STUDY GUIDE AND SOLUTIONS MANUAL

iGenetics

Bruce A. Chase

University of Nebraska at Omaha

Benjamin
Cummings

San Francisco • Boston • New York
Cape Town • Hong Kong • London • Madrid • Mexico City
Montreal • Munich • Paris • Singapore • Sydney • Tokyo • Toronto

Sponsoring Editor: Michele Sordi
Project Editor: Peggy Williams
Publishing Assistant: Caroline Smith
Compositor: R. Kharibian & Associates
Manufacturing Buyer: Vivian McDougal
Marketing Manager: Josh Frost

About the Cover: The front cover shows a computer screen display of a human DNA sequence generated by an automated sequencing procedure as part of the Human Genome Project to decipher the sequence and function of the three billion base pairs of DNA in our genome. Each color represents one of the four bases in DNA. This image was photographed at the Joint Genome Project, part of the Human Genome Project, in Walnut Creek, California. © David Parker, Science Source/Photo Researchers. The chromosome image is a photomicrograph of a set of normal human metaphase chromosomes. © ISM, Phototake.

ISBN 0-8053-4545-0

2 3 4 5 6 7 8 9 10–MV–04 03 02 01
www.aw.com/bc

CONTENTS

1

GENETICS: AN INTRODUCTION

CHAPTER OUTLINE

BUILDING CONCEPT MAPS USING GENETICS TERMS

Every chapter of the text introduces new terms are used in the "language of genetics." Like new words of a foreign language, each term has a precise meaning and contextual use. To help develop your ability to "speak" the language of genetics, each chapter of this guide will provide lists of key terms, symbols and concepts. After reading a chapter in the text, review the lists. Without consulting the text and in your own words, write a brief, precise definition of each term. Check your definition against that in the text. Then, visualize the relationships between the terms by constructing a concept map using the terms in each list.

What is a concept map? A concept map is a visual image that depicts the relationships between ideas. Terms are arranged on a page and related terms are connected with lines. A word or phrase that explains the relationship of the concepts is placed next to the lines. Different concept maps can be constructed from the same list of terms, depending on how the relationships between the concepts are viewed. Here is a sample concept map illustrating relationships between ancestral canines and modern dogs.

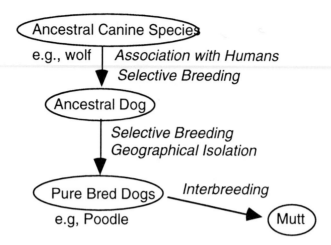

Here are some hints* to help you build concept maps using the end-of-chapter lists:

1. Write the terms on small pieces of paper. In some lists, specific examples of a term will be given. For example, in this chapter, one list contains "genetic material", "DNA", and "RNA." DNA and RNA could be considered to be examples of genetic material. Keep the examples separate, perhaps even using different colored paper for them.

2. Arrange the terms on a larger sheet of paper, with the broadest or most abstract ideas at the top and the most specific ideas at the bottom.

3. Arrange the concepts so that two related ideas are placed near (e.g., under) each other.

4. Draw lines between related concepts. Rearrange the pieces of paper as you see fit.

5. On the connecting lines, write words or phrases that explain the relationship between the concepts. Be as precise and succinct as you can. This is challenging, so be patient.

6. Put examples under the concepts they belong with. Connect examples to a concept using an explanatory phrase - "e.g.," or "specifically."

7. Copy the results onto a single sheet of paper. Draw circles around the concepts, but not the examples.

While concept maps can be generated with a pencil and paper, computer tools for concept mapping also exist. The site *http://users.edte.utwente.nl/lanzing/cm_home.htm* provides a useful list of links.

REVIEW OF KEY TERMS, SYMBOLS, AND CONCEPTS

In your own words, write a brief, precise definition of each term in the groups below. Check your definitions using the text. Then, develop a concept map using the terms in each list.

---

*Adapted from http://www.dc.peachnet.edu/~shale/humanities/composition/handouts/concept.html

1	2	3	4
genome	gene	genetics	eukaryote
eukaryotes	gene expression	genome project	diploid
nucleus	enzyme	genetic map	haploid
prokaryotes	polypeptide	gene locus	gamete
bacteria	protein	mutation	zygote
eubacteria	one gene-one enzyme	recombination	homolog
archaebacteria	hypothesis	selection	homologous
chromosome	one gene–one	hypothetico-	chromosome
gene	polypeptide	deductive	Nonhomologous
Allele	hypothesis	investigation	chromosome
genotype	operon	transmission genetics	sex chromosome
phenotype	messenger RNA	molecular genetics	autosome
homozygous	transfer RNA	population genetics	centromere
heterozygous	ribosomal RNA	quantitative	p arm
dominant	small nuclear RNA	genetics	q arm
recessive	ribosomes	recombinant DNA	metacentric
DNA	nucleolus	technology	chromosome
RNA	transcription	PCR	submetacentric
nucleotide	translation	basic research	chromosome
ribose	genetic code	applied research	acrocentric
deoxyribose	codon	model organisms	chromosome
adenine (A)	amino acid	clone	telocentric
guanine (G)	RNA polymerase	DNA typing	chromosome
cytosine (C)	centrioles	genetic database	karyotype
thymine (T)	endoplasmic	BLAST	ideogram
uracil (U)	reticulum	GenBank	band
	mitochondria	PubMed	G-banding
	chloroplast	OMIM	
		NCBI	

5	6	7	8
mitosis	meiosis I, II	meiosis	meiosis
karyokinesis	prophase I, II	sexual reproduction	meiospore
cytokinesis	metaphase I, II	spermatogenesis	gametogenesis
cell cycle	anaphase I, II	oogenesis	sporogenesis
M, G_1, S, G_2	telophase I, II	spermatozoa	gametophyte
sister chromatid	leptonema	primary	sporophyte
chromatid	zygonema	spermatogonia	stamen
daughter	pachynema	primary	pistil
chromosome	diplonema	spermatocytes	alternation of
prophase	diakinesis	meiocyte	generations
prometaphase	pairing	secondary	ovule
metaphase	crossing over	spermatocyte	pollen

5	6	7	8
anaphase	synapsis	spermatid	anther
telophase	synaptonemal	primary oogonia	gametophyte
mitotic spindle	complex	secondary oogonia	generation
microtubule	bivalent	primary oocyte	sporophyte
tubulin	tetrad	unequal cytokinesis	generation
centriole	dyad	secondary oocyte	spore
kinetochore	chiasma, chiasmata	first polar body	
microtubule	genetic	second polar body	
metaphase plate	recombination	ovum	
scaffold	recombinant		
disjunction	chromosome		
cell plate	pseudoautosomal		
	region		

THINKING ANALYTICALLY

Learning genetics is more than just learning a set of facts. Geneticists use analytical reasoning to incorporate new results into established conceptual frameworks. Analytical reasoning is essential to use new data to expand, and sometimes refute established concepts.

Following each chapter is a set of questions and problems. The questions ask you to recall and integrate information, while the problems require you to apply analytical reasoning. Solving problems using analytical reasoning is essential to learn genetics. It reinforces what you have read, and promotes an understanding of the relationships between terms, facts and concepts.

Unfortunately, learning to reason analytically is not always straightforward. It also takes time. The time will be well spent however, as you will grow tremendously in your reasoning ability. Here are some pointers that will be helpful to keep in mind as you work on problems.

1. Read the problem straight through without pausing. Get the sense of what it is about.

2. Then read it again, slowly and critically. This time,
    a. Jot down pertinent information.
    b. Scan the problem carefully analyzing the *terms* it uses. Often, clues to an answer can be found in the way the problem is stated. (Geneticists use very precise language!)

3. If you are unsure how to continue, ask yourself, "What are the options here?"
    a. Write down all the options you perceive.
    b. Carefully analyze whether a particular option will provide a solution.

4. When arrive at a solution, read the problem again, making sure that your analysis is consistent with *all* the data in the problem. Try to see if there is a more general principle behind the solution, or for that matter, a clearer or more straightforward solution.

5. If you get stuck (everyone does!), DON'T GO IMMEDIATELY TO THE ANSWER KEY. This only gives an *illusion* of solving a problem. On an exam, and in real life, there is no answer key. Don't be tempted "to just know the answer." Go on to another problem. Come back to this one later. Your mind can use the time to sort through loose ends.

6. If you cannot solve the problem after coming back to it a second time, read through the answer key. Then, close the answer key and try the problem once more. The next day, try it a third time without the answer key.

Applying Rules of Probability

To solve some problems in this and subsequent chapters, you will need to apply rules of probability. Two rules are commonly employed in genetics:

Product Rule: The probability of two independent events occurring simultaneously is the product of each of their individual probabilities.

Sum Rule: The probability of either one of two independent mutually exclusive events occurring is the sum of their individual probabilities.

To apply these rules, first consider the possible outcomes of a situation. Then, identify the mutually exclusive independent events leading to these outcomes. Apply the rules after rephrasing the question. Suppose there are two mutually exclusive, independent events: *A* and *B*. If you can rephrase the question to ask for the chance that *both A and B* occur (together), multiply the individual probabilities: $P(A \text{ and } B) = P(A) \times P(B)$. If you can rephrase the question statement to ask for the chance that *either A or B* occur (separately), add the individual probabilities: $P(A \text{ or } B) = P(A) + P(B)$.

QUESTIONS FOR PRACTICE

Multiple Choice Questions

1. Transmission genetics is primarily concerned with
    a. the distribution and behavior of genes in populations.
    b. the passing of genes from generation to generation and their recombination.
    c. the structure and function of genes at the molecular level.
    d. the means by which mutations are retained in nature.

2. Which one of the following is not a criterion to choose an organism for genetic experimentation?
    a. The organism should be able to be used in applied research.
    b. The organism should be easy to handle.
    c. The organism should exhibit genetic variation.
    d. The organism should have a relatively short life cycle.

3. Which one of the following eukaryotic cell structures does not contain DNA?
    a. a nucleus
    b. a mitochondrion
    c. the endoplasmic reticulum
    d. a chloroplast

4. Which one of the following is *not* an accurate description of a chromosome?
   a. It is a colored body localized in the nucleus.
   b. It is a protein and nucleic acid complex.
   c. It is the cellular structure that contains the genetic material.
   d. In eukaryotes, it is composed of many DNA molecules attached end to end.

5. Which one of the following is *not* true?
   a. genes encode proteins
   b. genes are proteins
   c. genes are transcribed into RNA molecules
   d. mRNA molecules are translated into proteins on ribosomes

6. A eukaryotic organism is one that
   a. is multicellular.
   b. has a plasma membrane.
   c. has genetic material encapsulated in a nuclear membrane.
   d. all of the above.

7. A centriole is an organelle that is
   a. present in the center of a cell's cytoplasm.
   b. composed of microtubules and important for organizing the spindle fibers.
   c. surrounded by a membrane.
   d. part of a chromosome.

8. The rough endoplasmic reticulum is
   a. an intracellular double-membrane system to which ribosomes are attached.
   b. an intracellular membrane that is studded with microtubular structures.
   c. a membranous structure found within mitochondria.
   d. only found in prokaryotic cells.

9. Which one of the following is available at the NCBI website and is a search tool that is useful to compare a nucleotide sequence with other nucleotide sequences in a database?
   a. PubMed
   b. BLAST
   c. OMIM
   d. GenBank
   e. PCR

10. Which one of the following can be translated?
    a. rRNA
    b. tRNA
    c. snRNA
    d. mRNA
    e. DNA

11. What two events occur in leptonema of prophase I?
    a. synapsis and crossing-over
    b. terminalization and disjunction
    c. synaptonemal complex formation and crossing-over

    d. pairing and chiasma formation

    e. pairing and the beginning of crossing-over

12. Which one of the following is *not* true?

    a. Crossing-over begins in leptonema.

    b. Chiasmata are visible manifestations of crossing-over.

    c. Chiasmata are visible in pachynema.

    d. Chiasmata are visible before terminalization.

13. Which one of the following statements is true about mitosis?

    a. The nucleolus disappears during metaphase.

    b. Nuclear membranes reform at the end of telophase.

    c. Centromeres are aligned on an equatorial plane at prophase.

    d. The nucleolus reforms at the end of anaphase.

14. Sister chromatids are

    a. synonymous with homologous chromosomes.

    b. present only in meiosis and not in mitosis.

    c. identical products of chromosome duplication held together by a replicated, but unseparated centromere.

    d. visible in interphase just after S phase.

Answers: 1b; 2a; 3c; 4d; 5b; 6c; 7b; 8a; 9b; 10d, 11e, 12c, 13b, 14c.

Thought Questions

1. Why is it difficult to draw a sharp boundary between molecular genetics, transmission genetics, population genetics and quantitative genetics?

2. Geneticists use the hypothetico-deductive method of investigation. How does this rational approach still allow research projects to go in exciting unpredictable directions?

3. How are basic and applied research interrelated in the following research areas:

    a. studies of mutations that affect the production of alcohol (ethanol) in yeast

    b. recombinant DNA technology

    c. studies of mutations that result in pesticide resistance in *Drosophila melanogaster*

    d. studies of mutations affecting the timing of seed ripening in *Arabidopsis*

    e. studies of transposons in corn

4. What features make an organism well-suited for genetic experimentation?

5. What is the relationship between a genotype and a phenotype?

6. What is a gene?

7. When during meiosis does the chromosomal behavior underlying Mendel's laws occur?

8. What different types of analyses can be made using genetic databases?

9. How are genetic maps different from ideograms? How is each used?

10. What hopes and concerns are associated with the field of genomics?

Thought Questions for Media

After reviewing the media on the *iGenetics* CD-ROM, try to answer these questions.

1. How are centromeres, centrioles and centrosomes different in terms of their cellular location and function during mitosis?
2. At what point in the cell cycle are chromosomes replicated? At what point are replicated chromosomes so extended that individual chromatids cannot be seen? When can they first be visualized? When are they maximally condensed?
3. When do centromeres replicate? When do replicated centromeres split apart?
4. During anaphase, chromosomes move to opposite poles and polar and kinetochore microtubules change length. Which type of microtubule shortens, and which type of microtubule elongates?
5. During anaphase, why do chromosomes appear V-shaped, I-shaped or J-shaped?
6. How do the chromosomes of daughter cells produced by mitosis compare to the chromosomes of the parental cell?

SOLUTIONS TO TEXT PROBLEMS

In 1.1 through 1.3, select the correct answer.

1.1   Interphase is a period corresponding to the cell cycle phases of
    a. mitosis
    b. S
    c. $G_1 + S + G_2$
    d. $G_1 + S + G_2 + M$

    Answer: c.

1.2   Chromatids joined together by a centromere are called
    a. sister chromatids
    b. homologs
    c. alleles
    d. bivalents (tetrads)

    Answer: a.

1.3   Mitosis and meiosis always differ in regard to the presence of
    a. chromatids
    b. homologs
    c. bivalents
    d. centromeres
    e. spindles

Answer: c.

1.4   State whether each of the following statements is true or false. Explain your choice.

    a. The chromosomes in a somatic cell of any organism are all morphologically alike.

    b. During mitosis the chromosomes divide and the resulting sister chromatids separate at anaphase, ending up in two nuclei, each of which has the same number of chromosomes as the parental cell.

    c. At zygonema, any chromosome can synapse with any other chromosome in the same cell.

Answer:

    a. False. Chromosomes can have different sizes, and can have their centromeres positioned differently. For many organisms, this statement will be false. However, in a diploid cell, a pair of homologous chromosomes will be morphologically alike.

    b. True.

    c. False. In meiosis I, only homologous chromosomes will synapse together.

1.5   For each mitotic event described in the following table, write the name of the event in the blank provided in front of the description. Then put the events in the correct order (sequence); start by placing a 1 next to the description of interphase and continue through 6, which should correspond to the last event in the sequence.

NAME OF EVENT		ORDER OF EVENT
_____	The cytoplasm divides and the cell contents are separated into two separate cells.	_____
_____	Chromosomes become aligned along the equatorial plane of the cell.	_____
_____	Chromosome replication occurs.	_____
_____	The migration of the daughter chromosomes to the two poles is complete.	_____
_____	Replicated chromosomes begin to condense and become visible under the microscope.	_____
_____	Sister chromatids begin to separate and migrate toward opposite poles of the cell.	_____

Answer: Try to visualize the events of mitosis dynamically as you solve this problem.

NAME OF EVENT		ORDER OF EVENT
cytokinesis	The cytoplasm divides and the cell contents are separated into two separate cells.	6
metaphase	Chromosomes become aligned along the equatorial plane of the cell.	3
interphase	Chromosome replication occurs.	1
telophase	The migration of the daughter chromosomes to the two poles is complete.	5
prophase	Replicated chromosomes begin to condense and become visible under the microscope.	2
anaphase	Sister chromatids begin to separate and migrate toward opposite poles of the cell.	4

1.6   Determine whether the answer to these statements is "yes" or "no." Explain the reasons for your answer.
   a. Can meiosis occur in haploid species?
   b. Can meiosis occur in a haploid individual?

Answer:
   a. Yes. Providing that a sexual mating system exists in the species, two haploid cells can fuse to produce a diploid cell that can then go through meiosis to produce haploid progeny. The fungi *Neurospora crassa* and *Saccharomyces cerevisiae* exemplify this life cycle.
   b. No. Meiosis only can occur in a diploid cell. A haploid individual cannot form a diploid cell, so meiosis cannot occur.

1.7   Select the correct answer. The general life cycle of a eukaryotic organism has the sequence
    a. 1N→meiosis→2N→fertilization→1N
    b. 2N→meiosis→1N→fertilization→2N
    c. 1N→mitosis→2N→fertilization→1
    d. 2N→mitosis→1N→fertilization→2N

Answer: b. Only diploid (2N) cells can undergo meiosis, and haploid cells (1N) fuse at fertilization, regenerating the diploid state.

1.8   Which statement is true?
    a. Gametes are 2N; zygotes are 1N.
    b. Gametes and zygotes are 2N.
    c. The number of chromosomes can be the same in gamete cells and in somatic cells.
    d. The zygotic and the somatic chromosome numbers cannot be the same.
    e. Haploid organisms have haploid zygotes.

Answer: c. In a haploid organism, gametes and somatic cells are both 1N. This provides an example of how (c) is true.

1.9   All of the following happen in prophase I of meiosis *except*
    a. chromosome condensation
    b. pairing of homologs
    c. chiasma formation
    d. terminalization
    e. segregation

Answer: e.

1.10   Give the name of the stage of mitosis or meiosis at which each of the following events occurs:
    a. Chromosomes are located in a plane at the center of the spindle.
    b. The chromosomes move away from the spindle equator to the poles.

Answer:
    a. Metaphase: Metaphase in mitosis, metaphase I and metaphase II in meiosis.
    b. Anaphase: Anaphase in mitosis, anaphase I and anaphase II in meiosis.

1.11   Given the diploid, meiotic mother cell shown below, diagram the chromosomes as they would appear

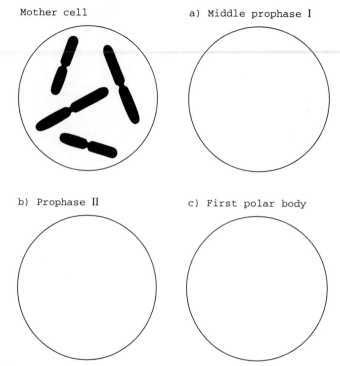

a. in late pachynema
b. in a nucleus at prophase of the second meiotic division
c. in the first polar body resulting from oogenesis in an animal

Answer:

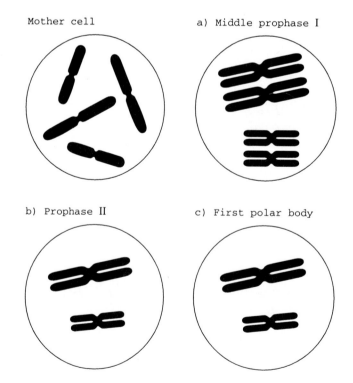

1.12   The cells in the following figure were all taken from the same individual (a mammal). Identify the cell division events occurring in each cell and explain your reasoning. What is the sex of the individual? What is the diploid chromosome number?

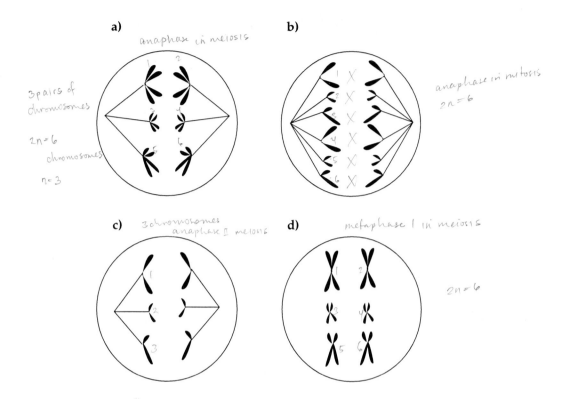

Answer: To reconcile how all the cells illustrated could come from one individual, consider that the cells shown could come from either somatic or germline cells. Cell (a) shows 3 pairs of previously synapsed homologs disjoining and must therefore illustrate anaphase I of meiosis. That three pairs of chromosomes are present indicates that the organism has 2N = 6 chromosomes, so that N = 3. Cell (b) shows the disjoining of chromatids. Since the organism has 2N = 6 chromosomes, and the daughter cells that will form as a result of this cell division will have 6 chromosomes, (b) must illustrate part of mitosis, specifically anaphase. Figure (c) also shows the disjoining of chromatids. Since the daughter cells will receive three chromosomes, this must be anaphase II of meiosis. Figure (d) shows the pairing of homologs and therefore illustrates metaphase I of meiosis. As the individual has three pairs of identically appearing chromosomes, there are two identical sex (= X) chromosomes, indicating that the animal is female.

1.13   Does mitosis or meiosis have greater significance in the study of heredity? Explain your choice.

Answer: Meiosis has greater significance. While mitosis generates progeny cells that are genetically identical to a parent cell, meiosis generates gametes that are genetically diverse. Gamete diversity is obtained when nonparental combinations of genes are obtained in two ways: the random assortment of maternal and paternal chromosomes at anaphase I of meiosis I and crossing-over events in prophase I of meiosis I. When gametes from different parents fuse at fertilization, more diversity is obtained. Hence, meiosis provides a means for genetic variation.

1.14   Consider a diploid organism that has three pairs of chromosomes. Assume that the organism receives chromosomes A, B, and C from the female parent and A', B', and C' from the male parent. To answer the following questions, assume that no crossing-over occurs.
   a. What proportion of the gametes of this organism would be expected to contain all the chromosomes of maternal origin?
   b. What proportion of the gametes would be expected to contain some chromosomes from both maternal and paternal origin?

Answer:
   a. The chance that a gamete would have a particular maternal chromosome is 1/2. Apply the product rule to determine the chance of obtaining a gamete with all three maternal chromosomes: $P(A \text{ and } B \text{ and } C) = P(A) \times P(B) \times P(C) = (1/2)^3 = 1/8$.
   b. There are two approaches to this question.
   1. List all of the possible options to obtain gametes that satisfy the specified condition - that some maternal and paternal chromosomes are present. Then use the product rule to determine the probability of each, and then, using the sum rule, determine the proportion of the gametes having maternal and paternal chromosomes. Gametes which satisfy the condition that both maternal and paternal chromosomes are present are ABC', AB'C, A'BC, AB'C', A'BC', and A'B'C. For each one of these six gamete types, the chance of obtaining it is 1/8. This is based on applying the product rule and logic similar to that used in part (a) of this question. Apply the sum rule to determine the chance of obtaining one of these types of gametes: $P(ABC' \text{ or } AB'C \text{ or } A'BC \text{ or } AB'C' \text{ or } A'BC' \text{ or } A'B'C) = 1/8 + 1/8 + 1/8 + 1/8 + 1/8 + 1/8 = 6/8 = 3/4$.
   2. Realize that the set of gametes with some maternal and paternal chromosomes is composed of all gametes *except* those that have only maternal or only paternal chromosomes. That is, P(gamete with *both* maternal *and* paternal chromosomes) = 1 – P(gamete with *only* maternal *or* only paternal chromosomes). From part (a), the chance of a gamete having chromosomes from only one parent is 1/8. Using the sum rule, P(gamete with both maternal and paternal chromosomes) = $1 - (1/8 + 1/8) = 3/4$.

1.15   Normal diploid cells of a theoretical mammal are examined cytologically at the mitotic metaphase stage for their chromosome complement. One short chromo-some, two medium-length chromosomes, and three long chromosomes are present. Explain how the cells might have such a set of chromosomes.

Answer: Since the cells are normal and the cell is diploid, the chromosomes should exist in pairs. The cell could have come from a male mammal with one medium-length pair, one long-length pair and a heteromorphic sex chromosome (X, Y) pair.

1.16   Is the following statement true or false? Explain your decision. "Meiotic chromosomes can be seen after appropriate staining in nuclei from rapidly dividing skin cells."

Answer: False. Skin cells consist entirely of mitotic, not meiotic, cells.

1.17   Is the following statement true or false? Explain your decision. "All the sperm from one human male are genetically identical."

Answer: False. Genetic diversity in the male's sperm is achieved during meiosis. There is crossing-over between non-sister chromatids as well as independent assortment of the male's maternal and paternal chromosomes during spermatogenesis.

1.18   The horse has a diploid set of 64 chromosomes, and a donkey has a diploid set of 62 chromosomes. Mules (viable but usually sterile progeny) are produced when a male donkey is mated to a female horse. How many chromosomes will a mule cell contain?

Answer: A female horse has ova with 32 chromosomes, while a male donkey has sperm with 31 chromosomes. A mule has $32 + 31 = 63$ chromosomes.

1.19   The red fox has 17 pairs of large, long chromosomes. The arctic fox has 26 pairs of shorter, smaller chromosomes.
   a. What do you expect to be the chromosome number in somatic tissues of a hybrid between these two foxes?
   b. The first meiotic division in the hybrid fox shows a mixture of paired and single chromosomes. Why do you suppose this occurs? Can you suggest a possible relationship between this fact and the observed sterility of the hybrid?

Answer:
   a. The red fox will have gametes with 17 chromosomes, and the arctic fox will have gametes with 26 chromosomes. The hybrid will have $17 + 26 = 43$ chromosomes. Once the fertilized egg is formed, mitotic division will produce somatic cells with 43 chromosomes.
   b. Similar chromosomes pair in meiosis. The pairing pattern seen in the hybrid indicates that some of the chromosomes in the arctic and red foxes share evolutionary similarity, while others do not. Unpaired chromosomes will not segregate in an orderly manner, giving rise to unbalanced meiotic products with

either extra or missing chromosomes. This can lead to sterility for two reasons: First, meiotic products that are missing chromosomes may not have genes necessary to form gametes. Second, even if gametes are able to form, a zygote generated from them will not have the chromosome set from either the hybrid, the red, or the arctic fox. The zygote will be an aneuploid with missing or extra genes, causing it to be inviable.

1.20   At the time of synapsis preceding the reduction division in meiosis, the homologous chromosomes align in pairs, and one member of each pair passes to each of the daughter nuclei. In an animal with five pairs of chromosomes, assume that chromosomes 1, 2, 3, 4, and 5 have come from the father, and 1', 2', 3', 4', and 5' have come from the mother. Assuming no crossing-over, in what proportion of the gametes of this animal will all the paternal chromosomes be present together?

Answer: The chance of getting a particular paternal chromosome is 1/2. Using the product rule, and logic similar to that in the answer presented in question 1.14a, the chance of getting all five paternal chromosomes is $(1/2)^5 = 1/32$.

2

DNA: *The Genetic Material*

CHAPTER OUTLINE

REVIEW OF KEY TERMS, SYMBOLS, AND CONCEPTS

In your own words, write a brief definition of each term in the groups below. Check your definitions using the text. Then, develop a concept map using the terms in each list.

1	2	3	4
macromolecule	genetic material	Chargaff's rules	viral genome
chromosome	DNA	% GC	prokaryotic genome
genome	RNA	X-ray diffraction	single-, double-
nucleic acid	transformation	Ångstrom unit	stranded
DNA, RNA	transforming	3' OH, 5' P	circular chromosome
nucleotide	principle	polarity	linear chromosome
nucleoside	nuclease	antiparallel strands	circularly permuted
nitrogenous base	ribonuclease	complementary base	terminal redundancy
adenine, guanine	(RNase)	pairs	denature, renature
cytosine, thymine	deoxyribonuclease	double helix	reanneal
uracil	(DNase)	major groove	T-even phage
purine	Avery's experiment	minor groove	λ, ΦX174 phage
pyrimidine	Griffith's experiment	oligomer	headful packaging

5	6	7

nuclear matrix
MARs
evolutionary
    conservation
	telomere-associated
	    sequences
	transposons	

THINKING ANALYTICALLY

This chapter presents a large amount of complex, related information. As such, its information and problems require attention to detail. To comprehend and retain this information, organize it and develop strategies to place it in context. In addition to concept maps, it will help to construct labeled diagrams that display information contextually. Sketch labeled diagrams of nucleic acid structure, chromosome packaging, and sequence organization of chromosomes.

This chapter starts with a presentation of the key experimental evidence for the nature and structure of the genetic material. What we now accept as fact once was hotly debated. These insightful experiments resolved fundamental questions in biology. To organize this information and place it in context, pay close attention to the subtleties of the experiments that are presented, and strive to see *how* they provided evidence for or against a particular view.

It is essential to know the chemical structures of nucleic acids to fully understand the material in coming chapters. Start by drawing out the structures, using paper and pencil. Copy the component parts of a nucleotide (the sugar, the bases, the phosphodiester linkages) from the text figures, paying close attention to their polarity. Practice them for a few days in a row, so that you can draw them easily from memory.

Having a good sense of the dimensions involved in nucleic acid structure and chromosomal packaging is helpful in grasping a mental image of these physical processes. For this reason, it is important to learn (or review) units of measurement and to be able to make conversions between different dimension units. In solving problems, it is helpful to convert values presented in many different units to a smaller set of units. Particularly important unit conversions are:

UNIT/CONVERSION	EXAMPLE
$1 \text{ Å} = 1$ Ångstrom $= 1 \times 10^{-10}$ meter	distance between 2 protons in $H_2 = 0.74\text{Å}$
$1 \text{ nm} = 1$ nanometer $= 1 \times 10^{-9}$ meter	width of a DNA double helix $= 2 \text{ nm}$
$1 \text{ μm} = 1$ micrometer $= 1 \times 10^{-6}$ meter	typical red blood cell diameter $= 7 \text{ μm}$
1 dalton (unit of mass) $= 1.66 \times 10^{-24}$ gram	1 H atom $= 1$ dalton

The chromosomal organization and packaging of DNA varies in different organisms. Consequently, while there are general principles that underlie DNA packaging, there are also organism-specific requirements. As you study this chapter, first identify the general principles used to organize and package genetic material. Then relate these principles to specific examples of organization and packaging in viruses, prokaryotes and eukaryotes.

DNA packaging occurs in three dimensions, and so it helps to visualize DNA packaging by making sketches. You do not have to be a great artist—the point is to convey the different strategies that organisms use to fit a molecule, that if left unpackaged would be larger than most cells, into a cell and have it remain functional.

Not everyone visualizes well in three dimensions and so it can be especially challenging to visualize supercoiling in a circular DNA molecule. The following exercise might help: Take a spiral telephone cord and hold the ends together to circularize it. Sequentially introduce 1, 2, 3, or 4 additional twists that *tighten* the spirals. For each complete twist that is introduced, a supercoil is added. Since the twist tightens the spiral, it introduces a positive supercoil. If you let the cord "relax," and then introduce additional twists that *loosen* the spirals, you will be introducing negative supercoils. To determine whether your phone cord is a right- or left-handed helix, wrap your right hand around the spiral, and trace the direction of the spiral with your right index finger. If, while you hold the spiral with your right hand, your index finger traces up the spiral in the same direction that your right thumb points, you are holding a right-handed helix. If it traces down the spiral in an opposite direction, you are holding a left-handed helix. Notice that the orientation of the helix remains the same regardless of whether your right thumb points up or down.

QUESTIONS FOR PRACTICE

Multiple Choice Questions

1. DNA and RNA are polymers of
    a. nucleosides.
    b. nucleotides.
    c. pentose sugars connected by phosphodiester bonds.
    d. ribonucleotides.

2. A molecule consisting of ribose covalently bonded to a purine or pyrimidine base is a
    a. ribonucleoside.
    b. ribonucleotide.
    c. nuclease.
    d. deoxyribonucleotide.

3. The transforming principle was found to be
    a. a cellular material that could alter a cell's heritable characteristic.
    b. a substance derived from killed viruses.
    c. modified RNA that could change a living cell.
    d. a transmissible substance that revives dead cells.

4. When Griffith injected mice with a mixture of live *R* pneumococcus derived from a *IIS* strain and heat-killed *IIIS* bacteria,
    a. the mice survived and he recovered live type *IIIR* organisms.
    b. the mice died, but he recovered live type *IIIR* cells.
    c. the mice died, but he recovered live type *IIS* cells.
    d. the mice died, but he recovered live type *IIIS* cells.

5. In the Hershey-Chase experiment, T2 phage were radioactively labeled with either ^{35}S or ^{32}P, and allowed to infect *E. coli.* What results proved that DNA was the genetic material?
    a. The ^{35}S was found in progeny phage, and the ^{32}P was found in phage ghosts
    b. The ^{35}S was found in phage ghosts, and the ^{32}P was found in progeny phage.
    c. The ^{35}S was found in both progeny phage and in phage ghosts.
    d. The ^{32}P was found in both progeny phage and in phage ghosts.

6. Analysis of the bases of a sample of nucleic acid yielded these percentages: A–20 percent, G–30 percent, C–20 percent, T–30 percent. The sample must be
    a. double-stranded RNA.
    b. single-stranded RNA.
    c. double-stranded DNA.
    d. single-stranded DNA.

7. Which of the following is *not* true about a linear molecule of double-stranded DNA?
    a. It is a double helix composed of antiparallel strands.
    b. Bases are paired via hydrogen bonds.
    c. At one end, two 5' phosphate groups can be found.
    d. Pentose sugars are linked via covalent phosphodiester bonds.

8. Which kind of DNA is *not* likely to be found in cells?
    a. A-form DNA
    b. B-form DNA
    c. Z-form DNA
    d. none of the above

9. Physical evidence indicates that DNA is not a rigid, rod-like molecule. How might bending DNA be important?
    a. It might facilitate the binding of DNA by regulatory proteins.
    b. Certain enzymes that cleave DNA may bend it in the cleavage process.
    c. It plays an important role in enzyme-mediated recombination events.
    d. All of the above.

10. Two double-stranded 25-base-pair DNA fragments are heated in solution. Fragment A has 60% GC, and fragment B has 40% GC. Which observation(s) might be made as the solution temperature increases?
    a. At a low enough temperature, both fragments will remain double stranded.
    b. A will separate into single strands at a lower temperature than B.
    c. B will separate into single strands at a lower temperature than A.
    d. At a high enough temperature, both A and B will separate into single strands.
    e. a, c, and d.

11. The chromosome of *E. coli* is packaged in the nucleoid region in a
    a. nuclear membrane.
    b. semicircular form.
    c. relaxed form.
    d. supercoiled form.

12. Circularly permuted chromosomes are found in
    a. T2 and T4 phage.
    b. only certain bacteria.
    c. all eukaryotes.
    d. lambda phage.

13. The DNA of viruses ΦX174 and Qβ is
    a. single stranded.
    b. double stranded.
    c. circularly permuted.
    d. extensively supercoiled.

14. Topoisomerases are enzymes that do all of the following except:
    a. untwist relaxed DNA.
    b. introduce negative supercoils into relaxed DNA.
    c. introduce positive supercoils into relaxed DNA.
    d. change the topological form of the DNA, but not the DNA sequence.

15. The total amount of DNA in the haploid genome of any organism is
    a. its karyotype.
    b. its C value.
    c. twice its GC content.
    d. an indication of its organizational and structural complexity.

16. Facultative heterochromatin
    a. is always inactive.
    b. is inactive only in certain cells.
    c. contains only moderately repetitive DNA.
    d. can contain unique-sequence DNA.
    e. both b and d.
    f. both a and c.

17. Which of the following is not true about both centromeres and telomeres?
    a. They are characteristically heterochromatic.
    b. They are associated with CEN sequence elements.
    c. They are essential for eukaryotic chromosome function.
    d. They contain a short, species-specific sequence that is repeated hundreds to thousands of times.

18. The fundamental unit of chromatin packaging in eukaryotes is
    a. a histone protein.
    b. a nucleosome.
    c. a 30-nm chromatin fiber.
    d. a looped domain.

19. Examples of tandemly repeated DNA sequences include all of the following except:
    a. genes for ribosomal RNA.
    b. LINEs.
    c. genes for histones.
    d. simple telomeric sequences.

20. Which type of chromatin contains expressed genes?
    a. constitutive heterochromatin
    b. facultative heterochromatin
    c. euchromatin
    d. Barr bodies

Answers: 1b; 2a; 3a; 4d; 5b; 6d; 7c; 8a; 9d; 10e; 11d; 12a; 13a; 14c; 15b; 16e; 17d; 18b; 19b; 20c.

Thought Questions

1. The histones, H1, H2A, H2B, H3, and H4, are the most highly conserved of all proteins. It has been proposed that they serve a basic function in all eukaryotes. What are the implications of this assertion for evolutionary theory?

2. The histones are highly basic proteins that interact with DNA (specifically, with the acidic sugar-phosphate backbone). What kinds of proteins are the nonhistones? How might they differ from the histones in their interactions with DNA?

3. How do you account for the presence of both unique and repetitive sequences in the genomes of eukaryotes? Why are the latter mostly lacking in prokaryotes?

4. Explain one of the fundamental puzzles of life: An amphibian that lives in a swamp has 30-fold more DNA than a human that lives on the 48th floor of a luxury apartment complex. In what way is the amphibian richer?

5. Summarize the structural composition and organization of the chromosomes of eukaryotic cells. How do they compare with the chromosomes of viruses and of prokaryotes?

6. Consider two phage: λ and T4. What different consequences would there be on chromosome packaging if 20 percent of the genome of each phage were deleted? What if the mutation were a 20 percent insertion?

7. Describe the logic behind the series of experiments that conclusively demonstrated that DNA was the genetic material in some cells. Why was this hotly debated for so long? When RNA was found to be the genetic material for some viruses, was the debate rekindled, or was this "the exception that proved the rule"?

8. In a double-stranded DNA molecule, how many strands of DNA exist in a single chromosome during the following stages of the cell cycle, mitosis and meiosis: G_1, G_2, prophase, metaphase, anaphase, pachynema, diplonema, anaphase I, and anaphase II?

9. Describe the various forms of DNA (A, B, Z) that have been identified. What are their most significant differences? Are any of these differences likely to have functional significance? If so, what are they?

10. Watson and Crick reputedly deduced the structure of DNA by applying observations made by others to molecular models, without any direct experimental observations of their own. Is this legitimate scientific procedure? If so, why? If not, why not?

11. Draw out the chemical structure of a double-stranded DNA molecule so that one strand has the sequence 5'-ATG-3'. Indicate the polarity of each strand, the location and the kinds of bonds that exist, and the approximate dimensions of the molecule.

12. Double-stranded DNA molecules have negatively charged sugar-phosphate backbones, and a major and minor groove into which the chemical groups of the bases project. Some proteins that interact with DNA do so in a highly sequence-specific manner, while others interact in a largely sequence-nonspecific manner. What different features of the DNA molecule might these two classes of protein be recognizing?

Thought Questions for Media

After reviewing the media on the *iGenetics* CD-ROM, try to answer these questions.

1. In the animation depicting the experiment by Avery and his colleagues that showed that bacteria could be transformed with DNA, how did they show that <u>polysaccharides</u> were not the transforming principle?
2. In the animation depicting the Hershey-Chase experiment, how were the T2 phage *initially* labeled with either ^{35}S or ^{32}P?
3. The T2 phage labeled with ^{32}P only had their DNA labeled. Why doesn't this information, by itself, provide evidence that DNA is the genetic material of T2?
4. What *experiment* was done to provide evidence that DNA is the genetic material?
5. In the animation depicting how the *E. coli* chromosome is supercoiled, is the DNA of *E. coli* compacted by adding negative or positive supercoils?
6. Which enzyme is responsible for adding negative supercoils?
7. Which enzyme is responsible for removing negative supercoils?

1. We now know that the genetic material of viruses can be either RNA or DNA, and that it can be either single- or double-stranded. Why is it still important to determine the type of nucleic acid associated with a new virus?
2. Once you determine the type of nucleic acid of a new virus, how can you determine which one of several known viruses is most closely related to it?

SOLUTIONS TO TEXT PROBLEMS

2.1   Griffith's experiment injecting a mixture of dead and live bacteria into mice demonstrated that (choose the correct answer):
   a. DNA is double stranded.
   b. mRNA of eukaryotes differs from mRNA of prokaryotes.
   c. A factor was capable of transforming one bacterial cell type to another.
   d. Bacteria can recover from heat treatment if live helper cells are present.

   Answer: c.

2.2   In the 1920s, while working with *Streptococcus pneumoniae*, the agent that causes pneumonia, Griffith injected mice with different types of bacteria. For each of the following bacteria types injected, indicate whether the mice lived or died:
   a. type *IIR* ⌐
   b. type *IIIS* ▽
   c. heat-killed *IIIS* ⌐
   d. type *IIR* + heat-killed *IIIS* ▽

   Answer:
   a. lived
   b. died
   c. lived
   d. died (DNA from the *IIIS* bacteria transformed the *IIR* bacteria to a virulent form)

2.3   Several years after Griffith described the transforming principle, Avery, MacLeod, and McCarty investigated the same phenomenon.
   a. List the steps they used to show that DNA from dead *S. pneumoniae* cells was responsible for the change from nonvirulent to a virulent state.
   b. Did their work affirm Griffith's work or disaffirm it and how?
   c. What was the role of the enzymes used in their experiments?

   Answer:
   a. They made extracts from *S* cells, and showed that they could transform *R* cells by exposing them to these extracts. These extracts contained different cellular macromolecules, such as lipids, polysaccharides, proteins and nucleic acids. They first showed that nucleic acids were the only macromolecular component that could transform the *R* cells. Then, by treating the nucleic acid component with either ribonuclease or deoxyribonuclease, they showed that the transforming principle co-purified with DNA. This strongly suggested that the genetic material was DNA. Although the work suggested that the genetic material was DNA, it could be criticized because the nucleic acids were contaminated by proteins.
   b. Their work affirmed and extended Griffith's work in that it identified the probable nature of Griffith's transforming principle as being DNA.
   c. Enzymes were used to destroy one of the two components of the nucleic acid mixture, and served to identify which of two nucleic acids was the genetic material. Ribonuclease did not destroy the transforming principle, but deoxyribonuclease did abolish transforming activity. This result supported the contention that DNA was the genetic material.

2.4   Hershey and Chase showed that when phages were labeled with ^{32}P and ^{35}S, the ^{35}S remained outside the cell and could be removed without affecting the course of infection, whereas the ^{32}P entered the cell and could be recovered in progeny phages.

What distribution of isotope would you expect to see if parental phages were labeled with isotopes of

a. C?

b. N?

c. H?

Explain your answer.

Answer: a, b, and c. Phage ghosts (supernatant) and progeny would have isotope. Both amino acids and nucleic acids have carbon, nitrogen and hydrogen. If a parental phage was labeled with isotopes of C, N, or H, one would expect the phage to have a labeled protein coat as well as labeled DNA. As a consequence, these isotopes would be recovered in the DNA of the progeny phage, as well as in the phage ghosts left behind in the supernatant after phage infection. This experiment would not be very helpful to determine whether DNA or protein was the genetic material, as neither material would be selectively labeled. The elegance of the Hershey-Chase experiment was that the isotopes used *selectively* labeled only one component of the phage, so that it could be followed from one generation to the next.

2.5   What is the evidence that the genetic material of (tobacco mosaic virus) is RNA?

Answer: Initial evidence that RNA is the genetic material of TMV came from the experiments of Gierer and Schramm. They showed that tobacco plants inoculated with RNA purified from TMV developed typical virus-induced lesions, and that these effects were specifically due to RNA, as they were not seen following RNase treatment. Fraenkel-Conrat and Singer confirmed this when they showed that reconstituted hybrid viruses, which had RNA from one strain and protein from another strain, produced progeny viruses that had protein subunits specified by the RNA component of the hybrid.

2.6   The X-ray diffraction data obtained by Rosalind Franklin suggested (choose the correct answer):

a. DNA is a helix with a pattern which repeats every 3.4 nanometers.

b. Purines are hydrogen bonded to pyrimidines.

c. Replication of DNA is semiconservative.

d. mRNA of eukaryotes differs from mRNA of prokaryotes.

Answer: a.

2.7   What evidence do we have that in the helical form of the DNA molecule the base pairs are composed of one purine and one pyrimidine?

Answer: Two different lines of evidence support the view that a base pair is composed of one purine and one pyrimidine.

(1) When the chemical components of double-stranded DNA from a wide variety of organisms were analyzed quantitatively by Chargaff, it was found that the amount of purines equaled the amount of pyrimidines. More specifically, it was found that the amount of adenine equaled the amount of thymine, and that the amount of cytosine equaled the amount of guanine. The simplest hypothesis to explain these observations was the existence of complementary base pairing, A on one strand paired with T on the other strand, and G paired with C.

(2) More direct physical evidence was provided by X-ray diffraction studies. These established the dimensions of the DNA double helix and allowed for comparison with the known sizes of the bases. The diameter of the double helix is constant throughout its length at 2 nm. This is the right size to accommodate a purine paired with a pyrimidine, but too small for a purine-purine pair, and too large for a pyrimidine-pyrimidine pair.

2.8   What exactly is a deoxynucleotide made up of and how many different deoxynucleotides are there in DNA? Describe the structure of DNA and describe the bonding mechanism of the molecule (i.e., what kind of bonds are on the sides of the "ladder" and what kind of bonds hold the two complementary strands together?). Base pairing in DNA consists of purine-pyrimidine pairs, so why can't A-C and G-T pairs form?

Answer. A deoxynucleotide consists of 2'-deoxyribose plus a phosphate group (PO_4^{-2}) attached to its 5' carbon, plus a nitrogenous base attached to its 1' carbon. Since there are four different nitrogenous bases in DNA, adenine (A), thymine (T), guanine (G) and cytosine (C), there are four different nucleotides. In a DNA molecule, one finds monophosphate nucleotides, so that there is deoxyadenosine monophosphate (dAMP), thymidine monophosphate (TMP), deoxyguanosine monophosphate (dGMP) and deoxycytidine monophosphate (dCMP). Along the sides of the "ladder," the 5' carbon of one deoxyribose is connected by a covalent, phosphodiester (O–P–O) bond to the 3' carbon of another. A phosphate group is found at the 5' end of a DNA polynucleotide chain, and a hydroxyl (OH) group is found at the 3' end of a DNA polynucleotide chain. Weaker hydrogen bonds between complementary A-T and G-C bases hold the complementary strands together. A-T pairs have two hydrogen bonds, while G-C pairs have three hydrogen bonds. See text Fig. 2.11.

Although A-C and G-T pairs would be purine-pyrimidine base pairs, they do not form because of their inability to pair using hydrogen bonding. Note that A-T base pairs have two hydrogen bonds while G-C base pairs have three hydrogen bonds. This is consistent with the evidence provided by Chargaff. Quantitative measurements of the four bases in double-stranded DNA isolated from a wide variety of organisms indicated that, in all cases, the amount of A equaled the amount of T, and the amount of G equaled the amount of C. Moreover, different DNAs exhibited different base ratios so that while (A) = (T) and (G) = (C), in most organisms (A + T) ≠ (G + C). Put another way, the percent GC content of different DNA samples varies.

The simplest hypothesis is that there are two base pairs in DNA, A–T and G–C, and the proportion of the two base pairs varies from organism to organism.

2.9   What is the base sequence of the DNA strand that would be complementary to the following single-stranded DNA molecules?

a. 5' AGTTACCTGATCGTA 3'
b. 5' TTCTCAAGAATTCCA 3'

Answer:
a. 3' TCAATGGACTAGCAT 5' (or 5' TACGATCAGGTAACT 3').
b. 3' AAGAGTTCTTAAGGT 5' (or 5' TGGAATTCTTGAGAA 3').

2.10   Describe the bonding properties of G-C and T-A. Which would be the hardest to break? Why?

Answer: The adenine-thymine base pair has two hydrogen bonds, while the guanine-cytosine base pair has three hydrogen bonds. Thus, the guanine-cytosine base pair requires more energy to break apart and so is harder to break apart.

2.11   The double-helix model of DNA, as suggested by Watson and Crick, was based on data gathered on DNA by other researchers. The facts fell into the following two general categories; give two examples of each:
a. chemical composition
b. physical structure

Answer: The double-helix model of DNA suggested by Watson and Crick had to incorporate existing information about its chemical composition and physical structure. In terms of its chemical composition, it was known that DNA is composed of polynucleotides, that (A) = (T) and (G) = (C) (Chargaff's rules), and that while the percent GC varies between organisms, the A/T and G/C ratios do not. In terms of its physical structure, the structure and molecular dimensions of the component molecules (the bases, sugars, and phosphates) were known. It was also known from studies of Franklin and Wilkins that the molecule is organized in a highly ordered, helical structure, and that there are two distinctive regularities at 0.34 and 3.4 nm along the molecule's axis.

2.12   For double-stranded DNA, which of the following base ratios always equals 1?
a. $(A + T)/(G + C)$
b. $(A + G)/(C + T)$
c. C/G
d. $(G + T)/(A + C)$

Answer: Since (G) = (C), and (A) = (T), it follows that (G + A) = (C + T), and (G + T) = (A + C). Thus, b, c, and d are all equal to 1.

2.13   If the ratio of (A + T) to (G + C) in a particular DNA is 1.00, does this result indicate that the DNA is probably constituted of two complementary strands of DNA or a single strand of DNA, or is more information necessary?

Answer: More information is needed. That (A + T)/(G + C) = 1 indicates only that (A + T) = (G + C). If the DNA was double stranded, (G) = (C), and (A) = (T). For the observed ratio, there would need to be 25 percent A, 25 percent T, 25 percent C, and 25 percent G. However, if the DNA were single stranded, one could still observe this ratio. In single-stranded DNA, there are no restrictions on the relative amounts of the different bases. There are many ways in which one could observe (A + T)/(G + C) = 1. For example, suppose there were 35 percent A, 15 percent T, 20 percent G, and 30 percent C.

2.14   The percentage of cytosine in a double-stranded DNA is 17. What is the percentage of adenine in that DNA?

Answer: In double-stranded DNA, if (C) = 17 percent, then (G) = 17 percent. This means that the DNA has 34 percent G–C, and 66 percent A–T base pairs. Hence, the DNA will have (66/2)(100%) = 33% A.

2.15   A double-stranded DNA polynucleotide contains 80 thymidylic acid and 110 deoxy-guanylic acid residues. What is the total nucleotide number in this DNA fragment?

Answer: Since the DNA molecule is double stranded, (A) = (T), and (G) = (C). If there are 80 T residues, there must be 80 A residues. If there are 110 G residues, there must be 110 C residues. The molecule has (110 + 110 + 80 + 80) = 380 nucleotides, or 190 base pairs.

2.16   Analysis of DNA from a bacterial virus indicates that it contains 33 percent A, 26 percent T, 18 percent G, and 23 percent C. Interpret these data.

Answer: First, notice that (A) ≠ (T), and (G) ≠ (C). Thus, the DNA is not double stranded. The bacterial virus appears to have a single-stranded DNA genome.

2.17   The following are melting temperatures for different double-stranded DNA molecules. Arrange these molecules from lower to higher content of GC pairs.
   a. 73°C
   b. 69°C
   c. 84°C
   d. 78°C
   e. 82°C

Answer: G–C base pairs have three hydrogen bonds, while A–T base pairs have two. As a consequence, G–C base pairs are stronger than A–T base pairs. If a double-stranded molecule in solution is heated, the thermal energy will "melt" the hydrogen bonds, denaturing the double-stranded molecule into single strands. Double-stranded molecules with more G–C base pairs require more thermal energy to break the hydrogen bonds, and so dissociate into single strands at higher temperatures. Put another way, the higher the GC content of a double-stranded DNA molecule, the higher its melting temperature. Reordering the molecules from lowest to highest percent GC, one has b (69°), then a (73°), d (78°), e (82°), and c (84°).

2.18   What is a DNA oligomer?

Answer: A DNA oligomer is a short stretch of DNA containing a small number of bases. It is often referred to as an oligonucleotide, or an oligo, for short. Sometimes, when the exact size of the oligomer can be specified, this information might be included. For example, a single-stranded oligomer having 20 bases might be referred to as a 20-base oligomer, a 20-base oligo, or a 20-mer.

2.19   The genetic material of bacteriophage ΦX174 is single-stranded DNA. What base equalities or inequalities might we expect for single-stranded DNA?

Answer: No predictions can be made regarding the base content of single-stranded DNA. Any base-pair equality would depend on the overall sequence of the chromosome: (A) might be equal to (T), but that need not be the case, as that is only one of many possibilities.

2.20   Through X-ray diffraction analysis of crystallized DNA oligomers, different forms of DNA have been identified. These forms include A-DNA, B-DNA, and Z-DNA, and each has unique molecular attributes.
   a. Which of these forms is the most common form in living cells?
   b. Z-DNA has an unusual conformation resulting in more base pairs per helical turn than B-DNA. What is the conformation? Does this molecule have any function in living cells?
   c. Which of these forms is never found in living cells?

Answer:
   a. B-DNA is the form most common to living cells.
   b. To understand why Z-DNA is considered to have an unusual conformation, it helps to compare it to B-DNA. Z-DNA is a long and thin (about 2 nm wide) double helix, like B-DNA. Unlike the right-handed B-DNA however, Z-DNA is left-handed. It has an axis that runs through the minor groove, and has 12 base pairs per helical turn that are inclined 8.8° from a plane perpendicular to the axis. In contrast, B-DNA has an axis that runs through the base pairs, and has 10 base

pairs per helical turn that are inclined 2° from a plane perpendicular to the axis. The major groove of Z-DNA is not very distinct, as it is thin and flattened out along the helix surface, while the major groove of B-DNA is wide and intermediate in depth (between that of A-DNA and Z-DNA). The minor groove of Z-DNA is extremely narrow and very deep, while that of B-DNA is narrow and of intermediate depth. It has been proposed that regions with Z-DNA provide a stretch of left-handed helical turns that are involved in replication, recombination and transcription. Stretches of left-handed turns may aid in unwinding right-handed helical turns in B-DNA during these processes. Z-DNA may also be more stable under extreme environmental conditions.

   c. A-DNA is found only when the DNA is dehydrated, so it is unlikely that lengthy sections of A-DNA would be found in living cells.

2.21   If a virus particle contains double-stranded DNA with 200,000 base pairs, how many complete 360° turns occur in this molecule?

Answer: With 10 base pairs per complete 360° turn of a B-form double-stranded DNA molecule, there are 200,000/10 = 20,000 complete turns in the viral DNA.

2.22   A double-stranded DNA molecule is 100,000 base pairs (100 kb) long.
   a. How many nucleotides does it contain?
   b. How many complete turns are there in the molecule?
   c. How long is the DNA molecule?

Answer:
   a. Each base pair has 2 nucleotides, so the molecule has 200,000 nucleotides.
   b. There are 10 base pairs per complete 360° turn, so there will be 100,000/10 = 10,000 complete turns in the molecule.
   c. There are 0.34 nm between the centers of adjacent base pairs. There will be 100,000 x 0.34 nm = 3.4×10^4 nm = 34 μm.

2.23   Organisms have vastly different amounts of genetic material. *E. coli* has about 4.6 million base pairs of DNA in one circular chromosome, the haploid budding yeast (*S. cerevisiae*) has 12,057,500 base pairs of DNA in 17 chromosomes, and the gametes of humans have about 2.75 billion base pairs of DNA in 23 chromosomes.
   a. If all of the DNA were B-DNA, what would be the average length of a chromosome in these cells?
   b. On average, how many complete turns would be in each chromosome?
   c. Would your answers to (a) and (b) be significantly different if the DNA were composed of, say, 20 percent Z-DNA and 80 percent B-DNA?
   d. What implications do your answers to these questions have for the packaging of DNA in cells?

Answer:

a. For *E. coli*, the length is $[(4.6 \times 10^6 \text{ bp}) \times (0.34 \text{ nm/bp})] = 1.6 \times 10^6 \text{ nm} = 1,600 \text{ μm}$ (microns). Since *E. coli* has a circular chromosome, this would be a chromosome with a diameter of about 510 μm. For yeast, the average chromosome length is $[(12,057,500 \text{ bp/16 chromosomes}) \times (0.34 \text{ nm/bp})] = 2.56 \times 10^5 \text{ nm} = 256 \text{ μm}$. For humans, the average chromosome length is $[(2.75 \times 10^9 \text{ bp/23 chromosomes}) \times (0.34 \text{ nm/bp})] = 4.07 \times 10^7 \text{ nm} = 40,700 \text{ μm}$.

b. For B-DNA, there are 10 bp per helical turn. Therefore, the *E. coli* chromosome would have $[(4.6 \times 10^6 \text{ bp/chromosome}) \times (1 \text{ turn/10 bp})] = 4.6 \times 10^5$ turns. The average yeast chromosome would have $[(12,057,500 \text{ bp/17 chromosomes}) \times (1 \text{ turn/10 bp})] = 7.1 \times 10^4$ turns. The average human chromosome would have $[(2.75 \times 10^9 \text{ bp/23 chromosomes}) \times (1 \text{ turn/10 bp})] = 1.2 \times 10^7$ turns.

c. While Z-DNA and B-DNA differ in the distance between successive base pairs and the number of bp per turn, these are not large compared to chromosome length. Thus, the answers to (a) and (b) will not be very different.

    Z-DNA has more space between successive base pairs, as there is about 0.57 nm between successive base pairs instead of the 0.34 nm found in B-DNA. Thus, if 20% of each chromosome were Z-DNA, each chromosome would be 20% × $[(0.57 - 0.34)/0.34] = 13.5\%$ longer. A full turn of the double helix in Z-DNA utilizes more base pairs, as there are 12 bp/turn in Z-DNA instead of the 10 bp/turn in B-DNA. Thus, if 20% of each chromosome were Z-DNA, each chromosome would have 20% × $[(12-10)/12] = 3.33\%$ fewer turns.

d. These answers point out the need for DNA to be flexible so that it can be packaged and "fit" into a cell. Other forms of DNA, including Z-DNA, do not necessarily shorten a chromosome but they can affect its flexibility. In the examples considered in this problem, the cells are hundreds to tens of thousands of times smaller than the length of their (average) chromosome. *E. coli* is about 2 μm × 0.5 μm, with a 510 μm diameter chromosome, a yeast cell is about 20 μm wide, with 16 chromosomes that average 256 μm, and a "typical" human cell is about 10 μm wide, with 46 chromosomes that average 40,700 μm. Thus chromosomes cannot remain as unpackaged molecules inside cells.

2.24   If nucleotides were arranged at random in a single-stranded RNA 10^6 nucleotides long, and if the base composition of this RNA was 20 percent A, 25 percent C, 25 percent U, and 30 percent G, how many times would you expect the specific sequence 5'-GUUA-3' to occur?

Answer: The chance of finding the sequence 5' GUUA 3' is $(0.30 \times 0.25 \times 0.25 \times 0.20) = 0.00375$. In a molecule 10^6 nucleotides long, there are nearly 10^6 groups of four bases: the first group of four is bases 1, 2, 3, and 4, the second group is bases 2, 3, 4, and 5, etc. Thus, the number of times this sequence is expected to appear is $0.00375 \times 10^6 = 3,750$.

2.25   Two double-stranded DNA molecules from a population of T2 phages were denatured to single strands by heat treatment. The result was the following four single-stranded DNAs:

1 TAGCTCC →   3 GCTCCTA →

and

2 ← ATCGAGG   4 ← CGAGGAT

These separated strands were then allowed to renature. Diagram the structures of the renatured molecules most likely to appear when **(a)** strand 2 renatures with strand 3 and **(b)** strand 3 renatures with strand 4. Label the strands and indicate sequences and polarity.

Answer:

a.   The sequence C G A G G in molecule 2 is complementary to the sequence G C T C C in molecule 3. When these pair up, one has:

3 ← GCTCCTA →

2 ATCGAGG

Each strand has two unpaired bases sticking out. These bases are complementary to each other, so that if the molecule bends, one has:

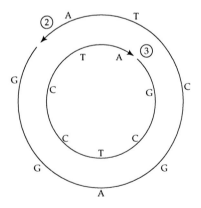

b.   The sequence in molecule 3 is complementary to the sequence in molecule 4. It also has opposite polarity, so that the two strands can pair up. One has:

③ ── G C T C C T A →

← ── C G A G G A T ④

2.26   Define topoisomerases and list the function(s) of these enzymes.

Answer: Topoisomerases are a class of enzymes that convert one topological form of DNA to another. Topoisomerases untwist relaxed DNA to produce negative supercoils. or twist negatively supercoiled DNA to convert it to a more relaxed state. These enzymes allow DNA to be converted between negatively supercoiled, compact DNA and a more relaxed, less compact state.

2.27   What is the relationship between cellular DNA content and the structural or organizational complexity of the organism?

Answer: There is, paradoxically, no simple relationship between the haploid DNA content of a cell and its structural or organizational complexity. This is the "C value paradox." While organisms in some taxa show little variation, organisms in other taxa show as much as tenfold variation in their C values. In addition, organisms do not have C values corresponding to their organizational or structural complexity. At least one reason for this is that there is considerable variation in the amount of repetitive-sequence DNA in the genome.

2.28   In a particular eukaryotic chromosome (choose the best answer):
   a. Heterochromatin and euchromatin are regions where genes make functional gene products (where they are active).
   b. Heterochromatin is active but euchromatin is inactive.
   c. Heterochromatin is inactive but euchromatin is active.
   d. Both heterochromatin and euchromatin regions are inactive.

Answer: c.

2.29   Compare and contrast eukaryotic chromosomes and bacterial chromosomes considering the following features:

FEATURES

a.	centromeres	f.	nonhistone protein scaffolds
b.	hexose sugars	g.	DNA
c.	amino acids	h.	nucleosomes
d.	supercoiling	i.	circular chromosome
e.	telomeres	j.	looping

Answer:
   a. Only eukaryotic chromosomes have centromeres, the sections of the chromosome found near the point of attachment of mitotic or meiotic spindle fibers. In some organisms, such as *S. cerevisiae*, they are associated with specific CEN sequences. In other organisms, they have a more complex repetitive structure.
   b. Hexose sugars are not found in either eukaryotic or bacterial chromosomes, as *pentose* sugars are found in DNA.

c. Amino acids are found in proteins that are involved in chromosome compaction, such as the proteins that hold the ends of looped domains in prokaryotic chromosomes, and the histone and nonhistone proteins in eukaryotic chromatin.

d. Both eukaryotic and bacterial chromosomes share supercoiling.

e. Telomeres are only found at the ends of eukaryotic chromosomes, and are required for replication and chromosome stability. They are associated with specific types of sequences: simple telomeric sequences and telomere-associated sequences.

f. Nonhistone protein scaffolds are found only in eukaryotic chromosomes, and have structural (higher-order packaging) and possibly other functions.

g. DNA is found in both prokaryotic and eukaryotic chromosomes. (Although, some viral chromosomes have RNA as their genetic material.)

h. Nucleosomes are the fundamental unit of packaging of DNA in eukaryotic chromosomes, and are not found in prokaryotic chromosomes.

i. Circular chromosomes are only found in prokaryotes, not in eukaryotes.

j. Looping is found in both eukaryotic and prokaryotic chromosomes. In eukaryotic chromosomes, the 30-nm nucleofilament is packed into looped domains by nonhistone chromosomal proteins. In bacterial chromosomes such as that of *E. coli*, there are about 100 looped domains, each containing about 40 kilobases of supercoiled DNA.

2.30 Discuss the structure of nucleosomes, the hierarchical packaging, and the composition of a core particle of a nucleosome. Also discuss the functions of nucleosomes.

Answer: Nucleosomes are the fundamental unit of DNA packaging in eukaryotic chromosomes. In a nucleosome core particle, a short segment of DNA is wrapped about one-and-three-quarters times around a protein core. This protein core is an octamer consisting of two copies of each of four histone proteins: H2A, H2B, H3, H4. This nucleosome core particle packs the DNA into a flattened disk about 5.7 × 11 nm. This packing effectively condenses the DNA into a smaller size, condensing it by a factor of about seven. The interactions between the histones and the DNA are not sequence specific, but rather are based on the basic, positively charged histone proteins interacting with the acidic, negatively charged sugar-phosphate backbone of the DNA. Nucleosome core particles serve to package double-stranded DNA at regular intervals, with short stretches of linker DNA between particles. At this level of packaging, DNA is packed into a "beads-on-a-string" form of chromatin known as the 10-nm nucleofilament. This condensation of DNA also forms the basis for subsequent packaging, first through associations between nucleosomes and then by associations with nonhistone chromosomal proteins. Associations between nucleosomes result in further compaction of the 10-nm nucleofilament, producing a 30-nm chromatin fiber that condenses the DNA another six fold. Histone H1 plays an important role in this coiling. The 30-nm chromatin fiber is further condensed into looped domains, with each loop containing between 10 and 100s of kilobases of DNA. The looped domains are anchored inside the nuclear envelope to a filamentous structural framework of protein, the nuclear matrix.

2.31   Answer the following questions after setting up the following "rope trick." Start with a belt (representing a DNA molecule; imagine the phosphodiester backbones lying along the top and bottom edges of the belt) and a soda can. Holding the belt buckle at the bottom of the can, wrap the belt flat against the side of the can, counterclockwise three times around the can. Now remove the "core" soda can and, holding the ends of the belt, pull the ends of the belt taut. After some reflection, answer the following questions.

a.   Did you make a left- or a right-handed helix?

b.   How many helical turns were present in the coiled belt before you pulled it taut?

c.   How many helical turns were present in the coiled belt after you pulled it taut?

d.   Why does the belt appear more twisted when pulled taut?

e.   About what percentage of the length of the belt was decreased by this packaging?

f.   Is the DNA of a linear chromosome that is coiled around histones supercoiled?

g.   Why are topoisomerases necessary to package linear chromosomes?

Answer:

a.   The belt forms a right-handed helix. Although you wrapped the belt around the can axis in a counterclockwise direction from your orientation (looking down at the can), the belt was winding up and around the side of can in a clockwise direction from its orientation. With the belt wrapped around the can, curve the fingers of your right hand over it, and use your index finger to trace the direction of the belt's spiral. Your right index finger will trace the spiral upward, the same direction your thumb points when you wrap your hand around the can. Therefore the belt has formed a right-handed helix. If you do this with your left hand, your thumb will point away from the direction the helix twists, indicating that it has not formed a left-handed helix.

b.   Three.

c.   Three. The number of helical turns is unchanged, although the twist in the belt is changed.

d.   The belt appears more twisted because the pitch of the helix was altered, and the edges of the belt (positioned much like the complementary base pairs of a double helix) are twisted more tightly.

e.   While twisted around the can, the length of the belt decreases by about 70–80 percent, depending on the initial length of the belt and the belt diameter.

f.   Yes. The DNA of linear chromosomes becomes supercoiled as it is wrapped around histones to form the 10-nm nucleofilament. Just as you must add twists to the belt in order for it to lie flat on the surface of the can, supercoils must be introduced into the DNA for it to wrap around the histones.

g.   Topoisomerases increase or reduce the level of supercoiling in DNA. In order for it to be packaged, negative supercoils must be added to linear DNA.

2.32   Arrange the following figures in increasing order of eukaryotic chromosome condensation. Designate the simplest chromosome organization as number 1 and the most complex chromosome organization as number 6.

A. Chromatin fiber
    of packed
    nucleosomes

B. Metaphase
    chromosome

C. DNA double helix

D. Extended section
    of chromosome

E. "Beads-on-a-string"
    form of chromatin

F. Condensed section
    of chromosome

From Alberts et al., *Molecular Biology of the Cell*, 2nd ed., p. 504. New York: Garland Publishing, Inc., 1989. Copyright © 1989 by Bruce Alberts, Dennis Bray, Julian Lewis, Martin Raff, Keith Roberts, and James D. Watson. Reprinted by permission.

Answer: 1 = C, DNA double helix

↓

2 = E, "Beads-on-a-string" form of chromatin

↓

3 = A, chromatin fiber of packed nucleosomes

↓

4 = D, extended section of chromosome

↓

$$5 = F, \text{ condensed section of chromosome}$$

$$\downarrow$$

$$6 = B, \text{ metaphase chromosome}$$

2.33   What are the main molecular features of yeast centromeres?

Answer: The centromeres of *S. cerevisiae* have similar, though not identical, DNA sequences, called CEN sequences. Each contains three sequence domains, called centromere DNA elements (CDEs). CDEII, a 76–86-bp region that is >90% AT, is flanked by CDEI, a conserved RTCACRTG sequence (R = A or G), and CDEIII, a 26-bp AT-rich conserved domain. The CDEs interact with kinetochore proteins that mediate the attachment of centromeres to spindle fiber microtubules. In one model, CDEI binds centromere-binding factor I (CBFI), CDEII is wrapped once around a histone octamer, and CDEIII binds the protein complex CBF3. In turn, a linker protein may attach CBF3 to the spindle microtubule. Some yeast centromeres are quite different. For example, those of the fission yeast, *S. pombe*, are 40 to 80 kb long. They contain complex rearrangements of repeated sequences. Nonetheless, all centromeres provide the same function - to insure accurate chromosome segregation during mitosis and meiosis.

2.34   Telomeres are unique repeated sequences. Where on the DNA strand are they found? How are they synthesized (in the presence of which enzyme)? Do they serve a function?

Answer: Telomeres are characteristically heterochromatic sequences found at the ends of a linear, eukaryotic chromosome. For most organisms, the telomeric sequences at the extreme end of a chromosome are simple, highly repeated, and species specific. As will be discussed in Chapter 3, these sequences are synthesized by the enzyme telomerase. Nearby, but not at the very end of a chromosome, are telomere-associated sequences. These are repeated, complex sequences, and extend for thousands of bases from the simple telomeric sequences. These sequences are replicated, along with other chromosomal DNA sequences, by a set of enzymes that include DNA polymerases. Telomere organization is quite different in some organisms. In organisms such as *Drosophila*, telomeres consist of transposons belonging to the LINE family of repeated sequences. Telomeres function in DNA replication and provide chromosome stability.

2.35   Would you expect to find most protein-coding genes in unique-sequence DNA, in moderately repetitive DNA, or in highly repetitive DNA?

Answer: In unique-sequence DNA.

2.36   Both histone and nonhistone proteins are essential for DNA packaging in eukaryotic cells. However, these classes of proteins are fundamentally dissimilar in a number of ways. Describe how these classes of proteins differ in terms of

a. their protein characteristics
b. their presence and abundance in cells
c. their interactions with DNA
d. their role in DNA packaging

Answer:

a. The five histones (H1, H2A, H2B, H3, and H4) are small, basic, positively charged proteins that are rich in arginine and lysine. Histones H2A, H2B, H3, and H4 are among the most highly conserved of all proteins. In contrast to the small number of histones, there are many types of nonhistones. They are variable in size, and are usually negatively charged, acidic proteins.

b. The five histones are present in all cells of all eukaryotic organisms. Relative to the total amount of DNA, they are present in fairly constant amounts. In contrast, nonhistones differ in number and type between cell types in an organism, at different times in the same cell type, and from organism to organism. As a class, nonhistones may be between 50 and 100 percent of the mass of DNA.

c. Histones are positively charged and mostly interact with the negatively charged sugar-phosphate backbone of DNA. Nonhistones are typically negatively charged, and can interact with the positively charged histones or with DNA. The HMG class of nonhistones binds to the minor groove of the DNA and causes DNA bending.

d. The histones H2A, H2B, H3, and H4 are fundamental to packaging DNA into nucleosome core particles and the formation of the 10-nm nucleofilament. Histone H1 is involved in compaction of this nucleofilament to produce a 30-nm chromatin fiber. Nonhistones are important in higher-order packaging of DNA. They form the protein scaffold that anchors the looped domains of the 30-nm chromatin fiber and they control the degree of chromosome condensation.

2.37   Rearrangements at the end of 16p (the short arm of chromosome 16) underlie a variety of common human genetic disorders, including β-thalassemia (a defect in hemoglobin metabolism caused by mutations in the β-globin gene), mental retardation, and the adult form of polycystic kidney disease. Recently, the determination of approximately 285 kilobase (kb) pairs of DNA sequence at the end of human chromosome 16p has allowed for very detailed analysis of the structure of this chromosome region. The first functional gene lies about 44 kb from the region of simple telomeric sequences, and about 8 kb from the telomere-associated sequences. Analysis of sequences proximal (nearer the centromere) to the first gene reveals a sinusoidal variation in GC content, with GC-rich regions associated with gene-rich areas and AT-rich regions associated with *Alu*-dense areas. The β-globin gene lies about 130 kb from the telomere-associated sequences.

a. Discuss these findings in light of the current view of telomere structure and function as presented in the text.

b. What new information have these data revealed about the distribution of SINEs in the terminus of 16p? (SINEs and LINEs are short and long interspersed nuclear elements, respectively, and are transposable elements called retroposon.)

Answer:

a. These findings support the view that telomeres are specialized chromosome structures with two distinct structural components, simple telomeric sequences and telomere-associated sequences. They show that functional genes do not reside in the telomeric region, consistent with the view that telomeres are heterochromatic and function in DNA replication and stability. They document the structure of telomeric and near-telomeric regions. For example, they show the considerable distance over which the telomere-associated sequences are found, about 36 kb, and give a sense of the number, size, and density of genes in the region near this telomere.

b. At least in this region, Alu sequences are found more often in AT-rich areas. These areas are not as gene-rich as adjacent GC-rich areas. Thus, this class of moderately repetitive sequences, as well as the genes in this area, appear to have a nonrandom distribution.

3

DNA REPLICATION

CHAPTER OUTLINE

REVIEW OF KEY TERMS, SYMBOLS, AND CONCEPTS

In your own words, write a brief definition of each term in the groups below. Check your definitions using the text. Then, develop a concept map using the terms in each group.

1	2	3
semiconservative DNA replication	semidiscontinuous DNA replication	Semidiscontinuous DNA replication
conservative DNA replication	origin of replication	supercoiling
dispersive DNA replication	replication bubble	DNA gyrase
Meselson-Stahl experiment	DNA helicase, primase	rolling circle model
CsCl equilibrium gradient	primosome	λ phage
^{15}N, ^{14}N	replisome	temperate phage
buoyant density	RNA primer	lytic pathway

1	2	3
harlequin chromosomes	SSB protein	Lysogenic pathway
BUdR	replication fork	"sticky" ends
base analog	Okazaki fragments	*cos* site
DNA polymerase I, II, III	bidirectional replication	concatemer
dNTP, dNMP, Mg^{++}	DNA polymerase I, III	*ter*
Kornberg enzyme	5'-to-3' synthesis	leading strand
template strand	proofreading	lagging strand
non-template strand	3'-to-5', 5'-to-3' exonuclease	
primer	leading, lagging strand	
	DNA ligase	
	polA1, *polA1ex1* mutants	
	conditional mutant	

4
eukaryote
cell cycle
checkpoint
START
cyclins
Cdk, MPF
nucleus, mitochondrion
DNA polymerase α, β, δ, γ, ε
DNA replication
DNA repair
proofreading ability
replicon
ARS
telomere
telomerase
reverse transcription
reverse transcriptase
TLC1, EST1, TEL1, TEL2 genes

THINKING ANALYTICALLY

Because of its fundamental importance in genetics and to treating diseases such as cancer, there has been a considerable interest in understanding the mechanism of DNA replication. At this point, we understand the mechanism of DNA replication in considerable detail. For example, we know that DNA replicates semiconservatively, as well as the nature of the complex set of proteins and enzymes that act in a sequential, coordinated fashion to replicate DNA. The best way to understand and retain the details of this complex process is to place them in context. Start by developing a general understanding of the steps of DNA replication. Ask yourself: What must happen first? How is this accomplished? What happens next? How is that accomplished? Then focus on understanding the activities of each of the enzymes and proteins used in each step. To help develop a contextual understanding and establish a mental image of each of the steps, refer to the text figures that summarize the key events of DNA replication.

The following related exercise will help you assess your understanding and retention of the material. After reading each section, close the text and sketch out the aspect of DNA replication that has just been presented. Then relate the figure you have sketched to the previous steps of DNA replication. This will force you to confront unclear concepts and help you identify details you might have missed.

QUESTIONS FOR PRACTICE

Multiple Choice Questions

1. Consider the Meselson and Stahl experiment where *E. coli* were grown in ^{15}N medium. Which model of DNA replication is eliminated by analyzing DNA after exactly one round of replication in ^{14}N medium?
   a. semiconservative
   b. dispersive
   c. conservative

2. The enzymes most directly concerned with catalyzing DNA synthesis are DNA
   a. ligases.
   b. exonucleases.
   c. polymerases.
   d. primases.

3. Which of the following is not essential for the *in vitro* synthesis of DNA?
   a. magnesium ions
   b. DNA polymerase I
   c. DNA primase
   d. a DNA fragment

4. Which enzyme untwists the parent strands of DNA during replication?
   a. DNA primase
   b. DNA helicase
   c. DNA gyrase
   d. DNA ligase

5. Which of the following *do not provide evidence for* semiconservative DNA replication?
   a. The Meselson-Stahl experiment
   b. Harlequin chromosomes
   c. The existence of ARS elements
   d. Okazaki fragments

6. Which of the following *E. coli* polymerases have proofreading activity?
   a. DNA polymerase I
   b. DNA polymerase II
   c. DNA primase

d. DNA polymerase III

e. a, b, and d

7. DNA replication in certain viruses, such as the circular φX174, is achieved

a. using a rolling circle model and semidiscontinuous DNA replication.

b. using a rolling circle model and continuous DNA replication.

c. without using an origin of replication.

d. using DNA fragmentation.

8. During chromosome replication, new histones are synthesized during

a. G_1 and S, and nucleosomes are reformed using new and old histones.

b. G_1 and S, and new nucleosomes are formed with only these new histones.

c. G_1, S, and G_2, and nucleosomes are reformed using new and old histones.

d. G_1, S, and G_2, and new nucleosomes are formed with only these new histones.

9. During the eukaryotic cell cycle, checkpoints serve to determine

a. whether the mitochondria of a cell should replicate their DNA.

b. whether the cell is infected with a virus.

c. whether the cell requires the activity of telomerase.

d. whether the cell is able to or should continue to the next phase of the cell cycle.

10. What is the function of the enzyme telomerase in mammals?

a. to replicate telomeres in all cell types.

b. to replicate and expand simple telomeric repeats in germ cells and tumor cells.

c. to expand the length of simple telomeric repeats in brain cells.

d. to replicate telomere-associated sequences and simple telomeric repeats in all cells.

Answers: 1c; 2c; 3c; 4b; 5c; 6e; 7a; 8b; 9d; 10b.

Thought Questions

1. Describe the mechanism of semidiscontinuous DNA replication.

2. In his investigation of the requirements for *in vitro* synthesis of DNA, Kornberg found that an absolute minimum of four components was necessary. What were these components, and why in particular were each and all necessary? Also, what limitations did his *in vitro* method have as compared to *in vivo* synthesis, which involves other components, such as helicase, primase, and ligase?

3. Describe how eukaryotic DNA is assembled into nucleosomes after DNA replication. Where do the new nucleosomes come from? How might you experimentally determine whether new nucleosomes are composed of all new, or some old and some new, histone proteins (Hint: Consider the Meselson and Stahl approach.)

4. What phenotype would you expect to see in a mutant in the *E. coli polA* gene that showed heat-sensitive 3'-to-5' exonuclease activity, but normal 5'-to-3' exonuclease activity at all temperatures?

5. In humans, how are simple telomeric repeats replicated in a fast dividing population of cells such as epithelial cells? Are all of them replicated at each cell division?

6. The text describes evidence that telomere length is under genetic control, and that in mammals, only immortal cells (e.g., tumor cells, germ cells) have telomerase activity. Why might this be important? In particular, why might it be important for some cells *not* to have telomerase activity?

Thought Questions for Media

After reviewing the media on the *iGenetics* CD-ROM, try to answer these questions.

1. In the animation depicting the experiment by Meselson and Stahl that showed that DNA replication was semiconservative, how did they initially label DNA with ^{15}N?
2. In the animation depicting DNA synthesis using DNA polymerase, when proofreading occurs, what type of molecule is released?
3. In the animation depicting the semidiscontinuous model of DNA replication, in which direction is DNA synthesis on the lagging strand and which direction is this relative to the movement of the replication fork?

1. How can you experimentally determine if a replication fork proceeds bidirectionally or unidirectionally?
2. How can you experimentally determine whether DNA primase randomly starts synthesizing an RNA primer or whether it primes DNA synthesis only at specific sites?
3. In the text, the function(s) of *E. coli* DNA polymerase II was not described. Based on the iActivity, what genetic analysis could you perform to demonstrate that it is involved in DNA repair?

SOLUTIONS TO TEXT PROBLEMS

3.1 Describe the Meselson-Stahl experiment and explain how it showed that DNA replication is semiconservative and not conservative.

Answer: By growing *E. coli* for many generations in media containing "heavy" nitrogen, or ^{15}N, bacterial DNA was uniformly labeled with heavy nitrogen. Such ^{15}N DNA has a greater buoyant density than ^{14}N DNA, and can be differentiated from ^{14}N DNA by its banding position in a CsCl density gradient. Semiconservative DNA replication was demonstrated by placing *E. coli* with ^{15}N DNA into ^{14}N media, and following the density of the DNA that was present in cells after growth proceeded through each of several successive generations. If DNA replication were conservative, after one cell division and one round of DNA replication one would expect to see two distinct, equally dense bands, one corresponding to ^{14}N DNA and one corresponding to ^{15}N DNA. This was not seen. If DNA replication were either semiconservative or dispersive, after one cell division and one round of DNA replication one would expect to see one band, consisting of DNA with a density halfway between ^{14}N DNA and ^{15}N DNA. This was seen. To further distinguish between semiconservative and dispersive replication, the consequences of another round of cell division and DNA replication were examined. In semiconservative replication, one would expect two bands, one of density halfway between ^{14}N DNA and ^{15}N DNA, and one having ^{14}N DNA density. In dispersive replication, only DNA with both ^{14}N DNA and ^{15}N DNA would be seen. The density of the two bands seen (one at the level of ^{14}N DNA and one at the level of half ^{14}N DNA and half ^{15}N DNA) supported the semiconservative model. See text Figure 3.2.

3.2   In the Meselson-Stahl experiment, ^{15}N-labeled cells were shifted to ^{14}N medium at what we can designate as generation 0.

a. For the semiconservative model of replication, what proportion of ^{15}N-^{15}N, ^{15}N-^{14}N, and ^{14}N-^{14}N would you expect to find after 1, 2, 3, 4, and 6 replication cycles?

b. Answer (*a*) in terms of the conservative model of DNA replication.

Answer:

GENERATION	SEMICONSERVATIVE MODEL			CONSERVATIVE MODEL		
	^{15}N-^{15}N	^{15}N-^{14}N	^{14}N-^{14}N	^{15}N ^{15}N	^{15}N-^{14}N	^{14}N-^{14}N
1	0	1	0	1/2	0	1/2
2	0	1/2	1/2	1/4	0	3/4
3	0	1/4	3/4	1/8	0	7/8
4	0	1/8	7/8	1/16	0	15/16
6	0	1/32	31/32	1/64	0	63/64

3.3   A spaceship lands on Earth carrying a sample of extraterrestrial bacteria. You are assigned the task of determining the mechanism of DNA replication in this organism.

You grow the bacteria in unlabeled medium for several generations, then grow it in the presence of ^{15}N for exactly one generation. You extract the DNA and subject it to CsCl centrifugation. The banding pattern you find is as follows:

It appears to you that this is evidence that DNA replicates in the semiconservative manner, but you are wrong. Why? What other experiment could you perform (using the same sample and technique of CsCl centrifugation) that would further distinguish between semiconservative and dispersive modes of replication?

Answer: The CsCl centrifugation result eliminates the possibility of the conservative model of replication, but is still consistent with either semiconservative or dispersive models of DNA replication. To distinguish between these two possibilities using the same sample and the technique of CsCl centrifugation, one could denature the DNA, and then subject the single-stranded sample to CsCl centrifugation. This could be done in practice by using an alkaline CsCl gradient, as the two DNA strands will denature at high pH. The expected results are shown below.

3.4   The elegant Meselson-Stahl experiment was among the first experiments to contribute to what is now a highly detailed understanding of DNA replication. Reconsider this experiment in light of current molecular models by answering the following questions.
   a. Does the fact that DNA replication is semiconservative mean that it must be semidiscontinuous?
   b. Does the fact that DNA replication is semidiscontinuous ensure that it is also semiconservative?
   c. Do any properties of known DNA polymerases ensure that DNA is synthesized semiconservatively?

Answer:
   a. That DNA replication is semiconservative does not mean that it also must be semidiscontinuous. For example, if DNA polymerase were able to synthesize DNA in both the 3'-to-5' and 5'-to-3' directions, DNA replication could proceed continuously on both DNA strands, while still being semiconservative. Alternatively, if each of the two old strands were completely (or even substantially) unwound, and replication were initiated from the 3' end (or 3' region) of each, it could proceed continuously (or mostly continuously) in a 5'-to-3' direction along each strand.
   b. That DNA replication is semidiscontinuous does ensure that it is semiconservative. In the semidiscontinuous model, each old, separated strand serves as a template for a new strand. This is the essence of the semiconservative model.

c. That DNA polymerase synthesizes just one new strand from each "old" single-stranded template and can synthesize in only one direction (5'-to-3') ensures that replication is semiconservative.

3.5   List the components necessary to make DNA in vitro by using the enzyme system isolated by Kornberg.

Answer: DNA can be synthesized *in vitro* using the Kornberg enzyme (DNA polymerase I), all four dNTPs (dATP, dGTP, dCTP, dTTP), magnesium ions (Mg^{2+}), and a fragment of DNA that will serve as a template.

3.6   Give two lines of evidence that the Kornberg enzyme is not the enzyme involved in DNA replication for chromosome duplication in growth of *E. coli*.

Answer: Two lines of evidence that the Kornberg enzyme, DNA polymerase I, is not the enzyme involved in the replication of DNA for the duplication of chromosomes came from (1) an analysis of the growth and biochemical phenotypes of mutations in the *E. coli* gene encoding DNA polymerase I and (2) the discovery and analysis of DNA polymerases II and III.

Biochemical analysis of DNA polymerase I purified from the *polA1* mutant showed that the mutant enzyme has less than 1 percent of normal polymerizing activity, but near-normal 5'-to-3' exonuclease activity. Despite the lack of polymerizing activity, the mutant strain grew and divided normally, suggesting that DNA polymerase I is not the enzyme used to replicate DNA for the duplication of chromosomes. However, the *polA1* mutants did exhibit a high mutation rate when exposed to UV light and chemical mutagens, suggesting that DNA polymerase I has an important function in repairing damaged DNA. These inferences were supported by the biochemical and phenotypic analysis of the conditional mutant *polAex1*. Biochemical analysis of DNA polymerase I purified from *polAex1* showed that the mutant DNA polymerase I is temperature-sensitive for 5'-to-3' exonuclease activity. The *polAex1* DNA polymerase I has normal catalytic activity at 37°C, but at the restrictive temperature of 42°C, *polAex1* DNA polymerase I is defective in 5'-to-3' exonuclease activity, although it has near-normal polymerizing activity. Unlike the *polA1* mutant, the *polAex1* mutant is lethal at 42°C, indicating that while DNA polymerase I synthetic activity is not needed for DNA replication, the 5'-to-3' exonuclease activity is essential for DNA replication. In this way, the analysis of the *polA1* and *polAex1* mutants indicated that there must be other DNA-polymerizing enzymes in the cell. The discovery and analyses of DNA polymerases II and III identified DNA polymerase III as the main enzyme involved in the replication of DNA for chromosomes in the growth of *E. coli*.

3.7   Kornberg isolated DNA polymerase I from *E. coli*. DNA polymerase I has an essential function in DNA replication. What are the functions of the enzyme in DNA replication?

Answer: DNA polymerase I functions to remove the RNA primer synthesized during the initiation of DNA replication and replace this RNA with DNA. When DNA polymerase III, the main synthetic enzyme for DNA polymerization, reaches an RNA primer, it dissociates from the DNA. DNA polymerase I functions to continue synthesis of the DNA in a 5'-to-3' direction. It simultaneously removes the RNA primer using its 5'-to-3' exonuclease activity, and replaces the RNA with DNA nucleotides.

3.8   Assume you have a DNA molecule with the base sequence T-A-T-C-A going from the 5' to the 3' end of one of the polynucleotide chains. The building blocks of the DNA are drawn as in the following figure. Use this shorthand system to diagram the completed double-stranded DNA molecule, as proposed by Watson and Crick.

Answer: The deoxyribonucleotides have a triphosphate group at the 5' end of the molecule, and a hydroxyl group at the 3' end of the molecule. This information establishes the polarity of each of the deoxyribonucleotides (dATP, dGTP, dTTP, and dCTP). Since the phosphodiester bond will form between the 5' and 3' ends of adjacent nucleotides, the 5'-to-3' bonding of the T-A-T-C-A oligonucleotide can be represented as:

The complementary strand will base pair with antiparallel orientation:

3.9   Base analogs are compounds that resemble the natural bases found in DNA and RNA, but are not normally found in those macromolecules. Base analogs can replace their normal counterparts in DNA during in vitro DNA synthesis. Four base analogs were studied for their effects on in vitro DNA synthesis using *E. coli* DNA polymerase. The results were as follows, with the amounts of DNA synthesized expressed as percentages of the DNA synthesized from normal bases only.

ANALOG	NORMAL BASES SUBSTITUTED BY THE ANALOG			
	A	T	C	G
A	0	0	0	25
B	0	54	0	0
C	0	0	100	0
D	0	97	0	0

Which bases are analogs of adenine? of thymine? of cytosine? of guanine?

Answer: None are analogs for adenine, B and D are analogs of thymine, C is an analog of cytosine, and A is an analog of guanine.

3.10   Imagine that you are charged with the task of designing a DNA replicating machine. Describe (draw) models of continuous, semidiscontinuous and discontinuous DNA replication. What was the contribution of Reiji and Tuneko Okazaki and colleagues with regard to those replication models?

Answer: Since DNA replication is known to be semidiscontinuous, its helpful to first consider the details of this model. As the other models are constructed, reference to the semidiscontinuous model can identify the problems associated with them.

   (b) A semidiscontinuous model is shown in text Figures 3.5 and 3.6. Its main features are that:

   i.   DNA replication proceeds only in the 5'-to-3' direction.
   ii. Because DNA replication proceeds only in one direction, it is continuous on the 3'-to-5' template strand (the leading strand), while it is discontinuous on the 5'-to-3' template strand (the lagging strand). This is why it is *semi*discontinuous.
   iii. Replication initiates at a replication origin, where a complex of proteins and enzymes forms at a replication fork. Initially, helicase untwists the DNA and SSBs (single-strand binding proteins) bind the single-stranded DNA to protect it from nuclease attack and keep it unwound.
   iv. Since DNA polymerase can only polymerize DNA if a 3'-OH is provided, an RNA primer must be synthesized by a primase-enzyme complex (the primo-

some). The primosome binds to the single-stranded DNA and synthesizes a short RNA primer in the 5'-to-3' direction.

v. Once an RNA primer is synthesized, DNA polymerase III (a complex of proteins) adds nucleotides onto the 3'-OH in the 5'-to-3' direction, using the unwound DNA as a template. The newly synthesized DNA is thus synthesized onto an RNA primer. This is referred to as an Okazaki fragment. On the lagging strand, synthesis moves "away" from the fork, and synthesis must be reinitiated frequently. On the leading strand, synthesis proceeds "into" the fork. The proteins involved in replication are associated into a replisome, so that the DNA polymerase III of the lagging strand is complexed with DNA polymerase III on the leading strand. The replisome that forms at a replication fork moves as a unit along the DNA, enabling new DNA to be synthesized efficiently on both the leading and lagging strands.

vi. On the lagging strand, DNA polymerase III will (after about 1,000–2,000 bp) encounter the 5' end of an RNA primer of the previously synthesized Okazaki fragment. At this point, it dissociates and is replaced by DNA polymerase I, which uses its 5'-to-3' exonuclease activity to excise the RNA primer and replace it with DNA.

vii. Once the RNA primer is replaced with DNA, the gap between adjacent DNA fragments is sealed by DNA ligase.

(a) A continuous model would need to consider what we know about the semiconservative nature of DNA replication, as well as the enzymes known to be involved in DNA replication. In particular, the model would have to

- produce new double helices that each have one old and one new strand,
- use DNA polymerases that synthesize DNA only in the 5'-to-3' direction,
- use DNA polymerases requiring a 3'-to-5' template,
- use DNA polymerases that need a primer to initiate replication.

One problem to be solved by any model of continuous-only DNA replication is to insure that the DNA is completely replicated. For example, if DNA replication starts in the middle of a linear chromosome, and proceeds continuously in only a 5'-to-3' direction using a 3'-to-5' template strand, half of that template strand will remain unreplicated. This problem might be overcome in different ways depending on whether the chromosome is circular or linear. Each solution however, presents additional problems.

Suppose DNA replication occurs in a circular chromosome. As in the semidiscontinuous model, a protein or set of proteins would recognize an origin-of-replication site within the DNA molecule. To create a site for initiation of DNA synthesis, an endonuclease would nick one strand. Helicase would then bind the free 5' end and start unwinding it. DNA primase would not be needed, as the free 3'-OH would serve as the end of a "primer." The complementary (3'-to-5') strand would be used as a template for new DNA synthesis. A protein such as SSB would bind to the unwound, non-template strand (the strand with an exposed 5'-end) to keep it separate from the template strand. In some unknown manner, this strand would need to be kept separate and perhaps unwound throughout the replication of the template strand. This raises a first problem, as this might be a daunting task given the size of a chromosome compared to the size of a cell. Since DNA replication is semiconservative, this strand (which lacks a priming site) would also need to be replicated. The mechanism by which this would occur is unknown, and raises a second problem. In a replication fork proceeding down the length of the template strand, DNA polymerase III would add nucleotides based on the sequence of the 3'-to-5' template strand, continuously until the site of the origin was reached. Some mechanism would be needed to mark this site, so that DNA polymerase III would stop synthesis. A ligation reaction would be needed to join the two ends of the newly synthesized DNA. There are multiple approaches to solving the two problems posed by this model, but in reality, neither problem occurs, due to the semidiscontinuous nature of DNA replication.

For linear eukaryotic chromosomes, it would be difficult to initiate DNA synthesis at the very ends of chromosomes. But this would not be always be required, as in germ-line cells of eukaryotes, the simple telomeric repeats at the very ends of chromosomes are replicated by telomerase. However, in somatic cells, a distinct mechanism would be needed to identify "origin-of-replication" sites very near to, but not at the ends of the chromosomes. After an endonuclease made a nick near the end of a linear chromosome, a DNA polymerase III-like enzyme could add nucleotides 5'-to-3' based on the sequence of the 3'-to-5' template strand. A replication fork would proceed down the length of the template strand, replicating just one of the strands. Presumably, the other strand would be bound by a SSB-like protein as it was unwound. (Recall the first problem above.) At the other end of a linear chromosome, a similar process would occur.

In both of these models of continuous DNA replication, no DNA primase was required, and no RNA primer was used. Certainly, other models of continuous DNA replication might be devised that use DNA primase and RNA primers. However, there is then the question of how to remove the primers, and so a DNA polymerase I-like enzyme must be used. One significant problem with these models is that they require one of the two strands of the parental DNA molecule to remain separate from the template strand until it is replicated. Given the sizes of chromosomes in prokaryotes and eukaryotes relative to their cell sizes, this is a considerable problem. It is a problem that is solved by having a replication fork synthesize DNA semidiscontinuously, so that there are only very short stretches of unwound, SSB-bound DNA.

(c) A discontinuous model of DNA replication would be nearly identical to the semidiscontinous model [presented in (b)], except that DNA replication would be discontinuous not only on the lagging strand, but also on the leading strand. Presumably, DNA polymerase III would "fall off" the "leading-strand" template periodically, and then come back "on board" to continue synthesizing DNA. No new priming would be required, as there would be a free 3'-OH available for DNA polymerase III to add deoxyribonucleotides onto.

Reiji Okazaki provided the primary evidence that DNA synthesis must be discontinuous on at least one strand. He demonstrated the existence of Okazaki fragments, short segments of DNA that have short RNA primers at their 5' ends. Their existence indicated that DNA synthesis must be periodically re-primed on the lagging strand, and therefore that it must be discontinuous on that strand. See also the answer to question 3.16.

3.11   How long would it take *E. coli* to replicate its entire genome (4.2×10^6 base pairs) assuming a replication rate of 1,000 nucleotides per second at each fork with no pauses?

Answer: In *E. coli*, replication proceeds bidirectionally from the replication origin (*oriC*). Thus, each replication fork proceeds halfway down the length of the circular *E. coli* chromosome, at which point the replication forks meet and replication is complete. Thus, it will take:

$$\frac{4.2 \times 10^6 \text{ base pairs}}{2 \text{ replication forks}} \times \frac{1 \text{ second}}{1000 \text{ basepairs}} \times \frac{1 \text{ minute}}{60 \text{ seconds}} = 35 \text{ minutes}$$

3.12   A diploid organism has 4.5×10^8 base pairs in its DNA. This DNA is replicated in 3 minutes. Assuming all replication forks move at a rate of 10^4 base pairs per minute, how many replicons (replication units) are present in this organism's genome?

Answer: Since a replication fork moves at a rate of 10^4 bp per minute and each replicon has two replication forks moving in opposite directions, in one replicon, replication would be occurring at a rate of 2×10^4 bp/minute. Since all of the organism's DNA is replicated in 3 minutes, the number of replicons in the diploid genome is

$$\frac{4.5 \times 10^8 \text{ bp}}{3 \text{ minutes}} \times \frac{1 \text{ replicon}}{2 \times 10^4 \text{ bp/minute}} = 7,500.$$

3.13   The following events, steps or reactions occur during *E. coli* DNA replication. For each entry in Column A, select the appropriate entry in Column B. Each entry in Column A may have more than one answer, and each entry in Column B can be used more than once.

	COLUMN A		COLUMN B
__ a.	Unwinds the double helix	A.	Polymerase I
__ b.	Prevents reassociation of complementary bases	B.	Polymerase III
__ c.	Is an RNA polymerase	C.	Helicase
__ d.	Is a DNA polymerase	D.	Primase
__ e.	Is the "repair" enzyme	E.	Ligase
__ f.	Is the major elongation enzyme	F.	SSB protein
__ g.	A 5'-to-3' polymerase	G.	Gyrase
__ h.	A 3'-to-5' polymerase	H.	None of these
__ i.	Has 5'-to-3' exonuclease function		
__ j.	Has 3'-to-5' exonuclease function		
__ k.	Bonds free 3'-OH end of a polynucleotide to a free 5' monophosphate end of polynucleotide		
__ l.	Bonds 3'-OH end of a polynucleotide to a free 5' nucleotide triphosphate		
__ m.	Separates daughter molecules and causes super-coiling		

Answer: a. C; b. F; c. D; d. A, B; e. A; f. B; g. A, B, D; h. H; i. A; j. A, B; k. E; l. A, B, (D, after the first two bases of the RNA primer are positioned); m. G.

3.14   Describe the molecular action of the enzyme DNA ligase. What properties would you expect an *E. coli* cell to have if it had a temperature-sensitive mutation in the gene for DNA ligase?

Answer: DNA ligase catalyzes the formation of a phosphodiester bond between the 3'-OH and the 5'-monophosphate groups on either side of a single-strand DNA gap, sealing the gap. See Figure 3.7. Temperature-sensitive ligase mutants would be unable to seal such gaps at the restrictive (high) temperature, leading to fragmented lagging strands, and presumably cell death. If a biochemical analysis were performed on DNA synthesized after *E. coli* were shifted to a restrictive temperature, there would be an accumulation of DNA fragments the size of Okazaki fragments. This would provide additional evidence that DNA replication must be discontinuous on one strand.

3.15   Chromosome replication in *E. coli* commences from a constant point, called the origin of replication. It is known that DNA replication is bidirectional. Devise a biochemical experiment to prove that the *E. coli* chromosome replicates bidirectionally. (Hint: Assume that the amount of gene product is directly proportional to the number of genes.)

Answer: Assume the amount of a gene's product is directly proportional to the number of copies of the gene present in the *E. coli* cell. Assay the enzymatic activity of genes at various positions in the *E. coli* chromosome during the replication period. Then, some genes (those immediately adjacent to the origin) will double their activity very shortly after replication begins. Relate the map position of genes having doubled activity to the amount of time that has transpired since replication was initiated. If replication is bidirectional, there should be a doubling of the gene products both clockwise and counterclockwise from the origin.

3.16   Reiji Okazaki concluded that both strands could not replicate continuously. What evidence led him to this conclusion?

Answer: Reiji Okazaki and his colleagues added a pulse of radioactive DNA precursor, ^{3}H-thymidine, to cultures of *E. coli* for a small fraction of its generation time (0.5 percent). To prevent the further incorporation of additional radioactive precursor into the DNA after this period, they chased this pulse with a large amount of nonradioactive thymidine. They then sampled the bacterial DNA at successive intervals as DNA replication continued. When DNA was sampled soon after the labeling period, most of the radioactivity was found in DNA with very low molecular weights, in DNA fragments between 100 and 1000 nucleotides long. When DNA was sampled at longer intervals, the radioactivity was found in DNA with much higher molecular weight, in much longer DNA fragments. The short DNA fragments seen in the early samplings indicate that DNA replication normally involves the synthesis of short DNA segments – the Okazaki fragments – that are then linked together. This provided evidence that DNA replication occurs in a discontinuous fashion on the lagging strand.

3.17   A space probe returns from Jupiter and brings with it a new microorganism for study. It has double-stranded DNA as its genetic material. However, studies of replication of the alien DNA reveal that, while the process is semiconservative, DNA synthesis is continuous on both the leading-strand and the lagging-strand templates. What conclusions can you make from that result?

Answer: Clearly DNA replication in the Jovian bug does not occur as it does in *E. coli*. Assuming that the double-stranded DNA is antiparallel as it is in *E. coli*, the Jovian DNA polymerases must be able to synthesize DNA in the 5'-to-3' direction (on the leading strand) as well as in the 3'-to-5' direction (on the lagging strand). This is unlike any DNA polymerase on Earth.

3.18   Compare and contrast eukaryotic and prokaryotic DNA polymerases.

Answer: A number of different DNA polymerases have been identified in both pro-karyotes and eukaryotes. All DNA polymerases can synthesize DNA using a tem-plate and a primed strand. The primer provides a 3'-OH onto which nucleotides are added in the 5'-to-3' direction. There are three DNA polymerases in *E. coli* (I, II, and III) and five in mammalian cells (α, β, γ, δ, and ε). All of the enzymes synthesize DNA in a 5'-to-3' direction.

In *E. coli*, at least DNA polymerase I and III are essential for viability. DNA po-lymerase I and II each consist of one polypeptide coded for by one gene, while DNA polymerase III consists of ten polypeptides coded for by many genes. Both DNA polymerase I and III are involved in DNA replication, with DNA polymerase III being the main synthetic enzyme. Less is known about DNA polymerase II. All three *E. coli* DNA polymerases also have proofreading activity, as they have 3'-to-5' exonuclease activity. However, only DNA polymerase I has 5'-to-3' exonuclease activity, the activity needed to excise the RNA primer at the 5' end of Okazaki fragments.

In mammalian cells, only two DNA polymerases, α and δ, function in nuclear DNA replication. They function much like *E. coli* DNA polymerase III functions in chromosomal DNA replication. DNA polymerases β and ε are nuclear and function in DNA repair. DNA polymerase γ is found in mitochondria and catalyzes mito-chondrial DNA replication. In contrast to the *E. coli* polymerases, only a subset of mammalian enzymes (δ, ε, and γ), have proofreading 3'-to-5' exonuclease activity. Like the *E. coli* polymerases, the nuclear polymerases α and δ, as well as the mito-chondrial polymerase δ, use RNA primers.

3.19   In eukaryotes, cellular proliferation is tightly controlled. Explain why this is im-portant and outline how key regulatory proteins control the progression of the cell cycle.

Answer: Cellular proliferation is tightly controlled at a series of cell cycle check-points. At each checkpoint, a system of checks and balances assesses whether the cell is able to or should be allowed to continue into the next phase of the cell cycle. This is important for many reasons. To proceed through the G_1-S checkpoint, a cell must be large enough, and the environment must be favorable for future growth. This ensures that cells will not expend their energy on DNA replication unless there is a good chance for successful future growth. As will be seen in Chapter 18, G_1-S is also a major checkpoint to ensure that DNA damage is repaired, so that only healthy, undamaged cells progress through the cell cycle. To proceed through the G_2-M checkpoint, a cell must have completed DNA replication, be large enough, and be in a favorable environment. This maximizes the probability that daughter cells will have a euploid genome, and that the energy expended on mitosis will result in viable daughter cells. To proceed through the third checkpoint in M, chromosomes must be attached properly to the mitotic spindle, ensuring their correct segregation and the production of euploid daughter cells.

The cyclins and cyclin-dependent kinases (Cdks) are interacting regulatory proteins that control whether cells will proceed past each cell cycle checkpoint. Cyclin-Cdk interactions lead to the activation and inactivation of other cellular proteins, often by altering their phosphorylation state. For example, at the G_1-S (START) checkpoint, one or more G_1 cyclins bind to the Cdk CDC28/cdc2 kinase and activate it. This Cdk in turn phosphorylates key proteins needed for progression of the cell into S. Following activation of the Cdk, the level of cyclins is decreased through increased proteolysis.

3.20   Autoradiography is a technique that allows radioactive areas of chromosomes to be observed under the microscope. The slide is covered with a photographic emulsion, which is exposed by radioactive decay. In regions of exposure the emulsion forms silver grains on being developed. The tiny silver grains can be seen on top of the (much larger) chromosomes. Devise a method for finding out which regions in the human karyotype replicate during the last 30 min. of the S period. (Assume a cell cycle in which the cell spends 10 hours in G_1, 9 hours in S, 4 hours in G_2, and 1 hour in M.)

Answer: If cells spend 4 hours in G_2, then there will be about 4.5 to 5 hours between the last 30 minutes of S and metaphase in M. To see which chromosomal regions replicate during the last 30 minutes of S, add ^{3}H-thymidine for a 5-minute pulse, chase it with (cold, unlabeled) thymidine, wait 4.5–5 hours and prepare a spread of metaphase chromosomes on a glass slide. (Cells can be blocked at metaphase by adding colchicine, a drug that blocks the separation of the chromatids by interfering with microtubule function.) Immerse the slide in photographic emulsion, and after a suitable exposure period, develop the exposed silver grains and stain the chromosomes. Examine which regions of the chromosomes have silver grains lying over them to infer where ^{3}H-thymidine was incorporated.

3.21   In typical human fibroblasts in culture, the G_1 period of the cell cycle lasts about 10 hours, S lasts about 9 hours, G_2 takes 4 hours, and M takes 1 hour. Imagine you were to do an experiment in which you added radioactive (^{3}H) thymidine to the medium and left it there for 5 minutes and then washed it out and put in ordinary medium.
   a. What percentage of cells would you expect to become labeled by incorporating the ^{3}H-thymidine into their DNA?
   b. How long would you have to wait after removing the ^{3}H medium before you would see labeled metaphase chromosomes?
   c. Would one or both chromatids be labeled?

d. How long would you have to wait if you wanted to see metaphase chromosomes containing ^{3}H in the regions of the chromosomes that replicated at the beginning of the S period?

Answer:

a. Assuming that the fibroblast culture is completely asynchronous, and that cells are distributed in all stages of the cell cycle, 10/24 of the cells would be in G_1, 9/24 in S, 4/24 in G_2, and 1/24 in M. Only cells in S are replicating their DNA, so only 9/24 of the cells are capable of incorporating ^{3}H-thymidine into their DNA. $(9/24)(100\%) = 37.5\%$.

b. If a cell in the very last stages of S phase incorporated ^{3}H-thymidine into its DNA, it would have to proceed through G_2 (four hours) before entering M. Not until M are metaphase chromosomes seen. Therefore, wait a little over four hours to see labeled metaphase chromosomes.

c. DNA replication is semiconservative, meaning that each of the two double strands is used as a template for the synthesis of a new, complementary strand. When ^{3}H-thymidine is incorporated into the newly synthesized DNA, it will be incorporated into each new complementary strand, and so be in each chromatid that is synthesized.

d. Cells that took up ^{3}H-thymidine into their DNA at the beginning of S phase would need to complete the S phase, and then go through G_2 and mitotic prophase before label could be seen in metaphase chromosomes. This would take a little over 13 hours.

    The experiment that is outlined in this problem gives one an elegant means to determine which chromosomal region replicates early in S phase and which chromosomal region replicates late in S phase. Proceed by systematically collecting cells at various time points after the ^{3}H-thymidine pulse. Spread their chromosomes on slides; cover the chromosomes with a photographic emulsion that is able to detect decay of ^{3}H particles. After a period of time, develop the emulsion to detect sites on chromosomes that were replicating at a given stage of S phase. This kind of experimentation supported a view that there are early- and late-replicating regions of eukaryotic chromosomes. The late-replicating regions are characteristically heterochromatic and include centromeric regions.

3.22   Assume you did the experiment in Question 3.21, but left the radioactive medium on the cells for 16 hours instead of 5 minutes. How would your answers change?

Answer:

a. 16 hours is longer than any single stage of the cell cycle. In particular, a cell that just entered G_2 at the beginning of the labeling period would, at the end of a 16-

hour labeling period, be in early S phase. Therefore, it would be labeled. Indeed, every cell would be labeled.

b. Labeled metaphase chromosomes would already be present by the time the ^{3}H-thymidine was removed, as some of the cells in G_1 at the beginning of the labeling period would go through S and G_2, and be in M after 16 hours.

c. Both chromatids would be labeled, as in a 5-min pulse of ^{3}H-thymidine.

d. Consider what would happen if metaphase chromosomes were examined in cells collected periodically after the radioactive medium was washed out. Start with cells sampled immediately after the radioactive medium is washed out. Since these cells were left in the radioactive medium for 16 hours, and there is only a little over 13 hours between the beginning of the S period and metaphase of mitosis, the previous S phase of these cells was spent entirely in the presence of radioactive thymidine. Any metaphase chromosomes seen at this time point would be labeled in their entirety, so these chromosomes would not be useful to identify regions replicated at a particular time during the S period. Suppose instead that cells were sampled after about 6 hours in nonradioactive medium. These cells would have been in the first part of G_1 when the radioactive medium was added and spent about the first 8 hours of their S period in the radioactive medium. All of their chromosomal regions would be labeled except for the regions that replicated late in the S period. By sampling cells over increasing lengths of time, and comparing the results of different samplings, chromosomal regions that replicated at successively earlier stages could be identified. Finally, consider the cell sample taken after 13 hours in nonradioactive medium. These cells would have just entered the S period when the nonradioactive medium had been washed out. Since they have only spent the beginning of their S period in radioactive medium, chromosomal regions that replicated early in the S period would be labeled. However, since the culture was left in radioactive medium for 16 hours, the parents of these cells spent about the last hour of their S period in the presence of radioactive thymidine. Thus, these cells would have chromosomes that were labeled both at the beginning and at the end of the S period. Only by comparison of this sample to samples obtained at earlier time points might these regions be distinguished.

3.23 In Figure 3.3, semiconservative DNA replication is visualized in eukaryotic cells using the harlequin chromosome-staining technique.

a. Explain what the harlequin chromosome-staining technique is and how it provides evidence for semiconservative DNA replication in eukaryotes.

b. Propose a hypothesis to explain why, in Figure 3.3, some chromatids appear to contain segments of both DNA containing T and DNA containing BUdR, and others appear to consist entirely of DNA with T or DNA with BUdR.

Answer:

a. Harlequin chromosomes are prepared by allowing tissue culture cells to undergo two rounds of DNA replication in the presence of BUdR. After BUdR (a base analog that replaces T) becomes incorporated in the DNA, metaphase chromosomes stained with Giemsa stain and a fluorescent dye have one darkly stained and one lightly stained chromatid. Since DNA with BUdR stains less intensely than DNA with T, the presence of two differently stained chromatids indicates that one chromatid has two strands with BUdR while the other has one with BUdR and one with T.

This supports the semiconservative model of DNA replication. After one round of replication, the DNA molecule contains one new strand with BUdR and one old strand with T. After two rounds of replication, these molecules will each produce a DNA molecule where both strands have BUdR (the light chromatid) and a DNA molecule where one strand has BUdR- and one strand has T (the dark chromatid).

b. Chromosomes with chromatids that appear to contain segments of with both T and BUdR might have had a sister-chromatid exchange (mitotic crossing-over).

3.24   When the eukaryotic chromosome duplicates, the nucleosome structures must duplicate. Discuss the synthesis of histones in the cell cycle and discuss the model for the assembly of new nucleosomes at the replication forks.

Answer: New histones are synthesized to complex with newly synthesized DNA. The five histone genes are transcribed starting near the end of G_1, just prior to S. The mRNAs that are produced are translated throughout S, producing new histones that will be assembled into nucleosomes as the chromosomes are duplicated. Nucleosomes assemble and disassemble from DNA as the replication fork passes a replicating DNA region. There is a 200–300-bp zone around the replication fork free of nucleosomes. Different types of experiments have strongly suggested that new nucleosomes are assembled from an all-new set of histones, while the old nucleosomes are conserved.

3.25   A mutant *Tetrahymena* has an altered repeated sequence in its telomeric DNA. What change in the telomerase enzyme would have this phenotype?

Answer: Telomerase synthesizes the simple-sequence telomeric repeats at the ends of chromosomes. The enzyme is made up of both protein and RNA, and the RNA component has a base sequence that is complementary to the telomere repeat unit. The RNA component is used as a template for the telomere repeat, so that if the RNA component were to be altered, the telomere repeat would be as well. Thus, the mutant in this question is likely to have an altered RNA component.

3.26   Given what you know about these repeats of short, GC-rich sequences and that the exact sequence of the repeat in a telomere is species-specific, what is the function of telomeres. (Hint: normal mammalian somatic cells lack telomerase, but germ cells retain it. Cancer cells also have telomerase; this information is important in understanding the implications of the function of telomeres.)

Answer: The short, GC-rich repeats associated with the simple telomeric sequences are species specific because the telomeric repeats found on all chromosomes of an individual are synthesized by the enzyme telomerase, which uses an RNA template that is complementary to the repeat. The observations that mammalian somatic cells lack telomerase, but that telomerase is found in cells that are "immortal" – such as germ cells and cancer cells, suggest two things. First, they suggest that telomere length is regulated by the availability of telomerase activity. Second, since the chromosomes of cells that lack telomerase activity will have progressively shorter telomeres as the cells proceed through repeated cycles of mitosis, they suggest that telomeres are somehow important for cell viability or cell immortality. That is, cells without telomerase are able to divide only a finite number of times before they become inviable because of the eventual loss of their telomeric sequences. Telomeres must therefore function in a process essential for cell viability, perhaps related to chromosome stability and/or replication. The view that telomere length is necessary for long-term cell viability is also supported by analysis of yeast mutations that affect telomerase function (e.g., *TLC1*) and telomere length (*EST1*).

4

GENE CONTROL OF PROTEINS

CHAPTER OUTLIN

GENE CONTROL OF ENZYME STRUCTURE
Garrod's Hypothesis of Inborn Errors of Metabolism
The One Gene–One Enzyme Hypothesis

GENETICALLY BASED ENZYME DEFICIENCIES IN HUMANS
Phenylketonuria
Albinism
Lesch-Nyhan Syndrome
Tay-Sachs Disease

GENE CONTROL OF PROTEIN STRUCTURE
Sickle-Cell Anemia
Other Hemoglobin Mutants
Biochemical Genetics of the Human ABO Blood Groups
Cystic Fibrosis

GENETIC COUNSELING
Carrier Detection
Fetal Analysis

REVIEW OF KEY TERMS, SYMBOLS, AND CONCEPTS

In your own words, write a brief definition of each term in the groups below. Check your definitions using the text. Then, develop a concept map using the terms in each group.

1	2
inborn error of metabolism	enzyme
metabolic pathway	nonenzymatic protein
biochemical pathway	ABO blood type
nutritional mutant	antigen, antibody
auxotroph	polysaccharide
prototroph	glycosyltransferase
ascus, asci, ascospore, conidia	cystic fibrosis (CF)
minimal medium	transmembrane conductance regulator
mating type	active transport
one gene–one enzyme hypothesis	sickle-cell anemia, sickle-cell trait
one gene–one polypeptide hypothesis	hemoglobin

1	2
amino acid	α-, β-polypeptide
polypeptide	electrophoresis
protein	amino-acid substitution
N-, C-terminus	hydrophilic
pleiotropic	multiple alleles
alkaptonuria (AKU)	autosomal recessive mutation
phenylketonuria (PKU)	genetic counseling
albinism	pedigree analysis
Lesch-Nyhan syndrome	carrier detection
Tay-Sachs disease	fetal analysis
recessive trait	amniocentesis
OMIM	chorionic villus sampling

THINKING ANALYTICALLY

The problems in this chapter require you to make multiple connections. You need to:
   (1) relate the genetic properties of a mutation to its visible phenotype,
   (2) relate the visible phenotype to a biochemical deficit (a 'biochemical phenotype'),
   (3) relate the biochemical deficit of a mutation back to its genetic properties.

As you make these connections, layers of complexity will unfold in a problem. Clues at one level (genetic properties of the mutations, mutant phenotypes, biochemical abnormalities found in the mutant) can be used to infer what might be happening at another level. Approach the problems systematically, attempting to connect these levels wherever possible.

To relate biochemical pathways to mutant phenotypes, diagram as much of the biochemical pathway as you can, and then try to understand how specific phenotypic consequences arise when a particular step is blocked. Go slowly and be thorough. It is essential to remember that mutations in different steps of a biochemical pathway do not always cause identical mutant phenotypes. In addition, mutations affecting a particular step can have multiple consequences. They may lead to the absence of the final product and cause one phenotype. They may also lead to the accumulation of intermediate metabolites of the pathway and cause a different phenotype. Furthermore, mutations at different steps of a pathway may be able to be "rescued" if different biochemical intermediates are provided to the mutant.

QUESTIONS FOR PRACTICE

Multiple Choice Questions

1. An inborn error of metabolism is
   a. any biochemical abnormality that results from taking a drug.
   b. any heritable biochemical abnormality.
   c. any recessive mutation.
   d. any dominant mutation.

2. Why was the one gene–one enzyme hypothesis recast as the one gene–one polypeptide hypothesis?
   a. Genes can encode proteins that are not enzymes.
   b. Some enzymes are not polypeptides.
   c. Some enzymes have more than one polypeptide subunit.
   d. Some polypeptides are not enzymes.

3. Suppose an individual was diagnosed with PKU as a child and was successfully treated. If that individual and a normal, noncarrier (pku^+/pku^+) partner have children, what is the probability that they will have offspring that are carriers for PKU?
   a. 0.00
   b. 0.25
   c. 0.50
   d. 1.00

4. In individuals affected with AKU,
   a. a block in the pathway leads to the accumulation of homogentisic acid.
   b. if homogentisic acid is provided, the pathway can be completed.
   c. a block in the pathway leads to the accumulation of phenylalanine.
   d. if phenylalanine is provided, the pathway can be completed.

5. Two *Neurospora* auxotrophs are unable to grow on minimal medium but are able to grow on minimal medium supplemented with arginine. When each is tested, only one can grow on minimal medium supplemented with ornithine, a biochemical precursor to arginine. Which statement(s) below are supported by these findings?
   a. The auxotrophs are blocked in different biochemical steps.
   b. At least one auxotroph is blocked in a step before ornithine is made.
   c. Both of the auxotrophs are blocked in a step before ornithine is made.
   d. Both of the auxotrophs accumulate ornithine.
   e. Both a and b.

6. In complex metabolic pathways such as the phenylalanine-tyrosine metabolic pathway,
   a. blocks at different steps always result in the same phenotype.
   b. a block at one step results solely in the accumulation of the biochemical made just before that step.
   c. blocks at different steps can lead to very different phenotypes.
   d. a block at one step can lead to the accumulation of potentially toxic derivatives of biochemicals synthesized before that step.
   e. a and b.
   f. c and d.

7. What is the difference between sickle-cell anemia and sickle-cell trait?
   a. None, they refer to individuals with the same disease that are equally affected.
   b. Individuals with sickle-cell anemia have severe disease and have two abnormal alleles, while individuals with the sickle-cell trait have a less severe form of the disease, as they are heterozygotes with one disease and one normal allele.
   c. Individuals with sickle-cell anemia have severe disease. The term "sickle-cell trait" refers to the disease allele present in their families, and not to symptomatic status.

    d. Individuals with sickle-cell anemia have severe disease and are homozygous for a severe disease allele. Individuals with sickle-cell trait have mild disease and are homozygous for a less severe disease allele.

8. Both Tay-Sachs disease and Lesch-Nyhan syndrome are examples of human diseases that are
   a. pleiotropic.
   b. caused by a deficiency in one enzyme activity.
   c. recessive.
   d. a, b and c.

9. An example of a heritable disease that results from a biochemical defect in a non-enzymatic protein is
   a. PKU.
   b. AKU.
   c. sickle-cell anemia.
   d. Tay-Sachs disease.

10. Which of the following is *not* true about both amniocentesis and chorionic villus sampling?
    a. Both can be performed with an acceptably low risk as early as the eighth week of pregnancy.
    b. Each procedure has a risk of fetal loss.
    c. One is more likely than the other to provide an accurate diagnosis.
    d. Both are valid, useful procedures in genetic counseling.

Answers: 1b; 2c; 3d; 4a; 5e; 6f; 7b; 8d; 9c; 10a.

Thought Questions

1. If you were a genetics counselor, how would you counsel the following couple that is contemplating having children? The prospective father is apparently normal, except for a nervous twitch of his nose, but his maternal uncle had PKU as a child and his brother, who plays in a heavy metal band, is hard of hearing. The prospective mother also appears normal, but her father has hemophilia and her brother, who plays in the same band as her brother-in-law, is also hard of hearing. You know that hemophilia is often X-linked, and that PKU and sometimes deafness are autosomal recessive.

2. Distinguish between the procedures of amniocentesis and chorionic villus sampling. How is each useful in genetic counseling? What reasons are there for or against choosing each procedure?

3. All states currently require testing for PKU in infants. Do you expect the frequency of PKU to decline, or increase, over time? Justify your answer.

4. In the US, the frequency of PKU is about 1 in 16,000 newborns. The frequency of cystic fibrosis is about 1 in 4,000 newborns. While all states currently require testing for PKU in infants, not all states require testing for cystic fibrosis. Both are autosomal recessive disorders. What are the risks associated with screening for an inherited disease? What reasons might there be not to routinely test for cystic fibrosis (or PKU) in new-

borns? What reasons might there be to routinely test for PKU (or cystic fibrosis) in newborns?

5. Over two hundred hemoglobin mutants have been detected. Explain why some hemoglobin mutations do not lead to as severe sickle-cell anemia phenotypes as others.

6. Some alleles of sickle-cell anemia, when heterozygous with a normal allele, confer some resistance to malarial infection. What consequences might this have on selection for this allele in different human populations?

7. Keep in mind your answer to questions 5 and 6 as you respond to the following question. Suppose you have the ability to make point mutations in a gene that encodes an enzyme, and are able to determine the percentage of normal enzyme activity that remains in the mutant enzyme. What effects would you expect to see if you systematically mutate the gene for the enzyme, changing only one amino acid at a time?

8. Different diseases are more prevalent in different ethnic groups. For example, within the US population, Tay-Sachs disease is more prevalent in individuals of Ashkenazi Jewish descent, while certain types of sickle-cell anemia are more prevalent in some individuals of Hispanic, Native American, and African American descent. Given this situation and a history of documented discrimination based on ethnicity in the US, what concerns must be addressed if genetic testing is to be used for carrier testing and prenatal diagnosis with the aim of improving the quality of health-care?

9. As you have seen in the study of PKU, Tay-Sachs disease, Lesch-Nyhan syndrome, and sickle-cell anemia, mutations that result in the blockage of a single enzymatic step, or the function of a single protein, can have pleiotropic phenotypes. Generate an hypothesis about a potentially general principle from these data.

10. What functions do (should) genetic counseling services provide? What do they look for, how do they proceed, what do they recommend, and what, if any, advice do (should) they give?

11. In many states in the US, legislation is being developed to address the use and privacy of information obtained from genetic testing. What specific protections can be legislated for genetic testing to be performed without fears of stigmatization and discrimination? Under what circumstances, if any, should genetic testing be allowed for diseases for which there is no treatment? no cure? For some diseases with very similar symptoms, genetic tests may be useful to distinguish between diseases, and improve therapy. Should laws governing the use of genetic tests as diagnostic tests (in symptomatic individuals) differ from laws governing the use of genetic tests as tests for predicting risk (in asymptomatic individuals)?

12. What is meant by "obtaining informed consent" prior to undergoing a genetic test? What information is needed to give informed consent prior to undergoing a genetic test?

Thought Questions for Media

After reviewing the media on the *iGenetics* CD-ROM, try to answer these questions.

1. In the animation depicting the experiments by Beadle and Tatum, how can *Neurospora* be propagated asexually?
2. How did Beadle and Tatum obtain nutritional mutations?
3. Why did Beadle and Tatum use two rounds of screening for auxotrophs?

1. Why is the arginine pathway present in *Neurospora* also present in humans?
2. Suppose a block is made in a single enzymatic step of the arginine pathway in either humans or *Neurospora*. What is the consequence to the level of the precursor compound synthesized before the blocked enzymatic step?
3. How might citrullinemia, argininosuccinic aciduria, or OTC deficiency lead to ammonia buildup? How might you implement effective therapeutic treatments?

SOLUTIONS TO TEXT PROBLEMS

4.1   Phenylketonuria (PKU) is an inheritable metabolic disease of humans; its symptoms include mental deficiency. This phenotypic effect results from:
a. accumulation of phenylketones in the blood
b. absence of phenylalanine hydroxylase
c. deficiency of phenylketones in the blood
d. deficiency of phenylketones in the diet

Answer: a.

4.2   If a person were homozygous for both PKU and alkaptonuria (AKU), would you expect him or her to exhibit the symptoms of PKU, or AKU, or both? Refer to the following pathway.

Phenylalanine

↓ (blocked in PKU)

tyrosine → DOPA → melanin

↓

ρ-Hydroxyphenylpyruvic acid

↓

Homogentisic acid

↓ (blocked in AKU)

Maleylacetoacetic acid

Answer: Given the pathway that is presented, a double homozygote will have PKU, but not AKU. The PKU block will prevent homogentisic acid from being formed, so that it could not accumulate to high levels and cause AKU.

4.3   Refer to the pathway shown in Question 4.2. What effect, if any, would you expect PKU or AKU to have on pigment formation? Explain your answer.

Answer: The block in PKU leads to decreased tyrosine levels and so should lead to a decrease in melanin formation and pigmentation. However, some tyrosine will be obtained from food, and so the block in the pathway can be partially circumvented in this way. It has been reported that PKU patients are sometimes lighter in pigmentation than their normal relatives.

Since the block in AKU patients lies after (downstream of) the formation of melanin, pigmentation should not be affected in AKU patients. However, the levels of the products of an enzymatic reaction can affect the efficiency with which that reaction proceeds. If the products of an enzymatic reaction accumulate, the reaction may be inhibited. This in turn can lead to the accumulation of the substrates of the reaction. In this case, the accumulation of homogentisic acid in AKU individuals may ultimately lead to elevation of tyrosine levels. This tyrosine might be available for conversion to melanin. Hence, if AKU has any effect, it may be to increase pigmentation levels.

Using the same logic as in question 4.2, an individual with both PKU and AKU will show symptoms of PKU, but not AKU. Therefore, it is likely that there will be decreased tyrosine levels, and a decrease in melanin formation and pigmentation.

4.4   Upon infection of *E. coli* with bacteriophage T4, a series of biochemical pathways result in the formation of mature progeny phages. The phages are released after lysis of the bacterial host cells. Suppose that the following pathway exists:

enzyme   enzyme

↓   ↓

A → B → mature phage

Also suppose that we have two temperature-sensitive mutants that involve the two enzymes catalyzing these sequential steps. One of the mutations is cold-sensitive (*cs*) in that no mature phages are produced at 17°C. The other is heat-sensitive (*hs*) in that no mature phages are produced at 42°C. Normal progeny phages are produced when phages carrying either of the mutations infect bacteria at 30°C. However, let us assume that we do not know the sequence of the two mutations. Two models are therefore possible:

hs   *cs*

(1)   A → B → phage

cs   *hs*

(2)   A → B → phage

Outline how you would experimentally determine which model is the correct model without artificially lysing phage-infected bacteria.

Answer: Consider what will happen under each model if *E. coli* is infected with a doubly mutant phage (one step is cold-sensitive, one step is heat-sensitive), and the growth temperature is shifted between 17° and 42° during phage growth.

Suppose model (1) is correct and cells infected with the double mutant are first incubated at 17° and then shifted to 42°. Progeny phages will be produced and the cells will lyse as each step of the pathway can be completed in the correct order. In model (1), the first step, *A* to *B*, is controlled by a gene whose product is heat-sensitive, but not cold-sensitive. At 17°, the enzyme works, and *A* will be converted to *B*. While at 17°, the second, cold-sensitive step of the pathway prevents the production of mature phage. However, when the temperature is shifted to 42°, the accumulated *B* product can be used to make mature phage, so that lysis will occur.

Under model (1), a temperature shift performed in the reverse direction does not allow for growth. When *E. coli* cells are infected with a doubly mutant phage, and placed at 42°, the heat-sensitive first step precludes the accumulation of *B*. When the culture is shifted to 17°, *B* can accumulate, but now, the second step cannot occur, so that no progeny phage can be produced. Therefore, if model (1) is correct, lysis will be seen only in a temperature shift from 17° to 42°.

If model (2) is correct, growth will be seen only in a temperature shift from 42° to 17°, and not in a temperature shift from 17° to 42°. Hence, the correct model can be deduced by performing the temperature-shift experiment in each direction, and observing which direction allows progeny phage to be produced.

4.5   Four mutant strains of *E. coli* (*a*, *b*, *c*, and *d*) all require substance X in order to grow. Four plates were prepared, as shown in the following figure. In each case the medium was minimal, with just a trace amount of substance X, to allow a small amount of growth of the mutant cells. On plate *a*, cells of mutant strain *a* were spread over the entire surface of the agar and grew to form a thin lawn (continuous bacterial growth over the plate). On plate *b* the lawn is composed of mutant *b* cells, and so on. On each plate, cells of the four mutant types were inoculated over the lawn, as indicated by the circles. Dark circles indicate luxuriant growth. This experiment tests whether the bacterial strain spread on the plate can feed the four strains inoculated on the plate, allowing them to grow. What do these results show about the relationship of the four mutants to the metabolic pathway leading to substance X?

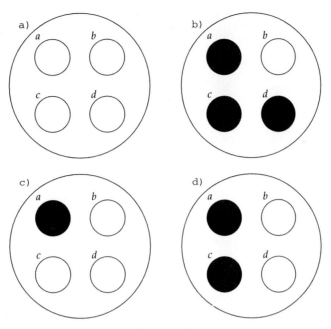

Figure 4.B

Answer: A strain blocked at a later step in the pathway accumulates a metabolic intermediate that can "feed" a strain blocked at an earlier step. It will secrete the metabolic intermediate into the medium, thereby providing a nutrient to bypass the earlier block of another strain. Consequently, a strain that feeds all others (but itself) is blocked in the last step of the pathway, while a strain that feeds no others is blocked in the first step of the pathway. Mutant *a* is blocked in the earliest step in the pathway, as it cannot feed any of the others. Mutant *c* is next, as it can supply the substance *a* needs, but cannot feed *b* or *d*. Mutant *d* is next, and mutant *b* is last in the pathway, as it can feed all the others. The pathway is $a \rightarrow c \rightarrow d \rightarrow b$.

4.6   The following growth responses (where 1 = growth and 0 = no growth) of mutants *1–4* were seen on the related biosynthetic intermediates A, B, C, D, and E. Assume that all intermediates are able to enter the cell, that each mutant carries only one mutation, and that all mutants affect steps after B in the pathway.

	GROWTH ON				
MUTANT	A	B	C	D	E
1	+	0	0	0	0
2	0	0	0	+	0
3	0	0	+	0	0
4	0	0	0	+	+

B $\xrightarrow{1}$ A $\xrightarrow{4}$ E $\xrightarrow{2}$ D

$\xrightarrow{3}$ C

Which of the schemes in the figure best fits the data with regard to the biosynthetic pathway?

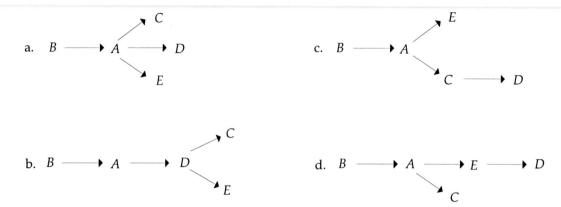

Answer: One approach to this problem is to try to sequentially fit the data to each pathway, as if each were correct. Check where each mutant *could* be blocked (remember, each mutant carries only one mutation), whether the mutant would be able to grow if supplemented with the *single* nutrient that is listed, and whether the mutant would *not* be able to grow if supplemented with the "no growth" intermediate. It will not be possible to fit the data for mutant 4 to pathway a, the data for mutants 1 and 4 to pathway b, or data for mutants 3 and 4 to pathway c. The data for all mutants can be fit only to pathway d. Thus, d must be the correct pathway.

A second approach to this problem is to realize that in any linear segment of a biochemical pathway (a segment without a branch), a block early in the segment can be circumvented by *any* metabolites that normally appear later in the same segment. Consequently, if two (or more) intermediates can support growth of a mutant, they normally are made after the blocked step in the same linear segment of a pathway. From the data given, compounds D and E both circumvent the single block in mutant 4. This means that compounds D and E lie after the block in mutant 4 on a linear segment of the metabolic pathway. The only pathway where D and E lie in an unbranched linear segment is pathway d. Mutant 4 could be blocked between A and E in this pathway. Mutant 4 cannot be fit to a *single* block in any of the other pathways that are shown, so the correct pathway is d.

4.7   A breeder of Irish setters has a particularly valuable show dog that he knows is descended from the famous bitch Rheona Didona, who carried a recessive gene for atrophy of the retina. Before he puts the dog to stud, he must ensure that it is not a carrier for this allele. How should he proceed?

Answer: One method is to testcross the male to a retinal atrophic female. Retinal atrophic pups (expected half of the time) would indicate that the male is heterozygous. If the retinal atrophy is associated with a known biochemical phenotype (e.g., altered enzyme activity), a preferred method is to take a tissue biopsy or blood sample from the male, and assess whether normal levels of enzyme activity are present in the male. Recessive mutations in genes for many enzymes, when heterozy-gous with a normal allele, lead to reduced levels of enzyme activity even though no visible phenotype is observed.

4.8   Glutathione (GSH) is important for a number of biological functions, including pre-vention of oxidative damage in red blood cells, synthesis of deoxyribonucleotides from ribonucleotides, transport of some amino acids into cells, and maintenance of protein conformation. Mutations that have lowered levels of glutathione syn-thetase (GSS), a key enzyme in the synthesis of glutathione, result in one of two clinically distinguishable disorders. The severe form is characterized by massive urinary excretion of 5-oxoproline (a chemical derived from a synthetic precursor to glutathione), metabolic acidosis (an inability to regulate physiological pH appro-priately), anemia, and central nervous system damage. The mild form is character-ized solely by anemia. The characterization of GSS activity and the GSS protein in two affected patients, each with normal parents, is shown below.

PATIENT	DISEASE FORM	GSS ACTIVITY IN FIBROBLASTS (PERCENT OF NORMAL)	EFFECT OF MUTATION ON GSS PROTEIN
1	severe	9%	Arginine at position 267 replaced by tryptophan
2	mild	50%	Aspartate at position 219 replaced by glycine

a. What pattern of inheritance do you expect these disorders to exhibit?
b. Explain the relationship of the form of the disease to the level of GSS activity.
c. How can two different amino acid substitutions lead to dramatically different phenotypes?
d. Why is 5-oxoproline only produced in significant amounts only in the severe form of the disorder?
e. Is there evidence that the mutations causing the severe and mild forms of the disease are allelic (in the same gene)?
f. How might you design a test to aid in prenatal diagnosis of this disease?

Answer:
a. Since normal parents have affected offspring, the disease appears to be reces-sive. However, since patients with 50 percent of GSS activity have a mild form of the disease, an individual may show mild symptoms if they are heterozygous (mutant/+) for a mutation that eliminates GSS activity. In a population, indi-viduals having the disease may not all show identical symptoms, and some may have more severe disease than others. The severity of the disease in an individ-ual will depend on the nature of the person's GSS mutation, and possibly, whether they are heterozygous or homozygous for the disease allele. The alleles discussed here appear to be recessive.

b. Patient 1, with 9 percent of normal GSS activity, has a more severe form of the disease, while patient 2, with 50 percent of normal GSS activity, has a less severe form of the disease. Thus, increased disease severity is associated with less GSS enzyme activity.

c. The two different amino acid substitutions may disrupt different regions of the enzyme's structure (consider the effect of different amino acid substitutions on hemoglobin function that are discussed in the text). As amino acids vary in their polarity and charge, different amino acid substitutions within the same structural region could have different chemical effects on protein structure. This too could lead to different levels of enzymatic function. (For a discussion of the chemical differences between amino acids, see Chapter 6).

d. By analogy with the disease PKU discussed in the text, 5-oxoproline is produced only when a precursor to glutathione accumulates in large amounts due to a block in a biosynthetic pathway. When GSS levels are 9 percent of normal, this occurs. When GSS levels are 50 percent of normal, sufficient GSS enzyme is present to partially complete the pathway and prevent high levels of 5-oxoproline.

e. The mutations are allelic (in the same gene), since both the severe and the mild forms of the disease are associated with alterations in the same polypeptide that is a component of the GSS enzyme. (Note that while the data in this problem suggest that the GSS enzyme is composed of a single polypeptide, they do not exclude the possibility that GSS has multiple polypeptide subunits encoded by different genes.)

f. If GSS is normally found in fetal fibroblasts, one could, in principle, measure GSS activity in fibroblasts obtained via amniocentesis. The GSS enzyme level in cells from at-risk fetuses could be compared to that in normal control samples to predict disease due to inadequate GSS levels. Some variation in GSS level might be seen, depending on the allele(s) present. Since more than one mutation is present in the population, it is important to devise a functional test that assesses GSS activity, rather than a test that identifies a single mutant allele.

4.9 Some methods used to gather fetal material for prenatal diagnosis are invasive and therefore pose a small but very real risk to the fetus.

a. What specific risks and problems are associated with chorionic villus sampling and amniocentesis?

b. How are these risks balanced with the benefits of each procedure?

c. Fetal cells are reportedly present in maternal circulation after about 8 weeks of pregnancy. However, the number of cells is very low, perhaps no more than one in several million maternal cells. To date, it has not been possible to isolate fetal cells from maternal blood in sufficient quantities for routine genetic analysis. If the problems associated with isolating fetal cells from maternal blood were overcome, and sufficiently sensitive methods were developed to perform genetic tests on a small number of cells, what would be the benefits of performing genetic tests on these fetal cells?

Answer:

a. Amniocentesis is typically done after 12 weeks of pregnancy (after the first tri-
mester), while chorionic villus sampling can be done between 8 and 12 weeks of
pregnancy. In either sampling method, there is a risk of fetal loss. While chorionic villus sampling can allow parents to learn if the fetus has a genetic defect
earlier than amniocentesis, there is more risk of fetal loss, and more chance of
an inaccurate diagnosis due to the contaminating presence of maternal cells.

b. These sampling methods offer parents an opportunity to learn about the genetic
constitution and health of the fetus early in a pregnancy. If the fetus is diseased, early prenatal diagnosis allows parents to make an informed decision
about the pregnancy. They can seek genetic counseling and consider what options might be available to them: to treat the diseased fetus *in utero*, to plan for
the care of a diseased child, or to terminate the pregnancy.

c. Such a method would allow for early, *noninvasive* prenatal diagnosis. This
would substantially reduce the risk to the fetus, and the discomfort to the
mother. Since a blood sample could be obtained by many health professionals
and shipped off-site for processing, it would also eliminate the need for a highly
skilled physician and sophisticated on-site support services to perform the
sampling procedure. Consequently, it would allow for more accessible prenatal
testing at lower cost.

4.10   Refer to Figure 4.10. What would you expect the phenotype to be in people heterozygous for the following two hemoglobin mutations?
a. Hb-Norfolk and Hb-S
b. Hb-C and Hb-S

Answer:

a. From Figure 4.10, Hb-Norfolk affects the α-chain, while Hb-S affects the β-
chain, of hemoglobin. Since each chain is encoded by a separate gene, there remains one normal allele at the genes for each of α- and β-chains in a double heterozygote. Thus, some normal hemoglobin molecules form and double heterozygotes do not have severe anemia. However, unlike double heterozygotes for two
different, completely recessive mutations that lie in one biochemical pathway,
these heterozygotes exhibit an abnormal phenotype. This is because some mutations in the α- and β-chains of hemoglobin show partial dominance. In particular, Hb-S/+ heterozygotes show symptoms of anemia if there is a sharp drop
in oxygen tension, and so these double heterozygotes exhibit mild anemia.

b. Both Hb-C and Hb-S affect the sixth amino acid of the β-chain. The Hb-C mutation alters the normal glutamate to lysine, while the Hb-S mutation alters it to
valine. Since both mutations affect the β-chain, no normal hemoglobin molecules are present. According to the text, only one type of β-chain is found in any
one hemoglobin molecule. Therefore a Hb-C/Hb-S heterozygote has two types of
hemoglobin, those with Hb-C β-chains and those with Hb-S β-chains.

Inferences about the phenotype of the heterozygote come from analysis of the homozygote phenotypes. Homozygotes for the Hb-S allele have severe anemia, while homozygotes for the Hb-C mutation have only mild anemia. Therefore, the two hemoglobin molecules present in the Hb-C/Hb-S heterozygote provide for different, abnormal levels of function. The heterozygote has a level of anemia between the Hb-S/Hb-S and Hb-C/Hb-C homozygotes, and shows moderate levels of the sickle-cell trait.

4.11   In evaluating my teacher, my sincere opinion is that:
   a. He/she is a swell person whom I would be glad to have as a brother-in-law/sister-in-law.
   b. He/she is an excellent example of how tough it is when you do not have either genetics or environment going for you.
   c. He/she may have okay DNA to start with, but somehow all the important genes got turned off.
   d. He/she ought to be preserved in tissue culture for the benefit of other generations.

Answer: Your choice!

4.12   A *Neurospora* mutant has been isolated in the laboratory in which you are working. This mutant cannot make an amino acid we will call Y. Wild type *Neurospora* cells make Y from a cellular product X through a biochemical pathway involving three intermediates called c, d, and e. How would you establish that your mutant contains a defective gene for the enzyme that catalyzes the d–e reaction?

Answer: If the enzyme that catalyzes the $d \rightarrow e$ reaction is missing, the mutant strain should accumulate d and be able to grow on minimal medium to which e is added. In addition, it should not be able to grow on minimal medium or on minimal medium to which X, c or d are added, but should grow if Y is added. Therefore, plate the strain on these media, and test which allow for growth of the mutant strain, and which intermediate is accumulated if the strain is plated on minimal medium.

4.13   Consider thalassemia as a devastating disease that is clearly the result of an autosomal genetic mutation on a specific chromosome. Explain what a molecular or genetic disease is. Compare and contrast this disease with a disease caused by an invading microorganism such as a bacterium or virus.

Answer: A genetic disease is one that is caused by a change in DNA. This change can result in altered levels or forms of one or more gene products. In turn, the altered forms or levels of gene products result in changes in cellular functions, which in turn cause a disease state. In this chapter, the examples of genetic diseases that have been given have demonstrated that diseases can be associated with mutations in single genes, and affect their protein products. For example, mutations in the gene for β-globin can cause sickle-cell anemia. For some diseases, such as PKU, the disease can be treated by altering diet. This is an example of a more general principle that the environment can have a significant effect on disease severity. Unlike diseases caused by an invading microorganism, an external agent, genetic diseases are caused by heritable changes in DNA that are associated with altered levels or forms of one or more gene products. While the severity of the disease can be influenced by environmental factors in some cases, the primary cause of the disease is not the infection of an external agent.

4.14   What problems might we encounter if we accept the one gene-one enzyme concept as completely accurate, and what have we discovered about this concept? What work led to this discovery?

Answer: If the one gene : one enzyme concept is accepted as completely accurate, it would impossible to explain how mutations in different genes can affect the same enzyme. This finding led to the identification that this concept is not completely accurate. The inaccuracy associated with the one gene : one enzyme concept is that some enzymes are composed of multiple, different polypeptides, and that these different polypeptides can be encoded by different genes. Therefore, while mutations in genes can affect the function of an enzyme, they do so by affecting *just one* of the polypeptides that makes up an enzyme. The one gene : one enzyme concept is a special case of the more general concept of "one gene : one polypeptide" and is true only for enzymes that are made of one type of polypeptide.

The work that led to the discovery that one gene specified one enzyme is the work of Beadle and Tatum. They showed that nutritional mutations (auxotrophs) in *Neurospora* were associated with defects in specific steps of a biochemical pathway. Mutations in different steps accumulated the biochemical intermediate made before the enzymatic block, and could be rescued, or grown, if there were addition of a biochemical intermediate made after the enzymatic block. This genetic analysis indicated that the normal gene specified an enzyme in the pathway that converted one biochemical intermediate to another.

4.15   You have been introduced to the functions and levels of proteins and their organization. List as many protein functions as you can and give an example of each.

Answer: Proteins serve a multitude of different functions. Here are some possibilities and examples:

Protein Function	Examples And Their Roles
Enzyme	DNA polymerase I - synthesizes DNA, proofreads, excises an RNA primer
	DNA ligase - seals a nick in a DNA sugar-phosphate backbone
	phenylalanine hydroxylase - converts phenylalanine to tyrosine
	topoisomerase - introduces/removes negative supercoils in DNA
Structural Protein	tubulin - polymerizes to form microtubules, used in chromosome segregation at anaphase
	myosin - a muscle protein used in muscle contraction
	actin - polymerizes to form actin filaments which provide structural integrity to the cell
Viral Protein	proteins making up the coat of T2, TMV
Receptor	acetylcholine receptor - binds the neurotransmitter acetylcholine, found on the surface of muscle cells
Transporter	Hemoglobin - transports oxygen
Ion Channel	CFTR - transports chloride ions
Regulatory Molecule	Transcription factors - determine where mRNA transcripts are produced (see Chapter 5)
Bind DNA	Single Stranded Binding Protein - keeps single-stranded DNA strands intact and from renaturing within a replication bubble during DNA synthesis.
Antibody	Immunoglobulins - immune function
Blood Type	A, B, O glycoproteins - specify blood type

4.16   We have discovered that most enzymes are proteins but not all proteins are enzymes. What are the functions of enzymes and why are they essential for living organisms to carry out their biological functions?

Answer: Enzymes are macromolecules which function to catalyze chemical reactions. These reactions can be quite simple, such as the addition of a hydroxyl (-OH) group onto a simple compound, or they can be exceedingly complex, such as the replication of an entire chromosome. Enzymes are absolutely essential to biological systems. This is because enzymes provide catalytic power, and usually increase reaction rates (the rate of production of the product of the chemical reaction) by at least a millionfold. Nearly all of the chemical transformations that are made in the body proceed at very low rates in the absence of enzymes. Therefore, they are necessary to catalyze reactions that produce needed compounds and perform essential processes.

4.17   We know that the function of any protein is tied to its structure. Give an example of how a disruption of structure by mutation can lead to a distinctive phenotypic effect.

Answer: Many examples are given in the text. Here are two.

Hb-S mutations in the β-globin gene change the sixth amino acid from the N-terminus of the β-globin polypeptide. This amino acid is changed from a negatively charged, acidic amino acid (glutamic acid) to an uncharged, neutral amino acid (valine). This single amino acid change causes the β-globin polypeptide to fold in an abnormal way, which in turn causes sickling of red-blood cells and sickle-cell anemia.

The most common mutation causing cystic fibrosis (CF) is a mutation in the CFTR (cystic fibrosis transmembrane regulator) gene called ΔF508. This mutation deletes three consecutive base pairs of DNA, and results in the deletion of a single amino acid in the CFTR protein. This amino acid is deleted in a region of the CFTR protein important for binding ATP. Since this region contributes to the function of the protein – to transport chloride ions across cell membranes – this single amino acid deletion affects the function of the protein, and causes CF.

4.18   Define the term *autosomal recessive mutation* and give some examples of diseases that are caused by autosomal recessive mutation. Explain how two parents who do not display any symptoms of a given disease (albinism, or any of the diseases you have named) can have two or even three children who have the disease. How can these same parents have no children with the disease?

Answer: Autosomes are chromosomes which are found in two copies in both males and females. That is, an autosome is any chromosome except the X and Y chromosome. Since individuals have two of each type of autosome, they have two copies of each gene on an autosome. The forms of the gene, or the alleles at the gene, can be the same or different. They can have either two normal alleles (homozygous for the normal allele), one normal allele and one mutant allele (heterozygous for the normal and mutant alleles), or two mutant alleles (homozygous for the mutant allele). A recessive mutation is one that exhibits a phenotype only when it is homozygous. Therefore, an autosomal recessive mutation is a mutation on any chromosome except the X or Y, and which causes a phenotype only when homozygous. Heterozygotes exhibit a normal phenotype.

Of the diseases discussed in this chapter, many are autosomal recessive diseases. For example, phenylketonuria, albinism, Tay-Sachs disease, and cystic fibrosis are all autosomal recessive diseases. Heterozygotes for the disease allele are normal, but homozygotes with the disease allele are affected. For phenylketonuria and albinism, homozygotes are affected because they lack a required enzymatic function. In these cases, heterozygotes have a normal phenotype because their single normal allele provides sufficient enzyme function.

Parents contribute one of their two autosomes to their gametes, so that each offspring of a couple receives an autosome from each parent. If, in a particular conception, each of two heterozygous parents contributes a chromosome with the normal allele, the offspring will be homozygous for the normal allele, and be normal. If, in a particular conception, one of the two heterozygous parents contributes a chromosome with the normal allele and the other parent contributes a chromosome with the mutant allele, the offspring will be heterozygous, but be normal. If, in a particular conception, each parent contributes the chromosome with the mutant allele, the offspring will be homozygous for the mutant allele, and develop the disease. Therefore, heterozygous parents can have both normal and affected children. Since each conception is independent, two heterozygous parents can have all normal, all affected, or any mix of normal and affected children.

4.19   The human β-globin gene provides an excellent example of how the sequence of nucleotides in a gene is eventually expressed as a functional protein. Explain how mutations in the β-globin gene can cause an altered phenotype. Give some examples.

Answer: Many single basepair mutations in the β-globin gene cause amino acid substitutions at different sites in the β–polypeptide chain. They can have different effects, depending on the type of amino acid substitution and its position. Some of them, such as the Hb-S mutation described in the answer to problem 4.17, alter the charge of an amino acid and thereby affect the folding of the protein. This in turn either affects the function of the hemoglobin molecule and/or the shape of the red-blood cell, causing anemia. Not all such mutations are equally severe. In the Hb-C mutation, the sixth amino acid from the N-terminus of the β–polypeptide chain is changed from glutamic acid to lysine. Both of these amino acids are hydrophilic. Consequently, the conformation of the hemoglobin molecule is not as altered as in the Hb-S mutation, and the Hb-C mutation causes only mild anemia.

4.20   What can prospective parents do to reduce the risk of having offspring who have genetically based enzyme deficiencies?

Answer: At one level, the answer to this question is straightforward. Couples who are prospective parents can undergo genetic testing for mutations that result in enzyme deficiencies. If both members of a couple are heterozygous for mutations in the same gene, then they may elect to undergo genetic counseling to assess the risk of having an affected child, and to discuss the options available to them concerning prenatal screening.

    In practice however, this question raises very complex issues. First, a decision to undergo genetic testing is associated with certain risks. While the risks associated with drawing blood for the testing procedure itself can be minimal, there are additional risks with very real, significant consequences. These include a risk of emotional discomfort upon learning that one is (or is not) a carrier, risks to personal and familial relationships, and potential risks to privacy, insurability, employment, discrimination, and stigmatization. Second, it is difficult to know which mutations to test for. Sometimes this issue can be rationally addressed if there is a clear family history of a particular inherited disease. However, this may not be the case. For example, for autosomal recessive diseases, family members may show no signs of a disease because they are heterozygous and some individuals will not know their familial history. In addition, because the genes we have are shared within our ethnic group, the risks we have for different inherited diseases are related to our ethnicity. Given this, genetic screening and testing can raise issues related to cultural and societal values, historical (and perhaps current) levels of discrimination, and the availability and quality of health-care services. Third, this question raises personal, philosophical and religious issues. Some individuals may not be willing to undergo genetic testing out of deeply held personal beliefs. While some couples may be willing to undergo genetic testing, and prenatal testing, so that they can use this information in planning, they may not be willing to electively terminate a fetus who has a genetically based enzyme deficiency. With current and anticipated advances in genomics (see Chapter 9), these and other policy, societal and ethical issues related to genetic screening and genetic testing are becoming more significant.

4.21   Proteins are the most abundant macromolecules found in cells. They are the end products of genes and play many diverse roles. List as many proteins as possible and give an example of the role the protein plays.

Answer: This list can be very long! The answer to question 4.15 provides a short list and descriptions of the roles some proteins play. Many more are found in the first four text chapters. To get a sense of the immense number of proteins that are known and their roles, do the following exercise. Visit the website listed below:

http://www.ncbi.nlm.nih.gov/entrez/query.fcgi?db=Protein

This site gives you access to a protein database. Search this database using a function you identified for a protein in your answer to question 4.15. For example, search the database using a term such as *enzyme, structural protein, viral protein, receptor, transporter, ion channel, regulatory, DNA binding, antibody*, etc. Assess how many different proteins are identified by your searches, and explore the links to a few of these.

5

GENE EXPRESSION: TRANSCRIPTION

CHAPTER OUTLINE

GENE EXPRESSION: AN OVERVIEW
THE TRANSCRIPTION PROCESS
    RNA Synthesis
    Initiation of Transcription at Promoters
    Elongation and Termination of an RNA Chain
TRANSCRIPTION IN EUKARYOTES
    Eukaryotic RNA Polymerases
    Transcription of Protein-Coding Genes by RNA Polymerase II
    Eukaryotic mRNAs
    Transcription of Other Genes

REVIEW OF KEY TERMS, SYMBOLS, AND CONCEPTS

In your own words, write a brief definition of each term in the groups below. Check your definitions using the text. Then, develop a concept map using the terms in each group.

1	2	3	4
central dogma	prokaryotic RNA polymerase	RNA polymerase II	RNA polymerase II
replication		protein-coding genes	transcription unit
transcription	transcription initiation	mRNA, snRNA	leader, trailer, coding sequences
translation		regulatory elements	
primary transcript	promoter	basal transcription factors	5'-, 3'-UTR
precursor RNA	closed, open promoter complex		precursor mRNA
mRNA		regulatory factors	pre-, mature mRNA
tRNA	holoenzyme	basal promoter elements	posttranscriptional modification
rRNA	core enzyme		
snRNA	sigma factor	promoter proximal elements	monocistronic
RNA polymerase	$\sigma^{70}, \sigma^{32}, \sigma^{54}, \sigma^{23}$		5' cap
RNA polymerases I, II, III	heat shock, stress	Goldberg-Hogness, TATA, CAAT, GC boxes	5' 7-methyl guanosine
	consensus sequence		5'-to-5', 2'-to-5' bonds
prokaryotic genes	$-10, -35$ regions		capping enzyme
eukaryotic genes	Pribnow box	enhancer element	methylation
structural gene	elongation	silencer elements	3' polyadenylation
protein-coding gene	transcription bubble	activator, repressor	poly(A) site, tail

1	2	3	4
α-amanitin	*rho*-dependent	adapter	poly(A) polymerase
nucleolus	termination	upstream activator	RNA endonuclease
nucleus	Type I, II terminators	sequences (UAS)	CPSF, CstF, CFI, CFII
gene regulatory	hairpin loop	TBP, TFIIB, D E, F,	introns, exons
elements	twofold symmetry	H	hnRNA, gRNA
5'-to-3', 3'-to-5'	coupled transcription	initial committed	mRNA splicing
coding strand	and translation	Complex	branch-point
template strand	transcription unit	minimal	sequence
nontemplate strand	leader, coding,	transcription	3', 5' splice sites
NTPs	trailer sequences	initiation complex	snRNA, snRNP
	5'-, 3'-UTR	complete	spliceosome
	polycistronic	transcription	U1, U2, U4, U5, U6
		initiation	RNA lariat structure
		complex	RNA editing
		preinitiation	
		complex	

5	6	7
E. coli RNA polymerase	RNA polymerase III	spliceosome
RNA polymerase I	5S rRNA genes	snRNPs (*snurps*)
sucrose density gradient	tRNA genes	self-splicing
Svedberg unit	tDNA	group I introns
S value	internal control region (ICR)	protein-independent reaction
30S, 50S subunits	pre-tRNA molecule	secondary structure
70S ribosome	codon	lariat molecule
23S, 16S, 5S rRNA	anticodon	*Tetrahymena* pre-mRNA
40S, 60S subunits	posttranscriptional	28S spacer sequence removal
80S ribosome	modification	28S intron removal
28S, 18S, 5.8S, 5S rRNA	TFIIIA, B, C	RNA enzyme
ribosomal protein	transcription initiation	ribozyme
rDNA	factor	RNA ligase
rRNA transcription unit	Cloverleaf	
(*rrn*)	stem loop structure	
Precursor rRNA	RNA ligase	
RNase III		
rDNA repeat unit		
spacer sequence		
nontranscribed spacer		
nontranscribed spacer		
external transcribed spacer		
(ETS)		
upstream control element		
(UCE)		
hUBF, SL1, TBP, TAFs		

THINKING ANALYTICALLY

As transcription and RNA processing are central to gene expression, they have been investigated intensely. Our substantial understanding of these processes is reflected in the wealth of detailed information presented in this chapter. As was the case for understanding DNA replication, the best way to understand and retain this information is to organize the details and place them in context. As you read the chapter, continually refer to the text figures that summarize the key events of transcription and RNA processing. Try explaining the figures to yourself out loud to enhance your understanding. To clarify and solidify your understanding of the material after you have read the chapter once, go through it again and categorize its detailed information.

To start categorizing the information, develop a list of terms and identify their chemical nature. Is the term a region of DNA, RNA or a part of a protein? After this, relate the term to its function in the overall process of gene expression. If it is DNA, how does it relate to the structure of a gene or a transcription unit? If it is RNA, how does it relate to the RNA being synthesized or being processed? If it is a part of a protein, how is it involved in transcription or RNA processing?

To help you relate a term to its function, construct sketches of the processes of transcription and transcript processing. Diagram how the structure of a gene at the DNA level relates to the structure of its primary transcript at the RNA level. Then, diagram how the structure of the primary transcript relates to the structure of the processed, mature transcript.

Next, distinguish between processes and characteristics in prokaryotes and eukaryotes. While there are some similarities between prokaryotes and eukaryotes, there are many, many differences. The fact that three RNA polymerases are active in eukaryotes results in three sets of data. For each RNA polymerase, there are distinct requirements for initiation and termination. Different DNA sequences are used, and different protein factors are involved in each case. It may help to prepare a list of analogous sites and factors, pairing prokaryotic elements with those doing similar jobs in eukaryotes.

QUESTIONS FOR PRACTICE

Multiple Choice Questions

1. Each row of the table below lists an item composed of DNA, RNA, and/or protein. Indicate an item's chemical composition by placing an X in the appropriate column(s).

ITEM	DNA	RNA	PROTEIN
sigma factor			
promoter			
terminator			
transcription factor			
regulatory factor			
Pribnow box			
transcription initiation complex			
spacer sequences			
NTS			
snRNP			
spliceosome			
rho			
promoter element			
RNA polymerase core enzyme			
ribozyme			
consensus sequence			
U2			
enhancer			

2. Now indicate whether each item is found only in prokaryotes, only in eukaryotes, or in both prokaryotes and eukaryotes by placing an X in the appropriate column.

ITEM	Found Only in Prokaryotes	Found Only in Eukaryotes	Found in Both
sigma factor			
promoter			
terminator			
transcription factor			
regulatory factor			
Pribnow box			
transcription initiation complex			
spacer sequences			
NTS			
snRNP			
spliceosome			
rho			
promoter element			
RNA polymerase core enzyme			
ribozyme			
consensus sequence			
U2			
enhancer			

3. Which one statement is correct?
    a. During transcription, the template strand is read in a 3'-to-5' direction.
    b. During transcription, the template strand is read in a 5'-to-3' direction.
    c. During transcription, the nontemplate strand is read in a 3'-to-5' direction.
    b. During transcription, the nontemplate strand is read in a 5'-to-3' direction.

4. Which one statement is correct?
    a. During transcription, an RNA is synthesized in the 5'-to-3' direction.
    b. During transcription, an RNA is synthesized in the 3'-to-5' direction.
    c. During transcription, DNA is synthesized in the 5'-to-3' direction.
    b. During transcription, DNA is synthesized in the 3'-to-5' direction.

5. Which one of the following is incorrect?
    a. DNA polymerases can proofread but RNA polymerases cannot.
    b. Some RNA polymerases, but no DNA polymerases, are sensitive to α-amanitin.
    c. Only RNA polymerases can initiate the formation of a polynucleotide.
    d. RNA polymerases synthesize in a 3'-to-5' direction while DNA polymerases synthesize in a 5'-to-3' direction.

6. Which one of the following is essential for RNA polymerase to bind an *E. coli* promoter?
    a. sigma factor
    b. snRNP
    c. TFIID
    d. U1

7. Which one of the following is essential for RNA polymerase II to bind a eukaryotic promoter?
    a. sigma factor
    b. *rho*
    c. TFIID
    d. U1

8. Which one of the following is incorrect?
    a. Prokaryotic and eukaryotic mRNAs have 5'-untranslated leader sequences.
    b. Only prokaryotic mRNAs are polyadenylated at their 3' ends.
    c. In prokaryotes, transcription and translation are coupled.
    d. Consensus sequences can be found in both DNA and RNA.
    e. In eukaryotes, RNA splicing occurs in the nucleus.

Answers:
1. A promoter, terminator, Pribnow box, NTS, promoter element, and enhancer are composed of DNA. U2 and a ribozyme are composed of RNA. A sigma factor, transcription factor, regulatory factor, *rho*, and the RNA polymerase core enzyme are composed of protein. Spacer and consensus sequences can be found in both RNA and DNA. A transcription initiation complex contains proteins that interact with DNA. Spliceosomes and snRNPs contain both RNA and proteins.
2. Sigma factor, the Pribnow box, *rho*, and the RNA polymerase core enzyme are only found in prokaryotes (*E. coli*). An NTS, snRNP, spliceosome, ribozyme, enhancer,

and U2 are only found in eukaryotes. A promoter, terminator, transcription factor, regulatory factors, transcription initiation complex, spacer sequence, promoter element, and consensus sequence can be found in both eukaryotes and prokaryotes. 3a; 4a; 5d; 6a; 7c; 8b.

Thought Questions

1. Compare and contrast each of the following pairs of terms with respect to location, function, and host organism (prokaryote or eukaryote).
   a. Pribnow box and TATA element
   b. promoter elements, enhancer elements, silencer elements, UAS
   c. transcription in T7 and T4 bacteriophage
   d. the promoters bound by RNA polymerase I, II, III
   e. promoters located internally within a gene
   f. rRNA genes

2. Do prokaryotes or eukaryotes have more RNA polymerase (per unit total protein)? Why should the two groups of organisms differ?

3. How does *rho*-dependent termination differ from *rho*-independent termination? What is the role of the hairpin loop in each of these events? Is the hairpin loop in DNA or RNA?

4. What takes the place of sigma factor in eukaryotes?

5. Recall that there was no simple relationship between the C-value and the structural and organizational complexity of an organism. Do you expect a relationship to exist between the number of rDNA repeat units and the structural or organizational complexity of the organism? The amount of hnRNA? The amount of cytoplasmic mRNA? Why or why not?

6. The promoters for RNA polymerase II have been highly conserved, and thus differ little among eukaryotes. However, the promoters for RNA polymerase I show significant differences among eukaryotes. Why might this be the case? (Hint: Consider the number of genes read by each polymerase.)

7. Consider what will happen to an mRNA once it is processed and then address the following questions. How precise does RNA splicing need to be? How precise does transcription initiation need to be? How precise does polyadenylation need to be?

8. What posttranscriptional modifications are routinely made to a eukaryotic mRNA? Where do they occur in the cell?

Thought Questions for Media

After reviewing the media on the *iGenetics* CD-ROM, try to answer these questions.

1. At which end of the template strand does transcription begin?
2. When trascription is complete, which strand of DNA is the final RNA molecule identical to, if the thymine in DNA is replaced with uracil in RNA?
3. What purpose does the sequence AAUAAA serve in a pre-mRNA's 3'-UTR?

1. Suppose a mutation in the β-globin gene introduced a new 3'-splice site within its first intron.

    a. In what different ways could the mutation affect the reading frame of the mature mRNA?

    b. If the mature mutant mRNA were translated in the same reading frame after the mutant site, what would its effect be on the β-globin protein?

    c. If the mutation caused the mRNA to be translated in a different reading frame, what would its effect be on the β-globin protein? (Remember that when mRNAs are "read" out of their correct reading frames, stop codons are often introduced.)

2. Suppose a point mutation occurred in the first intron of the β-globin globin, but did not change either the branch point, the 5'-splice site or the 3'-splice site sequence. Could such a mutation ever affect the level of mRNA transcripts available for translation? How might your answer change if the mutation were a deletion or insertion of 100 base pairs of DNA (Recall that the first intron is 130 base pairs long)?

3. In the iActivity, the first multiple-choice question describes two forms of beta-thalassemia: beta-plus and beta-zero. Beta-plus thalassemia occurs when a reduced amount of beta-globin protein is produced, while beta-zero thalassemia occurs when no beta-globin protein is produced.

    a. Do you expect the phenotypes of these forms of thalassemia to be identical in heterozygotes having a disease and a normal allele? Why or why not?

    b. Will they be identical in homozygotes for a disease allele? Why or why not?

SOLUTIONS TO TEXT PROBLEMS

5.1 Compare DNA and RNA with regard to structure, function, location and activity. Also, how do these molecules differ with regard to the polymerases used to carry out their specific functions?

Answer: While both DNA and RNA are composed of linear polymers of nucleotides, their bases and sugars differ. DNA contains deoxyribose and thymine, while RNA contains ribose and uracil. Their structures also differ. DNA is frequently double-stranded, while RNA is usually single-stranded. Single-stranded RNAs are capable of forming stable, functional, and complex stem-loop structures, such as those seen in tRNAs. Double-stranded DNA is wound in a double-helix, and packaged by proteins into chromosomes, either as a nucleoid body in prokaryotes or within the eukaryotic nucleus. RNA, after being transcribed from DNA, can be exported into the cytoplasm. If it is mRNA, it can be bound by ribosomes and translated. Eukaryotic RNAs are highly processed before being transported out of the nucleus. DNA functions as a storage molecule, while RNA functions either as a messenger (mRNA carries information to the ribosome) or in the processes of translation (rRNA functions as part of the ribosome, tRNA brings amino acids to the ribosome) or in eukaryotic RNA processing (snRNA functions within the spliceosome).

Both DNA polymerases and RNA polymerases catalyze the synthesis of nucleic acids in the 5'-to-3' direction. Both use a DNA template and synthesize a nucleic acid polynucleotide that is complementary to the template. However, DNA polymerases require a 3'-OH to add on to, while RNA polymerases do not. That is, RNA polymerases can initiate chains without primers, while DNA polymerases cannot. Furthermore, RNA polymerases usually require specific base-pair sequences as signals to initiate transcription.

5.2   All base pairs in the genome are replicated during the DNA synthesis phase of the cell cycle, but only some of the base pairs are transcribed into RNA. How is it determined which base pairs of the genome are transcribed into RNA?

Answer: The DNA sequences that are transcribed into RNA are determined using two general principles. First, signals in the DNA base sequences identify the specific region to be transcribed. Only regions bounded by transcription initiation and transcription termination signals are transcribed. In regions bounded by these signals, only one strand is ordinarily transcribed, so that transcripts are formed in a 5'-to-3' direction using a single DNA template strand. Second, transcription within a defined region occurs only if additional transcription-inducing molecules are present. Some of these molecules recognize the signals within the DNA that define the transcription unit and are used in the transcription process.

5.3   Discuss the similarities and differences between the *E. coli* RNA polymerase and eukaryotic RNA polymerases.

Answer: Both eukaryotic and *E. coli* RNA polymerases transcribe RNA in a 5'-to-3' direction using a 3'-to-5' DNA template strand. There are many differences between the enzymes, however. In *E. coli*, a single RNA polymerase core enzyme is used to transcribe genes. In eukaryotes, there are three types of RNA polymerase molecules, RNA polymerase I, II, and III. RNA polymerase I synthesizes 28S, 18S, and 5.8S rRNA and is found in the nucleolus. RNA polymerase II synthesizes hnRNA, mRNA, and some snRNAs and is nuclear. RNA polymerase III synthesizes tRNA, 5S rRNA, and some snRNAs and is nuclear.

Each RNA polymerase uses a unique mechanism to identify those promoters at which it initiates transcription. In prokaryotes such as *E. coli*, a sigma factor provides specificity to the sites bound by the four-polypeptide core enzyme, so that it binds to promoter sequences. The holoenzyme loosely binds a sequence about 35 bp before transcription initiation (the -35 region), changes configuration, and then tightly binds a region about 10 bp before transcription initiation (the −10 region) and melts about 17 bp of DNA around this region. The two-step binding to the promoter orients the polymerase on the DNA and facilitates transcription initiation in the 5'-to-3' direction. After about 8–9 bases are formed in a new transcript, sigma factor dissociates from the holoenzyme, and the core enzyme completes the transcription process. Although the principles by which eukaryotic RNA polymerases bind their promoters are similar in that they use a set of ancillary protein factors – transcription factors – the details are quite different. In eukaryotes, each of the three types of RNA polymerases recognizes a different set of promoters by using a polymerase-specific set of transcription factors, and the mechanisms of interaction are different.

5.4   What are the most significant differences between the organization and expression of prokaryotic genes and eukaryotic genes?

Answer: Prokaryotic and eukaryotic genes differ in their gene structure, in their RNA processing and in how transcription is coupled to translation.

Structure: Prokaryotic genes are defined by an upstream promoter, an RNA-coding sequence, and a downstream terminator. While these three features also exist in eukaryotic genes, eukaryotic promoters are more complex, and nearby or distant enhancer and silencer elements can strongly effect the level of transcription of eukaryotic genes. The RNA-coding sequences of eukaryotes can be interrupted with introns. Finally, prokaryotic mRNAs are often polycistronic, containing the amino-acid coding information for more than one gene. In contrast, eukaryotic mRNAs are monocistronic, containing the amino-acid coding information from just one gene.

Processing: Prokaryotic genes lack introns, while eukaryotic genes typically have one or more introns, and therefore a transcribed region can be larger than the size of a mature mRNA. The excision of introns from primary mRNAs is only one aspect of the processing of eukaryotic RNAs. In addition, eukaryotic mRNAs are modified at both their 5'- and 3'-ends: they are capped and polyadenylated.

Coupling of Transcription and Translation: Since prokaryotes lack a nucleus, transcription is directly coupled to translation. In eukaryotes, mRNAs must be processed, and then transported out of a nucleus, before they are translated by ribosomes in the cytoplasm.

These three differences provide cell types in a multicellular eukaryote three means to regulate gene expression. Gene expression can be regulated at each of these three levels: transcription, mRNA processing, and/or translation.

5.5   Discuss the molecular events involved in the termination of RNA transcription in prokaryotes. In what ways is this process fundamentally different in eukaryotes?

Answer: Termination of transcription in *E. coli* is signaled by controlling elements (sequences within the DNA) called terminators. Two classes of terminators exist, *rho*-independent (Type I) and *rho*-dependent (Type II). Both Type I and Type II termination events lead to the cessation of RNA synthesis and the release of both the RNA chain and the RNA polymerase from the DNA.

Type I terminators utilize sequences with two-fold symmetry lying about 16–20 bp upstream of the termination point to signal the termination site. See text Figure

5.5 The hairpin loop that forms when a two-fold symmetric sequence is transcribed, plus a string of Us lead to termination, perhaps by destabilizing the RNA-DNA hybrid in the terminator region. Type II terminators lack the structure of Type I terminators, and instead use an ATP-activated *rho* protein that binds to recognition sequences in the transcribed termination region. The binding of *rho* leads to the hydrolysis of the ATP, and the release of the transcript and the RNA polymerase from the DNA template.

In eukaryotes, transcription termination differs depending on the RNA polymerase under consideration. RNA polymerase I transcribes repeated 18S, 5.8S and 28S rDNA clusters as single transcription units. Transcription of each unit is terminated at a specific site. The termination site lies in the nontranscribed spacer (NTS) between adjacent rDNA transcription units.

RNA polymerase II transcribes genes for mRNAs and some snRNAs. These genes lack specific transcription termination sequences at their 3' ends, so that mRNA transcription can continue for hundreds or thousands of nucleotides downstream of the protein-coding sequence until it is past a poly(A) site in the RNA. The poly(A) site is recognized and cleaved by a complex set of proteins. It is positioned 10–30 nucleotides after an AAUAAA sequence and is followed by a GU-rich or U-rich sequence. Once the RNA is cleaved, poly(A) polymerase adds A nucleotides onto the 3'-OH of the RNA to produce a poly(A) tail.

RNA polymerase III transcribes genes for 5S rRNA, tRNA and some snRNAs. Simple sequences at the 3' ends of these genes signal transcription termination. For 5S rDNA, the signal is a cluster of four or more Ts surrounded by GC-rich sequences. For tDNA, the signal is a cluster of Ts.

5.6   Three different RNA polymerases are found in all eukaryotic cells, and each is responsible for the synthesis of a different class of RNA molecules. What are the characteristics of the different RNA polymerases in eukaryotic cells? (Hint: where is the cellular location and what is the product of each?)

Answer:

RNA POLYMERASE	CELLULAR LOCATION	PRODUCT & OTHER CHARACTERISTICS
I	nucleolus	28S, 18S, 5.8S rRNA: These are structural and functional components of the ribosome, which functions during translation. It is relatively insensitive to inhibition by α-amanitin.
II	nucleoplasm	1) mRNAs: These provide protein coding information to ribosome. 2) Some snRNAs (small nuclear RNAs): These function in a variety of nuclear processes, including RNA splicing and processing. It is very sensitive to inhibition by α-amanitin.

RNA POLYMERASE	CELLULAR LOCATION	PRODUCT & OTHER CHARACTERISTICS
III	nucleoplasm	tRNAs (transfer RNAs): These carry amino acids to the ribosome during translation. Some small nuclear RNAs: These function in a variety of nuclear processes. 5S rRNA: This is a functional and structural component of the ribosome's 60S (large) subunit. It is somewhat sensitive to inhibition by α-amanitin.

5.7   *E. coli* RNA polymerase can to transcribe all the genes of *E. coli*, but the three eukaryotic RNA polymerases transcribe only specific, nonoverlapping subsets of eukaryotic genes. What mechanisms are used to restrict the transcription of each of the three eukaryotic polymerases to a particular subset of eukaryotic genes?

Answer: The initiation of transcription at different genes by RNA polymerases I, II and III is restricted through the use of three distinct sets of transcription factors that recognize three distinct classes of promoters. Since the genes transcribed by each polymerase have uniquely organized controlling regions and the transcription factors that interact with each polymerase recognize only the regulatory elements in one type of controlling region, transcription by each polymerase is specific and nonoverlapping. See Figures 5.6, 5.19, and 5.23.

5.8   More than 100 promoters in prokaryotes have been sequenced. One of these promoters is sometimes called the Pribnow box, named after the investigator who compared several *E. coli* and phage promoters and discovered a region they held in common. Discuss the nature of this sequence (where it is located and why it is important?). Another consensus sequence appears a short distance from the Pribnow box. Diagram the positions of the two prokaryotic promoters relative to the start of transcription for a typical *E. coli* promoter.

Answer: The Pribnow box is the −10 element of the prokaryotic promoter. It is located at −10 bp relative to the starting point of transcription and has the consensus sequence 5'-TATAAT-3' (in the coding strand). A second consensus sequence is located about 35 bp before transcription initiation (the -35 region). Each of these sequences is important for the binding of RNA polymerase and initiation of RNA transcription. At the start of transcription initiation, the holoenzyme loosely binds the -35 region, then changes configuration and tightly binds the -10 region. It melts about 17 bp of DNA around this region. The two-step binding to the promoter orients the polymerase on the DNA and facilitates transcription initiation in the 5'-to-3' direction, as shown in Figure 5.4 and the cartoon below:

5.9   Eukaryotes have two major types of regulatory regions, one of which consists of nucleotide sequences that serve as the recognition point for RNA polymerase binding. These regions are called promoters. They function somewhat similarly in both eukaryotes and prokaryotes. What do you know about these sequences with regard to location, base make-up, and organization? A diagram with labels and a short explanation would suffice.

Answer: Eukaryotic promoters consist of two general types of elements: basal promoter elements and promoter proximal elements. The basal promoter elements are the TATA box (TATA element), and a pyrimidine-rich sequence near the transcription start site called the initiator element (Inr). Like the Pribnow box in prokaryotes, the AT-rich TATA box, being easier to denature than GC-rich sequences, facilitates strand separation for the initiation of transcription. The TATA box determines the exact start point for eukaryotic transcription. After it is recognized and bound by the TATA-binding protein (TBP), a subunit of TFIID, TFIIB is recruited, which in turn recruits RNA polymerase II and TFIIF to produce a minimal transcription initiation complex. Additional TFIIs (TFIIE, TFIIH) bind to produce the complete transcription initiation complex, or preinitiation complex (PIC).

Promoter proximal elements are upstream of the TATA box, between 50 and 200 nucleotides prior to the +1 transcription start site. These elements, which include CAAT and GC boxes, can work in either orientation and are present in one or multiple copies.

Both promoter proximal and basal promoter elements have only general activities in transcription initiation, and allow for low levels of transcription. For high levels of transcription to occur, other transcription factors called activators must bind to distinct DNA elements called enhancers. The activator proteins interact through adapter proteins with the preinitiation complex and stimulate transcription. See text Figure 5.6.

5.10   In addition to promoter regions, transcription of most eukaryotic genes is regulated by other DNA sequences called enhancers. How do these sequences differ from promoters?

Answer: An enhancer element is a DNA sequence that increases the amount of transcription of a gene lying in its vicinity. Enhancers are distinct from promoters, both in terms of location and in terms of the proteins which bind them. Promoters, if bound by a preinitiation complex, can provide only a low level of transcription. To obtain maximal transcription, enhancers are bound by activator proteins, (which are not basal transcription factors). The activator proteins interact with adapters to form bridges to the preinitiation complex, thereby stimulating transcription. Specific enhancer elements have consensus sequences, and are bound by particular activators. Since the activators are cell- and tissue-specific, enhancers contribute to tissue-specific gene expression. Enhancer elements are found singly or in multiple copies, and do not have a fixed position relative to the start of transcription. They can lie over a thousand base pairs in either direction from the start of transcription. In addition, they do not have to be in a particular orientation relative to the direction of transcription, although most lie upstream of the gene.

5.11   A piece of mouse DNA was sequenced as follows (a space is inserted after every 10th base for ease in counting; (...) means a lot of unspecified bases):

```
AGAGGGCGGT    CCGTATCGGC    CAATCTGCTC    ACAGGGCGGA
TTCACACGTT    GTTATATAAA    TGACTGGGCG    TACCCCAGGG
TTCGAGTATT    CTATCGTATG    GTGCACCTGA    CT(...)
GCTCACAAGT    ACCACTAAGC(...)
```

What can you see in this sequence to indicate that it might be all or part of a transcription unit?

Answer: By convention, DNA sequence is given 5'-to-3'. This is the same polarity as the antitemplate strand, the strand that is complementary to the 3'-to-5' template strand used for transcription. By using this convention, analyzing a DNA sequence is made easier. If a region of the sequence is transcribed, the RNA will have an identical sequence, except that U will replace T.

Transcription units should be flanked at their 5'-ends by promoter elements. Therefore, approach this problem by surveying the sequence for the GC, CAAT, and TATA box consensus sequences (see text Figure 5.6). The figure below summarizes their location and the approximate site of transcription initiation. An mRNA that could be produced (a conceptual mRNA) is given in lower-case letters. This mRNA has two signals (underlined) that could be used by the ribosome to recognize the start and termination of translation. Initiation of a polypeptide chain is signaled by a 5'-AUG-3' codon (encoding a methionine). Chain termination is signaled by a UAA stop codon. Features of translation are described in Chapter 6.

−80	−65		−50
GC element	*CAAT box*		*GC element*
5' AGA<u>GGGCGG</u>T	CCGTATC<u>GGC</u> <u>CAAT</u>CTGCTC		ACA<u>GGGCGG</u>A

	−30		
	TATA box		
TTCACACGTT	GTTA<u>TATAAA</u>	TGACTGGGCG	TACCCCAGGG

+1 (approx., conceptual)
transcription initiation potential translation start
TTCGAG *TATT*   *CTATCGT<u>ATG</u>*   *GTGCACCTGA*   *CT*(...)
mRNA 5'uauu   cuaucgu<u>aug</u>   gugcaccuga   cu(...)

potential translation stop
GCTCACAAGT   *ACCAC<u>TAA</u>GC*   (...)
gcucacaagu   accac<u>uaa</u>gc   (...)

5.12   How do the structures of mRNA, rRNA and tRNA differ? Hypothesize a reason for the difference.

Answer: Although mRNA, rRNA, and tRNA are single stranded, they can differ substantially in the secondary and tertiary structures achieved by intramolecular base-pairing interactions. These interactions, in the case of rRNA and tRNA, are essential for them to fulfill their different functions.

mRNA typically has a 5' untranslated leader sequence, a protein-coding sequence and a 3' untranslated trailer sequence (see Figure 5.7). In eukaryotes, mRNAs are processed to have 5' caps and 3' poly(A) tails, and to remove intronic sequences (see Figures 5.8b, 5.9, and 5.10).

rRNAs are of three sizes in prokaryotes (5S, 16S, 23S) and four sizes in eukaryotes (5S, 5.8S, 18S, and 28S). They are single stranded, and three rRNAs are produced by processing a single rRNA precursor transcript (exception = eukaryotic 5S rRNA) (see Figures 5.17 and 5.18). They fold in a complex manner and have both structural and functional roles in the ribosome.

tRNA molecules are small, about 4S, and consist of a single chain of 75–90 nucleotides. There is extensive base pairing between different parts of the tRNA molecule, allowing it to form a cloverleaf structure having three or four loops. The tRNA molecule functions to carry amino acids to the ribosome. An amino acid is attached to its 3' end in the cytoplasm for delivery to the ribosome. After an anticodon in loop II binds to the mRNA, the ribosome transfers the amino acid to a growing polypeptide chain. There is extensive posttranscriptional modification of tRNA bases, so that tRNAs contain modified bases such as inosine, ribothymidine, pseudouridine, dihydrouridine, methylguanosine, dimethylguanosine, and methylinosine. See Figures 5.21 and 5.22.

5.13   Many eukaryotic mRNAs, but not prokaryotic mRNAs, contain introns. Describe how these sequences are removed during the production of mature mRNA.

Answer: Introns are removed from a pre-mRNA molecule by the action of a spliceosome. Consensus sequences at the intron-exon boundaries and within the intron itself are recognized by spliceosome components as the spliceosome assembles around the intronic sequence. First, U1 snRNP binds to the 5' splice site by base-pairing interactions between the U1 snRNA and the 5' splice site sequence. Then, U2 snRNP binds to a branch point region inside of the intron. Following the association of a pre-assembled U4/U6/U5 particle with the bound U1 and U2 snRNPs, U4 snRNP dissociates from the complex, allowing the formation of an active spliceosome. Splicing proceeds via cleavage of the 5' exon-intron junction, attaching the 5' end of the intron sequence to a branch-point sequence via an unusual 2'-to-5' bond, and then cleavage at the 3' exon-intron junction. When the two exons are ligated together, a lariat structure composed of intron sequences is released. See Figures 5.12 and 5.13.

5.14   How is the mechanism of group I intron removal different from the mechanism used to remove the introns in most eukaryotic mRNAs? Speculate as to why these different mechanisms for intron removal might have evolved and how each might be advantageous to a eukaryotic cell.

Answer: Group I introns are self-splicing. Unlike the removal of introns from most eukaryotic mRNAs, removal of group I introns does not require a spliceosome containing snRNAs and protein splicing factors. In group I introns, the intron folds in a protein-independent manner to catalyze the splicing reaction.

While both splicing mechanisms result in the joining of RNA sequences flanking an intron, the more widespread use of spliceosomes to remove introns may reflect advantages associated with this mechanism. For example, it may allow greater flexibility in the sequence composition of an intron, as specific secondary structures do not have to form, while still allowing for the precise removal of intronic sequences (using consensus sequences at the 5′ and 3′ splice sites and the branch point). Spliceosome processing of introns may also allow for greater diversity in intron size. The group I intron in the Tetrahymena pre-rRNA is 413 bp. In contrast, introns processed by spliceosomes can be from tens to thousands of base pairs. As will be discussed in Chapters 8 and 17, intron removal using spliceosomes can also be regulated using protein factors. This allows for an additional level of control over gene expression. Thus, splicing mechanisms using spliceosomes allow for greater diversity in intron composition and gene expression than self-splicing mechanisms.

5.15   Distinguish between leader sequence, trailer sequence, coding sequence, intron, spacer sequence, nontranscribed spacer sequence, external transcribed spacer sequence, and internal transcribed sequence. Give examples of actual molecules in your answer.

Answer: **Leader and trailer sequences** are terms used in several related ways. First, these terms are used to denote untranslated sequences in mRNA not containing protein coding information that lie at the 5' end (for leader) or 3' end (for trailer). See text Figures 5.7 and 5.11. Second, these terms are sometimes used to denote the sequences that lie at the 5' end (for leader) or 3' end (for trailer) of pre-rRNA transcripts in prokaryotes. See text Figure 5.17.

Coding sequences are sequences in mRNA that are translated by the ribosome. These sequences encode information (in the form of a triplet code—see Chapters 1 and 6) that can be read by the ribosome to direct the synthesis of a polypeptide. **Introns** are sequences present in eukaryotic precursor RNA molecules that are spliced out in the mature, functional molecule. Introns are present in pre-mRNAs as well as in pre-rRNAs and pre-tRNAs.

Nontranscribed spacer sequences are sequences, such as those in the repeated rDNA genes, that lie between adjacent, repeating transcription units. **External transcribed spacer sequences** are found in pre-rRNA transcripts in eukaryotes (from transcription of 18S, 28S and 5.8S pre-rRNAs). They are located immediately upstream of the 5' end of the 18S sequence and downstream of the 3' end of the 28S sequence. The **internal transcribed spacer sequences** are located on either side of the 5.8S sequence. See text Figure 5.18.

5.16   Discuss the posttranscriptional modifications and processing events that take place on the primary transcripts of eukaryotic rRNA and protein-coding genes.

Answer: In eukaryotes, 18S, 28S, and 5.8S rRNA genes are transcribed from the rDNA into a single pre-rRNA molecule. The pre-mRNA is processed by removing the internal and external spacer sequences, leading to the production of the mature rRNAs. See text Figure 5.18 The eukaryotic 5S rRNA is transcribed separately to produce mature rRNA molecules that need no further processing. Eukaryotic 5S rRNAs are imported into the nucleolus where they are assembled with the other mature rRNAs and the ribosomal protein subunits to produce functional ribosomal subunits. Some *Tetrahymena* pre-rRNAs have self-splicing introns (group I) in the 28S rRNA. It is important to remember that the removal of the intron in the 28S rRNA via self-splicing is a separate process from the cleavage of spacer sequences from the mature rRNAs. See text Figure 5.20.

Protein-coding eukaryotic transcripts synthesized by RNA polymerase II are extensively processed. A 5'-5' bonded m^7Gppp cap is added to the 5' end of the nascent transcript when the chain is 20–30 nucleotides long. A poly(A) tail of variable length can be added to the 3' end of the transcript, and spliceosomes remove intronic sequences. The site of poly(A) addition, as well as splice-site selection, can be regulated, so that more than one alternatively processed mature mRNA is sometimes produced from a single precursor mRNA transcript.

5.17   Describe the organization of the ribosomal DNA repeating unit of a higher eukaryotic cell.

Answer: rDNA in a eukaryotic cell is organized into tandem arrays of repeating units, each of which have an 18S, 5.8S, and 28S rRNA gene. In between each repeating unit is a nontranscribed spacer. The three genes within each unit are transcribed by RNA polymerase I as a 45S precursor rRNA molecule in the nucleolus. 5' and 3' flanking spacer sequences (external transcribed spacer sequences) as well as internal spacer sequences are removed, leading to the production of 18S, 5.8S, and 28S rRNAs. See text Figure 5.18.

5.18   Which of the following kinds of mutations would be likely to be recessive lethals in humans? Explain your reasoning.
    a. deletion of the U1 genes
    b. deletion within intron 2 of β-globin
    c. deletion of four bases at the end of intron 2 and three bases at the beginning of exon 3 in β-globin

Answer: A recessive lethal is a mutation that results in lethality (death!) when the mutation is homozygous, that is, when only mutant alleles are present. Heterozygotes for such mutations can be viable. One way to think about recessive lethals is that they result in death because some essential function is missing. Neither copy of the gene functions, and so the organism dies.
    a. Deletion of the U1 genes will be recessive lethal, as U1 snRNA is essential for the identification of the 5' splice site in RNA splicing. Incorrect splicing would lead to nonfunctional gene products for many genes, a nonviable situation.
    b. If a deletion within intron 2 did not affect a region important for its splicing (e.g., the branch point, the regions near the 5' or 3' splice sites), it would have no effect on the mature mRNA produced. Consequently, such a mutation would lack a phenotype if it were homozygous. However, if splicing of intron 2 were affected and the mRNA altered, such a mutation, if homozygous, could result in the production of only nonfunctional hemoglobin, leading to severe anemia and death.
    c. The deletion described would affect the 3' splice site of intron 2, leading to, at best, aberrant splicing of intron 2. If it were homozygous, only a nonfunctional protein would be produced, resulting in severe anemia and death.

5.19   Figure 5.A shows the transcribed region of a typical eukaryotic protein-coding gene. What is the size (in bases) of the fully processed, mature mRNA? Assume in your calculations a poly(A) tail of 200 As.

Figure 5.A

Answer: 1 (5' m^{7}G cap) + 100 (exon 1) + 50 (exon 2) + 25 (exon 3) + 200 (poly(A) tail) = 376 bases.

5.20   Most human obesity does not follow Mendelian inheritance patterns because body fat content is determined by a number of interacting genes and environmental variables. Insights into how specific genes function to regulate body fat content have come from studies of mutant, obese mice. In one mutant strain, *tubby (tub)*, obesity is inherited as a recessive trait. Comparison of the DNA sequence of the *tub*$^+$ and *tub* alleles has revealed a single base-pair change: Within the transcribed region, a 5' GC base pair has been mutated to a TA base pair. The mutation causes an alteration of the initial 5' base of the first intron. Therefore, in the homozygous *tub/tub* mutant, a longer transcript is found. Propose a molecularly based explanation for how a single base change causes a nonfunctional gene product to be produced, why a longer transcript is found in *tub/tub* mutants, and why the *tub* mutant is recessive.

Answer: The first two bases of an intron are typically 5'-GU-3', which are essential for base pairing with the U1 snRNA during spliceosome assembly. A GC to TA mutation at the initial base pair of the first intron impairs base pairing with the U1 snRNA, so that the 5' splice site of the first intron is not identified. This causes the retention of the first intron in the *tub* mRNA and a longer mRNA transcript in *tub/tub* mutants. When the mutant *tub* mRNA is translated, the retention of the first intron could either result in the introduction of amino acids not present in the *tub*$^+$ protein, or, if the intron contained a chain termination (stop) codon, premature translation termination and the production of a truncated protein. In either case, a nonfunctional gene product is produced.

The *tub* mutation is recessive because the single *tub*$^+$ allele in a *tub/tub*$^+$ heterozygote produces mRNAs that are processed normally, and when these are translated, enough normal (*tub*$^+$) product is produced to obtain a wild-type phenotype. Only the *tub* allele produces abnormal transcripts. When both copies of the gene are mutated in *tub/tub* homozygotes, no functional product is made and a mutant, obese phenotype results.

5.21   Which of the following could occur in a single mutational event in a human? Explain.
   a. deletion of 10 copies of the 5S ribosomal RNA genes only
   b. deletion of 10 copies of the 18S rRNA genes only
   c. simultaneous deletion of 10 copies of the 18S, 5.8S, and 28S rRNA genes only
   d. simultaneous deletion of 10 copies each of the 18S, 5.8S, 28S, and 5S rRNA genes

Answer:
   a. This could occur. Since the 5S genes are clustered, 10 copies could be removed in one deletion.

b. This could not occur. The 18S genes are part of a cluster of 18S, 5.8S, and 28S genes. The 18S genes cannot be deleted without also deleting the others.

c. This could occur. The genes are clustered.

d. This could not occur. The 18S, 5.8S, and 28S genes are clustered at a locus separate from the 5S genes.

5.22   During DNA replication in a mammalian cell a mistake occurs: 10 wrong nucleotides are inserted into a 28S rRNA gene, and this mistake is not corrected. What will probably be the effect on the cell?

Answer: The cell will most likely be just fine. The remaining 1,000 copies of the 28S rRNA genes are normal, so this error will have little phenotypic consequence.

5.23   Choose the correct answers, noting that each blank may have more than one correct answer, and that each answer (1 through 4) could be used more than once.
Answers:

1. eukaryotic mRNAs
2. prokaryotic mRNAs
3. transfer RNAs
4. ribosomal RNAs

a. _____ Have a cloverleaf structure
b. _____ Are synthesized by RNA polymerases
c. _____ Display one anticodon each
d. _____ Are the template of genetic information during protein synthesis
e. _____ Contain exons and introns
f. _____ Are of four types in eukaryotes and only three types in *E. coli*.
g. _____ Are capped on their 5' end and polyadenylated on their 3' end

Answer:

a. 3
b. 1, 2, 3, 4
c. 3
d. 1 and 2
e. 1 (note that some tRNAs and rRNAs have introns)
f. 4
g. 1

6

GENE EXPRESSION: TRANSLATION

CHAPTER OUTLINE

PROTEINS
Chemical Structure of Proteins
Molecular Structure of Proteins
THE NATURE OF THE GENETIC CODE
The Genetic Code Is a Triplet Code
Deciphering the Genetic Code
Characteristics of the Genetic Code
TRANSLATION: THE PROCESS OF PROTEIN SYNTHESIS
The mRNA Codon Recognizes the tRNA Anticodon
Charging tRNA
Initiation of Translation
Elongation of the Polypeptide Chain
Termination of Translation
PROTEIN SORTING IN THE CELL

REVIEW OF KEY TERMS, SYMBOLS, AND CONCEPTS

In your own words, write a brief definition of each term in the groups below. Check your definitions using the text. Then, develop a concept map using the terms in each group.

1	2	3	4
protein	genetic code	translation	endoplasmic
polypeptide	triplet code	aminoacyl-tRNA	reticulum
amino acid	codon	synthetase	membrane-bound
α-carbon	frameshift mutation	codon recognition	ribosome
peptide bond	revertant	initiation	signal hypothesis
acidic, basic, netral,	reversion	elongation	signal sequence
polar, nonpolar	random copolymers	termination	signal recognition
amino acid	ribosome binding	charged tRNA	particle (SRP)
C-, N-terminus	assay	transformylase	docking protein
primary structure	cell-free, protein-	fMet, tRNA.fMet	cotranslational
secondary structure	synthesizing	tRNA.Met	transport
tertiary structure	system	30S initiation complex	signal peptidase

1	2	3	4
quaternary structure	genetic code	ribosome-binding site	Golgi complex
Conformation	reading frame	Shine-Dalgarno se-	cisternal space
α-helix	comma-free code	quence	glycoprotein
β-pleated sheet	nonoverlapping code	IF1, IF2, IF3; eIFs	*sec* mutants
	universal, degenerate	cap binding protein	secretory
	code	peptidyl transferase	pathway
	start, stop codon	P, A, E sites	
	sense, nonsense	EF-Tu, EF-Ts, EF-G	
	codon	translocation	
	wobble hypothesis	polyribosome	
	context effect	polysome	
	site-specific	termination factor	
	variation	RF1, RF2, RF3	
		UGA, UAG, UAA codon	

THINKING ANALYTICALLY

Much of the material presented in this chapter is detailed and descriptive. The initiation, elongation and termination of translation are all complex events. Each involves ribosomal subunits, RNAs and stage-specific factors that differ in prokaryotes and eukaryotes. As in the last two chapters, placing the information in context will help you learn and retain it.

There are several levels in which to organize this chapter's information. First, consider the level of spatial organization. Associate the different types of RNA (rRNA, mRNA, tRNA) and factors involved in translation with the different components of the translation machinery in the cell. Then construct a temporal framework to follow these components through the stages of translation. For prokaryotes, and then for eukaryotes, what RNAs and factors are components of the first initiation complex? What RNAs and factors are present during elongation? What new factors are required for termination? Then come back to the level of spatial organization. For eukaryotes, once proteins are synthesized, what factors are used to shuttle them to the appropriate location?

Keep in mind the polarity of DNA and RNA when analyzing DNA sequences, inferring transcripts that are produced, and identifying translation reading frames. Transcripts are always synthesized in the 5′-to-3′ direction using the 3′-to-5′ DNA template strand, and polypeptides are always synthesized starting at their N-terminus using codons that start relatively nearer to the 5′ end of the mRNA. The rhyme "5 to 3, N to C" may help you remember the orientations of mRNA and polypeptides. Pay close attention to maintain the correct mRNA, tRNA anticodon and DNA polarity.

One of the highlights of this chapter is the presentation of a set of elegant experiments used to decipher the genetic code. These technically demanding experiments addressed one of the fundamental questions in genetics: How is information in DNA used to code for proteins? Consider them carefully, and consider how interpreting them often uses probabilistic thinking. The product rule, which states that the frequency of two independent events occurring together is the product of their separate probabilities, allows one to deduce the appropriate codons that specify particular amino acids. Consider the following related problem:

(a) A synthetic mRNA is generated by randomly polymerizing adenine and guanine ribonucleotides. What codons would be formed, and what would be their relative frequency if the synthesis began with a limitless mixture of 3 adenine to 1 guanine?

(b) When the mRNAs generated in part (a) are added to a cell-free translation system, polypeptides are formed that, on average, have about 55 percent lysine, about 19 percent arginine, about 19 percent glutamic acid, and about 7 percent glycine. What can you infer about codon usage from these data (without consulting a table of the genetic code)?

Answer: First, determine what possible codons (three-nucleotide combinations) could be generated. Then, determine the frequency of that codon by multiplying together the probability of obtaining each base in one codon. Since there is a 3A:1 G ratio, the chance of finding an A is 3/4, and the chance of finding a G is 1/4.

$$P(AAA) = (3/4)^3 = 0.421875 \sim 42\%$$

$$p(AAG) = (3/4)^2(1/4) = 0.140625 \sim 14\%$$

$$p(AGA) = (3/4)^2(1/4) = 0.140625 \sim 14\%$$

$$p(AGG) = (3/4)(1/4)^2 = 0.046875 \sim 5\%$$

$$p(GAA) = (1/4)(3/4)^2 = 0.140625 \sim 14\%$$

$$p(GAG) = (1/4)^2(3/4) = 0.046875 \sim 5\%$$

$$p(GGA) = (1/4)^2(3/4) = 0.046875 \sim 5\%$$

$$p(GGG) = (1/4)^3 = 0.015625 \sim 2\%$$

Since AAA accounts for about 42 percent of the total codons that are translated, and only lysine constitutes at least 42 percent of the amino acid content of the polypeptides, AAA must encode lysine. By similar reasoning, GGG must encode glycine. Since there is only 7 percent glycine, and no codon alone accounts for 7 percent of the total codon usage, glycine must be encoded by at least two codons. GGG must be one of these, since if any other two codons encoded glycine, the amount of glycine would exceed 7 percent. The remaining glycine must be encoded by one of the GAG, GGA, or AGG codons, since they are represented 5 percent of the time. The remaining lysine must be encoded by either AAG, AGA, or GAA, as no combination of other codons would give 55 percent lysine. This leaves arginine to be encoded by one of the AAG, AGA, GAA codons and one of the AGG, GAG, GGA codons. Similarly, glutamic acid must be encoded by one of the AAG, AGA, GAA codons and one of the AGG, GAG, GGA codons. To make additional inferences, more experimentation (e.g., with different copolymers) must be done.

QUESTIONS FOR PRACTICE

Multiple Choice Questions

1. The term "secondary structure" refers to a polypeptide's
    a. sequence of amino acids.
    b. structure that results from local interactions between the residues of different amino acids.
    c. folding that results from local and distant interactions between the residues of different amino acids.
    d. interactions with a second polypeptide chain.

2. The eukaryotic equivalent of the Shine-Dalgarno sequence is the
    a. 60S large ribosomal subunit.
    b. 40S small ribosomal subunit.
    c. 5' cap of the mRNA.
    d. poly(A) tail.

3. In which stage of translation is GTP not used?
    a. initiation
    b. elongation
    c. translocation
    d. termination

4. Which of the following are the same in both prokaryotes and eukaryotes?
    a. Elongation factors
    b. Stop codons
    c. The use of fMet.tRNA
    d. AUG initiation codons
    e. Both b and d

5. Specificity in translation is obtained by all of the following except:
    a. using specific tRNA synthetases for each amino acid.
    b. using an anticodon.
    c. using a degenerate triplet code having codons for each amino acid.
    d. using RNA polymerase.

6. Where can coding sequences not be found?
    a. introns
    b. exons
    c. mRNA
    d. hnRNA

7. In an unprocessed, newly synthesized eukaryotic protein,
    a. the N-terminus is encoded by sequences in the 5' region of the mRNA.
    b. the C-terminus is encoded by sequences in the 5' region of the mRNA.
    c. the first amino acid is always f-methionine.
    d. the last amino acid is always encoded by the codon AAA.

8. During translation in *E. coli*,
    a. an intact 70S ribosome binds the mRNA during initiation.

b. Shine-Dalgarno sequences present in the mRNA align it with the 23S rRNA.

b. both initiation and elongation require energy in the form of GTP.

b. termination occurs when the ribosome recognizes a chain termination codon with the aid of EF-Tu.

9. The RNAs that are used in eukaryotic translation include all of the following except:
   a. 5S rRNA.
   b. 28S rRNA.
   c. mRNA.
   d. tRNA.
   e. snRNA.

10. In eukaryotes, proteins destined to remain in the cell are distributed by all of the following except:
   a. by packaging into secretory vesicles.
   b. after complexing with an SRP using an N-terminal signal sequence.
   c by using posttranslational transport.
   d. by using transit sequences.

   Answers: *1b; 2c; 3d; 4e; 5d; 6a; 7a; 8c; 9e; 10a.*

Thought Questions

1. The following sequence of bases in *E. coli* DNA is part of a gene. Mark the region that, if transcribed, will form the first codon to be translated. Mark the region that, if transcribed, will form a Shine-Dalgarno sequence. Is the strand shown the template or non-template strand? (Hint: Find the initiation codon. Be careful about polarity!)

   5′–CCGCATTCCTCCGGCGGGACCTACT–3′

2. Why is the code for methionine not degenerate? (Hint: What special role does methionine play in translation?)

3. What are the components of a cell-free, protein-synthesizing system? What is the function of each?

4. Describe three complementary methods by which the code was deciphered. Is any single method sufficient to completely decipher the code? What advantages and disadvantages does each method have?

5. The genetic code is nearly universal. To what extent does this indicate that the code was "settled on" very early in the evolution of cells?

6. Consider which bases can wobble to base pair with each other. What structural similarities exist between bases at the 3′ end of codon that can wobble to base pair with the base at the 5′ end of the anticodon?

7. What is the "context effect" in codon translation? Cite two examples.

8. What percentage of 70S ribosomes do you expect to be associated with mRNA in pro-karyotes? What percentage of 80S ribosomes do you expect to be associated with mRNA in eukaryotes?

9. Discuss the various ways in which proteins within a cell are targeted for secretion. How can a genetic approach be used to dissect the secretory pathway?

10. How do prokaryotes and eukaryotes differ in the mechanisms they use to identify the first codon in a reading frame? In what ways are the mechanisms similar?

Thought Questions for Media

After reviewing the media on the *iGenetics* CD-ROM, try to answer these questions.

1. How does the ribosome-IF-GTP complex identify where it should bind to the mRNA?
2. What are the functions of EF-Tu and EF-G in translation elongation?
3. At what points in translation is GTP hydrolysis required?
4. Review the A, E, and P sites on the ribosome. Which site never has a charged tRNA in it? Which site is only bound by a charged tRNA or a RF? Which site is almost always occupied by a tRNA with an attached polypeptide?
5. Peptidyl transferase provides two functions, one during translation elongation and one during translation termination. Are they the same enzymatic function?

4 Based on viewing the iActivity, what different features of a coding-region mutation would cause it to be associated with a mutant phenotype?
4 What type of coding-region mutations have no effect whatsoever on protein function?
3. What type of coding-region mutations are likely to have little, if any, effect on protein function?

SOLUTIONS TO TEXT PROBLEMS

6.1   The form of genetic information used directly in protein synthesis is (choose the correct answer):
a. DNA
b. mRNA
c. rRNA
d. tRNA

Answer: b.

6.2   Most genes encode proteins. What exactly is a protein, structurally speaking? List some of the functions of proteins.

Answer: A protein is composed of one or more polypeptides, each of which is composed of a folded, linear chain of amino acids. Proteins function in many different ways, including as enzymes to catalyze biochemical reactions, as structural molecules (e.g., actin, myosin, tubulin), as receptors (e.g., on the cell surface, for small signaling molecules such as neurotransmitters), as transporters (e.g., a protein that transports sugars across a membrane), as ion channels (e.g., the protein defective in cystic fibrosis, CFTR, transports Cl^- ions), and as regulatory molecules (e.g., transcription factors).

6.3   Various proteins are treated as specified. For each case indicate what level(s) of protein structure would change as the result of the treatment.
   a. Hemoglobin is stored in a hot incubator at 80° C.
   b. Egg white (albumin) is boiled.
   c. Rnase (a single polypeptide enzyme) is heated to 100° C.
   d. Meat in your stomach is digested (gastric juices contain proteolytic enzymes).
   e. In the β polypeptide chain of hemoglobin, the amino acid valine replaces glutamic acid at the number six position.

Answer:
   a. The hemoglobin would dissociate into its four component subunits, because the heat will destabilize the ionic bonds that stabilize the quaternary structure of the protein. An individual subunit's tertiary structure may also be altered, as the thermal energy of the heat may destabilize the folding of the polypeptide.
   b. The protein will denature. Its tertiary structure is destabilized by heating, so it does not retain a pattern of folding that allows it to be soluble.
   c. The protein will denature when its tertiary structure is destabilized by heating. Rnase, unlike albumin, will renature if cooled slowly, and re-establish its normal, functional tertiary structure.
   d. It is likely that the meat proteins will be denatured when their tertiary and quaternary structures are destabilized by the acid conditions of the stomach. Then the primary structure of the polypeptides will be destroyed as they are degraded into their amino acid components by proteolytic enzymes in the digestive tract.
   e. Valine is a neutral, nonpolar amino acid, unlike the acidic glutamic acid (see Figure 6.2). A change in the chemical properties of the number 6 amino acid may alter the function of the hemoglobin molecule by affecting multiple levels of protein structure. Since it is an amino acid substitution, it changes the primary structure of the β polypeptide. This change could affect local interactions between amino acids near the number 6 position and in doing so, alter the econddary structure of the β polypeptide. It could also affect the folding patterns of the protein and alter the tertiary structure of the β polypeptide. Finally, the number 6 amino acid residue is known to be important for interactions between the subunits of hemoglobin molecules (see Figures 4.8 to 4.10), as some

mutations that alter this amino acid result in sickle-cell anemia. Thus, this change could alter the quaternary structure of hemoglobin.

6.4   Several researchers have studied the structure and make-up of ribosomes because the best biochemical tradition of separating and reconstituting allows us to identify the components necessary for ribosomes to be active. Contrast prokaryotic ribosomes with eukaryotic ribosomes. What exactly is the function of ribosomes, and how do they carry out this function?

Answer: Prokaryotic and eukaryotic ribosomes each have two subunits with parallel functions and components. However, as presented in Chapter 5, the detailed constituents differ. The 70S prokaryotic ribosome has a 30S small subunit containing a 16S rRNA and 20 different proteins, and a 50S large subunit containing a 23S rRNA and 5S rRNA and 34 different proteins. The larger 80S eukaryotic ribosome has a 40S small subunit containing an 18S rRNA and about 35 proteins, and a 60S large subunit containing 28S, 5.8S, and 5S rRNAs and about 50 ribosomal proteins. In both eukaryotic and prokaryotic ribosomes, the proteins serve as structural units that help to organize the rRNA into key ribozyme elements.

Ribosomes function in translation, which proceeds through three phases: initiation, elongation and termination. During the initiation phase of translation, the small subunit, with the aid of initiation factors, is bound to the mRNA and the initiating aminoacyl tRNA (tRNA.fMet in prokaryotes, an initiator Met-tRNA in eukaryotes). The large subunit binds, forming an initiation complex with the initiator tRNA in the P site of the ribosome. During elongation, a second aminoacyl-tRNA is bound to the A site in the ribosome, the peptidyl transferase activity of the ribosome catalyzes the formation of the peptide bond, a now-uncharged tRNA is released (from the E site of the large subunit) and the ribosome translocates one codon down the mRNA. Translation elongation continues, so that codons are matched to amino acids in a growing polypeptide chain, until a stop (nonsense) codon is reached. Stop codons are recognized by release factors, which initiate three processes: the release of the polypeptide from the tRNA in the P site, the release of the tRNA from the ribosome, and the dissociation of the two ribosomal subunits and the release factor from the mRNA.

6.5   The term *genetic code* refers to the set of three-base code words (codons) in mRNA that stand for the 20 amino acids in proteins. What are some of the characteristics of the code?

Answer:
1. Triplet: Three nucleotides specify either the insertion of an amino acid into a polypeptide chain, or a chain termination event.
2. Continuous: An mRNA coding region is read in a continuous fashion without skipping nucleotides.
3. Nonoverlapping: A coding region is read in a nonoverlapping manner. Triplets are read sequentially.

4. Nearly universal: Nearly all organisms use the same code, with exceptions found in mammalian mitochondria and the nuclear genomes of some protozoa.
5. Degenerate: More than one codon typically codes for a single amino acid.
6. Signals start and stop: The code has translation stop (chain termination) and translation start signals. AUG, which encodes methionine within a coding region, is usually used as a start codon. One of three nonsense (*not sensing* an amino acid) codons are used as chain termination codons.
7. Wobble: The 5′ base of some anticodons wobbles, so that some tRNAs can recognize multiple codons (coding for the same amino acid).

6.6   If the codon were four bases long, how many codons would exist in a genetic code?

Answer: At each position of a codon four bases long, there will be one of four possible bases. So, there are $4 \times 4 \times 4 \times 4 = 4^4 = 256$ possible codons. This is far more than is needed to code for 20 amino acids. On the other hand, if there were only two bases in a codon, there would only be $4 \times 4 = 4^2 = 16$ possible codons, too few codons to uniquely specify 20 amino acids. Codons three bases long provide for $4 \times 4 \times 4 = 4^3 = 64$ possible codons.

6.7   Base-pairing wobble occurs in the interaction between the anticodon of the tRNAs and the codons. On a theoretical level, determine the minimum number of tRNAs needed to read the 61 sense codons.

Answer: Consider Figure 6.9, in answering this question.

AMINO ACID	TRNAS NEEDED	RATIONALE
Ile	1	3 codons can use 1 tRNA (wobble)
Phe	1	2 codons can use 1 tRNA (wobble)
Tyr	1	" " " " "
His	1	" " " " "
Gln	1	" " " " "
Asn	1	" " " " "
Lys	1	" " " " "
Asp	1	" " " " "
Glu	1	" " " " "
Cys	1	" " " " "
Trp	1	1 codon
Met	2	Single codon, but need one tRNA for initiation and one tRNA for elongation

AMINO ACID	TRNAS NEEDED	RATIONALE
Val	2	4 codons: 2 can use 1 tRNA (wobble)
Pro	2	" " " " "
Thr	2	" " " " "
Ala	2	" " " " "
Gly	2	" " " " "
Leu	3	6 codons: 2 can use 1 tRNA (wobble)
Arg	3	" " " " "
Ser	3	" " " " "
Total	**32**	**61 codons**

6.8   Antibiotics have been very useful in elucidating the steps of protein synthesis. If you have an artificial messenger RNA with the sequence

AUGUUUUUUUUUUUUU...,

it will produce the following polypeptide in a cell-free, protein-synthesizing system: fMet-Phe-Phe-Phe... In your search for new antibiotics you find one called putyermycin, which blocks protein synthesis. When you try it with your artificial mRNA in a cell-free system, the product is fMet-Phe. What step in protein synthesis does putyermycin affect? Why?

Answer: Since a dipeptide is formed, translation initiation is not affected, nor is the first step of elongation—the binding of a charged tRNA in the A site and the formation of a peptide bond. However, since *only* a dipeptide is formed, it appears that translocation is inhibited.

6.9   Describe the reactions involved in the aminoacylation (charging) of a tRNA molecule.

Answer: Aminoacylation of tRNAs occurs enzymatically using aminoacyl-tRNA synthetases. To provide for specificity in charging a tRNA, a separate aminoacyl-tRNA synthetase exists for each amino acid. This prevents an inappropriate amino acid from becoming attached to a tRNA. If an inappropriate amino acid were attached to a tRNA, the wrong amino acid would be inserted into a growing polypeptide chain, even with correct codon-anticodon base pairing between the mRNA and tRNA.

Aminoacyl-tRNA synthetases catalyze two sequential reactions to attach an amino acid to its appropriate tRNA. The first reaction results in the formation of an aminoacyl-AMP complex from the amino acid and ATP. The second reaction results in a covalent bond between the carboxyl group of the amino acid and the last ribose at the 3' end of the tRNA. See text Figures 6.10 and 6.11.

6.10   If the initiating codon of a mRNA became mutated, what might be the effect on the transcript?

Answer: In both prokaryotes and eukaryotes, the initiating codon of a transcript is AUG, and recognized by a special charged tRNA (tRNA.fMet in prokaryotes, initiator Met-tRNA in eukaryotes). This first codon is recognized in part because it is in a particular context: In prokaryotes, it is near the Shine-Dalgarno sequence, while in eukaryotes, it is embedded in a Kozak sequence. It is possible that if it were mutated, the 30S (in prokaryotes) or 40S (in eukaryotes) initiation complex would not form correctly, since the initiator tRNA would not find the correct initiator codon. The consequence of this would be that the mRNA would not be translated. On the other hand, if another AUG codon was very close by (and in eukaryotic mRNAs, embedded in a Kozak-type sequence), it might be used as an initiation codon, but the mRNA might be translated at a lower efficiency.

6.11   What differences would we find in protein synthesis initiation between prokaryotes and eukaryotes? What differences would we find in protein synthesis termination between prokaryotes and eukaryotes?

Answer: In both prokaryotes and eukaryotes, protein synthesis is initiated using special initiator tRNAs. In prokaryotes, methionine is attached to tRNA.fMet by methionine-tRNA synthetase, and transformylase catalyzes the addition of a formyl group to the methionine. The resulting fMet-tRNA.fMet is used at the AUG initiation codon. In eukaryotes, the N-terminal methionine is not formylated, but a special initiator methionine-tRNA is still used.

In both prokaryotes and eukaryotes, an initiation complex containing the small ribosomal subunit, initiator factors, GTP and the mRNA forms sequentially. In prokaryotes, after IF1, IF2, IF3 and GTP bind to the 30S ribosomal subunit, fMet-tRNA.fMet and the mRNA attach to form the 30S initiation complex. The mRNA is aligned using an internal ribosome-binding site (the Shine-Dalgarno sequence) lying near the AUG initiation codon that base pairs with sequences at the 3' end of the 16S rRNA. After the 50S ribosomal subunit binds, GTP is hydrolyzed and IF1 and IF2 are released, leaving a 70S initiation complex. In eukaryotes, after eIF4A binds to the 5' cap of the mRNA, a complex of the 40S ribosomal subunit, the initiator Met-tRNA.Met, GTP, and additional eIFs bind. Only after the 40S ribosomal subunit scans and finds the initiator codon does the 60S ribosomal subunit bind. This displaces the eIFs and produces the 80S initiation complex.

In both prokaryotes and eukaryotes, chain termination is signaled by one of three stop codons (UAG, UAA, UGA). These stop codons do not code for an amino acid, but are recognized with the help of termination factors or release factors. Of the three RFs in *E. coli*, RF1 recognizes UAA and UAG, RF2 recognizes UAA and UGA, and RF3 stimulates chain termination. Eukaryotes have a single release factor, eRF, that recognizes all three stop codons. The release factors trigger release of the polypeptide from the tRNA in the P site of the ribosome, release of the tRNA from the ribosome, and dissociation of the two ribosomal subunits from the mRNA. The initiating amino acid is usually cleaved from the completed peptide.

6.12   Random copolymers were used in some of the experiments that revealed the characteristics of the genetic code. For each of the following ribonucleotide mixtures, give the expected codons and their frequencies, and give the expected proportions of the amino acids that would be found in a polypeptide directed by the copolymer in a cell-free, protein-synthesizing system:

a. 4 A : 6 C
b. 4 G : 1 C
c. 1 A : 3 U : 1 C
d. 1 A : 1 U : 1 G : 1 C

Answer: Determine the expected amino acids in each case by calculating the expected frequency of each kind of triplet codon that might be formed, and inferring from these what types and frequencies of amino acids would be used during translation.

a. 4 A:6 C gives 2^3 = 8 codons, specifically AAA, AAC, ACC, ACA, CCC, ACA, CAC, CAA. Since there is 40% A and 60% C,

$$p(AAA) = 0.4 \times 0.4 \times 0.4 = 0.064, \text{ or } 6.4\% \text{ Lys}$$
$$p(AAC) = 0.4 \times 0.4 \times 0.6 = 0.096, \text{ or } 9.6\% \text{ Asn}$$
$$p(ACC) = 0.4 \times 0.6 \times 0.6 = 0.144, \text{ or } 14.4\% \text{ Thr}$$
$$p(ACA) = 0.4 \times 0.6 \times 0.4 = 0.096, \text{ or } 9.6\% \text{ Thr (24\% Thr total)}$$
$$p(CCC) = 0.6 \times 0.6 \times 0.6 = 0.216, \text{ or } 21.6\% \text{ Pro}$$
$$p(CCA) = 0.6 \times 0.6 \times 0.4 = 0.144, \text{ or } 14.4\% \text{ Pro (36\% Pro total)}$$
$$p(CAC) = 0.6 \times 0.4 \times 0.6 = 0.144, \text{ or } 14.4\% \text{ His}$$
$$p(CAA) = 0.6 \times 0.4 \times 0.4 = 0.096, \text{ or } 9.6\% \text{ Gln}$$

b. 4 G:1 C gives 2^3 = 8 codons, specifically GGG, GGC, GCG, GCC, CGG, CGC, CCC, CCG. Since there is 80% G and 20% C,

$$p(GGG) = 0.8 \times 0.8 \times 0.8 = 0.512, \text{ or } 51.2\% \text{ Gly}$$
$$p(GGC) = 0.8 \times 0.8 \times 0.2 = 0.128, \text{ or } 12.8\% \text{ Gly (64\% Gly total)}$$
$$p(GCG) = 0.8 \times 0.2 \times 0.8 = 0.128, \text{ or } 12.8\% \text{ Ala}$$
$$p(GCC) = 0.8 \times 0.2 \times 0.2 = 0.032, \text{ or } 3.2\% \text{ Ala (16\% Ala total)}$$
$$p(CGG) = 0.2 \times 0.8 \times 0.8 = 0.128, \text{ or } 12.8\% \text{ Arg}$$
$$p(CGC) = 0.2 \times 0.8 \times 0.2 = 0.032, \text{ or } 3.2\% \text{ Arg (16\% Arg total)}$$
$$p(CCC) = 0.2 \times 0.2 \times 0.2 = 0.008, \text{ or } 0.8\% \text{ Pro}$$
$$p(CCG) = 0.2 \times 0.2 \times 0.8 = 0.032, \text{ or } 3.2\% \text{ Pro (4\% Pro total)}$$

c. 1 A:3 U:1 C gives 3^3 = 27 different possible codons. Of these, one will be UAA, a chain-terminating codon. Since there is 20% A, 60% U and 20% C, the probability of finding this codon is $0.6 \times 0.2 \times 0.2 = 0.024$, or 2.4%. All of the remaining 26 (97.6%) codons will be sense codons. Proceed in the same manner as in a and b to determine their frequency, and determine the kinds of amino acids expected. To take the frequency of nonsense codons into account, divide the frequency of obtaining a particular amino acid considering all 27 possible codons by the frequency of obtaining a sense codon. This gives:

$(0.8/0.976)\% = 0.82\%$ Lys
$(3.2/0.976)\% = 3.28\%$ Asn
$(12.0/0.976)\% = 12.3\%$ Ile
$(9.6/0.976)\% = 9.84\%$ Tyr
$(19.2/0.976)\% = 19.67\%$ Leu
$(28.8/0.976)\% = 29.5\%$ Phe
$(4.0/0.976)\% = 4.1\%$ Thr
$(0.8/0.976)\% = 0.82\%$ Gln
$(3.2/0.976)\% = 3.28\%$ His
$(4.0/0.976)\% = 4.1\%$ Pro
$(12.0/0.976)\% = 12.3\%$ Ser

It is likely that the chains produced would be relatively short, due to the chain-terminating codon.

d. 1 A:1 U:1 G:1 C will produce $4^3 = 64$ different codons, all of those possible in the genetic code. The probability of each codon is 1/64, and so there will be a 3/64 chance of a codon being chain terminating. With those exceptions, the relative proportion of amino acid incorporation is directly dependent on the codon degeneracy for each amino acid. Inspecting the table of the genetic code in Figure 6.8, and taking the frequency of nonsense codons into account, there will be:

AMINO ACID	# CODONS	FREQUENCY
Trp	1	1/61 =1.64%
Met	1	1.64%
Phe	2	2/61 = 3.28%
Try	2	3.28%
His	2	3.28%
Gln	2	3.28%
Asn	2	3.28%
Lys	2	3.28%
Asp	2	3.28%
Glu	2	3.28%
Cys	2	3.28%
Ile	3	3/61 = 4.92%
Val	4	4/61 = 6.56%
Pro	4	6.56%
Thr	4	6.56%
Ala	4	6.56%
Gly	4	6.56%
Leu	6	6/61 = 9.84%
Arg	6	9.84%
Ser	6	9.84%

6.13   What would the minimum word (codon) size need to be if the number of different bases in the mRNA were, instead of four,

    a. two

    b. three

    c. five

Answer:

    a. If only two bases existed in mRNA and codons were four bases long, there would be $2^4 = 16$ possible codons, not enough to code for 20 amino acids. In order to encode 20 different amino acids, codons would need to be at least five bases long. For 5-base codons, there would be $2^5 = 32$ possible codons.

    b. If only three bases existed in mRNA, codons would need to be at least 3 bases long ($3^3 = 27$ possible combinations).

    c. If five bases existed in mRNA, codons would need to be at least 2 bases long ($5^2 = 25$ possible combinations).

6.14   Suppose that at stage A in the evolution of the genetic code only the first two nucleotides in the coding triplets led to unique differences and that any nucleotide could occupy the third position. Then, suppose there was a stage B in which differences in meaning arose depending on whether a purine (A or G) or pyrimidine (C or U) was present at the third position. Without reference to the number of amino acids or multiplicity of tRNA molecules, how many triplets of different meaning can be constructed out of the code at stage A? At stage B?

    Answer: Stage A: $4^2 = 16$ different meaningful triplets

                   Stage B: $4^2 \times 2 = 32$ different meaningful triplets

6.15   A gene encodes a polypeptide 30 amino acids long containing an alternating sequence of phenylalanine and tyrosine. What are the sequences of nucleotides corresponding to this sequence in the following:

    a. the DNA strand that is read to produce the mRNA, assuming Phe = UUU and Tyr = UAU in mRNA

    b. the DNA strand that is not read

    c. tRNAs

Answer:

    a. 3′ – TAC AAA ATA AAA ATA AAA ATA AAA ATA...–5′ (The first fMet or Met is removed following translation of the mRNA.)

    b. 5′ – ATG TTT TAT TTT TAT TTT TAT TTT TAT...–3′

    c. 3′ –AAA–5′ is the anticodon for Phe, and 3′ –AUA– 5′ is the anticodon for Tyr

6.16   A segment of a polypeptide chain is Arg-Gly-Ser-Phe-Val-Asp-Arg. It is encoded by the following segment of DNA:

Mutant *b* mutates the initiation codon, so that a polypeptide would be formed (if formed at all) using a downstream initiation codon. It results in a polypeptide missing amino acids at its N-terminus.

```
c:  AUG  UUC  UCG  AAU  UAC  ...  AUG  GGG  UGG  GUG  UAG
    met  phe  ser  asn  tyr  ...  met  gly  trp  val  stop
```

Mutant *c* changes a base in the 3' end of the codon. This does not alter the amino acid that is inserted. It will be "silent" and have no phenotypic effect.

```
d:  AUG  UUC  UCU  AAA  UAC  ...  AUG  GGG  UGG  GUG  UAG
    met  phe  ser  lys  tyr  ...  met  gly  trp  val  stop
```

Mutant *d* changes a base in the 3' end of the codon. This does alter the amino acid that is inserted. It is a missense mutation, resulting in the insertion of a Lys instead of an Asn.

```
e:  AUG  UUC  UCU  AAU  UC.  ..A  UGG  GGU  GGG  UGU  AG.
    met  phe  ser  asn  ser  ...  trp  gly  gly  cys  ?
```

Mutant *e* is a single base-pair deletion, and results in a frameshift mutation that alters the reading frame of the protein. All amino acids inserted following Asn are likely to be incorrect. It is conceivable that a stop codon could be read in the region that is indicated by the ..., leading to premature chain termination.

```
f:  AUG  UUC  UCU  AAU  UAC  ...  AUG  GGG  UGG  GUG  UGG
    met  phe  ser  asn  tyr  ...  met  gly  trp  val  trp..
```

Mutant *f* changes a base in the chain-terminating UAG codon so that the amino acid Trp will now be inserted. It will result in the placement of additional amino acids onto the C-terminus of the protein.

6.22   The normal sequence of a particular protein is given here, along with several mutant versions of it. For each mutant, explain what mutation occurred in the coding sequence of the gene; (...) = a multiple of three unspecified bases.
   Normal: Met-Gly-Glu-Thr-Lys-Val-Val-(...)-Pro
   Mutant 1: Met-Gly
   Mutant 2: Met-Gly-Glu-Asp
   Mutant 3: Met-Gly-Arg-Leu-Lys
   Mutant 4: Met-Arg-Glu-Thr-Lys-Val-Val-(...)-Pro

Answer: One approach to this problem is to infer the possible coding sequence(s) that could be used for the normal protein (using N = any nucleotide, R = purine, Y = pyrimidine), and then examine this sequence to deduce what possible mutations could have resulted in the mutant proteins.

Based on the normal amino acid sequence, the mRNA sequence is:

```
amino acid sequence: Met-Gly-Glu-Thr-Lys-Val-Val-...-Pro
potential mRNA: 5'-AUG GGN GAR ACN AAR GUN GUN ... CCN-3'
```

In mutant 1, premature chain termination has occurred. This could have occurred if, in the DNA transcribed into the third (GAR (Glu)) codon, a GC base pair was changed to a TA base pair. This would lead to a UAR (stop) codon.

```
normal sequence:  Met-Gly-Glu-Thr-Lys-Val-Val-...-Pro
```

```
normal mRNA: 5'-AUG GGN GAR ACN AAR GUN GUN ... CCN-3'
mutant mRNA: 5'-AUG GGN UAR ACN AAR GUN GUN ... CCN-3'
mutant sequence:  Met-Gly-stop
```

It could also have occurred if a TA base-pair insertion mutation occurred in the DNA, so that a U was transcribed in between the normal second and third codons, resulting in a UGA (stop) third codon.

```
amino acid sequence: Met-Gly-Glu-Thr-Lys-Val-Val-...-Pro
potential mRNA: 5' -AUG GGN GAR ACN AAR GUN GUN ... CCN-3'
mutant mRNA:  5' -AUG GGN UGA RAC NAA RGU NGU N.. .CC-3'
mutant sequence:    Met-Gly-stop
```

In mutant 2, premature chain termination has occurred after a wrong amino acid has been inserted. To explain both of these results as a consequence of a single mutational event, try either insertion or deletion mutations that would alter the reading frame. One possible explanation is that a GC base-pair insertional mutation in the DNA resulted in a G being inserted after the third codon. If the N of the fourth codon were a U, then such a frameshifting insertion would change the Thr to Asp, and also introduce a chain termination codon into the fifth codon position. If the R in the GAR coding for Glu (the third amino acid) is a G, this mutation could also be caused by a GC or AT base-pair insertional mutation after the first two nucleotides coding for Glu. As before, assume the N of the fourth codon is a U.

```
amino acid sequence: Met-Gly-Glu-Thr-Lys-Val-Val-...-Pro
potential mRNA: 5'-AUG GGN GAR ACN AAR GUN GUN ... CCN-3'
mutant mRNA:   5'-AUG GGN GAR GAC UAA RGU NGU N.. .CC-3'
mutant sequence:    Met-Gly-Glu-Asp-stop
```

In mutant 3, the situation is similar to that with mutant 2. This time, however, several wrong amino acids are inserted before chain termination. To explain all of these consequences as the result of a single mutational event, check for the consequences of deletions or insertions in the region of the second and third codons. One possible explanation is that a deletion mutation in the DNA resulted in the N of the second codon being deleted. If, as in mutant 2, the N of the fourth codon is a U, and the R of the third codon is a G, the R of the fifth codon is an A, and the N of the sixth codon is an A, the mutant sequence would be obtained.

```
normal sequence:  Met-Gly-Glu-Thr-Lys-Val-Val ... Pro
normal mRNA: 5'-AUG GGN GAR ACN AAR GUN GUN ... CCN-3'
normal mRNA: 5'-AUG GGN GAG ACU AAA GUA GUN ... CCN-3'
mutant mRNA: 5'-AUG GGG AGA CUA AAG UAG UN. ..C CN-3'
mutant sequence: Met-Gly-Arg-Leu-Lys-Stop
```

In mutant 4, the normal second amino acid (Gly) has been replaced with Arg. Arg is encoded by AGR or CGN, while Gly is encoded by GGN. If a GC base pair were substituted for a CG base pair in the DNA so that the first G of the second codon were replaced by a C, Arg would be inserted as the second amino acid.

```
normal sequence:  Met-Gly-Glu-Thr-Lys-Val-Val ... Pro
normal mRNA: 5'-AUG GGN GAR ACN AAR GUN GUN ... CCN-3'
mutant mRNA: 5'-AUG CGN GAR ACN AAR GUN GUN ... CCN-3'
mutant sequence: Met-Arg-Glu-Thr-Lys-Val-Val ... Pro
```

6.23   The N-terminus of a protein has the sequence Met-His-Arg-Arg-Lys-Val-His-Gly-Gly. A molecular biologist wants to synthesize a DNA chain that could encode this tRNA.Met for the recognition of the 5'-AUG-3' codon, and if successful, insert Ile into a protein where Met should be. Since a special tRNA.Met is used for initiation, only AUG codons other than the initiation AUG will be affected. Thus, this protein will have four different N-terminal sequences, depending on which tRNA occupies the A site in the ribosome when the codon AUG is present there:

```
Met-Val-Ser-Ser-Pro-Ile-Gly-Ala-Ala-Ile-Ser
Met-Val-Ser-Ser-Pro-Met-Gly-Ala-Ala-Ile-Ser
Met-Val-Ser-Ser-Pro-Ile-Gly-Ala-Ala-Met-Ser
Met-Val-Ser-Ser-Pro-Met-Gly-Ala-Ala-Met-Ser
```

6.20 The gene encoding an *E. coli* tRNA containing the anticodon 5'-GUA-3' mutates so that the anticodon now is 5'-UUA-3'. What will be the effect of this mutation? Explain your reasoning.

Answer: The normal tRNA recognizes the codon 5'-UAC-3', and so must have carried the amino acid tyrosine. The altered anticodon will recognize the codon 5'-UAA-3', a chain termination codon. Consequently, a tyrosine will be inserted when the nonsense codon UAA in an mRNA is positioned in the A site of the ribosome. This will result in read-through of the mRNA some of the time (when the termination factor does not compete for binding to the chain termination codon), and the addition of amino acids onto the C-terminus of the protein. mRNAs having UAG and UGA chain termination codons will not be affected.

6.21 The normal sequence of the coding region of an mRNA is shown below, along with six mutant versions of the same mRNA. Indicate what protein would be formed in each case; (...) = a multiple of 3 unspecified bases.

```
Normal:   AUGUUCUCUAAUUAC(...)AUGGGGUGGGUGUAG
Mutant a: AUGUUCUCUAAUUAG(...)AUGGGGUGGGUGUAG
Mutant b: AGGUUCUCUAAUUAC(...)AUGGGGUGGGUGUAG
Mutant c: AUGUUCUCGAAUUAC(...)AUGGGGUGGGUGUAG
Mutant d: AUGUUCUCUAAAUAC(...)AUGGGGUGGGUGUAG
Mutant e: AUGUUCUCUAAUUC(...)AUGGGGUGGGUGUAG
Mutant f: AUGUUCUCUAAUUAC(...)AUGGGGUGGGUGUGG
```

Answer: First rewrite the sequences so that the codons can be readily seen, noting the mutations (underlined):

```
normal: AUG UUC UCU AAU UAC (...) AUG GGG UGG GUG UAG
     a: AUG UUC UCU AAU UAG (...) AUG GGG UGG GUG UAG
     b: AGG UUC UCU AAU UAC (...) AUG GGG UGG GUG UAG
     c: AUG UUC UCG AAU UAC (...) AUG GGG UGG GUG UAG
     d: AUG UUC UCU AAA UAC (...) AUG GGG UGG GUG UAG
     e: AUG UUC UCU AAU UC. ..)A UGG GGU GGG UGU AG.
     f: AUG UUC UCU AAU UAC (...) AUG GGG UGG GUG UGG
```

Mutants *a, b, c, d,* and *f* are point mutations, in which one base has been substituted for another. Mutant *e* is a deletion of a single base that results in a shift in the reading frame of the mRNA (a frameshift mutation). Translating each sequence using the genetic code, determine the proteins that would be formed if these sequences were translated:

```
normal:    AUG UUC UCU AAU UAC ... AUG GGG UGG GUG UAG
           met phe ser asn tyr ... met gly trp val stop


     a:    AUG UUC UCU AAU UAG ... AUG GGG UGG GUG UAG
           met phe ser asn stop
```

Mutant *a* is a nonsense mutation, and results in premature chain termination.

```
     b:    AGG UUC UCU AAU UAC ... AUG GGG UGG GUG UAG
                                   met gly trp val stop
```

Mutant *b* mutates the initiation codon, so that a polypeptide would be formed (if formed at all) using a downstream initiation codon. It results in a polypeptide missing amino acids at its N-terminus.

```
     c:    AUG UUC UCG AAU UAC ... AUG GGG UGG GUG UAG
           met phe ser asn tyr ... met gly trp val stop
```

Mutant *c* changes a base in the 3' end of the codon. This does not alter the amino acid that is inserted. It will be "silent" and have no phenotypic effect.

```
     d:    AUG UUC UCU AAA UAC ... AUG GGG UGG GUG UAG
           met phe ser lys tyr ... met gly trp val stop
```

Mutant *d* changes a base in the 3' end of the codon. This does alter the amino acid that is inserted. It is a missense mutation, resulting in the insertion of a Lys instead of an Asn.

```
     e:    AUG UUC UCU AAU UC. ..A UGG GGU GGG UGU AG.
           met phe ser asn ser ... trp gly gly cys ?
```

Mutant *e* is a single base-pair deletion, and results in a frameshift mutation that alters the reading frame of the protein. All amino acids inserted following Asn are likely to be incorrect. It is conceivable that a stop codon could be read in the region that is indicated by the ..., leading to premature chain termination.

```
     f:    AUG UUC UCU AAU UAC ... AUG GGG UGG GUG UGG
           met phe ser asn tyr ... met gly trp val trp..
```

Mutant *f* changes a base in the chain-terminating UAG codon so that the amino acid Trp will now be inserted. It will result in the placement of additional amino acids onto the C-terminus of the protein.

6.22   The normal sequence of a particular protein is given here, along with several mutant versions of it. For each mutant, explain what mutation occurred in the coding sequence of the gene; (...) = a multiple of three unspecified bases.

Normal: Met-Gly-Glu-Thr-Lys-Val-Val-(...)-Pro
Mutant 1: Met-Gly
Mutant 2: Met-Gly-Glu-Asp
Mutant 3: Met-Gly-Arg-Leu-Lys
Mutant 4: Met-Arg-Glu-Thr-Lys-Val-Val-(...)-Pro

Answer: One approach to this problem is to infer the possible coding sequence(s) that could be used for the normal protein (using N = any nucleotide, R = purine, Y = pyrimidine), and then examine this sequence to deduce what possible mutations could have resulted in the mutant proteins.

Based on the normal amino acid sequence, the mRNA sequence is:

```
amino acid sequence: Met-Gly-Glu-Thr-Lys-Val-Val-...-Pro
potential mRNA: 5'-AUG GGN GAR ACN AAR GUN GUN ... CCN-3'
```

In mutant 1, premature chain termination has occurred. This could have occurred if, in the DNA transcribed into the third (GAR (Glu)) codon, a GC base pair was changed to a TA base pair. This would lead to a UAR (stop) codon.

```
normal sequence:  Met-Gly-Glu-Thr-Lys-Val-Val-...-Pro
normal mRNA: 5'-AUG GGN GAR ACN AAR GUN GUN ... CCN-3'
mutant mRNA: 5'-AUG GGN UAR ACN AAR GUN GUN ... CCN-3'
mutant sequence:  Met-Gly-stop
```

It could also have occurred if a TA base-pair insertion mutation occurred in the DNA, so that a U was transcribed in between the normal second and third codons, resulting in a UGA (stop) third codon.

```
amino acid sequence: Met-Gly-Glu-Thr-Lys-Val-Val-...-Pro
potential mRNA: 5' -AUG GGN GAR ACN AAR GUN GUN ... CCN-3'
mutant mRNA:  5' -AUG GGN UGA RAC NAA RGU NGU N.. .CC-3'
mutant sequence:   Met-Gly-stop
```

In mutant 2, premature chain termination has occurred after a wrong amino acid has been inserted. To explain both of these results as a consequence of a single mutational event, try either insertion or deletion mutations that would alter the

reading frame. One possible explanation is that a GC base-pair insertional mutation in the DNA resulted in a G being inserted after the third codon. If the N of the
fourth codon were a U, then such a frameshifting insertion would change the Thr to
Asp, and also introduce a chain termination codon into the fifth codon position. If
the R in the GAR coding for Glu (the third amino acid) is a G, this mutation could
also be caused by a GC or AT base-pair insertional mutation after the first two nucleotides coding for Glu. As before, assume the N of the fourth codon is a U.

```
amino acid sequence: Met-Gly-Glu-Thr-Lys-Val-Val-...-Pro
potential mRNA: 5'-AUG GGN GAR ACN AAR GUN GUN ... CCN-3'
mutant mRNA:   5'-AUG GGN GAR GAC UAA RGU NGU N.. .CC-3'
mutant sequence:   Met-Gly-Glu-Asp-stop
```

In mutant 3, the situation is similar to that with mutant 2. This time, however, several wrong amino acids are inserted before chain termination. To explain all of
these consequences as the result of a single mutational event, check for the consequences of deletions or insertions in the region of the second and third codons. One
possible explanation is that a deletion mutation in the DNA resulted in the N of the
second codon being deleted. If, as in mutant 2, the N of the fourth codon is a U, and
the R of the third codon is a G, the R of the fifth codon is an A, and the N of the
sixth codon is an A, the mutant sequence would be obtained.

```
normal sequence:  Met-Gly-Glu-Thr-Lys-Val-Val ... Pro
normal mRNA: 5'-AUG GGN GAR ACN AAR GUN GUN ... CCN-3'
normal mRNA: 5'-AUG GGN GAG ACU AAA GUA GUN ... CCN-3'
mutant mRNA: 5'-AUG GGG AGA CUA AAG UAG UN. ..C CN-3'
mutant sequence:  Met-Gly-Arg-Leu-Lys-Stop
```

In mutant 4, the normal second amino acid (Gly) has been replaced with Arg. Arg is
encoded by AGR or CGN, while Gly is encoded by GGN. If a GC base pair were
substituted for a CG base pair in the DNA so that the first G of the second codon
were replaced by a C, Arg would be inserted as the second amino acid.

```
normal sequence:  Met-Gly-Glu-Thr-Lys-Val-Val ... Pro
normal mRNA: 5'-AUG GGN GAR ACN AAR GUN GUN ... CCN-3'
mutant mRNA: 5'-AUG CGN GAR ACN AAR GUN GUN ... CCN-3'
mutant sequence:  Met-Arg-Glu-Thr-Lys-Val-Val ... Pro
```

6.23   The N-terminus of a protein has the sequence Met-His-Arg-Arg-Lys-Val-His-Gly-
Gly. A molecular biologist wants to synthesize a DNA chain that could encode this
portion of the protein. How many possible DNA sequences could encode this polypeptide?

Answer: Because of the redundancy in the genetic code, a number of different DNA
strands could serve as coding (nontemplate) strands for this sequence. If N = any of
the four nucleotides, Y = either pyrimidine nucleotide (C, T), and R = either purine

nucleotide (A, G), then the amino acid sequence could be encoded by any of the following strands:

```
Met-His-     Arg    -    Arg    -Lys-Val-His-Gly-Gly
ATG CAY (AGR or CGN) (AGR or CGN) AAR GTN CAY GGN GGN
```

Calculate the number of different sequences by multiplying the possibilities (using the product and sum rules):

```
ATG CAY (AGR or CGN)(AGR or CGN) AAR GTN CAY GGN GGN
 1 x  2 x  (2 + 4)    x  (2 + 4)  x 2 x 4 x 2 x 4 x 4 =18,432
```

6.24 In the recessive condition in humans known as sickle-cell anemia, the β-globin polypeptide of hemoglobin is found to be abnormal. The only difference between it and the normal β-globin is that the sixth amino acid from the N-terminal is valine, whereas the normal β-globin has glutamic acid at this position. Explain how this occurred in terms of differences in the DNA and the mRNA.

Answer: Both GAA and GAG code for glutamic acid, while GUU, GUC, GUA, and GUG code for valine. The simplest explanation is that there was an AT to a TA change in the DNA, at the 17th base pair in the coding region of the gene. In this event, the 6th codon, instead of being GAA or GAG, would be GUA or GUG and encode valine.

6.25 Cystic fibrosis is an autosomal recessive disease in which the cystic fibrosis transmembrane conductance regulator (CFTR) protein is abnormal. The transcribed portion of the cystic fibrosis gene spans about 250,000 base pairs of DNA. The CFTR protein, with 1,480 amino acids, is translated from an mRNA of about 6,500 bases. The most common mutation in this gene results in a protein that is missing a phenylalanine at position 508 (ΔF508).
  a. Why is the RNA coding sequence of this gene so much larger than the mRNA from which the CFTR protein is translated?
  b. About what percent of the mRNA together makes up 5' untranslated leader and 3' untranslated trailer sequences?
  c. At the DNA level, what alteration would you expect to find in the ΔF508 mutation?
  d. What consequences might you expect if the DNA alteration that you describe in (c) occurred at random in the protein-coding region of the cystic fibrosis gene?

Answer:
  a. If the primary mRNA for this gene is 250 kb (kilobase pairs), it must be substantially processed by RNA splicing (removal of introns) and polyadenylation to a smaller mature mRNA.

b. A 1,480 amino acid protein requires 1,480 x 3 = 4,440 bases of protein coding sequence. This leaves 6,500 – 4,440 = 2,060 bases of 5' untranslated leader and 3' untranslated trailer sequence in the mature mRNA, about 32 percent.

c. The ΔF508 mutation could be caused by a DNA deletion for the three base pairs encoding the mRNA codon for phenylalanine. This codon is UUY (Y = U or C), and the DNA sequence of the nontemplate strand is 5'-TTY-3'. The segment of DNA containing these bases would be deleted in the appropriate region of the gene.

d. If positioned at random and solely within a gene's coding region (i.e., not in 3' or 5' untranslated sequences, or in intronic sequences), a deletion of three base pairs results either in an mRNA missing a single codon, or an mRNA missing bases from two adjacent codons. If three of the six bases from two adjacent codons were deleted, the remaining three bases would form a single codon. In this case, an incorrect amino acid might be inserted into the polypeptide at the site of the left codon, and the amino acid encoded by the right codon would be deleted. If the 3' base of the left codon were deleted, it would be replaced by the 3' base of the right codon. Since the code is degenerate, and wobble occurs in the 3' base, this type of deletion might not alter the amino acid specified by the left codon. The adjacent amino acid would still be deleted, however.

6.26   Antibiotics have been useful in determining whether cellular events depend on transcription or translation. For example, actinomycin D is used to block transcription, and cycloheximide (in eukaryotes) is used to block translation. In some cases, though, surprising results are obtained after antibiotics are administered. Adding actinomycin D, for example, may result in an increase, not a decrease, in the activity of a particular enzyme. Discuss how this result might come about.

Answer: Some gene products can inhibit the activity of others. In this case, actinomycin D might block the transcription of a gene that codes for an inhibitor of an enzyme activity. In the absence of its inhibitor, the enzyme would have increased activity.

7

RECOMBINANT DNA CLONING TECHNOLOGY

CHAPTER OUTLINE

DNA CLONING
    Restriction Enzymes
    Cloning Vectors and DNA Cloning

RECOMBINANT DNA LIBRARIES
    Genomic Libraries
    Chromosome Libraries
    cDNA Libraries

FINDING A SPECIFIC CLONE IN A LIBRARY
    Screening a cDNA Library
    Screening a Genomic Library
    Identifying Genes in Libraries by Complementation of Mutations
    Identifying Specific DNA Sequences in Libraries Using Heterologous Probes
    Identifying Genes or cDNAs in Libraries Using Oligonucleotide Probes

ANALYZING GENES AND GENE TRANSCRIPTS
    Restriction Enzyme Analysis of Cloned DNA Sequences
    Restriction Enzyme Analysis of Genes in the Genome
    Analyzing Gene Transcripts
    DNA Sequencing

POLYMERASE CHAIN REACTION (PCR)

REVIEW OF KEY TERMS, SYMBOLS, AND CONCEPTS

In your own words, write a brief definition of each term in the groups below. Check your definitions using the text. Then, develop a concept map using the terms in each group.

1	2	3	4
recombinant DNA	genomic library	library screening	restriction map
genetic engineering	chromosome library	expression vector	preparative agarose
cloning vector	complementary DNA	autoradiogram	gel electrophoresis
molecular cloning	cDNA	autoradiography	Southern blot
restriction enzyme,	cDNA library	plaque lift	Technique
site endonuclease	partial digestion	replica plating	northern blot analysis

1	2	3	4
twofold rotational symmetry	insert size	random primer labeling	Sanger (dideoxy) sequencing
palindrome	flow cytometry	Klenow fragment	dideoxynucleotide
sticky, staggered, blunt ends	plasmid, λ, cosmid, YAC, BAC, shuttle vectors	nonradioactive labeling	sequencing ladder
5', 3' overhang	oligo(dT) chains	chemiluminescent, colorimetric detection	computer database
plasmid, λ, cosmid, YAC, BAC, shuttle vectors	reverse transcriptase	complementation	ORF, motif
polylinker	RNase H	digoxigenin	polymerase chain reaction (PCR)
multiple cloning site	restriction site linker adapter	heterologous probe	thermal cycler
ori vs. cos site	packaging	oligonucleotide probe	amplification
selectable marker	subcloning	GenBank	primer, amplimer
unique restriction site	TEL, CEN, ARS sequences		ancient DNA
blue/white selection	TRP1, URA3 markers		thermostable DNA polymerase
			Taq DNA polymerase
			DNA typing

THINKING ANALYTICALLY

The material in this chapter introduces core concepts in molecular genetics. It presents many techniques and ideas that are widely used throughout genetics. Many of these have been developed by coupling fundamental genetic principles with technological advances. For example, the development of the ability to clone DNA required the synthesis of information from bacterial genetics (e.g., how to transform cells, how to design and use selectable markers, how to perform bacterial crosses, how to design plasmids, an understanding of the λ-phage life cycle and genetics); DNA replication (the discovery, characterization and purification of DNA polymerases and ligases); and the discovery, characterization and purification of restriction enzymes. As you learn about molecular genetic methods, observe how they rely on a synthesis of information from different areas of genetics and biochemistry.

Learning this material requires you to understand the logic and fundamental genetic principles behind many different techniques. While it would be helpful to perform all of the techniques, this may not be an option. Indeed, the current repertoire of techniques is so great and so rapidly advancing that no one scientist has first-hand experience in all of them. Still, scientists learn to think effectively about them, and apply them to their research questions. As you approach a new method, think through the steps of the method and consider the rationale for each step. Then, consider how different methods can be used together or interchangeably.

This chapter discusses manipulations of DNA that cannot be directly sensed (with the eyes, ears, nose, or touch). Like material from the physical sciences—chemistry and physics—that considers molecular interactions, it requires visualization and abstract conceptualization. While the results of techniques presented in this chapter cannot be directly sensed, they are based on understanding, and developing a mental image of, the molecular structure, function and activity of nucleic acids and proteins in test tubes, cells and viruses under defined environmental conditions. When the techniques produce reasonable, expected results, they validate and sometimes expand our understanding of the structure and function of these molecules. For example, we have never *seen* the actual base sequences of a fragment of DNA, but we have developed a model of DNA structure from experimentation. *If* that model is correct, then a technique such as dideoxy sequencing of DNA should work. As you learn about an experimental method, identify the models being used. Consider how the results obtained with the method would be altered if the model were incorrect.

QUESTIONS FOR PRACTICE

Multiple Choice Questions

For questions 1–10, match each experimental goal with techniques useful to attain it. Multiple techniques may be used in achieving one goal. Some techniques will be used more than once.

EXPERIMENTAL GOAL	TECHNIQUE
1. Determine if a particular mRNA is expressed at a specific developmental stage.	a. restriction mapping
2. Separate mRNA from a mixture of mRNA, rRNA and tRNA prior to construction of cDNA.	b. partial digestion with a restriction enzyme that recognizes a 4-bp site
3. Isolate a particular cDNA clone in a cDNA library using an antibody.	c. polymerase chain reaction
4. Determine gene homology.	d. use expression vector to produce a particular protein
5. Determine the organization of introns in a gene.	
6. Produce relatively large genomic DNA fragments for cloning in a library.	e. northern blot analysis
7. Identify plasmids with inserted DNA sequences.	f. Southern blot analysis
8. Identify phage with inserts homologous to a probe sequence.	g. blue/white selection
	h. use oligo(dT) to isolate RNA with poly(A) tails
9. Amplify a specific genomic DNA sequence.	i. plaque lifts
10. Determine the size of a fragment of DNA inserted into a plasmid vector.	j. agarose gel electrophoresis

11. Why are antibiotic resistance markers important components of plasmid cloning vectors?
    a. The plasmid must have resistance to accept DNA inserts.
    b. They allow identification of bacteria that have taken up a plasmid.
    c. They ensure the presence of both the *ori* and *cos* sites.
    d. They ensure that the plasmid can be cut by a restriction enzyme.

12. When a PCR reaction is performed using genomic DNA as a template, a 1.5-kb product is amplified. When the same reaction is set up using cDNA as a template, a 0.8-kb product is amplified. A likely explanation for the different-sized products is that
    a. primers always bind to different sequences in different templates.
    b. there is a mutation in the genomic DNA.
    c. there is an intron in the gene.
    d. the cDNA is degraded.

13. Why is it advantageous to screen a genomic library constructed in a cosmid vector instead of a phage vector?
    a. Fewer inserts can be screened.
    b. More inserts can be screened.
    c. Phage libraries contain cDNA, not genomic DNA.
    d. Cosmid libraries can be screened with an antibody.

14. The restriction enzyme *Bam*HI cleaves a phosphodiester bond between two GC base pairs at a six base-pair site. The 5'-to-3' sequence of one of the sites is GGATCC. Which statement is true?
    a. *Bam*HI leaves a 5' overhang.
    b. *Bam*HI leaves a 3' overhang.
    c. *Bam*HI leaves a blunt end.
    d. DNA cleaved by *Bam*HI cannot be religated.

15. What advantages do BACs have over YACs?
    a. BACs can accommodate larger amounts of DNA than YACs.
    b. BACs are present in hundreds of copies per bacterium, making them easier to purify.
    c. BACs are selected for the *TRP1* and *URA3* markers, allowing an easier selection.
    d. BACs can be handled like regular plasmids, which are easier to manipulate.

Answers: 1e, j; 2h; 3d; 4a, f, j; 5a, c, f, j; 6b, j; 7g, (possibly also a, k); 8f, i, j; 9c; 10a, j; 11b; 12c; 13a; 14a, 15d.

Thought Questions

1. Contrast the *cos* site with the *ori* site.

2. For what purposes would you choose to use each of a plasmid, lambda, cosmid, YAC or BAC library? When you could use any of them, why would you choose one over the others?

3. What kinds of organisms naturally make restriction enzymes? Of what use are they to the organism where they are naturally made?

4. Address the following questions to explore the kinds of results that could be obtained on a Southern blot made with genomic DNA.
    a. DNA is digested with a restriction enzyme that cuts at a defined 6-bp sequence having 2 GC base pairs and 4 AT base pairs. The genome is 40% GC. What is the *average* fragment size?

b. The cleaved DNA is separated by size using agarose gel electrophoresis. When the gel is stained, a smear of DNA is seen. Why is a smear and not one, or a few bands of DNA seen?

c. The DNA is transferred in a Southern blot to a membrane. When sequences trans ferred to the membrane are hybridized to a unique-sequence probe made from a fragment that is 4 kb in length, bands that are 0.5, 3 and 9 kb are seen. How do you interpret this result?

d. The same blot is hybridized with a probe that has homology to moderately repeti tive DNA. The probe has been made from a fragment that is 1.2 kb in size. The blot has about 40 bands, ranging in size from 3 to 17 kb. How do you interpret this re- sult?

5. Construct a restriction map of a 10-kb DNA fragment using the following data:

ENZYMES USED	SIZES OF FRAGMENTS (in kb)
EcoRI	1, 4, 5
BamHI	4, 6
HindIII	0.8, 1.5, 7.7
EcoRI and BamHI	1, 2, 3, 4
EcoRI and HindIII	0.5, 0.8, 1, 3.2, 4.5
BamHI and HindIII	0.8, 1.5, 2.5, 5.2
BamHI, EcoRI, and HindIII	0.5, 0.8, 1, 2, 2.5, 3.2

6. Suppose you have cloned 11 kb of eukaryotic genomic DNA that includes a single gene. After analyzing the sequence of about 500 bp at each end of the clone, you believe you have evidence that these sequences contain the 5' UTR and 3' UTR sequences of the gene. What might this evidence be? How can you use the information you have in hand, together with Southern and northern blot analyses and PCR to (a) identify the length of the primary transcript of the gene, (b) identify the length of the mature mRNA of the gene, and (c) obtain a cDNA copy of the mature mRNA of the gene?

Thought Questions for Media

After reviewing the media on the *iGenetics* CD-ROM, try to answer these questions.

1. In the animation depicting restriction mapping, how is agarose gel electropho- resis able to separate fragments of cleaved DNA?

2. The rotating disk method is effective for orienting restriction fragment sites in a circular molecule relative to each other. Explain how it works.

3. Sometimes, when the rotating disk method is being used to locate restriction enzyme sites relative to each other, overlaying maps doesn't allow sites to be positioned. In some cases, an alternative mirror image map must be used. Why?

4. How could you modify the rotating disk method to map linear DNA fragments?

5. Automated DNA sequencers have made sequencing DNA both cheaper and easier. Why is it still important to know how to construct a restriction map?

6. The calibration curve shown in the animation is not linear over the entire length of the gel. However, it is approximately linear between about 1000 and 10,000 base pairs. Why might it be linear over only part of the length of the gel?

7. Each of two enzymes, Enzyme I and Enzyme II, cuts a plasmid giving fragments of 2506 and 5160 bp. What is the best means to *quickly* and unambigously determine how many different sites these enzymes recognize and their positions relative to each other?

1. What is the rationale behind deleting the *STA1*, *STA2*, and *STA2K* genes?

2. Why is it important to *entirely* delete each of the *STA1*, *STA2* and *STA2K* genes?

3. Why are there differences between the beers made with the three recombinant yeast strains, since each has a deletion of a gene responsible for glucoamylase production?

4. Why is the *CUP1* gene needed in these experiments? How would you demonstrate that it had no effect on fermentation characteristics or beer quality?

5. Refer back to the frame that asks you to insert the *STA1* gene into the YEpD vector. Suppose there were two *Sna*BI sites flanking the *STA1* gene. Even though there is a unique *Sna*BI site in the YEpD vector, why wouldn't you use it instead of the *Bgl*II site?

SOLUTIONS TO TEXT PROBLEMS

7.1 Restriction endonucleases are found in nature. What purposes do they serve?

Answer: Restriction enzymes serve to protect their hosts from infection by invading viruses, and degrade any potentially infectious foreign DNA taken up by the cell (for example, by transformation). Since restriction enzymes digest DNA (restrict it) at specific sites, any foreign DNA will be cut up. To protect its own DNA from digestion by its restriction enzyme(s), a bacterium modifies (methylates) the restriction sites its own enzymes recognize. This prevents them from cleaving at "host" sites.

7.2 A new restriction endonuclease is isolated from a bacterium. This enzyme cuts DNA into fragments that average 4,096 base pairs long. Like all other known restriction enzymes, the new one recognizes a sequence in DNA that has twofold rotational symmetry. From the information given, how many base pairs of DNA constitute the recognition sequence for the new enzyme?

Answer: The average length of the fragments produced indicates how often, on average, the restriction site appears. Here, the restriction site appears once every 4,096 bases. This can be related to the size of the site using the following logic. If the DNA is composed of equal amounts of A, T, C, and G, the chance of finding one specific base pair (AT, TA, GC, or CG) at a particular site is 1/4. The chance of finding two specific base pairs at a site is $(1/4)^2$. In general, the chance of finding n specific base pairs at a site is $(1/4)^n$. Here, $1/4,096 = (1/4)^6$, so the enzyme recognizes a six base-pair site.

7.3   An endonuclease called *Avr*II ("a-v-r-two") cuts DNA whenever it finds the sequence $\begin{array}{l}5\text{'-CCTAGG-3'}\\3\text{'-GGATCC-5'}\end{array}$. About how many cuts would *Avr*II make in the human genome, which is about 3×10^9 base pairs long and about 40% GC?

Answer: The enzyme recognizes a sequence that has two GC base pairs, two CG base pairs, one AT base pair and one TA base pair in a particular order. Since the genome has 40% GC, the chance of finding a GC or CG base pair is 0.20, and the chance of finding an AT or a TA base pair is 0.30. The chance of finding six base pairs with this sequence is $(0.20)^4(0.3)^2 = 0.000144$. A genome with 3×10^9 base pairs will have about 3×10^9 different groups of six base-pair sequences. Thus, the number of sites in the human genome is $(0.000144) \times (3 \times 10^9) = 432,000$.

7.4   About 40 percent of the base pairs in human DNA are GC. On average, how far apart (in terms of base pairs) will the following sequences be?
a.   two *Bam*HI sites
b.   two *Eco*RI sites
c.   two *Not*I sites
d.   two *Hae*III sites

Answer: Since the human genome has 40 percent GC, the probability of finding a GC or CG base pair is 0.20, and the probability of finding a TA or AT base pair is 0.30. [This assumes that in any region of the genome, one will find, on average, 40 percent GC or CG base pairs.] This information can be used to determine the probability of finding a particular restriction enzyme recognition sequence as follows:

ENZYME	RECOGNITION SEQUENCE	PROBABILITY OF FINDING SEQUENCE	AVERAGE DISTANCE BETWEEN SITES
*Bam*HI	5'-GGATCC-3' 3'-CCTAGG-5'	$(0.2)^4(0.3)^2 = 0.000144$	$1/0.000144 = 6,944$ bp
*Eco*RI	5'-GAATTC-3' 3'-CTTAAG-5'	$(0.2)^2(0.3)^4 = 0.000324$	$1/0.000324 = 3,086$ bp
*Not*I	5'-GCGGCCGC-3' 3'-CGCCGGCG-5'	$(0.2)^8 = 0.00000256$	$1/0.00000256 = 390,625$ bp
*Hae*III	5'-GGCC-3' 3'-CCGG-5'	$(0.2)^4 = 0.0016$	$1/0.0016 = 625$ bp

7.5   There are many varieties of cloning vectors. One type of cloning vector used to clone recombinant DNA in *E. coli* is plasmids. What features do these vectors have that make them useful for constructing and cloning recombinant DNA molecules?

Answer: Plasmids need three essential features to be utilized as cloning vectors:
1. A bacterial *ori*, or origin of replication sequence, to allow it to replicate in *E. coli*.
2. A dominant selectable marker, such as antibiotic resistance, to allow selection of cells harboring the plasmid.
3. At least one unique restriction enzyme cleavage site, so that DNA sequences cut with that enzyme can be spliced into the plasmid.
    Modern plasmid cloning vectors have been engineered to possess additional features that facilitate easier use as cloning vectors.
    1. They are present in a high copy number, which facilitates purification of plasmid DNA.
    2. They contain many unique restriction sites in a *polylinker* or *multiple cloning site*, to facilitate cloning fragments of DNA obtained after cleavage with a variety of different restriction enzymes.
    3. The polylinker is inserted near the 5' end of the *lacZ* gene, which encodes β-galactosidase. Cells harboring a plasmid with an intact *lacZ* gene, when grown on media with the β-galactosidase substrate X-gal, form blue colonies. Cells harboring a plasmid whose *lacZ* gene has been interrupted by a cloned segment of DNA will not express functional β-galactosidase, and will be white. Thus, one can tell if a bacteria colony harbors a plasmid with DNA insertion by the color of the colony.
    4. They contain phage promoters flanking each side of the polylinker. These promoters are used to make *in vitro* RNA copies of the cloned DNA. These promoters can then be used for a variety of purposes, including making radioactively labeled RNA probes.

7.6 *E. coli* is a commonly used host for propagating cloned sequences in plasmid vectors. Wild-type *E. coli* turns out to be an unsuitable host, however: Not only are the plasmid vectors "engineered," but so is the host bacterium. Based on your understanding of how DNA is cloned in plasmid vectors, speculate how each of the following bacterial mutations might enable a better host to be engineered.

MUTATION	DESCRIPTION
recA	Gene central to recombination and DNA repair. Mutation eliminates general recombination and renders bacteria sensitive to UV light.
rpsL	Mutation affects ribosomal protein S12, and makes cells resistant to streptomycin.
endA	Normal gene encodes the DNA-specific endonuclease I. Mutation eliminates endonuclease function.
mcrA	Normal gene encodes the McrA restriction endonuclease that restricts DNA when it is methylated at the internal cytosine in the site CCGG.
mrr	Normal gene encodes the Mrr restriction endonuclease that restricts DNA when it is methylated at the methylated adenine of GAC or CAG sites.
hsdR	Normal gene encodes EcoK restriction endonuclease, which restricts DNA that is *not* methylated at certain A residues.

Answer: It is important to modify the host bacterium for three reasons. First, it must not be pathogenic to those who work with it. Second, it should not survive outside of a laboratory environment. Third, it must allow for efficient propagation of plasmids with cloned inserts. Most laboratory host strains meet all three of these requirements.

The *recA* mutation assists in preventing recombination between the host chromosome and the plasmid vector. This restricts propagation of the plasmid to the cytoplasm and maintains the integrity of cloned sequences. It also makes the host cell less viable in the wild, as it is less efficient at DNA repair. The *rpsL* mutation allows selection for streptomycin resistance, which can aid in selection for certain recombinants or transformants. The *endA* mutation eliminates endonuclease I function, which improves the yield and quality of DNA in plasmid DNA preparation. This mutation may also make the host cell less viable in the wild, as it becomes more susceptible to phage infection. The *mcrA, mrr* and *hsdR* mutations eliminate some of the multiple *E. coli* restriction modification systems that are used by wild-type *E. coli* to prevent infection (e.g., by phage). These mutations have two advantages. "Outside" the laboratory, they make the host cell more susceptible to viral infection and hence less viable. "Inside" the laboratory, they allow for the cloning of DNA that may have been isolated from an organism that has a different restriction/modification system. The cloned DNA will not be restricted by the host cell, allowing it to be propagated.

7.7   The ability to clone DNA fragments gives molecular biologists the power to understand structure and function of our genes and to use fragments of DNA to produce proteins. What are the basic elements of research in recombinant DNA technology?

Answer: Recombinant DNA technology involves the isolation, cloning, manipulation and expression of DNA sequences. Fundamental to it is the ability to cleave DNA using restriction enzymes, insert it into cloning vectors (plasmids, phage, YACs, BACs) using an enzyme such as DNA ligase, and introduce (transform) these vectors into host cells where they can be propagated, and possibly, express DNA sequences (i.e., genes) of interest. DNA, once cloned, can be repurified and modified, altering parts of the DNA sequence. Since it is essential to be able to "identify" cloned sequences of interest, the "basic elements of research" may also include the ability to screen genomic and cDNA libraries in different ways (expression screens, oligonucleotide probe screens, heterologous probe screens, etc.) that allow the isolation of cloned sequences of interest. The ability to sequence DNA and amplify specific regions using PCR might also be considered basic elements of research, as these methods provide information about DNA molecules that is essential for research.

7.8   Much effort has been spent on developing cloning vectors that replicate in organisms other than *E. coli*.

    a. Describe several different reasons one might want to clone DNA in an organism other than *E. coli*.

    b. What is a shuttle vector and why is it used?

    c. Describe the salient features of a vector that could be used for cloning DNA in yeast.

Answer:

    a. Vectors have been developed for transforming yeast as well as plant and animal cells. These are useful for studying cloned eukaryotic genes in a eukaryotic environment, commercial production of eukaryotic gene products (e.g., drugs, antibodies), developing gene therapy, engineering crop plants and developing transgenic animals.

    b. Shuttle vectors are cloning vectors that can replicate in two or more host organisms. They are used to introduce DNA into organisms other than *E. coli*. A typical shuttle vector has the ability to replicate in *E. coli*, where it is usually easier and faster to do initial cloning and engineering steps. Once the appropriate recombinant DNA molecule is constructed in *E. coli*, it can be transferred into another organism without further subcloning.

    c. A yeast shuttle vector should contain dominant selectable markers for both yeast (e.g., *URA3*, which provides for uracil-independent growth when the vector is transformed into a *ura3* yeast) and *E. coli* (e.g., ampicillin resistance); a large number of unique restriction enzyme sites suitable for cloning foreign DNA; and if it is not integrated into the yeast chromosome, sequences that allow it to replicate autonomously, as a plasmid, in both yeast cells and bacteria.

7.9   Genomic libraries are important resources for isolating genes of interest and for studying the functional organization of chromosomes. List the steps you would use to make a genomic library of yeast in a lambda vector.

Answer: A genomic library made in a λ vector is a collection of λ phage that have had a portion of their genome replaced by different yeast genomic DNA sequences. Like two volumes of a book series, two λ phage will have identical external protein coats and λ vector sequences, but different yeast DNA inserts. Such a library is made as follows:

1. Isolate high-molecular-weight yeast genomic DNA by isolating nuclei, lysing them, and gently purifying their DNA.
2. Cleave the DNA into fragments that are an appropriate size for the λ vector being used. This can be done by cleaving the DNA with *Sau*3A for a limited time (i.e., performing a *partial* digest), and then selecting fragments of an appropriate size by either sucrose density centrifugation or agarose gel electrophoresis.
3. Remove the central portion of the λ vector by digestion with *Bam*HI.
4. Anneal, and then ligate the left and right arms of the λ vector to the yeast DNA. The sticky ends that are left by the *Sau*3A and *Bam*HI are complementary.
5. Package the recombinant DNA molecules *in vitro* into λ particles.
6. Infect *E. coli* cells with the λ phage population, and collect progeny phage produced by cell lysis. These phage have different yeast DNA inserts, and represent the yeast genomic library.

7.10   The human genome contains about 3×10^9 bp of DNA. How many 40-kb pieces would you have to clone into a library if you wanted to be 90 percent certain of including a particular sequence?

Answer: There are two ways to solve this problem.
   (1) Deduce the probability relationships from first principles.

p (identifying sequence in <u>one</u> 40-kb piece) $= 40{,}000 \, \text{bp}/3 \times 10^9 \, \text{bp}$
$$= 13.333 \times 10^{-6}$$

p (<u>not</u> finding sequence in <u>one</u> 40-kb piece) $= [1 - (13.333 \times 10^{-6})]$

p (<u>not</u> finding sequence in <u>n</u> clones) $= [1 - (13.333 \times 10^{-6})]^n$

If one wants to be 90 percent certain of finding the sequence, one is willing to allow a 10 percent chance that the sequence will not be found. Thus,

$$0.10 = [1 - (13.333 \times 10^{-6})]^n$$
$$n = \ln(0.10)/\ln[1 - (13.333 \times 10^{-6})]$$
$$n = 172{,}693 \text{ pieces.}$$

(2) Recall from the text presentation that the probability of having any sequence represented in a genomic library is given by $N = \ln(1 - p)/\ln(1 - f)$, where N = number of recombinant DNA molecules that must be screened, p = probability of finding at least one positive clone, f = fractional proportion of the genome in a single recombinant DNA molecule. Here, $p = 0.90$, $f = 40{,}000/(3 \times 10^9)$, so $N = 172{,}693$.

7.11   What is a cDNA library, and from what cellular genetic material is it derived? How is a cDNA library used in cloning particular genes?

Answer: A complementary DNA, or cDNA, is a DNA copy of an mRNA. A cDNA library is a collection of clones containing the different cDNAs synthesized from the entire population of mRNA of a particular (usually eukaryotic) tissue or cell. It is constructed as follows: Initially, the mRNAs expressed in a tissue or cell are isolated. The mRNA molecules are purified from the other RNAs present in cells by passing the total cellular RNA over an oligo-dT column, which binds the poly(A) tails of the mRNAs. After the other RNAs are washed through the column, the poly(A)+ mRNAs are eluted from the column. Then, cDNAs are synthesized by annealing an oligo(dT) primer to the poly(A) tail of each mRNA, and using the enzyme reverse transcriptase to synthesize a single-stranded DNA copy of each mRNA strand. This results in a collection of DNA-mRNA hybrids. RNase H is added to partially degrade the mRNA strands, leaving single-stranded complementary DNAs with short mRNA fragments attached. DNA polymerase I is added to synthesize a second DNA strand using the short mRNAs as primers. DNA ligase is used to ligate the DNA fragments of the second strand together. Finally, linkers or adapters are ligated onto the ends of the cDNAs (if linkers are used, the linkers are cleaved to generate sticky ends), and each member of the resulting collection of double-stranded DNAs is ligated into a restriction site in a cloning vector and propagated. Since there is a population of mRNA molecules in a particular tissue or cell, this procedure produces a population of clones, or a library, containing different cDNA inserts, that reflects the population of mRNA present in a particular tissue or cell. See text Figures 7.10 and 7.11.

If a cDNA library is constructed using mRNA isolated from a particular tissue, the cDNA inserts represent partial copies of genes transcribed in that tissue. Thus, each clone can be used to identify a gene expressed in that tissue. A cDNA library can be screened for cloned copies of particular mRNA transcripts either using the same methods that are used to screen genomic libraries, or by performing an expression screen. For example, just as for genomic libraries, a cDNA library could be screened by using a DNA probe containing part of the gene of interest, by using a heterologous probe, or by using an oligonucleotide probe. However, since a cDNA is a mature mRNA copy of a gene, if the cDNA library has been made in an expression vector, the cDNA can be expressed (i.e., transcribed, and the transcript translated). In this case, the protein a cDNA encodes can be produced in a bacterial cell. If an antibody is available that binds to a protein expressed in a particular tissue, the antibody can be radioactively or nonradioactively labeled and used as a probe to identify clones expressing the protein. Such clones have cDNAs that encode the protein. This method of screening an expression vector library is described in detail in text Figure 7.12.

7.12   Suppose a researcher wants to clone the genomic sequences that include a human gene for which a cDNA has already been obtained. The researcher has available a variety of genomic libraries that can be screened with a probe made from the cDNA, as described in Figures 7.13 and 7.14.

a. Assuming that each library has an equally good representation of the 3×10^9 base pairs in a haploid human genome, about how many clones should be screened if the researcher wants to be 95 percent sure of obtaining at least one hybridizing clone and
   i.   the library is a plasmid library with inserts that are, on average, 7 kb?
   ii. the library is a lambda library with inserts that are, on average, 15 kb?
   iii. the library is a cosmid library with inserts that are, on average, 40 kb?
   iv. the library is a YAC library with inserts that are, on average, 350 kb?

b. What advantages and disadvantages are there to screening these different libraries?

c. What kinds of information might be gathered from analyzing genomic DNA clones that could not be gathered from analyzing cDNA clones?

Answer:

a. As was discussed in the answer to problem 7.10, the number of clones that must be screened to have a specified probability of finding at least one copy of a DNA sequence represented in a genomic library is calculated using the formula $N = [\ln(1-p)]/[\ln(1-f)]$. Here, N is the number of recombinant DNA molecules that must be screened, p is the chance of finding at least one positive clone, and f is the fractional proportion of the genome in a single recombinant DNA molecule. Here, $p = 0.95$, and f varies: for (i), $f = 7/(3 \times 10^6)$; for (ii), $f = 15/(3 \times 10^6)$; for (iii), $f = 40/(3 \times 10^6)$; for (iv), $f = 350/(3 \times 10^6)$. The number of clones required for each vector is (i) 1.3×10^6 plasmids, (ii) 6.0×10^5 phage, (iii) 2.2×10^5 cosmids, and (iv) 2.6×10^4 YACs.

b. By screening libraries with larger average inserts, fewer clones must be screened. This advantage must be evaluated relative to the added difficulty of analyzing the larger inserts of positive clones. For example, restriction mapping 350 kb is substantially more difficult than restriction mapping 15 kb. Since a single gene ranges in size from hundreds of base pairs to hundreds of kilobase pairs, an essential question to consider is how the cloned sequences will be analyzed and used after they are identified.

c. Genomic clones provide for the analysis of gene structure: intron/exon boundaries, transcriptional control regions, and polyadenylation sites. This analysis is important for evaluating how a gene's expression is controlled. Since mutations in regulatory regions can affect the expression of the gene, analysis of these regions is important for understanding the molecular basis of a mutation.

7.13   A colleague has sent you a 4.5-kb DNA fragment excised from a plasmid cloning vector with the enzymes *Pst*I and *Bgl*II (see Table 7.1 for a description of these enzymes and the sites they recognize). Your colleague tells you that within the fragment there is an *Eco*RI site that lies 0.49 kb from the *Pst*I site. Suppose you wanted to clone this DNA fragment into the plasmid vector pUC19 (described in Figure 7.4).

    a. How do you proceed?

    b. How would you verify that you have cloned the correct fragment and determine the orientation of the fragment within the pUC19 cloning vector?

Answer:

    a. The *Bgl*II enzyme leaves a 5'-GATC overhang, while the *Pst*I enzyme leaves a 3'-ACGT overhang. If the polylinker of the pUC19 vector could be cleaved to leave two identical overhangs, the 4.5-kb fragment could be directionally cloned into the vector. Examination of the restriction enzyme sites available in the polylinker of pUC19 reveals a *Pst*I site, but no *Bgl*II sites. There are two approaches to obtain the required 5'-GATC overhang. Examine the polylinker further and compare the sites in the polylinker to the enzymes described in Table 7.1 to determine whether cleaving any of these sites leaves the same kind of overhang as *Bgl*II. This analysis identifies a *Bam*HI site that, if cut, would leave a 5'-GATC overhang, just like that of *Bgl*II. Thus, cleaving the vector with *Bgl*II would produce the appropriate sticky end. To directionally clone the insert, cleave the pUC19 vector with *Pst*I and *Bam*HI, allow the fragment to anneal to these sticky ends, and use DNA ligase to seal the gap in the phosphodiester backbones.

        Another approach to obtain appropriate sticky ends for directional cloning is to cut the polylinker with the enzyme *Sma*I (which leaves blunt ends), ligate a linker containing a *Bgl*II site onto the blunt end, and cleave the modified vector with *Bgl*II and *Pst*I.

    b. Transform the ligated DNA into a host bacterial cell, and plate the cells on bacterial medium containing ampicillin and a substrate (X-gal) for β-galactosidase that turns blue when cleaved. This selects for bacterial colonies that harbor pUC19 plasmids and allows for a blue/white selection to identify colonies that have plasmids with inserts. Pick white colonies (which have an interrupted *lacZ* gene, and so do not cleave the substrate) and isolate plasmid DNA from them. Cleave the DNA with restriction enzymes and analyze the products using agarose gel electrophoresis to verify that the appropriate-sized fragments are recovered. Restriction with *Eco*RI should give two fragments, one that is 2.686 + 0.49 = 3.176 kb (vector plus the 0.49-kb *Eco*RI fragment of the insert) and one that is 4.5 − 0.49 = 4.01 kb (the insert minus the 0.49-kb fragment of the insert). A set of double digests (*Eco*RI + *Pst*I; *Eco*RI + *Bam*HI) will also be informative.

7.14   Suppose you wanted to produce human insulin (a peptide hormone) by cloning. Assume that you could do this by inserting the human insulin gene into a bacterial host, where, given the appropriate conditions, the human gene would be transcribed and then translated into human insulin. Which would be better to use as your source of the gene, human genomic insulin DNA or a cDNA copy of this gene? Explain your choice.

Answer: It would be preferable to use cDNA. Human genomic DNA contains introns, while cDNA synthesized from cytoplasmic poly(A)$^+$ mRNA does not. Prokaryotes do not process eukaryotic precursor mRNAs having intron sequences, so genomic clones will not give appropriate translation products. Since cDNA is a complementary copy of a functional mRNA molecule, the mRNA transcript will be functional, and when translated human (pro-)insulin will be synthesized.

7.15   You are given a genomic library of yeast prepared in a bacterial plasmid vector. You are also given a cloned cDNA for human actin, a protein that is conserved in protein sequences among eukaryotes. Outline how you would use these resources to attempt to identify the yeast actin gene.

Answer: Radioactively (or nonradioactively) label the human actin cDNA, and use it as a heterologous probe to screen the yeast genomic library. To radioactively label the human actin cDNA using a random primer method, denature the double-stranded cDNA by boiling, allow "random" short oligonucleotides (primers) to anneal to a cDNA strand, and synthesize DNA complementary to the cDNA using one or more labeled dNTPs and the Klenow fragment of DNA polymerase I. Once a probe has been made, clones harboring plasmids with inserts encoding the yeast actin gene can be identified as follows: Plate the library onto bacterial media in Petri plates at a density that allows separate colonies to be identified. Overlay the bacterial colonies with a positively charged membrane that can bind DNA, and then lift it off so that some of each bacterial colony is attached to the membrane. Lyse the bacterial cells bound to the membrane *in situ* using an alkaline solution, so that the plasmid DNA harbored by the cells binds to the membrane in single-stranded form. Allow the probe to hybridize with sequences on the membrane. Detect the location of the bound probe (e.g., use autoradiography if the probe is radioactively labeled), and then align the membrane with the original Petri plate from which colonies were lifted. Identify the clone having the hybridizing cDNA insert. This clone will have a yeast genomic DNA insert that has sequence homology to the human actin gene probe, and most likely is a yeast actin gene. This can be assessed by obtaining and analyzing its DNA sequence.

7.16   A cDNA library is made with mRNA isolated from liver tissue. When a cloned cDNA from that library is digested with the enzymes *Eco*RI (E), *Hind*III (H) and *Bam*HI (B), the restriction map shown in Figure 7.A, part a) is obtained. When this cDNA is used to screen a cDNA library made with mRNA from brain tissue, three identical cDNAs with the restriction map shown in Figure 7.A, part b) are obtained. When either cDNA is used to synthesize a uniformly labeled 32P-labeled probe and the probe is allowed to hybridize to a Southern blot prepared from genomic DNA digested singly with the enzymes *Eco*RI, *Hind*III, and *Bam*HI, an autoradiograph shows the pattern of bands in Figure 7.A, part c). When either cDNA is used to synthesize a uniformly labeled 32P-labeled probe and used to probe a northern blot prepared with poly(A)+ RNA isolated from liver and brain tissues, the pattern of bands in part d) is seen. Fully analyze these data and then answer the following questions.

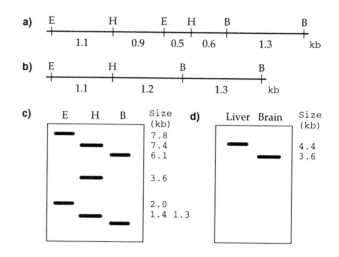

Figure 7.A

a. Do these cDNAs derive from the same gene?
b. Why are different sized bands seen on the northern blot?
c. Why do the cDNAs have different restriction maps?
d. Why are some of the bands seen on the whole-genome Southern blot different sizes than some of the restriction fragments in the cDNAs?

Answer:

a. Since both cDNAs hybridize to the same bands on a genomic Southern blot, they are copies of mRNAs transcribed from the same sequences. Therefore, it is likely that they are from the same gene.

b. Different bands on the northern blot indicate that the primary mRNA for this gene may be processed differently in brain and liver tissue. For example, it is possible that the 0.8-kb size difference between the two bands reflects a 0.8-kb intron that is spliced out in brain tissue that is not spliced out in liver tissue.

c. The two cDNAs are copies of mRNAs found in two different tissues. The northern blot indicates that there are some differences between the mRNAs in the different tissues. Thus, it is not surprising that the restriction maps are not identical. Note that the ends of the restriction maps are identical (the same EcoRI–HindIII and BamHI fragments), while the internal regions are not (the brain cDNA lacks the 0.5-kb EcoRI–HindIII fragment and some of each adjoining fragment).

d. The genomic Southern blot gives an indication of the gene organization at the DNA level, while the cDNA maps give an indication of the structure of the mRNA transcript(s). When the cDNA is used to probe genomic DNA sequences, it will hybridize to any sequences that are transcribed. Since restriction sites in the genome do not delineate where the transcribed regions are, the probe will hybridize to genomic DNA fragments that are only partly transcribed. That is, the probe will hybridize to transcribed sequences that are "connected to" non-transcribed sequences. Thus, the large (7.8, 7.4, 6.1 and 3.6 kb) bands reflect the parts of the cDNA that hybridize to genomic DNA fragments that are only partly transcribed. Since they are the same size fragments that appear in the liver cDNA, the smaller fragments (2.0, 1.4 and 1.3 kb) represent fragments that are entirely transcribed. Based on this data, a possible gene organization is illustrated below:

7.17   A researcher digests genomic DNA with the restriction enzyme EcoRI, separates it by size on an agarose gel, and transfers the DNA fragments in the gel to a membrane filter using the Southern blot procedure. What result would she expect to see if the source of the DNA and the probe for the blot is as described as follows?

a. The genomic DNA is from a normal human. The probe is a 2.0-kb DNA fragment obtained by excision with the enzyme EcoRI from a plasmid containing single-copy genomic DNA.

b. The genomic DNA is from a normal human. The probe is a 5.0-kb DNA fragment that is a copy of a LINE sequence that has an internal EcoRI site.

c. The genomic DNA is from a normal human. The probe is a 5.0-kb DNA fragment that is a copy of a LINE sequence that lacks an internal EcoRI site.

d. The genomic DNA is from a human heterozygous for a translocation (exchange of chromosome parts) between chromosomes 14 and 21. The probe is a 3.0-kb DNA fragment that is obtained by excision with the enzyme EcoRI from a plasmid containing single-copy genomic DNA from a normal chromosome 14. The translocation breakpoint on chromosome 14 lies within the 3.0-kb genomic DNA fragment.

e. The genomic DNA is from a normal female. The probe is a 5.0-kb DNA fragment containing part of the *testis determining factor* gene, a gene located on the Y chromosome.

Answer:

a. She should see a 2.0-kb band, as the 2.0-kb probe is a single-copy genomic DNA sequence.

b. LINE sequences are moderately repetitive DNA sequences, which may be distributed throughout the genome. Since the LINE sequence has an internal *Eco*RI site, each LINE element in the genomic DNA will be cut by *Eco*RI during preparation of the Southern blot. When the blot is incubated with the probe, both fragments will hybridize to the probe. The size of the fragments produced from each LINE element will vary according to where the element is inserted in the genome, and where the adjacent *Eco*RI sites are. Hence there will be many different-sized bands seen on the genomic Southern blot.

c. As in (b), there will be many different-sized bands on the genomic Southern blot. The sizes of the bands seen reflect the distances between *Eco*RI sites that flank a LINE element. All of the bands will be larger in size than the element, as the element is not cleaved by *Eco*RI. Counting the number of bands can give an estimate of the number of copies of the element in the genome.

d. Since the heterozygote has one normal chromosome 14, the probe will bind to the 3.0-kb *Eco*RI fragment derived from the normal chromosome 14. If the translocation is a reciprocal translocation, the remaining chromosome 14 is broken in two, and attached to different segments of chromosome 21. Since chromosome 14 has a breakpoint in the 3.0-kb *Eco*RI fragment, the 3.0-kb fragment is now split into two parts, each attached to a different segment of chromosome 21. Consequently, the 3.0-kb probe spans the translation breakpoint and will bind to two different fragments, one from each of the translocation chromosomes. The sizes of the fragments are determined by where the adjacent *Eco*RI sites are on the translocated chromosomes. Thus, the blot will have three bands, one of which is 3.0 kb.

e. Since the *testis determining factor* gene is on the Y chromosome, no signal should be seen in a Southern blot prepared with DNA from a female, since the female lacks a Y and has only X chromosomes.

7.18 Restriction endonucleases are used to construct restriction maps of linear or circular pieces of DNA. The DNA usually is produced in large amounts by recombinant DNA techniques. Generating restriction maps is like putting the pieces of a jigsaw puzzle together. Suppose we have a circular piece of double-stranded DNA that is 5,000 base pairs long. If this DNA is digested completely with restriction enzyme I, four DNA fragments are generated: fragment *a* is 2,000 base pairs long; *b* is 1,400 base pairs long; *c* is 900 base pairs long; and *d* is 700 base pairs long. If, instead, the DNA is incubated with the enzyme for a short time, the result is incomplete digestion of the DNA: Not every restriction enzyme site in every DNA molecule will be cut by the enzyme, and all possible combinations of adjacent fragments can be produced. From an incomplete digestion experiment of this type, fragments of DNA were produced from the circular piece of DNA that contained the following combinations of the above fragments: *a-d-b*, *d-a-c*, *c-b-d*, *a-c*, *d-a*, *d-b*, and *b-c*. Lastly, after digesting the original circular DNA to completion with restriction enzyme I, the DNA fragments are treated with restriction enzyme II under conditions conducive to complete digestion. The resulting fragments are: 1,400, 1,200, 900, 800,

400, and 300 bp. Analyze all the data to locate the restriction enzyme sites as accurately as possible.

Answer: Sort out the results for the first enzyme by tabulating the results:

COMPLETE DIGESTION		PARTIAL DIGESTION	
FRAGMENT	SIZE (BP)	FRAGMENT	SIZE (BP)
a	2,000	*d-a-c*	3,600
b	1,400	*a-d-b*	3,100
c	900	*c-b-d*	3,000
d	700	*a-c*	2,900
total plasmid	5,000	*d-a*	2,700
		b-c	2,300
		d-b	2,100

Consider the following: if an enzyme cuts a circular molecule once, it will produce one fragment. If an enzyme cuts a circular molecule twice, it will produce two fragments. (Diagram these situations to convince yourself of this.) Since four fragments are produced when enzyme I completely cleaves the plasmid, enzyme I must cut the plasmid at four sites. A partial digestion occurs when all four sites are not cut. For the partial digestion fragments that contain three fragments, two cuts were made in neighboring sites. Thus, the *d-a-c* fragment was released when two cuts were made at sites flanking fragment *b*, the *a-d-b* fragment was released when two cuts were made at sites flanking fragment *c*, and the *c-b-d* fragment was released when two cuts were made a sites flanking fragment *a*. For the partial digestion fragments containing only two fragments, cuts were made that flank both fragments. Thus, *a* is next to *c*, *d* is next to *a*, *b* is next to *c*, and *d* is next to *b*. This information can be used to order the fragments in the plasmid. Since *a* is next to *c* and *d*, the order must be *c-a-d*. Since *b* is next to *c* and *d*, the order must be *d-b-c*. Since *d* is next to *a* and *b*, the order must be *a-d-b*. Thus, the order of fragments in the plasmid is *c-a-d-b*.

When the plasmid is cleaved with both enzyme I and enzyme II, six fragments are produced. This indicates that the two enzymes together recognize six sites. Since enzyme I cleaves at four sites, enzyme II must cleave at two sites. Since the 1,400- and 900-bp fragments produced when enzyme I cleaves the plasmid remain intact in the double digestion, and the 2,000- and 700-bp fragments do not remain intact in the double digestion, enzyme II must cleave at sites within the 2,000- and 700-bp fragments (*a* and *d*). Given the 1,200- and 800-bp fragments produced with the double digestion, enzyme II must cleave *a* 800 bp from an enzyme I site. Given the 400- and 300-bp fragments produced with the double digestion, enzyme II must cleave *d* 300 bp from an enzyme I site. This gives the following map:

The ambiguities in enzyme II site positions could be resolved if one knew what size fragments were produced when the plasmid was digested to completion with enzyme II alone.

7.19   A piece of DNA 5,000 bp long is digested with restriction enzymes A and B, singly and together. The DNA fragments produced are separated by DNA electrophoresis and their sizes are calculated, with the following results:

DIGESTION WITH

A	B	A + B
2,100 bp	2,500 bp	1,900 bp
1,400 bp	1,300 bp	1,000 bp
1,000 bp	1,200 bp	800 bp
500 bp		600 bp
		500 bp
		200 bp

Each A fragment is extracted from the gel and digested with enzyme B, and each B fragment is extracted from the gel and digested with enzyme A. The sizes of the resulting DNA fragments are determined by gel electrophoresis, with the following results:

A FRAGMENT		FRAGMENTS PRODUCED BY DIGESTION WITH B	B FRAGMENT		FRAGMENTS PRODUCED BY DIGESTION WITH A
2,100 bp	→	1,900, 200 bp	2,500 bp	→	1,900, 600 bp
1,400 bp	→	800, 600 bp	1,300 bp	→	800, 500 bp
1,000 bp	→	1,000 bp	1,200 bp	→	1,000, 200 bp
500 bp	→	500 bp			

Construct a restriction map of the 5,000-bp DNA fragment.

Answer: Construct a map stepwise, considering the relationship between the fragments produced by double digestion and the fragments produced by single-enzyme digestion. Start with the larger fragments. The 1,900-bp fragment produced by digestion with both A and B is a part of the 2,100-bp fragment produced by digestion with A, and the 2,500-bp fragment produced by digestion with B. Thus, the 2,500-bp and 2,100-bp fragments overlap by 1,900 bp, leaving a 200-bp A-B fragment on one side and a 600-bp A-B fragment on the other. One has:

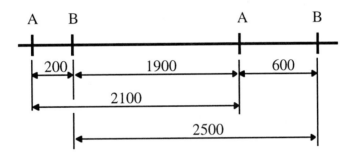

The map is extended in a stepwise fashion, until all fragments are incorporated into the map. The restriction map is:

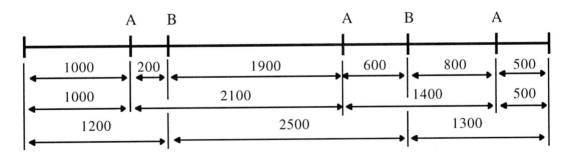

7.20   Draw the banding pattern you would expect to see on a DNA sequencing gel if you annealed the primer 5'-C-T-A-G-G-3' to the following single-stranded DNA fragment and carried out a dideoxy sequencing experiment. Assume the dNTP precursors were all labeled.

3'-G-A-T-C-C-A-A-G-T-C-T-A-C-G-T-A-T-A-G-G-C-C-5'.

Answer: The primer will anneal to the fragment, and be extended at its 3' end in four separate reactions, each with small amounts of a different dideoxynucleotide.

In each reaction, some chains will be prematurely terminated when the dideoxynucleotide is incorporated. By using labeled dNTP precursors, all extension products will be labeled, and be observed as distinct, labeled bands after separation on a denaturing polyacrylamide gel and signal detection.

GEL ANALYSIS

fragment: 3'-GATCCAAGTCTACGTATAGGCC-5'

ddNTP Added

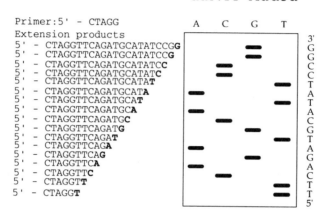

```
Primer:5' - CTAGG                        A   C   G   T
Extension products                                            3'
5' - CTAGGTTCAGATGCATATCCGG                      ==            G
5' - CTAGGTTCAGATGCATATCCG                       ==            G
5' - CTAGGTTCAGATGCATATCC               ==                     C
5' - CTAGGTTCAGATGCATATC                ==                     C
5' - CTAGGTTCAGATGCATAT                              ==        T
5' - CTAGGTTCAGATGCATA            ==                           A
5' - CTAGGTTCAGATGCAT                                ==        T
5' - CTAGGTTCAGATGCA              ==                           A
5' - CTAGGTTCAGATGC                     ==                     C
5' - CTAGGTTCAGATG                                ==           G
5' - CTAGGTTCAGAT                                    ==        T
5' - CTAGGTTCAGA                  ==                           A
5' - CTAGGTTCAG                                   ==           G
5' - CTAGGTTCA                    ==                           A
5' - CTAGGTTC                            ==                     C
5' - CTAGGTT                                         ==        T
5' - CTAGGT                                          ==        T
                                                              5'
```

7.21 PCR fragments can be separated by gel electrophoresis and the size of a fragment can be estimated. Explain the process involved in determining the size of the PCR fragment in question.

Answer: In gel electrophoresis, DNA fragments are separated by size. Since DNA is negatively charged due to its phosphates, it will migrate towards the positive pole in an electric field. Since, in an agarose gel, smaller DNA fragments will move more readily through the pores in the gel, smaller DNA fragments move through the gel more rapidly than larger DNA fragments. [Although larger DNA fragments have more phosphate groups, and hence more *total* negative charge, they have the same amount of charge density (negative charge per unit mass) as smaller DNA fragments. Hence, the DNA is separated by size in this gel, and not by charge.] To determine the size of a PCR fragment, it should be loaded into one well of an agarose gel, and a size standard, or marker, DNA sample should be loaded into another well of the gel. A current should be applied to induce the DNA samples to migrate through the gel. After electrophoresis, the gel should be stained with a dye that binds DNA, such as ethidium bromide. Ethidium bromide will complex with DNA, and fluoresces under ultraviolet light. The fluorescent image should be photographed, and the distance each DNA band has migrated from the loading should be measured. Since the molecular sizes of the DNA fragments in the marker lane are known, a calibration curve can be drawn to relate the DNA size (in log kb) to the migration distance (in mm). Then, the migration distance for the DNA band of the PCR product can be measured. By comparing it to the calibration curve, its size can be determined. See text Figure 7.16.

8

APPLICATIONS OF RECOMBINANT DNA TECHNOLOGY

CHAPTER OUTLINE

ANALYZING BIOLOGICAL PROCESSES
Regulation of Transcription: Glucose Repression of the Yeast *GAL1* Gene
Alternative Pre-mRNA Splicing: A Role in Sexual Behavior in *Drosophila*
Protein-Protein Interaction in the Cell: The Yeast Two-Hybrid System

DNA MOLECULAR TESTING FOR HUMAN GENETIC DISEASE MUTATIONS
Concept of DNA Molecular Testing
Purposes of Human Genetic Testing
Examples of DNA Molecular Testing
Availability of DNA Molecular Testing

ISOLATING HUMAN GENES
Cloning the Cystic Fibrosis Gene

DNA TYPING
DNA Typing in a Paternity Case
Other Applications of DNA Typing

GENE THERAPY

COMMERCIAL PRODUCTS

GENETIC ENGINEERING OF PLANTS
Transformation of Plant Cells
Applications for Plant Genetic Engineering

REVIEW OF KEY TERMS, SYMBOLS, AND CONCEPTS

In your own words, write a brief definition of each term in the groups below. Check your definitions using the text. Then, develop a concept map using the terms in each group.

1	2	3
recombinant DNA technology	genetic vs. diagnostic testing	positional cloning
transcriptional regulation	DNA molecular testing	reverse genetics
alternative mRNA splicing	newborn, disease screening	genetic linkage
regulatory gene	prenatal diagnosis	*in situ* hybridization
northern blotting	carrier detection	chromosome walking

1	2	3
PCR, RT-PCR	DNA typing, fingerprinting, profiling, marker	chromosome jumping
yeast two-hybrid system	polymorphism, mutation	jumping library
interaction trap assay	inclusion, exclusion result	zoo blot, Noah's Ark blot
Yeast *GAL GAL1, GAL4* genes	RFLP	pseudogene
glucose repression	STR, microsatellite	CpG island
Drosophila sexual behavior	VNTR, minisatellite	candidate gene
fruitless (fru) gene	monolocus, multilocus probe	
UAS$_G$ sequence	allele-specific	
DNA binding domain (BD)	oligonucleotide	
activation domain (AD)	(ASO) hybridization	
reporter gene, bait	reverse ASO hybridization	
fusion plasmid, fusion protein	multiplex PCR	
PEX genes, peroxisome	genetically modified	
	organism	

4
gene therapy
somatic gene therapy
transgene
transgenic cell, organism
biotechnology
Agrobacterium tumefaciens
crown gall disease
monocots vs. dicots
Ti plasmid
vir (virulence) region
T-DNA
plant cell transformation
electroporation
gene gun
DNA typing
antisense RNA

THINKING ANALYTICALLY

Much of the excitement in modern genetics comes as genetic principles and recombinant DNA technology are combined and applied to address fundamental biological questions as well as practical human problems. This material in this chapter introduces many examples – methods used to investigate biological processes, applications of technology for improving human health and agriculture, determination of paternity, and applications in forensics. As you read through the examples, look for how our understanding of genetic principles and recombinant DNA technology allows for inventive, pragmatic application. Analyze the example by asking –

- What questions are being asked?
- Why are they important? How do they relate to a fundamental biological question or practical problem?
- What methods are being used to address the questions?
- What genetic principles or recombinant DNA applications underlie a manipulation or investigation? (What did we need to know before being able to do this?)
- Are multiple investigatory approaches being combined?
- How is the method effective in answering the question?

After you have read through the examples, go back and reflect more generally on the types of questions and hypotheses that can be investigated, and whether there are limitations to the method or application.

Here is an example, using the yeast two-hybrid system.

- *What are the questions being asked?*
  - › Do two proteins physically (directly) interact *in the cell*?
  - › How can we identify which proteins interact with a known protein?
- *Why are they important?*
  - › It has been difficult to show that two proteins physically interact within cells.
  - › This system allows assessment of interactions in cells, not just in the test tube.
  - › We can better understand how a protein functions in cells.
  - › We can identify which other proteins, and infer which processes, a protein is involved with. This can be done in an unbiased manner, and with no previous knowledge of the other protein(s) or processes.
  - › We can gain insights into disease processes.
- *What methods are being used to address the questions?*
  - › Goal: Develop an *in vivo* system to monitor whether two proteins interact.
  - › Construct a fusion protein where the cDNA for a known protein of interest is fused to a cDNA for the binding domain of Gal4. Use this as a bait.
  - › Construct a library where cDNAs for genes expressed in a certain tissue are fused to a cDNA for the activation domain of Gal4.
  - › Construct a reporter gene (*lacZ*) with an upstream UAS$_G$.
  - › Transform yeast with the bait, clones from the library, and the reporter gene construct.
  - › Screen for interactions between proteins of the cDNA library and the bait. If two proteins interact, they will place the binding domain and activation domain of Gal4 in proximity, and the *lacZ* reporter gene will be expressed.
- *What genetic principles or recombinant DNA applications underlie a manipulation or investigation?*
  - › A detailed understanding of *GAL* gene transcriptional regulation.
  - › A detailed understanding of molecular cloning and library construction.
- *Are multiple investigatory approaches being combined?*
  - › Yes: This system combines investigations that address protein-protein interactions and transcriptional regulation with experimental strategies used by yeast geneticists.
- *How is the method effective in answering the question?*

› Normal interactions during *GAL4* gene expression are being modified to allow these interactions to serve as indicators of interactions between two unrelated proteins. Our detailed understanding of *GAL4* transcriptional regulation is being exploited to provide a more general tool to address protein-protein interaction.

- *What type of questions and hypotheses does this system allow us to investigate? What limitations might this method have?*
  › We can identify new genes whose products interact with a known protein causing a disease, providing new targets for therapeutic intervention.
  › We can test if two proteins interact, expanding our understanding of a protein's function.
  › We can test if a mutation inhibits a particular type of protein-protein interaction, thereby causing a disease.
  › What is the sensitivity of the method? Will the method ever give spurious results?

QUESTIONS FOR PRACTICE

Multiple Choice Questions

1. Positional cloning
   a. requires knowledge of the gene product before the gene can be cloned.
   b. generates a transgenic organism that expresses a gene only in certain tissues.
   c. isolates a disease gene based on its approximate chromosomal location.
   d. is when a cDNA has been cloned into a specific orientation in an expression vector.

2. Chromosome walking is
   a. used to obtain a set of overlapping clones from a genomic library.
   b. used to obtain a set of overlapping clones from a cDNA library.
   c. used to jump between chromosomal locations without cloning intervening DNA.
   d. impossible in eukaryotes because of the amount of interspersed repetitive DNA.

3. What is the difference between a gene and a pseudogene?
   a. A pseudogene is a special type of gene that contains sequences that hybridize with genes of other organisms.
   b. A pseudogene has a sequence resembling a functional gene, but lacks appropriate expression signals.
   c. A pseudogene is found within CpG islands, while genes are found next to them.
   d. A pseudogene is stored in heterochromatin, and is a non-functional copy of a gene.

4. During the positional cloning of a disease gene, four candidate genes are identified. What would provide the most convincing evidence that one of them is responsible for the disease?
   a. A zoo blot shows that one gene is also found in other organisms.
   b. Polymorphisms are present in one of the genes in affected individuals.
   c. One of them is expressed in the tissue affected by the disease.
   d. Mutational changes are present in one of the genes in affected individuals.

5. What is the difference between an STR and a VNTR?
    a. An STR is the same as a microsatellite, while a VNTR is the same as a minisatellite.
    b. Both are tandem repeats: STRs are 2-4 bp long; VNTRs are 5-10s of base pairs long.
    c. Both are tandem repeats: STRs are 5-10s of bp long; VNTRs are 2-4 bp long.
    d. STRs are simple tandem repeated sequences found only in one location, while VNTRs are always dispersed in different regions of the genome.

6. What is the difference between a monolocus probe and a multilocus probe?
    a. A monolocus probe detects alleles at one gene, while a multilocus probe detects alleles at different genes.
    b. A monolocus probe detects one of two alleles at one gene, while a multilocus probe detects both alleles at one gene.
    c. A monolocus probe detects STR or VNTR sequences at one locus (site) in the genome, while a multilocus probe detects STR or VNTR sequences at a number of loci (sites) in the genome.
    d. A monolocus probe detects STR sequences, while a multilocus probe detects VNTR sequences.

7. An ASO hybridization is a method
    a. to assess genotypes – allele-specific oligonucleotide hybridization. PCR products differing by one base are distinguished by hybridization with labeled oligonucleotides.
    b. used to screen jumping libraries – "all similar objects" hybridization. A probe is used to identify clones containing similar sequences.
    c. to distinguish between two similar transgenic animals – almost the same organisms. Blood taken from each is typed for a set of DNA markers, and the results compared.
    d. for testing for the presence of GMOs in foods – agriculturally sensitive oligonucleotide hybridization. Since transgenic plants are modified using expression vectors, an oligonucleotide probe can be used to test if foods contain it, and hence contain GM plant material.

8. Which one is *not* an example of a product produced by a biotechnology company?
    a. human growth hormone.
    b. DNase.
    c. bacteria that can accelerate the degradation of oil pollutants.
    d. aspirin.

9. How would you identify proteins that interact with PEX1, a protein important in peroxisomal biogenesis?
    a. Use cDNA clones for the *PEX1* gene to screen a cDNA expression library.
    b. Fuse a cDNA clone for the *PEX1* gene to the gene containing the GAL4 DNA binding domain, and use this as bait in a yeast two-hybrid screen.
    c. Fuse a cDNA clone for the *PEX1* gene to a reporter gene such as *lacZ*, and use it as bait in a yeast two-hybrid screen.
    d. Use a cDNA clone for the *PEX1* gene to screen a genomic library.

10. Suppose DNA typing is used in a paternity case. How do exclusion results differ from inclusion results?

a. Exclusion results are easier to prove - one just needs to show that the male in question has no alleles in common with the baby.

b. Inclusion results require positive identity to be established and usually requires testing for alleles at many genes.

c. Inclusion results require calculation of the relative odds that an allele came from the accused or from another person, and requires knowing the frequencies of VNTR and STR alleles in many ethnic groups.

d. All of the above.

Answers: *1c; 2a; 3b; 4d; 5b; 6c; 7a; 8d; 9b; 10d.*

Thought Questions

1. When cells are subjected to a heat shock (a transient high-temperature pulse), they become stressed and stop transcribing most genes. They start transcribing others that help them deal with the stress of the heat shock. How would you assess if transcription of a gene you have cloned is repressed or activated by heat shock?

2. After developing a GMO, some companies secure patents on it. Suppose a company sells seed for a GMO to a farmer, under the condition that the farmer may plant the seed, but may not retain seed stock from any crop that is harvested. The seed is expensive, and the farmer only buys seed from the company once. How would the company check if the farmer has used seed harvested from the first crop?

3. Suppose the farmer described in question 2 is quite poor, and also no longer retains the seed stock he used prior to planting seed for the GMO. What ethical issues arise?

4. While many mutations causing disease result in proteins that are non-functional or that have altered function (such as in sickle-cell anemia), some are caused by mutant alleles that fail to make a protein product. Therapeutic approaches will differ in this situation. Therefore, when a disease gene is cloned, it is important to address if the disease phenotype is caused by an abnormal protein, or by the absence of a protein. Suppose you have cloned a gene for a disease, and notice that a restriction site for *Eco*RI has been altered in a transcribed region of the gene. How would you experimentally address this issue, given a tissue biopsy from a patient with the disease?

5. How are DNA markers used to identify overlapping DNA clones containing a specific gene? How is the precise location of the gene then identified?

6. In US courts, DNA typing is not yet a generally accepted method for proving parenthood or guilt. However, it is often accepted as providing evidence that excludes an accused individual. What is the basis for the difference in the level of acceptance of DNA testing? Do you see this changing over time?

7. Some indigenous peoples have taken positions against the use of GMOs based on a cultural viewpoint that they alter the spiritual integrity of living organisms. Some Maori (an indigenous people in New Zealand), for example, have asked that transgenic sheep that produce milk with pharmaceutically important compounds not be raised on

their land, and that genetically modified trees harvested for lumber not be grown on their land. How do you respond to these types of concerns, and should these concerns be more generally raised (recall the text citing that "between 50 and 75% of produced and processed foods in a supermarket may be genetically modified or contain GMOs")?

8. Even though CF is the most common lethal genetic disease in the US today, it is not tested for routinely in newborns. Why might this be the case?

9. What is the difference between a genetic test and a diagnostic test, if each is also a DNA molecular test? How do the ethical and legal issues surrounding these two tests differ?

10. Somatic gene therapy holds great promise for treating genetic disease. What is the underlying basis for somatic gene therapy? What ethical and legal issues are associated with its implementation?

Thought Questions for Media

After reviewing the media on the *iGenetics* CD-ROM, try to answer these questions.

1. What is meant by a "bait gene?" How does the "bait" allow you to "fish" for interacting proteins?
2. When a yeast two-hybrid screen is done, what is the genotype of the transformed yeast strain? Why are both uracil <u>and</u> tryptophan left out of the medium on which the transformed yeast are grown?
3. Suppose a cDNA for the Y gene is fused to the Gal4 AD. This cDNA is expressed in a yeast cell that also expresses a cDNA for the X gene that is fused to the Gal4 BD, and which has a UAS_G promoter upstream of the *lacZ* gene. A blue colony is seen when the yeast is plated on a medium with X-gal. What control could you do to insure that the Y-Gal4 AD fusion protein activates *lacZ* expression specifically through its interaction with the X-Gal4 BD fusion protein, and not through some other mechanism?
4. How is a yeast two-hybrid screen done?

1. For one primer pair, how many different PCR products can be obtained in one individual? How many different alleles can be detected with one primer pair?
2. For five primer pairs, how many different PCR products can be obtained in one individual? How many different alleles can be detected with five primer pairs?
3. Are alleles detected as STRs dominant or recessive, or neither? Why?
4. For one primer pair, how many different patterns of PCR products can be obtained in two individuals? For five primer pairs, how many different patterns of PCR products can be obtained in two individuals?
5. Why is it important in forensics to perform DNA typing on loci that are highly polymorphic?
6. How is the profile probability used to determine the likelihood that two matching samples come from the same individual?

7. What is the advantage of using fluorescent primers and multiplex PCR? If you want to test multiple loci using PCR, what information would you need to know about each pair of primers, before labeling them and using them in a multiplex PCR?

SOLUTIONS TO TEXT PROBLEMS

8.1   Imagine that you have been able to clone the structural gene for an enzyme in a catecholamine biosynthetic pathway from the adrenal gland of rats. How could you use this cloned DNA as a probe to determine whether this same gene functions in the rat brain?

Answer: If the same gene functions in the brain, the gene for the enzyme must be transcribed into a precursor mRNA, processed to a mature mRNA and then translated to produce the functional enzyme. Thus, transcripts for the gene should be found in the brain. To address this issue, label the cloned DNA, and use it to probe a northern blot having mRNA isolated from brain tissue. If the mRNA is rare, it may be prudent to use mRNA isolated from a specific region of the brain, e.g., the hypothalamus. An alternative, quite sensitive approach would be to sequence the cloned DNA, analyze the sequence to identify the coding region, and then design PCR primers that could be used to amplify cDNA made from mRNA isolated from various brain regions. To perform this RT-PCR (reverse transcriptase PCR), one would isolate mRNA, reverse transcribe it into cDNA, and then perform PCR. Obtaining an RT-PCR product in such an investigation would provide evidence that the gene is transcribed in the brain. In this alternative method, it would be important to be sure that no genomic DNA was present in the PCR amplification mixture, as the gene for the enzyme would be found in genomic DNA in both tissues.

8.2   Imagine that you find an RFLP in the rat genomic region homologous to your cloned catecholamine synthetic gene from question 8.1 and that in a population of rats displaying this polymorphism there is also a behavioral variation. You find that some of the rats are normally calm and placid, but others are hyperactive, nervous, and easily startled. Your hypothesis is that the behavioral difference is caused by variations in your gene. How could you use your cloned sequence to test this hypothesis?

Answer: Initially, perform a genomic Southern analysis to see if the RFLP is limited to animals with or without the behavioral phenotype. Isolate DNA from the affected and normal rats, cleave it with the restriction enzyme that was used to identify the RFLP, separate the DNA by size on an agarose gel, blot the gel in the manner of Southern to a membrane, make a probe from DNA in the cloned catecholamine synthetic gene region, hybridize the probe to the Southern blot, and detect the location of the probe signal. If the data show that normally behaving rats and abnormally behaving rats share identical RFLPs, the hypothesis is not supported. If the data show that the presence of the RFLP correlates with the behavior of the rats (e.g., normally behaving rats never have the RFLP and abnormally behaving rats always have the RFLP), the hypothesis is supported. However, this data does not demonstrate that the behavioral difference is <u>caused</u> by the DNA difference.

To gather additional evidence that the DNA difference <u>causes</u> a variation in the gene which causes the behavioral difference, try to demonstrate that there is a correlation between the presence of the RFLP, an altered enzyme activity of the catecholamine synthetic gene, and the behavior. Determine if animals with the RFLP have different levels of enzymatic activity (for catecholamine synthesis) or catecholamine production than animals without the RFLP. With the earlier results, this provides a correlation between the presence of the RFLP, the behavioral trait, and the function of the gene.

Note that this still does not demonstrate that the RFLP itself is the mutation affecting the gene. There are two possibilities. First, the RFLP affects the catecholamine synthetic gene, either by affecting its transcription, transcript processing, or protein product. Second, the RFLP is close to another mutation that affects the gene. It is therefore important to determine the location of the RFLP relative to the location of the gene. If the RFLP lies within the coding region of the gene, it may result in a different, perhaps nonfunctional protein being produced. If it lies within a regulatory region (e.g., within the promoter, or in an enhancer or silencer), it could affect the amount of transcription of the gene, and so affect the amount of enzyme that is produced. If it lies within an intron, it may affect mRNA processing, and so affect the amount of mature mRNA and gene product produced. To address these issues, sequence the region containing the RFLP, and use this information, together with restriction mapping, to identify where the RFLP is relative to the transcribed region of the gene. If the RFLP lies in a region that might reasonably affect mRNA processing, or the level of transcription of the gene, experimentally assess if this is the case by using the methods described in the answer to question 8.1. That is, determine if the presence of the RFLP correlates with the level of mature mRNA produced from the gene. Alternatively, check to see if the RFLP causes a missense or nonsense mutation in the coding region of the gene, producing an altered protein.

If this analysis does not demonstrate that the RFLP itself causes a defect in transcription, transcript processing, or the protein product, it remains possible that another, nearby mutation is the cause of the gene alteration, or that the RFLP is the cause, but it affects the gene in a manner that is not easily recognized (e.g., it lies in an enhancer far from the gene that is not easily identified). To investigate this possibility, cross the affected and unaffected rats to control strains, and follow the segregation of the RFLP and the behavioral phenotype. If the two traits cosegregate, that is, if the RFLP is always present with one of the behavioral traits, this provides evidence that the two are linked. If the RFLP and the behavioral difference can be separated by recombination, the RFLP itself cannot be the molecular basis of the behavioral phenotype, but a closely linked mutation might be. The frequency of recombination will provide an estimate of how close the DNA region with the RFLP is to the site of the mutation causing the behavioral phenotype. Sequence analysis of the region may lead to the identification of the causal DNA alteration.

8.3   Sexual behavior in *Drosophila* (fruit fly) is under the control of several regulatory genes. Recently the *fru* gene has been molecularly cloned. Mutants homozygous for *fru* are considered sterile even though the fly has normal sexual organs and produces normal sperm. Explain.

Answer: *Drosophila* males and females display a stereotyped set of mating behaviors. Male *Drosophila* which are mutant for the *fru* gene are unable to perform male courtship behaviors, and so are unsuccessful at courting and mating with females. Even though the are morphologically normal, they are behaviorally abnormal. They can't persuade a female to allow copulation, and so are functionally sterile.

8.4   DNA was prepared from small samples of white blood cells from a large number of people. Ten different patterns were seen when these DNAs were all digested with *Eco*RI, then subjected to electrophoresis and Southern blotting. Finally, the blot was probed with a radioactively labeled cloned human sequence. The following figure shows the 10 DNA patterns taken from 10 people.

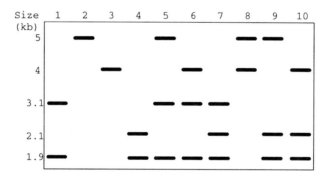

a.   Explain the hybridization patterns seen in the 10 people in terms of variation in *Eco*RI sites.

b.   If the individuals whose DNA samples are in lanes 1 and 6 on the blot were to produce offspring together, what bands would you expect to see in DNA samples from these offspring?

Answer:

a.   The probe hybridizes to the same genomic region in each of the ten individuals. Different patterns of hybridizing fragments are seen because of polymorphism of the *Eco*RI sites in the region. If a site is present in one individual, but absent in another, different patterns of hybridizing fragments will be seen. This provides evidence of restriction fragment length polymorphism. To distinguish between sites that are invariant and those that are polymorphic, analyze the pattern of bands that appear. Notice that the sizes of the hybridizing bands in individual 1 add up to 5 kb, the size of the band in individual 2 and the largest hybridizing band. This suggests that there is a polymorphic site within a 5-kb region. This is indicated in the diagram below, where the asterisk over site *b* depicts a polymorphic *Eco*RI site:

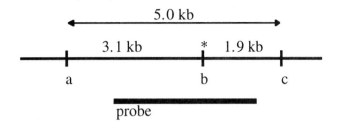

Notice also that the size of the band in individual 3 equals the sum of the sizes of the bands in individual 4. Thus, there is an additional polymorphic site in this 5-kb region. Since the 1.9-kb band is retained in individual 4, the additional site must lie within the 3.1-kb fragment. This site, denoted *x*, is incorporated into the diagram below. Notice that since the 1.0-kb fragment flanked by sites *a* and *x* is not seen on the Southern blot, the probe does not extend into this region.

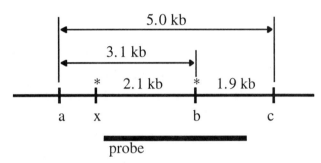

Depending on whether *x* and/or *b* are present, one will see either 5-kb, 3.1- and 1.9- kb, 2.1- and 1.9-kb, or 4-kb bands. In addition, if an individual has chromosomes with different polymorphisms, one can see combinations of these bands. Thus, individual 5 has one chromosome that lacks sites *x* and *b*, and one chromosome that has site *b*. The chromosomes in each individual can be tabulated as follows:

INDIVIDUAL	SITES ON EACH HOMOLOG	HOMOZYGOTE OR HETEROZYGOTE?
1	*a, b, c*	homozygote
2	*a, c*	homozygote
3	*x, c*	homozygote
4	*x, b, c*	homozygote
5	*a, c / a, b, c*	heterozygote
6	*x, c / a, b, c*	heterozygote
7	*a, b, c / x, b, c*	heterozygote
8	*a, c / x, c*	heterozygote
9	*a, c / x, b, c*	heterozygote
10	*x, c / x, b, c*	heterozygote

b. Since individual 1 is homozygous, chromosomes with sites at *a, b,* and *c* will be present in all of the offspring, giving bands at 3.1 and 1.9 kb. Individual 6 will contribute chromosomes of two kinds, one with sites at *x* and *c* and one with sites at *a, b,* and *c.* Thus, if this analysis is performed on their offspring, two equally frequent patterns will be observed: a pattern of bands at 3.1 and 1.9 kb, and a pattern of bands at 4, 3.1 and 1.9 kb. This is just like the patterns seen in the parents.

8.5   The maps of the sites for restriction enzyme R in the wild type and the mutated cystic fibrosis genes are shown schematically in the following figure:

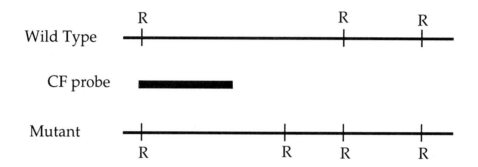

Samples of DNA obtained from a fetus (F) and her parents (M and P) were analyzed by gel electrophoresis followed by the Southern blot technique and hybridization with the radioactively labeled probe designated "CF probe" in the previous figure. The autoradiographic results are shown in the following figure:

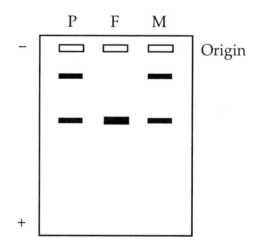

Given that cystic fibrosis is a recessive mutation, will the fetus be affected? Explain.

Answer: Chromosomes bearing CF mutations have a shorter restriction fragment than chromosomes bearing wild-type alleles. Both parent lanes (M and P) have two bands, indicating that each parent has a normal and a mutant chromosome. The parents are therefore heterozygous for the CF trait. The fetus lane (F) shows only one (lower molecular weight) band. The size of the band indicates that the fetus has only mutant chromosomes. The intensity of the band is about twice that of the same-sized band in the parent lanes. This is because the diploid genome of the fetus has two copies of the fragment, while the diploid genome of each parent only has one. Since the fetus is homozygous for the CF trait, it will have CF. (Do not confuse the black bands with the open boxes, which represent the origin, the location where the DNA was loaded before electrophoresis.)

8.6   Polymerase chain reaction (PCR) was introduced as a rapid and efficient way to amplify specific fragments of DNA. What is required to amplify a specific region (the target region) of DNA in a genome?

Answer: In order to amplify a specific region, one needs to know the sequences flanking the target region, so that primers able to amplify the target region can be designed. Once primers are synthesized, the polymerase chain reaction can be assembled. It contains a DNA template (in this case, genomic DNA), the pair of primers that flank the DNA segment targeted for amplification, a heat-resistant DNA polymerase (*Taq*), the four dNTPs (dATP, dTTP, dGTP and dCTP), and an appropriate buffer. See Figure 7.23.

8.7   What are the steps in one cycle of the polymerase chain reaction?

Answer: In the polymerase chain reaction, each cycle consists of a denaturation, annealing and extension step. These steps occur at different temperatures, and are repeated to amplify the desired fragment. In one cycle, the reaction mixture is first heated to 94°C to denature the DNA template. Then it is cooled to a temperature that allows the primers to anneal to specific sites on the DNA template. Then the reaction is heated to 72°C, where DNA polymerase extends the primers at their 3' ends. As shown in Figure 7.23, DNA fragments are produced in a unit length equal to the length of DNA between the two primer sites after the first cycle. After the second cycle, double-stranded fragments of unit length are produced. Subsequent cycles result in a geometric increase of the number of unit-length molecules, but linear amplification of longer-than-unit-length molecules. Consequently, the PCR reaction produces a large amplification of unit-length molecules.

8.8   Most enzymes are destroyed by hot temperatures. Explain why the enzyme used in PCR is not destroyed by heat.

Answer: The DNA polymerase used in PCR is purified from a thermophilic bacterium. For example, *Taq* DNA polymerase is purified from *Thermus aquaticus*, a bacterium that normally lives in hot springs. Since the bacterium normally lives in very hot environments, it has evolved to produce enzymes that are heat-stable.

8.9   Geneticists were trying to find the gene responsible for cystic fibrosis. They did not know the identity of its protein product. However, they did know that something about salt transport was disrupted, but they knew nothing about the nature of the defective protein. The geneticists used a powerful combination of classic and molecular approaches and in 1989 located the cystic fibrosis gene. What were the steps used to do so?

Answer: Cloning of the gene responsible for cystic fibrosis involved sequential homing in on the gene, using both genetic and molecular data.

1. *Linkage analysis:* First, RFLP markers linked to the CF gene were identified. As the patterns of inheritance of CF were tracked in families, DNA from family members was analyzed using Southern blot analysis to identify RFLP markers which showed genetic linkage to the CF locus.

2. *Chromosomal localization*: The RFLP marker was used as a probe in *in situ* hybridization to identify the chromosome on which the CF gene was located – chromosome 7. Additional nearby RFLPs were then identified. These were used in genetic linkage analysis to identify flanking markers that defined which region of chromosome 7 harbored the CF gene.

3. *Clone genomic DNA:* A combination of chromosomal walking and jumping was used to identify a large number of overlapping genomic DNA clones spanning about 500 kb in the CF region.

4. *Identify CF candidate gene:* To identify the CF gene among these DNA sequences, subcloned segments of the region were used as probes on zoo blots to detect if any were conserved among other organisms. Five clones with conserved gene sequences were identified. Linkage analysis excluded two from being responsible for CF. A third was excluded because it was a pseudogene. A fourth was excluded because it was not expressed in tissues affected in CF patients. The fifth subclone contained a CpG island. CpG islands are often found near promoters of expressed genes. This clone was used to synthesize a probe that was used to screen a cDNA library made from mRNA expressed in cultured sweat gland tissue cells. These cells were chosen since they might express genes involved in salt transport. The probe identified a single 6.5 kb band on a northern blot, and allowed the identification of a candidate cDNA clone. The cDNA clone was used to analyze the genomic clones in more detail.

5. *Confirm that candidate gene is responsible for CF.* The DNA sequences of the candidate CF gene were compared in normal and affected individuals. After a mutational change (a 3-bp deletion) was found in the gene from one CF patient, DNA changes were identified in the gene in additional CF patients.

6. *Characterize the protein produced by the CF gene.* Computerized analyses of the predicted CF protein provided a basis to propose a structure for the CF protein. In turn, this was used to develop testable hypotheses about its function.

8.10   Chromosome walking can be used to find a gene between flanking markers. Given that chromosome walking can be done in both directions, how could you feel confident that you are going toward the gene you are seeking?

Answer: Several different methods can be helpful to orient a chromosomal walk that has proceeded through several steps, or which includes one or more jumps. After restriction mapping is used to establish how the clones of the walk overlap, DNA markers such as RFLPs that have been positioned relative to each other using genetic mapping studies may be used to identify the orientation of a walk. If a walk has extended far enough, and includes two RFLP markers that have been previously oriented relative to the gene you are seeking, the orientation of the walk can be determined by using Southern blotting to identify which clone contains each marker. An alternative method is to use *in situ* hybridization to chromosomes. Probes can be made from unique sequences at the ends of a partially completed walk, and hybridized to chromosomes. The orientation of the walk relative to the centromere and telomere of the chromosome can be determined. A modification of this method using probes labeled with different fluorescent fluorochromes will be discussed in Chapter 9.

8.11   What is DNA fingerprinting? How could this method be used to establish parentage? How is it used in forensic science laboratories?

Answer: DNA fingerprinting is the characterization of an individual in terms of the set of DNA markers they have. For DNA fingerprinting, DNA markers are usually chosen so that they are highly polymorphic in a population, and may include RFLPs, simple tandem repeat polymorphisms of 2-4 bp in length (STR, microsatellite), and variable number of tandem repeat polymorphisms of 5 to 10s of bp in length (VNTR, minisatellite). They can be derived either from just one locus or more than one locus (monolocus or multilocus probes). Since all individuals except for identical (monozygotic) twins have different genomes, individuals of a species differ in terms of their DNA fingerprints.

Each parent donates one allele at a DNA marker to their offspring. Therefore, the set of DNA markers a child has come from his/her parents. If two parents and a child are tested, all of the DNA markers present in the child must also be present in the set of markers in the two parents. However, the parents can have additional markers, since they only donate one of their two alleles at each marker. If a child has no alleles in common with a suspected parent, the suspected individual can be excluded from consideration as the child's parent. If alleles are shared, the likelihood that the set of alleles came from the suspected parent must be calculated and compared to the likelihood that the set of alleles came from another person. If the alleles present in the child and one known parent are known, then one can infer a t least some of the alleles that were contributed by the other parent. Usually, multiple DNA markers are used to minimize possible inaccuracy and provide for a better statistical evaluation of the results – showing that the results obtained are not based on sampling variation. The calculation of the relative odds that a set of alleles derives from a suspected parent or from another person depends on knowing the frequencies of the marker alleles in the child's ethnic population. These types of data should be used together with other, non-DNA-based evidence to support a claim of parentage.

In forensic science laboratories, DNA fingerprinting is used to match, or exclude, the DNA fingerprint of a suspected individual with the DNA fingerprint provided by physical evidence (blood, skin, hair, semen, saliva, etc.) gathered at the scene of a crime. As in the analysis for parentage, DNA fingerprinting is very useful for excluding suspects who do not share alleles with that found in the physical evidence. Inclusion results, results where an individual is positively identified as being responsible for a crime, are more difficult to obtain. As for parentage, a calculation of the relative odds that a set of alleles derive from a suspect or from another person must be made, and this requires good population statistics. In addition, there must be evidence that there were no errors in collecting or processing samples. Thus, DNA evidence is often more useful for excluding suspects than for proving their guilt, and when used to support guilt, must usually be supported by additional, non-DNA based evidence.

8.12   One application of DNA fingerprinting technology has been to identify stolen children and return them to their parents. Bobby Larson was taken from a supermarket parking lot in New Jersey in 1978, when he was 4 years old. In 1990, a 16-year-old boy called Ronald Scott was found in California, living with a couple named Susan and James Scott, who claimed to be his parents. Authorities suspected that Susan and James might be the kidnappers and that Ronald Scott might be Bobby Larson. DNA samples were obtained from Mr. and Mrs. Larson, and from Ronald, Susan, and James Scott. Then DNA fingerprinting was done, using a polymorphic probe for a particular VNTR family, with the results shown in Figure 8.A. From the information in the figure, what can you say about the parentage of Ronald Scott? Explain.

Figure 8.A

Answer: James and Susan Scott are not the parents of "Ronald Scott." There are several bands in the fingerprint of the boy that are not present in either James or Susan Scott, and thus could not have been inherited from either of them (for example, bands **a** and **b** in the answer figure). In contrast, whenever the boy's DNA exhibits a band that is missing from one member of the Larson couple, the other member of the Larson couple has that band (for example, bands **c** and **d**). Thus, there is no band in the boy's DNA that he could not have inherited from one or the other of the Larsons. These data thus support an argument that the boy is, in fact, Bobby Larson. These data should be used together with other, non-DNA-based evidence to support the claim that the boy is Bobby Larson.

8.13   In 1990 the first human gene therapy experiment on a patient with adenosine deaminase deficiency was done. Patients who are homozygous for a defective gene for this enzyme have defective immune systems and risk death from diseases as simple as a common cold. Which cells were involved, and how were they engineered?

Answer: In this gene therapy experiment, T-cells were isolated from the patient and a viral vector was used to introduce the normal adenosine deaminase gene. The cells were then reintroduced into the patient.

8.14   You have inserted human insulin cDNA in the cloning vector pUC19 and transformed the clone into *E. coli*, but insulin was not expressed. Propose some hypotheses to explain why not.

Answer: If genomic DNA had been used, there could be concerns that an intron in the genomic DNA was not removed, since *E. coli* does not process RNAs as eukaryotic cells do. However, if the cDNA is a copy of a mature mRNA, this should not be a concern. There are other potential concerns however. First, depending on the nature of the sequence inserted, a fusion protein with β-galactosidase may have been produced, and not just human insulin. In pUC19, the polylinker is within the β-galactosidase gene. Sequences inserted into the polylinker, if inserted in the correct reading frame (the same one as used for β-galactosidase), will be translated into a β-galactosidase-fusion protein. If this was acceptable, it would be important to insure that only the ORF (the open reading frame) of the insulin gene is properly inserted into the polylinker of the pUC19 vector. In order for the insulin ORF to be properly inserted, it must be inserted in the correct reading frame, so that premature termination of translation does not occur, and the correct polypeptide is produced. One could not use a complete copy of the human mRNA transcript for insulin. If transcribed, it would have features of eukaryotic transcripts but not features required for prokaryotic translation. Indeed, some of its 5' UTR and 3' UTR sequences may interfere with prokaryotic transcription and translation. For example, it will lack a Shine-Dalgarno sequence to specify where translation should initiate and identify the first AUG codon. In the pUC19 vector, a Shine-Dalgarno sequence is supplied after the promoter for the *lacZ* gene, since without an insert in the polylinker, β-galactosidase is produced. However, the cDNA may have 5' UTR sequences which interfere with translation initiation in prokaryotes, or which contain stop codons, terminating translation of the β-galactosidase fusion protein. Second, the cDNA may encode a protein that is posttranslationally processed to become human insulin. The protein produced in *E. coli* may not be processed.

8.15   The ability to place cloned genes into plants raises the possibility of engineering new, better strains of crops such as wheat, maize, and squash. It is possible to identify useful genes, isolate them by cloning, and insert them directly into a plant host. Usually these genes bring out desired traits that allow the crops in question to flourish. Why is there such concern by consumers about this process? Do you feel that the concern is justified? Defend your answer.

Answer: There is clearly a huge potential for success in crop modification. In addition to the examples presented in the text, visit web sites listed below, two of many sites that describe the potential value of a modified, vitamin-A enhanced rice (golden rice). Such a product could, in principle, help millions of people suffering from vitamin A deficiency. Vitamin A deficiency is associated with blindness and increased disease susceptibility.

http://www.disasterrelief.org/Disasters/000808gmofoods/
http://www.monsantoindia.com/news/archives/August2000/040800monsanto.html

There are multiple, different reasons consumers have concerns about this and other GMOs. First, some individuals find that this type of genetic alteration is in conflict with their culturally held views of the spiritual integrity of living organisms (See Thought Question 7). Second, some individuals feel that the dangers associated with genetically modified organisms are unknown, or not well enough understood. Several different types of concerns exist. For example, a gene placed in a particular crop species might be transferred laterally, perhaps via some infectious agent, to another species, where it is undesirable; the gene may confer properties that are deleterious to the environment which only appear years after introduction, and which would not be apparent in controlled testing environments; the altered strain may deleteriously alter existing ecological balances; the altered gene may negatively impact on human health in unknown ways; there may be significant concerns about food safety. Third, there are concerns about the maintenance of genetic diversity in crops. What will be the effect on seed stocks if only a few, highly desirable strains of some crops are grown? Will this result in increased susceptibility to potential pathogens in the future? Fourth, there are economic concerns: How ethically sound are the business practices of companies involved in these efforts? Should science be financed by corporations? Are these developments in the best interests of underdeveloped nations? Finally, it is a new, and largely unknown area. There is much that is unknown, and regulatory agencies are themselves entering a new territory, and are being offered conflicting "expert" opinions.

9

GENOME ANALYSIS

CHAPTER OUTLINE

STRUCTURAL GENOMICS
Genome Sequencing Using a Mapping Approach
Genome Sequencing Using a Direct Shotgun Approach
Overview of Genomes Sequenced

FUNCTIONAL GENOMICS
Identifying Genes in DNA Sequences
Homology Searches to Assign Gene Function
Assigning Gene Function Experimentally
Describing Patterns of Gene Expression

COMPARATIVE GENOMICS
ETHICS AND THE HUMAN GENOME PROJECT

REVIEW OF KEY TERMS, SYMBOLS, AND CONCEPTS

In your own words, write a brief definition of each term in the groups below. Check your definitions using the text. Then, develop a concept map using the terms in each group.

1	2
structural genomics	genomics
physical vs. genetic mapping	structural genomics
Human Genome Project (HGP)	functional genomics
shotgun approach, direct shotgun approach	comparative genomics
sequencing, assembly, finishing	genome annotation
Map: genetic, physical, cytogenetic, FISH,	bioinformatics
restriction, radiation hybrid, clone contig	database
parental-type, recombinant-type gamete	ORF
genetic distance	homologous gene, homolog
polymorphism, DNA marker, genetic marker	homology
map unit (mu), centiMorgan (cM)	homology search
lod (logarithm of odds) score method	BLAST
RFLP, VNTR, STR, SNP	*FUN* gene
anonymous probe	orphan family, single orphan
minisatellite, microsatellite	protein domain
oligonucleotide hybridization analysis	gene knockout
high stringency hybridization	loss-of-function mutation
DNA microarray, DNA chip, GeneChip®	transcriptome

1	2
oligonucleotide array, probe array	proteome
high-density genetic map	gene expression profile
low-resolution physical map	transcriptional fingerprint
sequence tagged site (STS)	probe array
mapping panel	pharmacogenomics
expressed sequence tag (EST)	proteomics
chromosomal band; p, q chromosome arms	Human Genomic Project (HGP)
dideoxy sequencing	ELSI program
ORF, ECE	Bacteria, Archaea, Eukarya
NIH, DOE, NCBI, TIGR, CEPH	

THINKING ANALYTICALLY

Analysis of genomes is complex. Not only are there multiple approaches to mapping and sequencing a genome, but also a huge amount of information has been gathered through sequence analysis, and an entirely new area – bioinformatics – has emerged to analyze and apply this information. As in previous chapters, organizing information into a contextual framework will help you understand the logic behind the different approaches and retain information obtained from sequence analyses. It will help you to organize the information into separate units.

After reading through the chapter, sketch out answers to questions addressing its main topics such as: How is a genome mapped? What different types of markers are used? Why is mapping helpful to sequencing a genome? What is a direct shotgun approach? In what different ways are sequences analyzed? What similarities and differences have been seen in the genomes of organisms sequenced to date?

Once you can answer questions like these that relate to structural genomics, identify how sequence information is used in answering questions related to functional and comparative genomics. What are the aims of functional genomics? What methods are used in functional genomics? What new technologies have been developed that allow simultaneous analysis of many genes at once? What are the practical applications of these technologies? What are the aims of comparative genomics? What human problems can it help solve? What biological questions can it address? What tools are used in comparative genomics?

Finally, step back and consider that modern genetics increasingly interfaces with many different aspects of human health and human society. What ethical, legal and social issues arise with the advent of genomics and its related technologies? Ask yourself if all of these are unquestionably for the good of society, or whether some need to be carefully monitored and/or regulated? Step back and think outside the box wherein scientists only pursue information and research for its own sake, justified by the potential for positive benefit to society. What dangers are associated with genomics? How, as a society, can we insure that the "good" of genomics is utilized while minimizing its dangerous aspects?

QUESTIONS FOR PRACTICE

Multiple Choice Questions

1. Which of the following is *not* a goal of the Human Genome Project?
   a. Identify all the genes in human DNA.
   b. Store DNA sequence and gene-related information in public databases.
   c. Transfer technologies related to genomics to the private sector.
   d. Identify the gene(s) associated with each human disease.

2. Genetic crosses are used for all of the following *except*
   a. to establish the locations of genetic markers on chromosomes
   b. determine the genetic distance between markers
   c. determine the number of base pairs between markers
   d. determine the recombination frequency between markers

3. Which of the following is *not* a DNA marker?
   a. RFLP
   b. STS
   c. ECE
   d. VNTR

4. What is an anonymous probe?
   a. a random piece of DNA from a known gene.
   b. a piece of DNA that does not correspond to a known gene.
   c. any probe for an RFLP.
   d. an ORF without a known function.

5. Which DNA marker is most abundant in eukaryotic genomes?
   a. STR
   b. VNTR
   c. SNP
   d. EST

6. DNA microarrays are
   a. aligned sets of printed DNA sequences, ordered according to their map positions.
   b. ordered grids of DNA molecules of known sequence fixed at known positions on a solid substrate.
   c. aligned sets of printed STRs (microsatellites) in a database.
   d. ordered grids of homologous genes from different organisms.

7. A FISH map is a map of
   a. ordered DNA markers made using fluorescent in situ hybridization to chromosomes.
   b. sites in lakes where icthyologists have found large schools of particular game fish.
   c. ordered DNA markers (e.g., STSs) accurate to within 2 to 5 kilobase pairs of DNA.
   d. DNA markers on chromosomes from fish.

8. Which of the following statements is *not* true about radiation hybrid maps?
   a. Both gene markers and DNA markers can be used in generating these maps.
   b. The amount of radiation determines the resolution of the map.

c. For human radiation hybrids, the human DNA fragment is typically a few MB long.

d. If two markers are further apart, they are more likely to remain together in a hybrid.

9. An EST is an STS marker. Even though it is a unique DNA sequence and tags a specific site, it is not always an exact copy of genomic DNA. Why?

a. An EST contains vector sequences.

b. An EST is derived from cDNA, and so introns present in genomic DNA have been removed.

c. An EST is a fusion of 500 bp from the two ends of a 2-kb plasmid insert used for sequencing genomic DNA.

d. An EST is a clone of genomic DNA that has been modified to delete repetitive DNA sequences nearby unique sequences.

10. Which of the following annotation can be done using computerized algorithms for prokaryotic, but not eukaryotic genomes?

a. Identify the locations of all protein-coding regions.

b. Identify the locations of known repeated sequences.

c. Identify the locations of known transposable elements.

d. Identify the locations of all rRNA genes.

11. Which of the following is not true about Archaeon genomes?

a. Some have large main circular chromosomes as well as multiple circular extrachromosomal elements.

b. The genes involved in energy production, cell division, and metabolism are similar to their counterparts in the Bacteria.

c. The genes involved in DNA replication, transcription, and translation are similar to their counterparts in the Eukarya.

d. They have a higher GC content, when compared to either Bacteria or Eukarya.

12. Why could Celera Genomics only obtain the sequence of about 97% of the genomes of *Drosophila* and humans?

a. In both organisms, simple telomeric sequences are very difficult to sequence, and these make up about 3% of the genome.

b. In both organisms, long ribosomal DNA repeats comprise about 3% of the genome. Since these are identical, it is impossible to sequence each individual repeat.

c. In both organisms, approximately 3% of the sequences were in error.

d. In both organisms, heterochromatic regions mostly near the centromeres are unclonable, making sequences in these regions impossible to obtain.

13. Arguments can be made for using simpler organisms like *Drosophila* to study complex diseases like cancer. Which one reason below is the most compelling?

a. *Drosophila* do not get cancer, and it would be useful to understand why.

b. It has been impossible to find genes associated with cancer in humans.

c. *Drosophila* have homologs for about 61 percent (177 of 289) of human disease genes, making them good models to study the functions of genes involved in human disease.

d. *Drosophila* are usually found near human populations, and may cause cancer.

14. What is BLAST?
  a. The Basic Local Alignment Search Tool – used for homology searches when a DNA or amino acid sequence is compared to other sequences in a database.
  b. The Big Linear Accelerator Sequencing Tool – a device funded by the Department of Energy that is able to read 10,000 bp of DNA from one sequencing reaction.
  c. The Best Legal Analysis of Sequence Technology – a document from the American Bar Association that legally analyzes situations faced by biotechnology companies that introduce genetically modified organisms into the environment.
  d. The Beer Legal Age Screening Tool – a DNA chip used to detect the length of simple telomeric repeats. Since these shorten with each cell division in somatic cells, this can be used to quickly determine whether an individual is over the legal drinking age.

15. What is the ELSI program?
  a. The world's largest bioethics program.
  b. A program funding studies of the ethical, legal and social issues related to the availability of genetic information.
  c. A program that has is likely to impact legislation concerning the privacy of genetic information, the safe and effective introduction of genetic information in the clinical setting, the fair use of genetic information, and the education of professionals and the public.
  d. All of the above.

Answers: 1d; 2c; 3c; 4b; 5c; 6b; 7a; 8d; 9b; 10a; 11d; 12d; 13c; 14a; 15d.

Thought Questions

1. What are the arguments for and against the ability of states or the federal government to collect genetic data on their populace?

2. Huntington Disease is a neurodegenerative disorder inherited as an autosomal dominant disease and is caused by a single gene mutation. It affects about 30,000 Americans. A child of an affected parent has a 50% chance of inheriting the disease allele. While there is intensive research into treatments for Huntington Disease, there is at present no cure. Carriers of the disease allele will eventually get the disease. Why might someone who has a first-degree relative with the disease want to be tested for the disease allele? Why might the person not want to be tested? Should there be testing for a genetic disease for which there is no cure?

3. Unlike Huntington Disease, many different genes appear to be associated with other neurodegenerative diseases such as Alzheimer Disease. Having mutations at one of these genes increases the risk of getting the disease, but does not predict with certainty that an individual will get the disease. Other differences from Huntington Disease are that there are disease forms that are apparently not caused by gene mutations, and prevention and treatment options have been proposed. Alzheimer Disease affects over four million Americans. Would you modify your answers to the questions posed in Thought Question 2? Under what circumstances, if any, would genetic testing for genes related to Alzheimer Disease be warranted?

4. How are the challenges faced by proteomics different than the challenges faced by genomics?

5. What is pharmacogenomics? How can it, when combined with the use of DNA chips, be useful to develop drugs that are tailored to the needs of individuals?

6. DNA microarrays can be used to distinguish between two similar cancers affecting the same tissue. How is this done, and why might this be therapeutically helpful?

7. What impact does the completion of a high-resolution map and detailed sequence of the human genome have on positional cloning of disease genes?

8. Why are lod score analyses necessary to map human genes? Are these analyses still needed to map disease genes even though the sequence of the genome is known?

9. What is meant when two genes are referred to as homologs? For a gene encoding a protein product, is it better to search for homologs based on DNA sequence or amino acid sequence? Why?

10. Explore the NCBI website for BLAST at http://www.ncbi.nlm.nih.gov/BLAST/. What different forms of BLAST have been developed, and what are they used for? Why is it important to statistically evaluate matches between a sequence and others in a database as similar sequences are identified?

11. After the human genome sequence was completed, searches were performed to identify possible genes. About 35,000 were found. What different criteria might be used to quickly provide evidence that an DNA sequence was part of a functional gene? (Hint: think about the value of homology searches.)

12. Within different ethnic groups, some alleles are more common than others. Consequently, for diseases influenced by genetic factors, different ethnic groups vary in their frequency of disease alleles. What challenges does this present for genetic testing, and for preventative medicine that is based on the identification of genetically at-risk populations?

Thought Questions for Media

After reviewing the media on the *iGenetics* CD-ROM, try to answer these questions.

1. After shearing the DNA to fragments that are approximately 2 kb in size, why are the DNA fragments treated with S1 nuclease?

2. After the 2-kb DNA fragments are cloned into plasmid vectors, they are transformed into bacteria, the plasmids isolated and their inserts sequenced. Since only about 500 bp of insert DNA can be obtained from each end of an insert, how is the remaining 1 kb of DNA obtained?

3. How are overlapping clones identified to construct a clone contig?

4. Why might there be gaps in an assembled sequence?

5. What are the differences and similarities between a Southern blot and a colony blot?

6. The animation illustrated how microarrays can be designed to identify muta-
    tions in a gene as well as to analyze differences in patterns of gene expression.
    a.   What differences are there in the design of these two types of microarrays?
    b.   What differences are there in labeling the target DNA samples for these
         two types of analyses?

1. Why is it important to expose the microarray to two differently labeled probes
    simultaneously, instead of using two microarrays with a single probe on each?
2. What are the sources of the tissues for the mRNA samples used to develop the
    probes for the microarrays? How important is it for the tumor tissue sample to
    be composed only of tumor cells, and not be a mixture of tumor and normal
    cells?
3. Is the selection of drugs for Maeve's therapy based on a genotype? Tumor cells
    usually harbor multiple somatic mutations and often also contain chromoso-
    mal rearrangements. If the drug selection is based on a genotype, is it based on
    her genotype or the genotype of the tumor? If not, what is it based on?
4. Specific genes are placed on microarrays. What information was needed to de-
    sign the microarray used in this investigation?
5. How could you use microarrays to identify additional genes that might be
    helpful in identifying more effective therapies for breast cancer?

SOLUTIONS TO TEXT PROBLEMS

9.1   RFLP, VNTR, STR, and SNP are abbreviations for DNA markers used to map eu-
        karyotic genomes. How do they differ in terms of size, the methods that can be used
        for detection, their distribution within a genome, and their identified frequencies
        within the human genome?

        Answer: RFLPs are restriction fragment length polymorphisms, and reflect the
        presence or absence of a restriction enzyme site within DNA. A site present in one
        chromosome may be absent in another due to a change at a single base (in which
        case it would also be a SNP), although chromosomal aberrations can also result in
        an RFLP (e.g., a deletion removing the site, a chromosomal rearrangement reposi-
        tioning the site). If an RFLP is assessed in a genomic Southern blot, a probe span-
        ning the site will detect different patterns of hybridization. Probes for RFLPs are
        not obtained in any directed way, and so they are relatively uncommon markers.
        However, since SNPs (see below) often affect a restriction site, and SNPs are quite
        common, in principle, a great many RFLPs exist, but have not been detected or
        characterized. Although RFLPs were the first type of DNA markers studied, it is
        currently easier to detect an SNP. Consequently, RFLPs are not extensively used in
        current mapping studies.

        VNTRs and STRs are tandemly repeated sequences, with VNTRs (variable num-
        ber of tandem repeats, or minisatellites) being tandem repeats of 5 to a few 10s of
        base pairs and STRs (simple tandem repeats, or microsatellites) being repeats of 1

to 4 bp. Since STRs typically have 10 to 20 copes of the 1 to 4 bp repeat, they can be readily detected using PCR (which works well for amplifying sequences less than 300 bp long). Some VNTRs can also be detected by PCR using primers that flank the repeating sequence, but more often, they have many copies of a relatively long sequence, making them less than ideal for PCR detection. In this case, they are detected by restriction enzyme digestion (using enzymes that flank the repeat), Southern blotting and probing with a labeled DNA fragment containing several copies of the repeating sequence. Only about 100 VNTRs are known in the human genome. In contrast, STRs are evenly distributed throughout the genome, and are found at a higher frequency. There are about 100,000 loci at an average frequency of one every 30,000 bp. This, plus their easier detection using PCR, makes them more useful than VNTRs in mapping studies.

SNPs are single nucleotide polymorphisms found in at least one percent of the human population. They can be typed by oligonucleotide hybridization analysis: a short labeled oligonucleotide probe is hybridized under high stringency to target DNAs. Under these conditions, only a perfect match is allowed, and so target DNAs containing the same allele as the oligonucleotide are identified. Simultaneous typing of hundreds of SNPs can be done using DNA microarrays. SNPs are widely and uniformly distributed throughout the human genome: one SNP can be found in every 500-1,000 bp of DNA, and about three million SNPs can be found in the entire human genome. SNPs are therefore more frequent than the other types of DNA markers.

9.2   What different types of DNA markers are used to map a gene? Are there any DNA markers that cannot be used for mapping? If so, how are they used?

Answer: As discussed in the answer to Problem 9.1, RFLPs, VNTRs, STRs and SNPs are all useful as DNA markers for mapping. Some VNTRs reside in repetitive sequence DNA and therefore are present in multiple locations in the genome. Such VNTRs are not useful for mapping studies. These VNTRs can still be used for DNA typing when it is used in paternity or forensic analyses however. In addition to these DNA markers, STSs (sequence tagged site: DNA sequence that is unique in the genome) and ESTs (expressed sequence tag: marker produced using PCR and primers based on the sequence of a cDNA) are useful for mapping studies, since, like other DNA markers, they also provide a unique sequence that is anchored at a particular position in the genome. Note that if an STR defines a unique sequence, it is also an STS, but that not every STS (since it may not contain a simple repeating sequence) is an STR.

9.3   The frequency of individuals in a population with two different alleles at a DNA marker is called the marker's heterozygosity. Why would an STR DNA marker with 9 known alleles and a heterozygosity of 0.79 be more useful for mapping studies than a nearby STR having three alleles and a heterozygosity of 0.20?

Answer: If an individual is homozygous for an allele at an STR, all of their gametes have the same STR allele. The STR cannot be used as a marker to distinguish the recombinant- and parental-type gametes of the individual. In a population, individuals are more likely to be heterozygous for STRs with more alleles and higher levels of heterozygosity. The recombinant- and parental-type offspring may be able to be distinguished in individuals heterozygous for an STR, making crosses informative for mapping studies.

9.4   Abbreviations used in genomics typically facilitate the quick and easy representation of longer tongue-twisting terms. Explore the nuances associated with some abbreviations by answering the following questions.
   a. Could an RFLP, VNTR or STR be identified as an SNP? Why or why not?
   b. Are all STSs also ESTs? Are all ESTs capable of being STSs? Why or why not?

Answer:
   a. An SNP is a single nucleotide polymorphism. Since a single base change can alter the site recognized by a restriction endonuclease, an SNP can also be a RFLP. Since STRs and VNTRs are based on variable number of tandemly repeated sequences (1-4, and 5-10's of bp, respectively), they will not usually be SNPs.
   b. An STS, or sequence-tagged site, is a unique, known DNA sequence. Since it is not necessarily a transcribed DNA sequence, it is not an EST, or expressed sequence tag. Providing that an EST is derived from a cDNA for a unique gene, it will also be an STS.

9.5   What is the approximate level of resolution associated with each of the following physical mapping methods? Give your answers in units of kilobase pairs of DNA.
   a. chromosome banding
   b. FISH
   c. restriction maps generated with *Not*I
   d. radiation hybrid maps
   e. YAC clone contig maps

Answer:
   a. Since a chromosome band is on average about 6 Mb (pairs of DNA), or 6,000 kb (pairs of DNA), cytogenetic mapping to a chromosome band provides about this resolution. Note that some bands will be larger, and provide less resolution.
   b. In metaphase chromosomes, FISH methods have a resolution of 2-5 Mb, or 2,000 − 5,000 kb, for DNA markers. If chromosomes have been physically extended artificially, DNA markers can be resolved in a range of 5 - 700 kb.
   c. *Not*I cuts human DNA on average once every 10 Mb, providing a resolution of about 10,000 kb.
   d. The level of resolution associated with radiation hybrid maps depends on the amount of irradiation the human cells were subjected to. Typically, human

fragments in radiation hybrids are a few Mb in length, so radiation hybrid maps will provide a resolution of a few thousand (2,000 to 4,000) kb.

e. A single YAC can contain hundreds to thousands of kb, so localizing a gene to one YAC in a YAC-clone contig will provide at least this level of resolution. Finer resolution can be obtained if the gene can be shown to reside between two markers on one YAC, or on one but not another overlapping YAC in the contig. The degree of resolution will depend on marker positioning, and the number of YACs in the contig. For example, if markers are spaced, on average, every 200 kb, then this will be the approximate level of resolution.

9.6 Detailed physical maps of DNA markers can be generated from the analysis of radiation hybrids as well as clone contigs.

a. Why are these physical maps helpful for sequencing large genomes?

b. How is generating a physical map using radiation hybrids fundamentally different from generating a genetic map by following the inheritance of DNA markers through crosses in multiple generations?

c. The order of DNA markers in radiation hybrid and genetic maps is usually the same, but the relative distances between neighboring pairs of DNA markers in these maps are not always directly proportional. Why might this be the case?

d. Why can more precise radiation hybrid maps be generated when higher doses of X-rays are used to generate the hybrid cells?

e. What problems were associated with initial YAC-based clone-contig maps?

f. How can these problems be overcome by using radiation hybrid maps or BAC or PAC vectors?

Answer:

a. Since sequencing reactions typically only provide about 500 bp of sequence information, assembly of large sequences is a formidable task. Physical maps provide a means to anchor markers and position them relative to each other, so that sequence data can be assembled in the correct orientation and alignment.

b. Radiation hybrids are rodent cells that harbor one or more human DNA fragments, potentially from different regions of the genome. The frequency with which two markers appear together in a collection of radiation hybrids can be used to infer how close they are to each other physically, and radiation hybrid maps tend to better reflect physical distances between DNA markers. Radiation hybrid maps are based on a statistical evaluation of how often two markers are in the same hybrid – that is, the closer together they are physically, the more likely the will be in the same hybrid. In genetic maps, the frequency with which two markers appear together is a function of the recombination distance between them. For two markers on the same chromosome, this reflects the amount of crossing-over between them. This may not reflect the physical distance between two markers, as there is variation in the frequency of crossing-over in a given physical distance. That is, crossing-over frequency per unit DNA length varies in different regions of the genome.

c. The recombination (crossing-over) frequency per unit DNA length is not constant, and so genetic maps are not directly proportional to physical maps. The frequency of radiation-induced DNA breaks is more proportional to physical length, and so distances in radiation hybrid maps are more likely to reflect physical distances.

d. When higher doses of X-rays are used, DNA fragments are broken into smaller fragments. Hence, there is more resolution between closely spaced markers. That is, two markers that are close together will be separated more often in hybrids generated by using higher doses. This allows for better estimates of their map distance.

e. Initial YAC-based clone-contig maps had problems associated with YACs often being chimeric and/or subject to rearrangement. That is, during the construction of a YAC, two or more different genomic regions would be cloned into the same YAC clone, or a single DNA segment might be rearranged as it was cloned (e.g., a portion might be inverted).

f. Radiation hybrid mapping uses the frequency of two markers both being present in one hybrid to estimate a map distance between two markers. Making this measurement requires only that DNA is fragmented in a relatively uniform way. By using radiation hybrids, it is possible to order markers based on their physical distance, and so anomalies in YAC clone-contig maps due to rearrangements can be resolved.

Libraries constructed in BAC and P1 vectors do not show the same level of rearrangements and chimerism that YAC libraries do. They are more "stable."

9.7   STS mapping has been useful to generate clone-contig maps. Perform the following exercise to consider the logistics of locating STSs using PCR.

a. A plasmid library contains 500-bp inserts generated from randomly sheared mouse DNA. How would you identify clones harboring STRs with the dinucleotide repeat $(AT)_N$ or the trinucleotide repeat $(CAG)_N$?

b. How would you use these STRs as STSs in a mapping experiment?

c. Nusbaum and colleagues generated a YAC-based physical map of the mouse genome by localizing 8,203 STSs onto 960 YAC clones. If each of the STSs were assayed in each of the 960 YAC clones, how many different PCRs would need to be analyzed?

d. Although PCRs can be performed robotically, each reaction consumes time and material resources, and with each, there is a certain chance of a false positive result or other error. It is therefore advantageous to reduce the number of PCR reactions by pooling individual YACs together. First, yeast colonies containing the YACs are grown individually in the wells of ten 96-well plates. Suppose the plates are numbered I, II, ... X and the wells of each plate are arrayed in an 8 row $\times$ 12 column grid. The rows are coded A-H, and the columns coded 1-12. This allows the position of a single YAC to be uniquely specified by a code (e.g., II-C6 specifies the YAC from plate II, row C, column 6). In one pooling scheme, all YACs from each row of a plate are pooled into one well (e.g., those on plate II, A1-A12 are pooled together into a well designated II-A) and all YACs from each column of a plate are pooled into one well (those on plate II, A7-H7 are pooled together into a well designated II-7).

    i.   How many different pools would now have to be screened with each STS?

    ii. How many PCRs would have to be performed?

    iii. If the II6 and IIF pools had a positive result with a STS #6239, what is the code of the YAC containing this STS?

    iv. How would you interpret a result where only the IV3 pool was positive for a particular STS?

e. Construct a YAC contig based on the results in the following table.

STS Marker	Positive YAC Pools
63	II-6, II-A
210	II-6, II-A, IV-C, IV-3
522	VII-E, VII-12, X-G, I-C, I-8
713	I-C, I-8
714	VII-E, VII-12
719	X-H, X-9, IV-C, IV-3
991	X-H, X-9, VII-E, VII-12
1071	II-6, II-A, IV-C, IV-3, X-H, X-9
2631	II-6, II-A
3097	VII-E, VII-12, I-C, I-8
4630	VII-E, VII-12, I-C, I-8
5192	X-H, X-9, IV-C, IV-3
6193	X-H, X-9, VII-E, VII-12
6892	II-6, II-A, IV-C, IV-3

f. Devise a method to combine the YACs pooled in (c) to further reduce the number of PCRs. In your method, how many pools are there and how many PCRs would must be performed?

Answer:

a. Synthesize an oligonucleotide of, say, 30 bases, that is either $(AT)_N$ or $(CAG)_N$. Label the oligonucleotide with ^{32}P. Then use this as a probe in a colony hybridization to screen the colonies. Sequence the inserts of the positive clones using universal-primer sites near the multiple cloning site of the plasmids.

b. Sequence the positive clones, and then design primers (based on the unique sequences flanking the repetitive DNA sequences of each insert) for PCR. Have these synthesized, and use them in PCR amplifications of genomic DNA. The sizes of the PCR products will indicate the length of the amplified segment. If an STS is polymorphic, multiple alleles corresponding to different lengths of repeats will be found in different individuals. Polymorphic STSs can be used as markers in mapping experiments. The genotypes of individuals in a cross would be determined using PCR, and linkage between two different STSs, or between an STS and a phenotype (e.g., disease) can be assessed.

c. $960 \times 8,203 = 7,874,880$ PCR reactions.

d. i.   Under this scheme, the 96 wells on each plate are pooled into 12 (rows) + 8 (columns), or 20 samples. For 10 plates, there would be 200 samples.

ii. For 8,203 STSs, there would be $200 \times 8,203 = 1,640,600$ PCRs.

iii. Plate II, row F, column 6.

iv. It is probably a false-positive result – an artifact.

e. STS markers that are shared by a set of YACs define the regions of the YACs that overlap. Therefore, the process of assembling the contig involves identifying which YACs share the same markers and then drawing a possible contig.

To analyze the data in this example, first infer (see d-iii.) which YACs are positive for specific STS markers:

STS Marker	Positive YACs
63	II-6A
210	II-6A, IV-C3
522	VII-E12, I-C8 (X-G is a false positive)
713	I-C8
714	VII-E12
719	X-H9, IV-C3
991	X-H9, VII-E12
1071	II-6A, IV-C3, X-H9
2631	II-6A
3097	VII-E12, I-C8
4630	VII-E12, I-C8
5192	X-H9, IV-C3
6193	X-H9, VII-E12
6892	II-6A, IV-C3

STS markers that are shared by a set of YACs define the regions of the YACs that overlap. Rearrange the data to indicate which YACs share the same markers:

MARKER

YAC	63	210	522	713	714	719	991	1071	2631	3097	4630	5192	6193	6892
II-6A	X	X						X	X					X
IV-C3		X				X		X				X		X
VII-E12			X		X		X			X	X		X	
I-C8			X	X						X	X			
X-H9						X	X	X				X	X	

Rearrange the columns of this table so that markers in a single YAC are in columns positioned close together. Now the overlap between YACs becomes apparent.

MARKER

YAC	2631	63	210	6892	1071	5192	719	6193	991	714	3087	4630	522	713
II-6A	X	X	X	X	X									
IV-C3			X	X	X	X	X							
VII-E12								X	X	X	X	X	X	
I-C8											X	X	X	X
X-H9					X	X	X	X	X					

Now use this data to draw the contig. Note that the exact order of some sets of markers cannot be determined from these data. Some sets of markers may be in different orders than those shown below: 2631 and 63; 210 and 6892; 5192 and 719; 6193 and 991; 3097, 4630 and 522. Parentheses are shown around markers with ambiguous locations.

MARKER

YAC	(2631	63)	(210	6892)	1071	(5192	719)	(6193	991)	714	(3087	4630	522)	713
II-6A														
IV-C3														
X-H9														
VII-E12														
I-C8														

f. Multiple pooling schemes are possible, but not all insure that positive YACs can be identified unambiguously. One needs to consider what happens when more than one positive YAC is found with a given STS. Even the one presented in this problem may be ambiguous, or at least require further testing if two positive YACs reside in a single row (or column) in one plate. Try combining similarly positioned wells in each of the ten different microtiter plates: combine IA1, IIA1, … XA1 into pool A1, combine IB1, IIB1, …XB1 into pool B1, etc. This would give 96 pools. Also use the Plate-Row pools described in the question. Together, these would require 96 + 80 = 176 pools (176 $\times$ 8,203 = 1,443,728 PCRs), almost the same as the 200 pools previously described.

9.8 BACs I–VI have been aligned in the contig shown in the following figure after screening a BAC library with a series of numbered STS and EST markers.

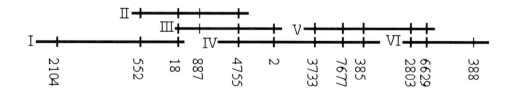

a. During the construction of BAC libraries, genomic DNA segments from different chromosomal regions sometimes are cloned together into a single BAC clone. This generates a chimeric BAC. How would you verify that none of the BACs in this contig was chimeric?

b. How would you identify the chromosomal region from which the contig derived?

c. How would you identify the orientation of the contig on a chromosome (that is, which end of the contig is closer to the telomere or centromere)?

d. How would you identify the distance (in bp) of the markers in each BAC from each other and from the end of the insert?

Answer:

a. Use FISH to verify that each fluorescently labeled BAC clone hybridizes to a single chromosomal site. In addition, use FISH to insure that each of the STS and EST markers present in the clone originate from approximately the same chromosomal region. This will provide evidence that a BAC is not chimeric.

b. When performing the FISH analysis in (a), identify the chromosomal location.

c. Label fragments at each end of the BAC clone contig with a different fluorochrome, and perform FISH with multiple probes. For example, label marker 2104 or part of BAC I with a yellow fluorochrome, label marker 388 or part of BAC VI with a red fluorochrome, and perform FISH. The orientation of the red and yellow signals relative to the centromere and telomere will reveal the orientation of the BAC clone contig.

d. A laborious, but precise approach is to sequence each BAC and use computerized algorithms to search for the sequences of the STSs relative to the entire BAC sequence. A faster, but approximate approach is to generate a restriction map of each BAC and identify which restriction fragments contain a STS or EST marker. This can be done by testing each restriction digest fragment for the presence of an STS using PCR, or using Southern blotting. For the latter, a Southern blot would be made after the restriction digests are separated by size using agarose gel electrophoresis, and probed with a labeled STS. Initially, this could be done using rare-cutting enzymes such as *Not*I and *Bss*HII to get an approximate position. To obtain a finer localization, single *Not*I or *Bss*HII restriction fragments could be subcloned and analyzed using more frequent cutting restriction enzymes.

9.9   Genomes can be sequenced either using a direct shotgun approach or a mapping approach.

a. What is the difference between these approaches?

b. What limitations have traditionally been associated with the direct shotgun approach and how have they been overcome?

c. Estimate the number of sequencing reactions needed to obtain 97 percent of the sequence of the human genome using the approach taken by the Celera group.

Answer:

a. In a direct shotgun approach, the genome is broken into partially overlapping fragments, each fragment is cloned and sequenced, and the genome sequence is assembled using computerized algorithms. The Celera group used a modification of this approach to sequence the human genome. They robotically sequenced 300 to 500 bp at the ends of many clones, keeping track of which sequences were from the ends of the same clone. In total, they obtained about five times the amount of sequence of the entire genome. This insured that they would have sufficient overlap among sequences, so that they could assemble a nearly complete (97%) sequence.

In a mapping approach, high resolution genetic and physical maps of the genome are obtained and integrated. This allows the position of DNA markers to be mapped onto clone contigs and gives an ordered assembly, without any gaps, of partially overlapping clones that comprise the DNA of each chromosome. For the human genome, this was done using BAC clones. The sequence of each BAC clone is obtained using a shotgun approach: the insert of the clone is cut out, sheared mechanically into a partially overlapping set of fragments appropriate for sequencing, cloned into a plasmid, the plasmid inserts sequenced, and the BAC clone sequence assembled using computerized algorithms. The contiguous sequence of each chromosome is obtained by assembling the sequences of the BAC contig.

b. The direct shotgun approach was used initially only for small genomes of less than 100 kb. This is because it was time-consuming and expensive to sequence the huge number of clones that would be required in a larger genome, and because it was difficult to accurately assemble the huge number of relatively small 300-500 bp sequence reads that would be obtained in larger genomes. It was difficult to assemble sequence reads because of the frequency of repetitive DNA sequences and because of the lack of sophisticated computer algorithms.

Two technical advances and several strategic changes allowed these difficulties to be overcome. The technical advances consisted of the development of sophisticated computer algorithms for assembling sequences and the development of robotic procedures for DNA sequencing. Strategically, the Celera group realized that they could obtain more complete sequence, even for regions that had some repetitive DNA sequences, if they sequenced the ends of many partially overlapping clones from two different libraries, one with 2-kb inserts and one with 10-kb inserts. Sequencing of the ends of the clones with 2-kb inserts and keeping track of pairs of sequence reads from one clone allowed them to assemble contigs covering most of the genome. However, since many repeated sequences are about 5 kb in length, one end of a clone with a 2-kb insert may be unique sequence, while the other end may lie in a repetitive sequence. The repetitive sequence will be found in many clones in the library and come from regions dispersed throughout the genome. Therefore, if one only had sequence data from the 2-kb insert clones, it would be impossible to determine, for a clone with a repetitive sequence at one end, which other clone is the true overlapping one from the genome. Now, if the repeat is about 5 kb in length, it can be found entirely within some of the 10-kb clones, so that some of them will have unique sequences flanking a repeated DNA sequence. Therefore, sequencing the ends of clones from the 10-kb library will circumvent the problem associated with this type of repetitive DNA sequence. Sequence information from the clones with 10-kb inserts also provides independent confirmation of contig-sequence structure.

c. Estimate the number of required sequencing reactions using estimates of the size of a haploid human genome (3×10^9 bp), the average number of bases that can be read in a sequencing reaction (500) and an aim of about 5-fold sequence coverage. In this case, obtaining 97% of the sequence would require $5 \times 0.97 \times (3 \times 10^9) /500 = 29.1 \times 10^6$ sequencing reactions. In fact, the assembled sequence of the Celera group consisted of 3.12×10^9 bp assembled from 26.4×10^6 sequence reads of 550 bp each, a total of 14.5×10^9 bp or 4.6-fold sequence coverage.

9.10 Eukaryotic genomes differ in their repetitive DNA content. For example, consider the typical euchromatic 50-kb segment of human DNA that contains the human β T-cell receptor. About 40 percent of it is composed of various genome-wide repeats, about 10 percent encodes three genes (with introns), and about 8 percent is taken up by a pseudogene. Compare this to the typical 50-kb segment of yeast DNA containing the *HIS4* gene. There, only about 12 percent is composed of a genome-wide repeat, and about 70 percent encodes genes (without introns). The remaining sequences in each case are untranscribed and either contain regulatory signals or have no discernible information. Whereas some repetitive sequences can be interspersed throughout gene-containing euchromatic regions, others are abundant near centromeres. What problems do these repetitive sequences pose for sequencing eukaryotic genomes? When can these problems be overcome, and how?

Answer: Repetitive sequences pose at least two problems for sequencing eukaryotic genomes. Highly repetitive sequences associated with centromeric heterochromatin consist of short, simple repeated sequences. These are unclonable, making it impossible to obtain the complete genome sequence of organisms with them. More complex repetitive sequences such as those found within euchromatic regions can be cloned and sequenced. However, since they are present in multiple copies in different genomic locations, and since sequencing reads are relatively short (500 bp), the assembly of overlapping sequences can be ambiguous, especially if the inserts are small (~ 2 kb). If the inserts are small, one end of a clone can be unique sequence, while the other may be repetitive sequence. It is therefore not possible to identify an overlapping clone from the same region of the genome, since many clones from different genomic regions have the same repetitive sequence. Some of the ambiguities can be resolved by comparing these sequences to overlapping sequences generated from sequencing clones with larger inserts, say of about 10 kb. Since many repetitive sequences are only about 5 kb in length, a larger insert may contain a repetitive sequence flanked by unique sequences. See the answer to Question 9.9 for more detail. Another approach is to sequence the clones of an assembled clone contig (e.g., a BAC clone contig).

9.11   How has genomic analysis provided evidence that the Archaea are a branch of life distinct from the Bacteria and the Eukarya?

Answer: Sequencing of the genomes of the Archaea has shown that their genes are not uniformly similar to those of either the Bacteria or the Eukarya. While most of the archaeon genes involved in energy production, cell division, and metabolism are similar to their counterparts in the Bacteria, the genes involved in DNA replication, transcription, and translation are similar to their counterparts in the Eukarya.

9.12   How do the following compare between *S. cerevisiae* and *C. elegans*?
a. the percentage of genes with introns
b. the number of tRNA genes
c. the number of ORFs
d. the (approximate) percentage of the genome devoted to exons

Answer:
a. In *S. cerevisiae*, there are 6,183 ORFs, 120-150 rRNA genes, 37 snRNA genes, and 262 tRNA genes. Of these 6,602-6,632 genes, 233 ORFs and 80 tRNA genes have introns, so about 4.7% have introns. In *C. elegans*, each gene has an average of five introns, so this percentage is close to (or perhaps at) 100%.
b. In *S. cerevisiae*, there are 262 tRNA genes. In *C. elegans*, there are 659 tRNA genes, about 2.5-fold more.
c. In *S. cerevisiae*, there are 6,183 ORFs. In *C. elegans*, there are 19,099 ORFs, about 3.1-fold more.
d. In *S. cerevisiae*, about 70% of the genome is devoted to ORFs, 95.3% of which have no introns, so about 70% of the genome is devoted to exons. In *C. elegans*, only about 27% of the genome is devoted to exons.

9.13   What is bioinformatics, and what is its role in structural, functional, and comparative genomics?

Answer: Bioinformatics is the use of computers and information science to study genetic information and biological structures. It results from the fusion of biology, mathematics, computer science and information science. It has become an important field with the widespread use of databases holding sequence, genetic, functional, structural (e.g., protein structure) and bibliographic information. In structural genomics, it is used to assemble genome (and other) sequences, find genes within databases containing sequence and genetic information, align sequences to determine their degree of matching, predict gene structure and identify the locations of putative genes, etc. In functional genomics, it is used to predict the function of genes based on homology to DNA or amino-acid sequences, and to analyze information on gene function (for example, databases containing information on how the function of a gene can alter the transcriptome or proteome). In comparative genomics, it is used to compare homologous gene sequences and compare genomes in terms of similarities and differences between gene and non-gene sequences.

9.14   What is the difference between a gene and an ORF? How might you identify the functions of ORFs whose functions are not yet known?

Answer: At the physical level, a gene is a sequence of DNA that includes both a transcribed DNA sequence that is an RNA gene product (for rRNA, snRNA, and tRNA) or used to direct the synthesis of a protein (for mRNA) and the regulatory sequences that direct its transcription (e.g., the promoter). At a functional level, genes are associated with the functions of their products, and by the phenotypes of mutations that alter or eliminate the functions of their products. In contrast, an ORF is a potential open reading frame, the segment of a mRNA (mature mRNA in eukaryotes) that directs the synthesis of a polypeptide by the ribosome. Therefore, genes have both transcribed and untranscribed sequences, and in eukaryotes, introns, which ORFs do not. For some ORFs, we have experimental evidence (cDNA sequence, detected protein products) that they exist. For other ORFs, we have predicted their existence based on genomic sequence information, but lack experimental proof.

To determine the function of ORFs whose functions are not yet known, two broad approaches can be used. First, homology searches can be performed. In these, computer-based comparisons are made between the ORF sequence and all sequences (DNA or protein) in a database. The extent of sequence similarity is used to infer whether the ORF encodes a protein with the same, or similar function to a gene in the database. Since proteins can have multiple functional domains (e.g., a catalytic domain and a DNA binding domain), sometimes this can give insight into the partial function of the protein product of the ORF. Second, an experimental approach can be used. In some organisms such as yeast or mice, this may involve "knocking out" the function of the gene by deleting it and analyzing the resulting mutant phenotype. In organisms such as humans, where this experimental approach would be unethical, a homolog in a model organism may be investigated instead. Alternate approaches may involve demonstrating that the ORF encodes a protein, and characterizing the protein product and its interactions within cells (e.g., using the yeast two-hybrid system described in Chapter 8).

9.15   Once a genomic region is sequenced, computerized algorithms can be used to scan the sequence to identify potential ORFs.
   a. Devise a strategy to identify potential prokaryotic ORFs by listing features assessable by an algorithm checking for ORFs.

b. Why does the presence of introns within transcribed eukaryotic sequences pre-clude direct application of this strategy to eukaryotic sequences?

c. How might you modify the strategy to overcome the problems posed by the presence of introns in transcribed eukaryotic sequences?

Answer:

a. Since prokaryotic ORFs should reside in transcribed regions, they should follow a bacterial promoter, containing –35 (TTGACA) and –10 (TATAAT) consensus sequences. Within the transcribed region, but before the ORF, there should be a Shine-Dalgarno sequence (UAAGGAGG) used for ribosome binding. Nearby should be an AUG (or GUG, in some systems) initiation codon. This should be followed by a set of in-frame, sense codons. The ORF should terminate with a stop (UAG, UAA, UGA) codon.

b. Eukaryotic introns introduce non-translated sequences into the coding region of a gene. These sequences will be spliced out of the primary mRNA transcript before it is translated. Their presence in eukaryotic DNA must be taken into ac-count, as the reading of introns as coding sequences would introduce amino acids not normally found in eukaryotic proteins, as well as frameshifts and chain termination signals.

c. Eukaryotic introns typically contain a GU at their 5′ ends, an AG at their 3′ ends, and a YNCURAY branch-point sequence 18 to 38 nucleotides upstream of their 3′ ends. To identify eukaryotic ORFs in DNA sequences, scan sequences following a eukaryotic promoter for the presence of possible introns by search-ing for sets of these three consensus sequences. Then try to translate sequences obtained if potential introns are removed, testing whether a long ORF with good codon usage can be generated. Codon usage refers to the finding that indi-vidual species vary in terms of which of the degenerate set of codons they use. For example, there are six codons for the amino acid arginine. A specific organ-ism will use some of these more frequently than others. A more difficult problem arises since alternative mRNA splicing exists at many genes. In these cases, more than one possible ORF may be found in a given DNA sequence. It is not yet possible to predict how a set of exons at a gene might be alternatively spliced, solely from knowledge of the DNA sequence.

9.16   Annotation of genomic sequences makes them much more useful to researchers. What features should be included in an annotation, and in what different ways can they be depicted? For some examples of current annotations in databases, see:

http://genome-www.stanford.edu/Saccharomyces/maps.html (*S. cerevisiae*)

http://www.flybase.org and http://flybase.bio.indiana.edu:82/annot/ (*Drosoph-ila*)

http://www.tigr.org/tbd/ath1/htmls/ath1.html (*Arabidopsis*)

http://www.ncbi.nlm.nih.gov/genome/guide/ (humans)

http://www.cybergenome.com/ (compilation of links to many organisms).

Answer: An annotation can vary in its level of completeness, depending on what can be inferred based on homology and what experimental data are available. An annotation could include:

1. The location of a transcribed region – graphically depicted with links embedded within the symbols used to depict transcripts
    a. Physical map coordinates
        i.   Links to clones, ESTs, STSs in the region
    b. Genetic map coordinates
        i.   Links to genes, mapping data, in the region
    c. Location of introns, exons, alternative splice sites, alternative promoters, poly(A) addition sites, etc.
        i.   Physical map coordinates
        ii. Graphical depictions
2. The types of evidence for a transcribed region
    a. Prediction based on computer algorithms that assess possible sequences of a promoter, conceptual ORF(s), appropriate splicing sites, homology with other genes, etc.
    b. Analysis of ESTs
    c. Documentation of splice sites, alternative transcript forms by comparison of cDNA and genomic sequences, etc.
3. The inferred function of the gene product
    a. Links to reports, database entries, publications.
    b. Evidence supporting the inferred function
        i.   Inferences based on homology
        ii. Experimental evidence
4. Information about gene regulation
    a. Genes regulated in a similar manner
    b. Unique features of the gene and its regulation

9.17   One of the central themes in genetics is that an organism's phenotype results from an interaction between its genotype and the environment. Because some diseases have strong environmental components, researchers have begun to assess how disease phenotypes arise from the interactions of genes with their environments, including the genetic background in which the genes are expressed. (See http//pga.tigr.org/desc.shtml for additional discussion.) How might DNA microarrays be useful in a functional genomic approach to understanding human diseases that have environmental components, such as some cancers?

Answer: One approach is to use model organisms (e.g., transgenic mice) that have been developed as models to study a specific human disease. Expose them and a control population to specific environmental conditions, and then simultaneously assess disease progression and alterations in patterns of gene expression using microarrays. This would provide a means to establish a link between environmental factors and patterns of gene expression that are associated with disease onset or progression.

9.18   How does a cell's transcriptome compare with its proteome?
   a. For a specific eukaryotic cell, can you predict which has more total members? Can you predict which has more unique members?
   b. Suppose you are interested in characterizing changes in the pattern of gene expression in the mouse nervous system during development. Describe how you would efficiently assess changes in the transcriptome from the time the nervous system forms during embryogenesis to its maturation in the adult.
   c. How would your analyses differ if you were studying the proteome?

Answer: The transcriptome is the set of RNAs present in a cell at a particular stage and time, while the proteome is the set of proteins present in the cell at that stage and time.
   a. It is likely that the proteome has both more total as well as unique members. It is likely that it has more total members since multiple copies of a protein can be translated from a single mRNA transcript. It is also likely that it has more unique members since a given transcript can in principle give rise to different protein isoforms. Once translated, proteins can be post-translationally or co-translationally modified in different ways: phosphorylation, glycosylation, methylation, proteolytic processing, etc. If proteins translated from a single transcript are modified in different ways, multiple protein isoforms are produced.
   b. This analysis could be performed using DNA chips. RNA could be isolated from the nervous system of different developmental stages, and the transcriptional profile in each stage could be assessed using DNA chips. To do this type of analysis, RNA from one developmental stage would be labeled with one fluorochrome – say a fluorescent-green dye. RNA from a second developmental stage would be labeled with another fluorochrome, say a fluorescent-red dye. The labeled probes would be hybridized to the DNA chip, and the relative red:green fluorescence bound to a single site on the chip can be used to infer the relative amounts of gene expression of the gene located at that site on the chip. This could be done for many different developmental stages.
   c. For the proteome, one would need to assess changes in the proteins produced over time. Thus, one would isolate proteins from the nervous system of different developmental stages, and assess the relative abundance of individual proteins using an analytical method such as quantitative two-dimensional gel electrophoresis.

9.19   Distinguish between structural, functional, and comparative genomics by completing the following exercise. The list describes specific activities and goals associated with genome analysis. Indicate the area associated with the activity or goal by placing a letter (S, structural; F, functional; C, comparative) next to each item. Some items will have more than one letter associated with them.

_____ Aligning DNA sequences within databases to determine the degree of matching

_____ Annotation of sequences within a sequenced genome

_____ Characterizing the transcriptome and proteome present in a cell at a specific developmental stage or in a particular disease state

_____ Comparing the overall arrangements of genes and non gene sequences in different organisms to understand how genomes evolve

_____ Describing the function of all genes in a genome

_____ Determining the functions of human genes by studying their homologs in nonhuman organisms

_____ Developing a comprehensive two-dimensional polyacrylamide gel electrophoresis map of all proteins in a cell

_____ Developing a physical map of a genome

_____ Developing DNA microarrays (DNA chips)

_____ Identifying of homologs to human disease genes in organisms suitable for experimentation

_____ Identifying a large collection of simple tandem repeat, or microsatellite sequences to use as DNA markers within one organism

_____ Identifying expressed sequence tags

_____ Making gene knockouts and observing the phenotypic changes associated with them

_____ Mapping a gene in one organism using the lod score method

_____ Sequencing individual BAC or PAC clones aligned in a contig using a shotgun approach

_____ Using oligonucleotide hybridization analysis to type an SNP

Answer:

S, F, C	Aligning DNA sequences within databases to determine the degree of matching
F, C	Annotating sequences within a sequenced genome
F	Characterizing the transcriptome and proteome present in a cell at a specific developmental stage or in a particular disease state
C	Comparing the overall arrangements of genes and non-gene sequences in different organisms to understand how genomes evolve
F	Describing the function of all genes in a genome

F, C	Determining the functions of human genes by studying their homologs in nonhuman organisms
F	Developing a comprehensive two-dimensional polyacrylamide gel electrophoresis map of all proteins in a cell
S	Developing a physical map of a genome
S, F, C	Developing DNA microarrays (DNA chips)
F, C	Identification of homologs to human disease genes in organisms suitable for experimentation
S	Identifying a large collection of simple tandem repeat, or microsatellite sequences to use as DNA markers within one organism
S, F, C	Identifying expressed sequence tags (ESTs)
F, C	Making gene knockouts and observing the phenotypic changes associated with them
S	Mapping a gene in one organism using the lod score method
S	Sequencing individual BAC or PAC clones aligned in a contig using a shotgun approach
S	Using oligonucleotide hybridization analysis to type an SNP

9.20   Genomic analyses of *Mycoplasma genitalium* have not only identified its 517 genes but also allowed identification of genes needed for life. The analyses are presented in detail at the Web site of the Institute for Genomic Research (http://www.tigr.org/minimal/). Explore this Web site and then address the following questions:

a. How many protein-coding genes have unknown functions?

b. How do we know which genes are required for life?

c. Are any of the protein-coding genes with unknown functions required for life?

d. What functional genomics approaches might be helpful to discern their function?

e. What practical value might there be in identifying the minimal gene set needed for life?

f. Is it possible to synthesize DNA sequences containing all the genes identified as essential for life and assemble these on one chromosome? Would this be enough to have a template for a new life form? If not, what additional sequence information would be needed to generate a new life form?

g. What is the difference between the life form generated in (f) and *Mycoplasma genitalium*?

h. What ethical issues arise from these analyses? Who should decide how to address them?

Answer:

a. There are about 180 genes with no known homologs outside of the mycoplasmas, which makes it difficult to assign their function.

b. Both theoretical and experimental paradigms can be used to provide evidence for which genes are required for life.

   A theoretical approach is to estimate how many genes are conserved across large phylogenetic distances, making the assumption that highly conserved genes provide essential functions. Comparison of the *Haemophilus influenzae* and *M. genitalium* genomes suggest that about 265 genes are needed. Comparison of two *Mycoplasma* species (*M. pneumoniae* and *M. genitalium*) shows that *M. pneumoniae* has all 480 of the *M. genitalium* protein-coding genes, plus an additional 197 genes.

   To test which of these 480 are essential for life an experimental approach can be used. One paradigm is to ask whether a mutation that "knocks out" a gene causes a visible mutation, affects the organism's ability to grow or affects its viability (ability to live). Hutchison et al. used transposons (DNA segments capable of moving and inserting themselves in other sites) to estimate the size of minimal mycoplasma genome. Their work suggested that between 265 and 300 of the 480 protein-coding genes were essential <u>under laboratory conditions</u> for growth. It is unclear whether any of the genes <u>not essential under laboratory conditions</u> might still be essential for growth in a human host. Thus, the approach begs the question – what "quality" of life? - or "life" under what conditions?

c. Yes. There are 180 genes without a functional assignment. While 69 of these could be disrupted by a transposon insertion without affecting the viability of the organism, 111 could not. This suggests that at least some of them are not dispensable, since if they were dispensable, transposon disruptions in them would have been recovered. The inference from this experiment is that at least some of them must encode essential cellular functions.

d. Multiple functional genomic approaches could be helpful to infer their function. Note that while the knock-out approach using transposon disruption suggested that these genes have an essential function, the results do *not* provide clues as to what they are. To understand the functions of individual genes, it might be helpful to understand when they are transcribed, and whether they are coordinately transcribed with other genes during the life cycle of the organism. This could provide some information about the cellular pathways utilizing these genes and so indirectly allow inferences as to their function. For this purpose, gene chips could be used to assess their expression profiles during growth or under different experimental conditions. For example, one might glean some information about the function of a gene by learning that its expression was up- or down-regulated during a particular growth phase, or in a mutant strain where a known function was disrupted. An alternate approach would be to generate mutations in a single gene (whose function is unknown) that did not disrupt its function entirely (e.g., by using a chemical mutagen), and then assess which genes had altered expression patterns as a result.

e. In principle, this would allow the design of cells that could be used as bioreactors to synthesize specific complex biological products that could be useful in improving health, crops or some other aspect of human existence. It might also provide a basis for designing cells that could be used in implementing some biological or chemical process (e.g., as agents to mediate gene therapy, as agents that could be designed with features to use in toxic-waste cleanup, as agents for germ warfare, etc.).

f. It is not likely that the assembly of the sequences, by itself, would be sufficient for generating a template for a new life form. Encoded in even a simple genome would have to be instructions for regulating the expression of its genes. Even in the smallest bacteriophage, there are enough instructions encoded to allow for the ordered synthesis of a set of genes, and the propagation of a life cycle. In a "cell" there must be at least these types of instructions, which would occur minimally at the level of transcriptional control.

g. *M. genitalium* is able to respond to its environment and grow as an autonomous cell. It has a set of genes that are "fitted" into regulatory circuits that interact and have the capacity to feedback into each other. The "life form" generated in (f) may make a set of gene products, but this may not "make" a cell. The cell is more than just the sum of the proteins it possesses.

h. There are multiple ethical issues. One can list some of them as a series of unanswered questions.

   1. Is there significant potential for the generation of a biohazard that could adversely affect existing life?

   2. How does the possibility of generating a "living" cell affect our religious and moral beliefs about the origin and sanctity of life?

   3. What are the benefits of pursuing this line of inquiry, relative to our goals for improving human health or the environment?

   4. Do we know enough about the safety, benefits, and risks to venture into such an undertaking?

   5. Since it is difficult to understand what the risks of this venture are, how does one evaluate how to proceed?

      It would be important that scientists, ethicists, the public, and representative groups who might be affected by this work be part of a team that discussed how to proceed and how to address ethical and other (legal, economic, biohazard) issues that might arise from these investigations. Even with this varied level of input, it might not be possible to anticipate all of the consequences of these types of investigations. There are both pragmatic as well as more philosophical concerns.

9.21 Comparative genomics offers insights into the relationship between homologous genes and the organization of genomes. When the genome of *C. elegans* was sequenced, it was striking that some types of sequences were distributed nonrandomly. Consider the data obtained for chromosome V and the X chromosome shown here. The figure shows the distribution of genes, the distribution of inverted and tandem repeat sequences, and the location of ESTs in *C. elegans* that are highly similar to yeast genes.

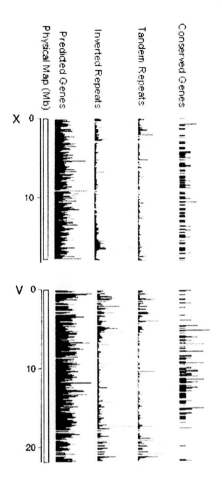

a. How do the distributions of genes, inverted and tandem-repeat sequences, and conserved genes compare?

b. Based on your analysis in **(a)**, what might you hypothesize about the different rates of DNA evolution (change) on the arms and central regions of autosomes in *C. elegans*?

c. Curiously, meiotic recombination (crossing-over, discussed in Chapter 13) is higher on the arms of autosomes, with demarcations between regions of high and low crossing-over at the boundaries between conserved and nonconserved genes seen in the physical map. Does this information support your hypothesis in **(b)**?

Answer:

a. On both chromosome V and the X chromosome, genes are distributed uniformly. However, especially on chromosome V, conserved genes are found more frequently in the central regions. In contrast, inverted and tandem-repeat sequences are found more frequently on the arms. It appears that at least on chromosome V, there is an inverse relationship between the frequency of inverted and tandem-repeats and the frequency of conserved genes.

b. Since there are fewer conserved genes on the arms, there appears to be a greater rate of change on chromosome arms than in the central regions.

c. Yes, since increased meiotic recombination provides for greater rates of exchange of genetic material on chromosomal arms.

10

MENDELIAN GENETICS

CHAPTER OUTLINE

GENOTYPE AND PHENOTYPE
MENDEL'S EXPERIMENTAL DESIGN
MONOHYBRID CROSSES AND MENDEL'S PRINCIPLE OF
SEGREGATION
> The Principle of Segregation

> Representing Crosses with a Branch Diagram

> Confirming the Principle of Segregation: The Use of Testcrosses

DIHYBRID CROSSES AND MENDEL'S PRINCIPLE OF
INDEPENDENT ASSORTMENT
> The Principle of Independent Assortment

> Branch Diagram of Dihybrid Crosses

> Trihybrid Crosses

THE REDISCOVERY OF MENDEL'S PRINCIPLES
STATISTICAL ANALYSIS OF GENETIC DATA: THE CHI-SQUARE TEST
MENDELIAN GENETICS IN HUMANS
> Pedigree Analysis

> Examples of Human Genetic Traits

REVIEW OF KEY TERMS, SYMBOLS, AND CONCEPTS

In your own words, write a brief definition of each term in the groups below. Check your definitions using the text. Then, develop a concept map using the terms in each group.

1	2
hereditary trait	probability
gene, particulate factor	product rule
locus, loci	sum rule
allele, allelomorph	principle of segregation
genotype	principle of independent assortment
phenotype	branch diagram
dominant	chi-square (χ^2) test
recessive	goodness-of-fit test
heterozygote, heterozygous	null hypothesis

1	2
homozygote, homozygous	expected values
self-fertilization, selfing	*P*
cross-fertilization, cross	significance
true-breeding, pure-breeding	degrees of freedom
P, F_1, F_2, F_3 generation, cross	pedigree analysis
monohybrid, dihybrid, reciprocal cross	proband, propositus, proposita
gamete, zygote	1:1, 3:1, all:none ratios
hybrid, dihybrid, trihybrid individual, cross	wild-type allele
testcross	rare homozygote
haploid, diploid	*AA*, *A–*, *Aa*, *a a*
gene segregation	loss of function, gain of function mutation
principle of segregation	recessive, dominant trait
principle of independent assortment	recessive, dominant pedigree

THINKING ANALYTICALLY

There are different levels of understanding of Mendelian genetics. You can certainly obtain some understanding of this material from a careful reading and outlining of the chapter, especially if you pay attention to detail and the logic of Mendel's experiments. Indeed, understanding why Mendel's approach gave insights into the principles of inheritance, when those for thousands of years before him failed, is a substantial accomplishment. However, it is through solving problems that you will develop a practical, useful understanding of this material. Solving the problems in this chapter will not only reinforce what you have read, it will help you develop an understanding of the relationships between its terms, ideas, and facts.

With some effort, you can discover one of the multiple "right" approaches to solving a Mendelian genetics problem. Pursuing any number of "right" approaches will serve to reinforce your understanding of Mendelian genetic principles, and help you gain a deeper understanding of relationships you read about in the chapter. Be warned, however, that there is also a "wrong" approach. It is easy to describe. In the wrong approach, you read through the problem, and then see if you can understand an answer presented in this guide or another key. This is about as beneficial as reading today's weather forecast after you have already stepped out into the rain. You have learned that its raining, but your'e already all wet. What use is your new knowledge? What will you do tomorrow? When you read a solution to a problem, you have not yourself devised the solution, so you have not developed the skills to analyze the situation, apply your knowledge of Mendelian principles, and identify a path that leads to a solution. You may understand the answer, but you won't have developed any of the skills to solve a similar problem. On an exam you will be stuck, and the purpose of doing the problems – to gain a deeper understanding of Mendelian principles – will have been thwarted.

What then, is a "right" approach? Its not the same thing as finding *the* correct answer, usually because there is more than one approach to solving the problem. Here are pointers, some repeated from Chapter 1 of this guide, that are worth emphasizing:

1. Read the problem straight through without pausing. Get the sense of what it is about.

2. Then read it again, slowly and critically. This time,
    a. Jot down pertinent information.
    b. Assign descriptive gene symbols. Use a dash (e.g., $--$ or $A-$) when unsure of a genotype.
    c. Scan the problem from start to finish, and then from the end to the beginning, and carefully analyze the *terms* used in the problem. Often, clues to the answer can be found in the way the problem is stated. (Geneticists use very precise language!)

3. If you are unsure how to continue, ask yourself, "What are the options here?"
    a. Write down all the options you perceive.
    b. Carefully analyze whether a particular option will provide a solution.

4. When you think you have a solution, read through the problem once more, and make sure that your analysis is consistent with *all* the data in the problem. Try to see if there is a more general principle behind the solution, or for that matter, a clearer or more straightforward solution.

5. If you do get stuck (and everyone does!), DO NOT GO IMMEDIATELY TO THE ANSWER KEY. This will only give you the *illusion* of having solved the problem. On an exam, or in real life, there won't be an answer key available. Learn to control the temptation "to just know the answer" and go on to another problem. Come back to this one another time, perhaps the next day. Your mind may be able to use the time to sort through loose ends.

6. If you cannot solve the problem after coming back to it a second time, read through the answer key. Then, close the answer key and try the problem once more. The next day, try it a third time without the answer key.

QUESTIONS FOR PRACTICE

Multiple Choice Questions

1. A dominant gene is one that
    a. suppresses the expression of genes at all loci.
    b. masks the expression of neighboring gene loci.
    c. masks the expression of a recessive allele.
    d. masks the expression of all the foregoing.

2. A dihybrid is an individual that
    a. is heterozygous for every gene.
    b. is heterozygous for two genes under study.
    c. is the result of a testcross.
    d. is used for a testcross.

3. The cross of an uncertain genotype with a homozygous recessive genotype at the same locus is a
    a. pure-breeding cross.
    b. monohybrid cross.

c. testcross.

d. dihybrid cross.

4. The genotypic ratio of the progeny of a monohybrid cross is typically

 a. 1:2:1

 b. 9:3:3:1

 c. 27:9:9:9:3:3:3:1

 d. 3:1

5. A typical phenotypic ratio of a dihybrid cross with dominant and recessive alleles is

 a. 9:1

 b. 1:2:1

 c. 3:1

 d. 9:3:3:1

6. Pedigrees showing rare recessive traits

 a. have about half of the progeny affected when one parent is affected.

 b. have heterozygotes that are phenotypically affected.

 c. have about 3/4 of the progeny affected when both parents are affected.

 d. often skip a generation.

7. In a chi-square test, a P value equal to 0.04 tells one that

 a. there is a 4 percent chance the hypothesis is correct.

 b. there is a 4 percent chance the hypothesis is incorrect.

 c. if the experiment were repeated, chance deviations from the expected values as large as those observed would be seen only 4 percent of the time.

 d. if the experiment were repeated, chance deviations from the expected values as large as those observed would be seen at least 96 percent of the time.

8. In a chi-square test, a P value equal to 0.04 indicates that

 a. the hypothesis is unlikely to be true.

 b. the hypothesis is false and must be rejected.

 c. the hypothesis is true.

 d. the hypothesis is likely to be true.

9. Gain of function mutations are associated with all of the following except

 a. dominant traits

 b. new properties in a gene

 c. phenotypes in heterozygous individuals

 d. a decrease in the normal activity of a gene

10. Two parents affected with a genetic disease have 5 children, all of whom are affected. Which one statement must be true?

 a. Both parents must have at least one mutant allele. The trait might be dominant or recessive.

 b. Both parents must be homozygous for a recessive trait.

 c. At least one parent must be homozygous.

 d. At least one parent must be homozygous for a dominant trait.

11. How many different genotypes are obtainable from the cross *Aa Bb* × *Aa Bb*?
    a. 3
    b. 4
    c. 9
    d. 16

12. What is the chance of obtaining a heterozygous individual from a testcross?
    a. 0%
    b. 50%
    c. At least 50%
    d. 100%

Answers: *1c; 2b; 3c; 4a; 5d; 6d; 7c; 8a; 9d; 10a; 11c; 12c.*

Thought Questions

1. When are Mendel's principles realized during meiosis?

2. How might the discovery of chromosomes toward the end of the nineteenth century have led to the rediscovery of Mendel's work?

3. Over a period of many years, numerous attempts were made to understand how physical traits are passed from one generation to the next. Gregor Mendel was first to make a breakthrough. How do you account for his success, in light of years of failure before him?

4. A gene codes for an enzyme that catalyzes a biochemical reaction. Two mutant alleles are identified. One is dominant to the wild-type allele, while the second is recessive to the wild-type allele. How is this possible? (Hint: consider gain of function, loss of function mutations.)

5. a. Clearly distinguish between an allele, a gene, and a locus.
      • Can an DNA marker identify a locus, but not a gene?
      • Do all STS markers identify loci that are genes?
      • Do all EST markers identify loci that are genes?
   b. Can you see an analogy between a gene and an allele and
      • a digit and an index finger?
      • a canine and a German Shepherd?
      • a dime and a mint, 1954 dime?
      Where do these analogies break down?

6. Why might the term "degrees of freedom" be so named, and why (for the problems in this chapter) is it equal to $(n-1)$?

7. Why are the frequencies of harmful recessive mutant alleles usually higher than the frequencies of harmful dominant mutations, even though individuals with the recessive trait are rare?

8. Construct a decision making tree (a flowchart) that can be used to decide if a pedigree shows a dominant or recessive trait.

9 . Why is it important to know if a trait is common or rare when analyzing a pedigree?

Thought Questions for Media

After reviewing the media on the *iGenetics* CD-ROM, try to answer these questions.

1. What is the difference between a locus, a gene and an allele? Can these terms be used interchangeably?
2. What is the difference between a phenotypic ratio and a genotypic ratio? Can these ever be the same in the offspring of a cross?
3. When a true-breeding plant is self-fertilized, why aren't plants with different traits ever produced? If two true-breeding plants are crossed, why do all of the offspring have just one phenotype?
4. In a cross between two true-breeding plants differing in two characteristics, will the F₁ offspring always exhibit both traits of just one parent? Will they always be dihybrids?
5. What does it mean for "genes on different chromosomes to behave independently in the production of gametes?"
6. How many types of gametes are produced by a monohybrid? By a dihybrid?
7. How many different zygote genotypes can be produced in a monohybrid cross? In a dihybrid cross?
8. How many different zygote phenotypes can be produced in a monohybrid cross? In a dihybrid cross?
9. Why doesn't a recessive trait ever appear in a heterozygote? How do we know that the recessive allele is still present in a heterozygote?

1. Two tagged tribbles wander out of the iActivity tribble laboratory and show up in your bed. One is tagged "male *bb ss* (solid yellow)", and one is tagged "female *Bb Ss* (spotted brown)". You recall that spotted (*S*) is dominant to solid (*s*) and brown (*B*) is dominant to yellow (*b*), that tribbles reproduce quickly, and seize on this opportunity to make a (small) fortune selling spotted-yellow tribbles. What crosses would you do to develop a true-breeding, spotted-yellow strain? Since it is important to keep the population of non-spotted-yellow tribbles to a minimum, you want to be sure that the animals chosen for the strain are true-breeding. How can you do this, since they cannot be selfed?
2. As you read the morning paper at breakfast, you notice that a (tiny) reward has been posted by the iActivity tribble laboratory for three missing tribbles. All the ad says is that one is a heterozygote and two are homozygotes. Midway through breakfast, three untagged tribbles waddle across your plate. One is a solid brown male, one is a solid brown female and the third is a spotted brown male. Assuming that these animals were not just stained with coffee, could they be the missing tribbles? If so, how would you determine, using crosses with just these animals, which animal is heterozygous, which animals are homozygous, and if the homozygotes are both homozygous dominant, both homozygous recessive or one is homozygous dominant and one is homozygous recessive?

SOLUTIONS TO TEXT PROBLEMS

10.1   In tomatoes, red fruit color is dominant to yellow. Suppose a tomato plant homozygous for red is crossed with one homozygous for yellow. Determine the appearance of (a) the F_1, (b) the F_2, (c) the offspring of a cross of the F_1 back to the red parent, and (d) the offspring of a cross of the F_1 back to the yellow parent.

Answer: Consider two ways to solve this problem.

i.   First, notice that this is a situation akin to Mendel's crosses. In such crosses, dominant traits mask the appearance of recessive traits, and when a true breeding dominant plant is crossed to a true breeding recessive plant, all the F_1 progeny show the dominant trait. Here the dominant trait is red, the recessive trait is yellow and the parents are true breeding, since they are homozygous.

(a) Just as in Mendel's crosses, the F_1 plants will be heterozygous and all show the dominant, red trait.

(b) The F_2 plants that result from the cross of two F_1 heterozygotes will also show the same ratios seen by Mendel, that is 3 dominant:1 recessive, or 3 red:1 yellow.

(c) When an F_1 plant is crossed back to the red parent, a heterozygous plant is crossed to a true-breeding dominant plant. Here, each offspring receives a dominant allele from the red parent and so all the progeny must show the dominant, red phenotype.

(d) When an F_1 plant is crossed back to the yellow parent, a heterozygous plant is crossed back to a true-breeding recessive plant. This is akin to one of Mendel's testcrosses, and so the progeny should show a 1:1 ratio of red:yellow plants.

ii.   Assign *R* as the allele symbol for dominant red color, and *r* as the allele symbol for recessive yellow color.

(a) Then the initial cross between two homozygous plants can be depicted as *RR* x *rr*, and the F_1 progeny obtain an *R* allele from the red parent, and a *r* allele from the yellow parent. Therefore, they are all heterozygotes and are *Rr*. As the *R* (red) allele is dominant to the *r* (yellow) allele, the *Rr* progeny are red.

(b) The F_2 are obtained from *Rr* x *Rr*, and so will be composed of 1 *RR*:2 *Rr*:1 *rr* types of progeny. There will be 3 red (*RR* or *Rr*):1 yellow (*rr*).

(c) The F_1 crossed back to the red parent can be depicted as *Rr* x *RR*. All the progeny will obtain an *R* allele from the red parent; the progeny can be written as *R–* (either *RR* or *Rr*) and all will be red.

(d) The F_1 crossed back to the yellow parent can be depicted as *Rr* x *rr*. There will be two equally frequent types of progeny, *Rr* and *rr*. Thus, half the progeny will be red and half yellow.

10.2   In maize, a dominant allele *A* is necessary for seed color as opposed to colorless (*a*). Another gene has a recessive allele *wx* that results in waxy starch, as opposed to normal starch (*Wx*). The two genes segregate independently. Give phenotypes and relative frequencies for offspring resulting when a plant of genetic constitution *Aa WxWx* is testcrossed.

Answer: A plant that is genotypically *Aa WxWx* has two types of gametes: *A Wx* and *a Wx* (notice that *Wx* is a symbol for one allele, not two). In a testcross, this plant is crossed to one homozygous for recessive alleles at both the color gene and the waxy gene, *aa wxwx*. The gametes of this plant are all *a wx*. This cross can be illustrated in the following Punnett square:

		Gametes of *Aa WxWx*	
		A Wx	*a Wx*
Gametes of *aa wxwx*	*a wx*	*Aa Wxwx*	*aa Wxwx*

Progeny will be of two equally frequent genotypes: *Aa Wxwx* and *aa Wxwx*. Thus, half will be colored (*Aa*), half will be colorless (*aa*), and all will have normal starch (*Wxwx*).

10.3 F_2 plants segregate 3/4 colored:1/4 colorless. If a colored plant is picked at random and selfed, what is the probability that both colored and colorless plants will be seen among a large number of its progeny?

Answer: In the F_2, there is a 3:1 colored:colorless phenotypic ratio. This reflects a 1 *CC*:2 *Cc*:1 *cc* genotypic ratio, where colored (*C*) is dominant to colorless (*c*). Thus, there are two types of colored plants (*CC, Cc*) that are present in a 1 *CC*:2 *Cc* ratio. If one is picked at random, there is a 1/3 chance of picking a homozygous *CC* plant, and a 2/3 chance of picking a heterozygous *Cc* plant. If selfed, the *CC* plant will only produce *CC* (colored) plants, while the *Cc* plant will produce both colored and colorless plants (in a 3:1 ratio). Thus, to see more than one type of plant in the progeny, a *Cc* plant must be chosen initially. The chance of this is 2/3. [Notice that the question asks for the chance that a particular colored plant will have two types of progeny, and *not* for the ratio of progeny types when two types are seen].

10.4   In guinea pigs, rough coat (*R*) is dominant over smooth coat (*r*). A rough-coated guinea pig is bred to a smooth one, giving eight rough and seven smooth progeny in the F_1.
a. What are the genotypes of the parents and their offspring?
b. If one of the rough F_1 animals is mated to its rough parent, what progeny would you expect?

Answer:
a. Since rough (*R*) is dominant over smooth (*r*), a rough parent is *RR* or *Rr* (i.e., *R–*). A cross between a rough and smooth guinea pig is *R– × rr*. If the cross is *RR × rr*, then all the progeny will be *Rr* and be rough. If the cross is *Rr × rr*, then half the progeny will be *Rr* (rough) and half will be *rr* (smooth). The 8 rough:7 smooth

progeny ratio approximates a 1:1 *Rr:rr* ratio, and so the initial cross must have been *Rr* × *rr*. The rough progeny must be *Rr* while the smooth progeny must be *rr*.

   b. If one of the rough F₁ animals is mated back to its rough parent, the cross is *Rr* × *Rr*. This cross would produce both rough (*R–*) and smooth (*rr*) progeny in a 3:1 ratio.

10.5   In cattle, the polled (hornless) condition (*P*) is dominant over the horned (*p*) phenotype. A particular polled bull is bred to three cows. Cow A, which is horned, produces a horned calf; polled cow B produces a horned calf; and horned cow C produces a polled calf. What are the genotypes of the bull and the three cows, and what phenotypic ratios do you expect in the offspring of these three matings?

Answer: First depict the phenotypes as genotypes: A polled animal exhibiting the dominant, hornless condition can be depicted as *P–*, while a horned animal exhibits the recessive condition and must be *pp*. Therefore, the three crosses and their progeny can be depicted as

cow phenotype	genotype	x	polled bull genotype	progeny phenotype	genotype
A: horned	*pp*	x	*P–*	horned	*pp*
B: polled	*P–*	x	*P–*	horned	*pp*
C: horned	*pp*	x	*P–*	polled	*P–*

Now follow how each set of parents contributed alleles to their progeny. In the crosses with cows A and B, a horned, *pp* offspring can only be obtained if each parent contributes a recessive *p* allele to the progeny. Therefore both the polled bull and cow B must be heterozygous: each is *Pp*. With this information, both the crosses with cows A and C appear to be testcrosses (*Pp* × *pp*) and will produce 1:1 phenotypic ratios of polled (*Pp*) and horned (*pp*) progeny. The cross with cow B is a cross between two heterozygotes (*Pp* × *Pp*) and will produce a 3:1 phenotypic ratio of polled to horned progeny.

10.6   In the jimsonweed, purple flowers are dominant to white. Self-fertilization of a particular purple-flowered jimsonweed produces 28 purple-flowered and 10 white-flowered progeny. What proportion of the purple-flowered progeny will breed true?

Answer: The ratio of 28 purple to 10 white plants is close to 3:1. A 3:1 ratio means that the purple plant that was initially selfed must have been heterozygous, or *Pp*. A cross of *Pp* × *Pp* would yield progeny with a genotypic ratio of 1 *PP*:2 *Pp*:1 *pp*. Thus, among the purple progeny, there would be 1/3 *PP* homozygotes and 2/3 *Pp* heterozygotes. Since the homozygous *PP* plants are the only purple plants that will breed true, only 1/3 of the purple-flowered progeny will breed true.

10.7   Two black female mice are crossed with the same brown male. In a number of litters, female X produced 9 blacks and 7 browns, and female Y produced 14 blacks. What is the mechanism of inheritance of black and brown coat color in mice? What are the genotypes of the parents?

Answer: Notice that the two crosses give very different results. Use both sets of results to answer the question. In the cross of black female X with the brown male, the 9 black and 7 brown progeny approximate a 1:1 phenotypic ratio. This suggests that this cross is similar to a testcross, and might be depicted $Bb \times bb$. However, it is not clear from this cross alone which color trait is dominant. This question can be answered by considering the cross of black female Y with the brown male, where only black progeny are seen. This is like a cross between two true-breeding individuals where black is dominant to brown, $BB \times bb$. Thus, the brown male is homozygous recessive (bb), female X is heterozygous (Bb), and female Y is homozygous dominant (BB).

10.8   Bean plants may have different symptoms when infected with a virus. Some show local lesions that do not seriously harm the plant; others show general systemic infection. The following genetic analysis was made:

P   local lesions x systemic infection
F_1 all local lesions
F_2 785 local lesions:269 systemic infection

What is probably the genetic basis of this difference in beans? Assign gene symbols to the genotypes occurring in the genetic analysis. Design a testcross to verify your assumptions.

Answer: In this question, note that the trait that is being examined is the *response* of plants to a virus. One envisions that crosses are performed between plants, and then, instead of looking at flower color or seed shape to score a trait, plants are individually tested for their response to viral infection. A cross of a plant showing only local lesions to one showing systemic lesions gives only plants that show local lesions, indicating that a local lesion response might be considered to be dominant to a systemic lesion response. If the allele for the local lesion response is depicted as L, and the allele for the systemic lesion response as l, the parental generation can be written as $LL \times ll$. Then, the F_1 would be all Ll and the F_2 would be 1 LL:2 Ll:1 ll. This fits with the observed numbers of 785 local and 269 systemic (3 L–:1 ll) lesion plants.

To test the hypothesis that the local lesion response is dominant to the systemic lesion response, testcross the F_2 plants to true-breeding plants that show a systemic lesion response (i.e., are ll). The progeny of this testcross can then be assayed for their response to viral infection so that the genotype of the F_2 can be determined. One would expect 2/3 of those F_2 plants showing a local lesion response to be heterozygotes, i.e., Ll. When they are testcrossed, half of their progeny should show local responses and half systemic responses. The remaining 1/3 will be *LL*, and give only progeny with local responses.

10.9 A normal *Drosophila* (fruit fly) has both brown and scarlet pigment granules in the eyes, which appear red as a result. Brown (*bw*) is a recessive allele on chromosome 2 that, in homozygous condition, results in the absence of scarlet granules (so that the eyes appear brown). Scarlet (*st*) is a recessive allele on chromosome 3 that, when homozygous, results in scarlet eyes because of the absence of brown pigment. Any fly homozygous for recessive brown and recessive scarlet alleles produces no eye pigment and has white eyes. The following results were obtained from crosses:

P   brown-eyed fly × scarlet-eyed fly

F_1 red eyes (both brown and scarlet pigment present)

F_2 9/16 red:3/16 scarlet:3/16 brown:1/16 white

a. Assign genotypes to the P and F_1 generations.
b. Design a testcross to verify the F_1 genotype and predict the results.

Answer: Here, two independently assorting genes affecting eye pigment are being followed. Use the symbols suggested in the problem to depict alleles at each locus. For the locus controlling scarlet granules, use *bw* to represent the recessive allele and *Bw* to represent the dominant allele. For the locus controlling brown granules, use *st* to represent the recessive allele and *St* to represent the dominant allele. When writing the genotypes of the flies being crossed, be certain to write the alleles present at both genes.

a. Our first task is to assign genotypes to the P and F_1 generations. Brown-eyed flies lack scarlet granules, so they must be *bwbw* (no scarlet) and *St–*; these flies do make brown granules. Note that they can either be *bwbw StSt* or *bwbw Stst*, and that we cannot tell their exact genotype yet. Using similar reasoning, scarlet-eyed flies must be *Bw– stst*. We can determine the exact genotype of these P-generation flies by considering what progeny they produce. Since each parent can be either of two genotypes, four different crosses are possible. These are illustrated in the following branch diagrams:

(i)   brown eyes × scarlet eyes
       bwbw StSt × BwBw stst

       bwbw × BwBw   StSt × stst

           Bwbw ——— *Stst* ——→ *Bwbw Stst*
       (scarlet granules) (brown granules)   (all red eyes)

(ii)   brown eyes × scarlet eyes
       bwbw Stst × BwBw stst

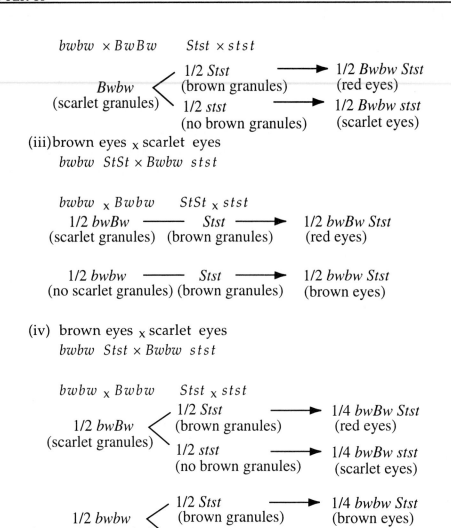

$$bwbw \times BwBw \qquad Stst \times stst$$

Bwbw
(scarlet granules)
⟨ 1/2 *Stst* (brown granules) → 1/2 *Bwbw Stst* (red eyes)
1/2 *stst* (no brown granules) → 1/2 *Bwbw stst* (scarlet eyes)

(iii) brown eyes ₓ scarlet eyes
bwbw StSt × *Bwbw stst*

$$bwbw \times Bwbw \qquad StSt \times stst$$

1/2 *bwBw* —— *Stst* → 1/2 *bwBw Stst*
(scarlet granules) (brown granules)   (red eyes)

1/2 *bwbw* —— *Stst* → 1/2 *bwbw Stst*
(no scarlet granules) (brown granules)   (brown eyes)

(iv) brown eyes ₓ scarlet eyes
bwbw Stst × *Bwbw stst*

$$bwbw \times Bwbw \qquad Stst \times stst$$

1/2 *bwBw*
(scarlet granules)
⟨ 1/2 *Stst* (brown granules) → 1/4 *bwBw Stst* (red eyes)
1/2 *stst* (no brown granules) → 1/4 *bwBw stst* (scarlet eyes)

1/2 *bwbw*
(no scarlet granules)
⟨ 1/2 *Stst* (brown granules) → 1/4 *bwbw Stst* (brown eyes)
1/2 *stst* (no brown granules) → 1/4 *bwbw stst* (white eyes)

Notice that even though the parents in each of the above crosses look the same, their progeny are not. The only way all red-eyed progeny can be obtained is if the cross is that shown in (i). To see if the observed F_2 is consistent with this view, use a branch diagram:

red eyes ₓ red eyes
Bwbw Stst × *Bwbw Stst*

$$Bwbw \times Bwbw \qquad Stst \times Stst$$

3/4 *Bw–*
(scarlet granules)
⟨ 3/4 *St–* (brown granules) → 9/16 *Bw– St–* (red eyes)
1/4 *stst* (no brown granules) → 3/16 *Bw– stst* (scarlet eyes)

1/4 *bwbw*
(no scarlet granules)
⟨ 3/4 *St–* (brown granules) → 3/16 *bwbw St–* (brown eyes)
1/4 *stst* (no brown granules) → 1/16 *bwbw stst* (white eyes)

b. To verify the F_1 genotype, cross the red-eyed F_1 to doubly homozygous recessive white-eyed flies of the genotype *bwbw stst*. One expects to see a 1:1:1:1 ratio of red:brown:scarlet:white flies, as shown in the following branch diagram.

red eyes × white eyes
Bwbw Stst × bwbw stst

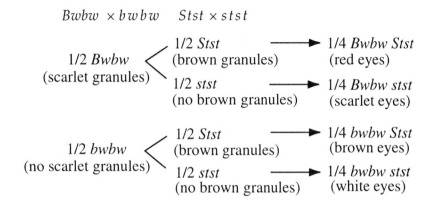

10.10 Grey seed color (*G*) in garden peas is dominant to white seed color (*g*). In the following crosses, the indicated parents with known phenotypes but unknown genotypes produced the listed progeny. Give the possible genotype(s) of each female parent based on the segregation data.

PARENTS	PROGENY		FEMALE PARENT
FEMALE × MALE	GREY	WHITE	GENOTYPE
grey × white	81	82	?
grey × grey	118	39	?
grey × white	74	0	?
grey × grey	90	0	?

Answer: First notice that white seeds are always *gg* while grey seeds are either *G G* or *Gg*. Thus, one can assign partial genotypes (either *G–* or *gg*) based on the phenotypes of the parents. The problem is to determine whether a grey parent is *GG* or *Gg*. In monohybrid crosses, there are three kinds of phenotypic ratios that can be generated. The cross *Gg × Gg* gives a 3 grey (*G–*):1 white (*gg*) ratio, the cross *Gg × gg* gives a 1 grey (*Gg*):1 white (*gg*) ratio, and the crosses *GG × gg* and *GG × G–* give all grey (*G–*) progeny. As the first cross of grey × white gives a 1:1 ratio, it must be *Gg × gg*. As the second cross of grey × grey gives a 3:1 ratio, it must be *Gg × Gg*. As the third cross of grey × white gives all grey, it must be *GG × gg*. In the fourth cross, only grey progeny are produced. The genotype of one of the parents must be *GG*, but the genotype of the other can only be specified as *G–*. One has:

PARENTS	PROGENY		FEMALE PARENT
FEMALE × MALE	GREY	WHITE	GENOTYPE
grey × white	81	82	Gg
grey × grey	118	39	Gg
grey × white	74	0	GG
grey × grey	90	0	GG or $G-$

10.11 Fur color in the babbit, a furry little animal and popular pet, is determined by a pair of alleles, B and b. BB and Bb babbits are black, and bb babbits are white.

A farmer wants to breed babbits for sale. True-breeding white (bb) female babbits breed poorly. The farmer purchases a pair of black babbits, and these mate and produce six black and two white offspring. The farmer immediately sells his white babbits, and then he comes to consult you for a breeding strategy to produce more white babbits.

a. If he performed random crosses between pairs of F_1 babbits, what proportion of the F_2 progeny would be white?

b. If he crossed an F_1 male to the parental female, what is the probability that this cross will produce white progeny?

c. What would be the farmer's best strategy to maximize the production of white babbits?

Answer: As the farmer starts with a pair of black babbits, he must be starting with animals that are either BB or Bb. Since his pair is not true breeding, and indeed, gives a 3:1 ratio of black to white progeny, he must have two heterozygotes, or Bb babbits. Therefore, one expects to find a 1 BB:2 Bb genotypic ratio among the black F_1 progeny that were not sold.

a. Consider that, in order for a white babbit to be obtained in a cross between a pair of F_1 babbits, both babbits must be Bb in genotype, and a bb offspring must be produced by these parents. Now ascertain the chance of these events occurring. If one picks randomly among the black F_1 progeny, there will be a 1/3 chance of picking a BB individual and a 2/3 chance of picking a Bb individual. The chance of two Bb parents giving a bb offspring is 1/4. Using the product rule, one has:

P(white offspring) = P(both F_1 babbits are Bb and a bb offspring is produced)
= P(both F_1 babbits are Bb) × P(bb offspring)
= (2/3 × 2/3) × (1/4)
= 1/9

b. If he crosses an F_1 male (Bb or BB) to the parental female (Bb), two types of crosses are possible. The crosses and probabilities are:

(i) Bb (F_1 male) × Bb (parental female) p = 2/3 × 1 = 2/3

(ii) BB (F_1 male) × Bb (parental female) p = 1/3 × 1 = 1/3

Here, only the first cross can produce white progeny, 1/4 of the time. Using the product rule, the chance that this strategy will yield white progeny is

p = 2/3 (chance of Bb × Bb cross) × 1/4 (chance of bb offspring) = 1/6.

c. As neither of the strategies in (b) work very well, evaluate other potential strategies (use trial and error). One that works better in the long run, but is more work initially, is as follows. Re-mate the initial two black babbits (which we have determined to be Bb) to obtain a white male offspring [$P = 1/4$ (white bb) $\times$ 1/2 (male) $= 1/8$]. Retain this male (note that the fertility of white males is not affected) and breed it back to its mother. This cross would be $Bb \times bb$ and give 1/2 white (bb) and 1/2 black (Bb) offspring. The progeny of this cross could be used to develop a "breeding colony" consisting of black (Bb) females and white (bb) males. These would consistently produce half white and half black offspring.

10.12 In the jimsonweed, purple flower (P) is dominant to white (p), and spiny pods (S) are dominant to smooth (s). In a cross between a jimsonweed homozygous for white flowers and spiny pods and one homozygous for purple flowers and smooth pods, determine the phenotype of (a) the F_1; (b) the F_2; (c) the progeny of a cross of the F_1 back to the white, spiny parent; (d) the progeny of a cross of the F_1 back to the purple, smooth parent.

Answer: Since you are told that each parent is homozygous, the parental genotypes can be determined from their phenotypes. One has a white (pp) spiny (SS) plant crossed to a purple (PP) smooth (ss) plant. This initial information can be used with branch diagrams to solve each part of the problem as follows:

P: white, spiny $\times$ purple, smooth
$pp\ SS \times PP\ ss$
Gametes: $p\ S$ $P\ s$
F_1: $Pp\ Ss$ (purple, spiny)
$F_1 \times F_1$: $Pp\ Ss \times Pp\ Ss$
$Pp \times Pp$ $Ss \times Ss$

```
                   3/4 S-  ——→  9/16 P- S- (purple, spiny)
       3/4 P- <
                   1/4 ss  ——→  3/16 P- ss (purple, smooth)

                   3/4 S-  ——→  3/16 pp S- (white, spiny)
       1/4 pp <
                   1/4 ss  ——→  1/16 pp ss (white, smooth)
```

F_1 x white, spiny: $Pp\ Ss \times pp\ SS$
$Pp \times pp$ $Ss \times SS$
$1/2\ Pp$ —— $S-$ ——→ $1/2\ Pp\ S-$ (purple, spiny)
$1/2\ pp$ —— $S-$ ——→ $1/2\ pp\ S-$ (white, spiny)

F_1 x purple, smooth: $Pp\ Ss \times PP\ ss$
$Pp \times PP$ $Ss \times ss$

$$P- \begin{cases} 1/2 \ Ss \longrightarrow 1/2 \ P- \ Ss \text{ (purple, spiny)} \\ 1/2 \ ss \longrightarrow 1/2 \ P- \ ss \text{ (purple, smooth)} \end{cases}$$

10.13   Cleopatra normally is a very refined cat. When she finds even a small amount of catnip, however, she purrs madly, rolls around in the catnip, becomes exceedingly playful, and appears intoxicated. Cleopatra and Antony, who walks past catnip with an air of indifference, have produced five kittens who respond to catnip just like Cleopatra. When the kittens mature, two of them mate and produce four kittens that respond to catnip and one that does not. When another of Cleopatra's daughters mates with Augustus (a nonrelative), who behaves just like Antony, three catnip-sensitive and two catnip-insensitive kittens are produced. Propose a hypothesis for the inheritance of catnip sensitivity that explains these data.

Answer: Try fitting the data to a model in which catnip sensitivity/insensitivity is controlled by a pair of alleles at one gene. Hypothesize that, since sensitivity is seen in all of the progeny of the initial mating between catnip-sensitive Cleopatra and catnip-insensitive Antony, sensitivity is dominant. Let S represent the sensitive allele, and s the insensitive allele. Then the initial cross would have been $S- \times ss$, and the progeny are Ss. If two of the Ss kittens mate, one would expect 3 Ss (sensitive):1 ss (insensitive) kittens. In the mating with Augustus, the cross would be $Ss \times ss$, and should give a 1 Ss (sensitive):1 ss (insensitive) progeny ratio. The observed progeny ratios are not far off from these expectations.

An alternative hypothesis is that sensitivity (s) is recessive, and insensitivity (S) is dominant. For Antony and Cleopatra to have sensitive (ss) offspring, they would need to be Ss and ss, respectively. When two of their ss progeny mate, only sensitive, ss offspring should be produced. Since this is not observed, this hypothesis does not explain the data.

10.14   Using the information in Problem 10.12, what progeny would you expect from the following jimsonweed crosses? You are encouraged to use the branch diagram approach.

a. $PP \ ss \times pp \ SS$ d. $Pp \ Ss \times Pp \ Ss$
b. $Pp \ SS \times pp \ ss$ e. $Pp \ Ss \times Pp \ ss$
c. $Pp \ Ss \times Pp \ SS$ f. $Pp \ Ss \times pp \ ss$

Answer: Using branch diagrams, one has:
a. $PP \ ss \times pp \ SS$

$$PP \times pp \qquad ss \times SS$$

$$Pp \text{ ——— } Ss \longrightarrow \text{all } Pp \ Ss \text{ (purple, spiny)}$$

b. *Pp SS* × *pp ss*

Pp × *pp*   *SS* × *ss*

1/2 *Pp* ——— *Ss* ——→ 1/2 *Pp Ss* (purple, spiny)

1/2 *pp* ——— *Ss* ——→ 1/2 *pp Ss* (white, spiny)

c. *Pp Ss* × *Pp SS*

Pp × *Pp*   *Ss* × *SS*

3/4 *P*– ——— *S*– ——→ 3/4 *P*– *S*– (purple, spiny)

1/4 *pp* ——— *S*– ——→ 1/4 *pp S*– (white, spiny)

d. *Pp Ss* × *Pp Ss*

Pp × *Pp*   *Ss* × *Ss*

3/4 *P*– ⟨ 3/4 *S*– ——→ 9/16 *P*– *S*– (purple, spiny)

1/4 *ss* ——→ 3/16 *P*– *ss* (purple, smooth)

1/4 *pp* ⟨ 3/4 *S*– ——→ 3/16 *pp S*– (white, spiny)

1/4 *ss* ——→ 1/16 *pp ss* (white, smooth)

e. *Pp Ss* × *Pp ss*

Pp × *Pp*   *Ss* × *ss*

3/4 *P*– ⟨ 1/2 *Ss* ——→ 3/8 *P*– *Ss* (purple, spiny)

1/2 *ss* ——→ 3/8 *P*– *ss* (purple, smooth)

1/4 *pp* ⟨ 1/2 *Ss* ——→ 1/8 *pp Ss* (white, spiny)

1/2 *ss* ——→ 1/8 *pp ss* (white, smooth)

f. *Pp Ss* × *pp ss*

Pp × *pp*   *Ss* × *ss*

10.15   In summer squash, white fruit (*W*) is dominant over yellow (*w*) and disk-shaped fruit (*D*) is dominant over sphere-shaped fruit (*d*). The following problems give the appearances of the parents and their progeny. Determine the genotypes of the parents in each case.

a.   White, disk × yellow, sphere gives 1/2 white, disk and 1/2 white, sphere.

b.   White, sphere × white, sphere gives 3/4 white, sphere and 1/4 yellow, sphere.

c.   Yellow, disk × white, sphere gives all white, disk progeny.

d.   White, disk × yellow, sphere gives 1/4 white, disk; 1/4 white, sphere; 1/4 yellow, disk; and 1/4 yellow, sphere.

e.   White, disk × white, sphere gives 3/8 white, disk; 3/8 white, sphere; 1/8 yellow, disk; and 1/8 yellow, sphere.

Answer: First define symbols for the alleles specifying each trait. Then use information about which allele is dominant or recessive to make initial assignments of possible genotypes. For example, if a plant is white, it must have a dominant *W* allele, but as it may be either *WW* or *Ww*, it would be initially noted as *W*–. If a plant is yellow, it has to be *ww*. Then, by considering just one pair of allelic traits at a time, and recalling the Mendelian progeny ratios you have seen [a 1:1 ratio follows from a testcross (*Aa* × *aa*), an all-to-none ratio follows if at least one parent is homozygous dominant (*AA* × *A*– or *aa*), and a 3:1 ratio follows from a monohybrid cross (*Aa* × *Aa*)], you can ascertain whether a parental *W*– plant is *Ww* or *WW*.

CROSS	PARENTS	PROGENY
a.	white, disk × yellow, sphere *WW Dd* *ww dd*	1/2 white, disk; 1/2 white, sphere
b.	white, sphere × white, sphere *Ww dd* *Ww dd*	3/4 white, sphere; 1/4 yellow, sphere
c.	yellow, disk × white, sphere *ww DD* *WW dd*	all white, disk
d.	white, disk × yellow, sphere *Ww Dd* *ww dd*	1/4 white, disk; 1/4 white, sphere; 1/4 yellow, disk; 1/4 yellow, sphere
e.	white, disk × white, sphere *Ww Dd* *Ww dd*	3/8 white, disk; 3/8 white, sphere 1/8 yellow, disk; 1/8 yellow, sphere

10.16   Genes *a*, *b*, and *c* assort independently and are recessive to their respective alleles *A*, *B*, and *C*. Two triply heterozygous (*Aa Bb Cc*) individuals are crossed.

a. What is the probability that a given offspring will be phenotypically *A B C*, that is, will exhibit all three dominant traits?

b. What is the probability that a given offspring will be genotypically homozygous for all three dominant alleles?

Answer: First consider just one pair of alleles, say *A* and *a*. Since the cross is *Aa* × *Aa*, the progeny will be 1 *AA*:2 *Aa*:1 *aa*, or 3 *A*–:1 *a a*.

a. Since the three genes assort independently, one can use the product rule to determine the chance of obtaining an *A– B– C–* offspring.

$$p = (\text{chance of } A\text{–})(\text{chance of } B\text{–})(\text{chance of } C\text{–})$$
$$p = (3/4)(3/4)(3/4)$$
$$p = (27/64)$$

b. Since the chance of obtaining an *AA* offspring will be 1/4, and the three genes assort independently, use the product rule to determine the chance of obtaining an *AA BB CC* offspring.

$$p = (\text{chance of } AA)(\text{chance of } BB)(\text{chance of } CC)$$
$$p = (1/4)(1/4)(1/4)$$
$$p = (1/64)$$

You can also solve this problem by setting up a branch diagram, or much more laboriously, by setting up a Punnett square.

10.17 In garden peas, tall stem (*T*) is dominant over short stem (*t*), green pods (*G*) are dominant over yellow pods (*g*), and smooth seeds (*S*) are dominant over wrinkled seeds (*s*). Suppose a homozygous short, green, wrinkled pea plant is crossed with a homozygous tall, yellow, smooth one.

a. What will be the appearance of the F_1?

b. If the F_1's are interbred, what will be the appearance of the F_2?

c. What will be the appearance of the offspring of a cross of the F_1 back to its short, green, wrinkled parent?

d. What will be the appearance of the offspring of a cross of the F_1 back to its tall, yellow, smooth parent?

Answer: First note that the problem asks only for the *appearance* of the offspring of the various crosses, and not the genotypes. Then write out the genotype of the parental cross: *tt GG ss* × *TT gg SS*.

a. For each pair of traits, a homozygous dominant plant is crossed to a homozygous recessive plant. Thus, all the F_1 progeny will show the dominant trait, and be tall, green, and smooth (*Tt Gg Ss*).

b. The F_2 results from selfing the F_1, i.e., *Tt Gg Ss* × *Tt Gg Ss*. The appearance of the F_2 is most readily determined by employing a branch diagram.

Tt × Tt   Gg × Gg   Ss × Ss

                                    3/4 S– ——→ 27/64 T– G– S– (tall, green, smooth)
                        3/4 G– <
                                    1/4 ss ——→ 9/64 T– G– ss (tall, green, wrinkled)
            3/4 T– <
                                    3/4 S– ——→ 9/64 T– gg S– (tall, yellow, smooth)
                        1/4 gg <
                                    1/4 ss ——→ 3/64 T– gg ss (tall, yellow, wrinkled)

                                    3/4 S– ——→ 9/64 tt G– S– (short, green, smooth)
                        3/4 G– <
                                    1/4 ss ——→ 3/64 tt G– ss (short, green, wrinkled)
            1/4 tt <
                                    3/4 S– ——→ 3/64 tt gg S– (short, yellow, smooth)
                        1/4 gg <
                                    1/4 ss ——→ 1/64 tt gg ss (short, yellow, wrinkled)

c. The branch diagram of the cross *Tt Gg Ss × tt GG ss* is:

Tt × tt   Gg × GG   Ss × ss

                                    1/2 Ss ——→ 1/4 Tt G– Ss (tall, green, smooth)
        1/2 Tt —— all G– <
                                    1/2 ss ——→ 1/4 Tt G– ss (tall, green, wrinkled)

                                    1/2 Ss ——→ 1/4 tt G– Ss (short, green, smooth)
        1/2 tt —— all G– <
                                    1/2 ss ——→ 1/4 tt G– ss (short, green, wrinkled)

d. The branch diagram of the cross *Tt Gg Ss × TT gg SS* is:

Tt × TT   Gg × gg   Ss × SS

                            1/2 Gg —— all S– ——→ 1/2 T– Gg S– (tall, green, smooth)
        all T– <
                            1/2 gg —— all S– ——→ 1/2 T– gg S– (tall, yellow, smooth)

10.18   *C* and *c*, *O* and *o*, and *I* and *i* are three independently segregating pairs of alleles in chickens. *C* and *O* are dominant alleles, both of which are necessary for pigmentation. *I* is a dominant inhibitor of pigmentation. Individuals of genotype *cc*, or *oo*, or *Ii*, or *II* are white, regardless of what other genes they possess. Assume that white leghorns are *CC OO II*, White Wyandottes are *cc OO ii*, and White Silkies are *CC oo ii*. What types of offspring (white or pigmented) are possible, and what is the probability of each, from the following crosses?

a. White Silkie × White Wyandotte

b. White Leghorn × White Wyandotte

c. (Wyandotte–Silkie F₁) × White Silkie

Answer: In order for an individual to be pigmented, they must have one of each of the dominant *C* and *O* alleles and not have any of the dominant *I* alleles. That is, they must be *C– O– ii*.

a. White Silkie (*CC oo ii*) x White Wyandotte (*cc OO ii*). These are two true-breeding strains at each of three genes, and differ from each other at two loci, the *C/c* and *O/o* loci. The progeny will be dihybrids, are all *Cc Oo ii* and are all pigmented.

b. White Leghorn (*CC OO II*) x White Wyandotte (*cc OO ii*). These two are also true-breeding at each of three genes, and differ from each other at two loci, the *C/c* and *I/i* loci. Their progeny will be dihybrids, are all *Cc OO Ii* and are all white (because of *Ii*).

c. Wyandotte-Silkie F_1 (*Cc Oo ii*) x White Silkie (*CC oo ii*). As both parents are *ii*, all the progeny will be as well, and so, if they are *C– O–*, they will be pigmented. The proportions of white and pigmented progeny can be determined by using a branch diagram, or considering each locus separately as follows: At the *C/c* locus, the cross is *Cc × CC*, so all the progeny will be *C–*. At the *O* locus, the cross is *Oo x oo*, a testcross, so half the progeny will be *Oo* and half will be *oo*. Thus, half of the progeny will be *C– Oo ii* and be pigmented, and half will be *C– oo ii* and be white.

10.19   Two homozygous strains of corn are hybridized. They are distinguished by six different pairs of genes, all of which assort independently and produce an independent phenotypic effect. The F_1 hybrid is selfed to give an F_2.

a. What is the number of possible genotypes in the F_2?

b. How many of these genotypes will be homozygous at all six gene loci?

c. If all gene pairs act in a dominant-recessive fashion, what proportion of the F_2 will be homozygous for all dominants?

d. What proportion of the F_2 will show all dominant phenotypes?

Answer: Although this problem can be solved using a branch diagram, the branch diagram analysis of six genes is tedious. Therefore approach it in a different manner. A general relationship exists between the number of possible genotypes and phenotypes. At any one locus having alleles that act in a dominant-recessive fashion, there are two possible phenotypes (*A–* and *aa*) and three possible genotypes (*AA, Aa* and *aa*). When several independently assorting loci are considered, the number of possibilities grows according to the number of combinations of alleles possible. For two loci, independent assortment of the alleles at each locus allows for $2 \times 2 = 4$ phenotypes (two possible phenotypes at each locus assorted with either of two possible phenotypes at a second locus) and 3×3 genotypes (three possible genotypes at one locus assorted with any of three possible genotypes at a second locus). For three loci, independent assortment of the alleles at each locus allows for $2 \times 2 \times 2 = 8$ phenotypes and $3 \times 3 \times 3 = 27$ genotypes. For *n* loci, the relationship becomes 2^n possible phenotypes and 3^n possible genotypes.

To determine the frequency of a particular phenotypic or genotypic class, consider that at one locus, an F_1 hybrid cross gives 3/4 phenotypically dominant and 1/4 phenotypically recessive progeny and 1/4 homozygous dominant, 1/2 heterozygous and 1/4 homozygous recessive progeny. The fraction of progeny of a particular genotypic or phenotypic class can be determined by considering the combinations that are possible. For example, for two independently assorting loci A/a and B/b, 3/4 of the progeny of a cross of $Aa\ Bb \times Aa\ Bb$ will show the $A-$ phenotype and 3/4 of the progeny will show the $B-$ phenotype. When independent assortment of these two loci is considered, $3/4 \times 3/4 = 9/16$ of the progeny will show both the $A-$ and the $B-$ phenotypes. (Multiply the individual probabilities using the product rule.) Thus, when n loci are involved, $(3/4)^n$ of the progeny will show all dominant phenotypes, $(1/4)^n$ of the progeny will show all recessive phenotypes, $(1/4)^n$ of the progeny will be homozygous dominant at all loci, $(1/4)^n$ of the progeny will be homozygous recessive at all loci, and $(1/2)^n$ of the progeny will be heterozygous at all loci.

a. For six loci, $3^6 = 729$ possible genotypes will be seen.

b. Notice that the question asks for how many of the *genotypes* will be homozygous. For just one locus, two (AA, aa) of three possible (AA, Aa, aa) genotypes are homozygous. Thus, for six loci, $2^6 = 64$ genotypes will be homozygous for all loci. Note that included in these genotypes are those that are homozygous dominant at each locus, those that are homozygous recessive at each locus, and those that are homozygous dominant at one or more loci and homozygous recessive at the other loci.

c. In a monohybrid cross, 1/4 of the progeny will be homozygous dominant. For the F_2 in this cross, $(1/4)^6 = 1/4{,}096$ of the progeny will be homozygous dominant. Notice that this fraction of the progeny derives from a single genotype.

d. In a monohybrid cross, 3/4 of the progeny show a dominant phenotype. For the F_2 in this cross, $(3/4)^6 = 729/4{,}096 = 17\%$ of the progeny will show all six dominant phenotypes.

10.20   The coat color of mice is controlled by several genes. The agouti pattern, characterized by a yellow band of pigment near the tip of the hairs, is produced by the dominant allele A; homozygous aa mice do not have the band and are non-agouti. The dominant allele B determines black hairs, and the recessive allele b determines brown. Homozygous $c^h c^h$ individuals allow pigments to be deposited only at the extremities (e.g., feet, nose, and ears) in a pattern called Himalayan. The genotype $C-$ allows pigment to be distributed over the entire body.

a. If a true-breeding black mouse is crossed with a true-breeding brown, agouti, Himalayan mouse, what will be the phenotypes of the F_1 and F_2?

b. What proportion of the black agouti F_2 will be of genotype $Aa\ BB\ Cc^h$?

c. What proportion of the Himalayan mice in the F_2 are expected to show brown pigment?

c. What proportion of all agoutis in the F_2 are expected to show black pigment?

Answer:

a. The cross is $aa\ BB\ CC \times AA\ bb\ c^h c^h$. Since the parents are true breeding at each of three different loci, the F_1 must be a trihybrid, or $Aa\ Bb\ Cc^h$. The F_1 will be agouti with black hairs and pigmented over the entire body. In the F_2, a branch diagram will identify eight possible phenotypic classes: agouti, black, full pigmentation ($A-B-\ C-$); non-agouti, black, full ($aa\ B-\ C-$); agouti, brown, full ($A-$

bb C–); non-agouti, brown, full (*aa bb C–*); agouti, black, Himalayan (*A– B– c^h c^h*); non-agouti, black, Himalayan (*aa B– c^h c^h*); agouti, brown, Himalayan (*A– bb c^h c^h*); and non-agouti, brown, Himalayan (*aa bb c^h c^h*).

b. F_2 animals that are black and agouti (and either Himalayan or have full-body pigmentation) have the genotypes *A– B– C–* and *A– B– c^h c^h*. Among the *A–* animals, 2/3 are *Aa*. Among the *B–* animals, 1/3 are *BB*. Among the *C–* and *c^h c^h* animals, 1/2 are *Cc^h*. Thus, among all of the black, agouti F_2, $2/3 \times 1/3 \times 1/2 = 1/9$ are *Aa BB Cc^h*. If one limits the animals under consideration to those that are black, agouti, *and not Himalayan* (i.e., *A– B– C–*), then 2/3 of the *C–* animals are *Cc^h*, and the proportion of *Aa BB Cc^h* animals is $2/3 \times 1/3 \times 2/3 = 4/27$.

c. From the cross *Aa Bb Cc^h × Aa Bb Cc^h*, 1/4 of the progeny will be *bb* and show brown pigment. This will be the case regardless of whether the animals are pigmented over their entire body or are Himalayan. Thus, 1/4 of the Himalayan mice will show brown pigment. [Be careful not to misread this question: It does *not* ask what proportion of the progeny are both brown *and* Himalayan.]

d. From the cross *Aa Bb Cc^h × Aa Bb Cc^h*, 3/4 of the progeny will be *B–* and show black pigment. This will be the case regardless of whether the animals are agouti or non-agouti. Thus, 3/4 of the agouti mice will show black pigment. [Be careful not to misread this question: It does *not* ask what proportion of the progeny are both black *and* agouti.]

10.21   In cocker spaniels, solid coat color is dominant over spotted coat. Suppose a true-breeding, solid-colored dog is crossed with a spotted dog, and the F_1 dogs are interbred.

a. What is the probability that the first puppy born will have a spotted coat?

b. What is the probability that if four puppies are born, all of them will have solid coats?

Answer: First, assign symbols to the alleles, and write down the cross. Let solid color be *S* and spotted be *s*. Then, if a true-breeding, solid-colored dog is bred to a spotted dog, the cross is *SS × ss*, the F_1 all *Ss* and interbreeding the F_1 will give 3/4 *S–* (solid) and 1/4 *ss* (spotted) progeny.

a. The chance that the first puppy born is spotted is just the chance of getting an *ss* offspring from an *Ss × Ss* cross, or 1/4.

b. The chance of getting four puppies all having solid coats is the chance of getting an *S–* offspring the first time, *and* the second time, *and* the third time, *and* the fourth time. Apply the product rule to get $p = 3/4 \times 3/4 \times 3/4 \times 3/4 = 81/256$.

10.22   In the F_2 of his cross of red-flowered × white-flowered *Pisum* (pea plant), Mendel obtained 705 plants with red flowers and 224 with white.

a. Is this result consistent with his hypothesis of factor segregation, from which a 3:1 ratio would be predicted?

b. In how many similar experiments would a deviation as great as or greater than this one be expected? (Calculate χ^2 and obtain the approximate value of P from Table 10.5.)

Answer:

a. It is important to *think through* this problem, and not just plug numbers into a chi-square formula. Here, we want to test the hypothesis of factor segregation. The hypothesis states that each allele in a monohybrid will segregate into gametes independently, so that zygotes have a half-chance of obtaining either allele from a heterozygous parent. Drawing a Punnett square shows that a 3:1 ratio of progeny phenotypes would be expected from an $F_1 \times F_1$ cross. Mendel observed 705 red and 224 white plants in the F_2, a ratio of 3.14:1. Thus, this ratio seems consistent with his hypothesis.

b. To test *how* significant this result is, use the χ^2 test to determine how frequently these types of numbers would be obtained in similar experiments.

CLASS	OBSERVED	EXPECTED	d	d^2	d^2/e
red	705	697	8	64	0.09
white	224	232	-8	64	0.28
Total	929	929	0	–	$\chi^2 = 0.37$

$\chi^2 = 0.37$; df = 1; $0.50 < P < 0.70$

According to the χ^2 test, then, Mendel's result is consistent with this hypothesis. More specifically, in approximately 60 percent of similar experiments, one would expect a deviation (i.e., a value of χ^2) as great as or greater than this one. One therefore does not reject the hypothesis.

10.23 In tomatoes, cut leaf and potato leaf are alternative characters, with cut (C) dominant to potato (c). Purple stem and green stem are another pair of alternative characters, with purple (P) dominant to green (p). A true-breeding cut, green tomato plant is crossed with a true-breeding potato, purple plant, and the F_1 plants are allowed to interbreed. The 320 F_2 plants were phenotypically 189 cut, purple; 67 cut, green; 50 potato, purple; and 14 potato, green. Propose a hypothesis to explain the data, and use the chi-square test to test the hypothesis.

Answer: First, use the symbols defined in the problem to write the genotypes of the parents and expected offspring if the two loci assort independently. One has:

$$P: \quad CC\ pp \times cc\ PP$$
$$F_1 \times F_1: \quad Cc\ Pp \times Cc\ Pp$$
$$F_2: \quad 9\ C\text{--}\ P\text{--}:3\ C\text{--}\ pp:3\ cc\ P\text{--}:1\ cc\ pp$$
(9 cut, purple:3 cut, green:3 potato, purple:1 potato, green)

If the two loci assort independently then, one expects to see a 9:3:3:1 phenotypic ratio in the F_2. Therefore, test the hypothesis of independent assortment using the χ^2 test.

CLASS	OBSERVED	EXPECTED	d	d^2	d^2/e
cut, purple	189	180	9	81	0.45
cut, green	67	60	7	49	0.81
potato, purple	50	60	-10	100	1.66
potato, green	14	20	-6	36	1.80
Total	320	320	0	–	$\chi^2 = 4.72$

$\chi^2 = 4.72$; df = 3; $0.10 < P < 0.20$

Therefore, in experiments similar to this one, a deviation at least as great as that observed here would be seen about 20 percent of the time. Thus, the hypothesis of two independently assorting genes is accepted as being possible.

10.24   The simple case of two mating types (male and female) is by no means the only sexual system known. The ciliated protozoan *Paramecium bursaria* has a system of four mating types, controlled by two genes (*A* and *B*). Each gene has a dominant and a recessive allele.

The four mating types are expressed according to the following scheme:

GENOTYPE	MATING TYPE
AA BB	*A*
Aa BB	*A*
AA Bb	*A*
Aa Bb	*A*
AA bb	*D*
Aa bb	*D*
aa BB	*B*
aa Bb	*B*
aa bb	*C*

It is clear, therefore, that some of the mating types result from more than one possible genotype. We have four strains of known mating type —"*A*," "*B*," "*C*," and "*D*"— but unknown genotype. The following crosses were made with the indicated results:

	MATING TYPE OF PROGENY			
CROSS	*A*	*B*	*C*	*D*
"*A*" × "*B*"	24	21	14	18
"*A*" × "*C*"	56	76	55	41
"*A*" × "*D*"	44	11	19	33
"*B*" × "*C*"	0	40	38	0
"*B*" × "*D*"	6	8	14	10
"*C*" × "*D*"	0	0	45	45

Assign genotypes to "*A*," "*B*," "*C*," and "*D*."

Answer: First summarize what you know about the mating types:

$$A = A\!-\!B\!- \qquad B = aa\ B\!- \qquad C = aa\ bb \qquad D = A\!-\!bb$$

Then rewrite the table in terms of what is known.

	MATING TYPE OF PROGENY			
CROSS	*A*	*B*	*C*	*D*
	A– B–	*aa B–*	*aa bb*	*A– bb*
"*A*" × "*B*"	24	21	14	18
A– B– × aa B–				
"*A*" × "*C*"	56	76	55	41
A– B– × aa bb				
"*A*" × "*D*"	44	11	19	33
A– B– × A– bb				
"*B*" × "*C*"	0	40	38	0
aa B– × aa bb				
"*B*" × "*D*"	6	8	14	10
aa B– × A– bb				
"*C*" × "*D*"	0	0	45	45
aa bb × A– bb				

Notice that a cross involving mating type C is similar to a testcross, as C is *aa bb*. The progeny ratios in crosses involving "C" will therefore reflect the gametes from the non-"C" parent. In the cross of "B" × "C", both the parents are *aa*, and the 1 B:1 C (1 *aa B–*:1 *aa bb*) ratio in the progeny reflects the fact that "B" is *Bb*. Therefore, "B" is *aa Bb*. In the cross "C" × "D," both parents are *bb*, and the 1 C:1 D progeny ratio indicates that "D" is *Aa*. "D" is therefore *Aa bb*. To determine the genotype of "A," consider that the cross of "A" × "C" produces progeny of all four mating types. This would be expected only if "A" were *Aa Bb*.

10.25   In bees, males (drones) develop from unfertilized eggs and are haploid. Females (workers and queens) are diploid and come from fertilized eggs. *W* (black eyes) is dominant over *w* (white eyes). Workers of genotype *RR* or *Rr* use wax to seal crevices in the hive; *rr* workers use resin instead. A *Ww Rr* queen founds a colony after being fertilized by a black-eyed drone bearing the *r* allele.

a.   What will be the appearance and behavior of workers in the new hive, and what are their relative frequencies?

b.   Give the genotypes of male offspring, with relative frequencies.

c.   Fertilization normally takes place in the air during a nuptial flight, and any bee unable to fly would effectively be rendered sterile. Suppose a recessive mutation, *c*, occurs spontaneously in a sperm that fertilizes a normal egg and that the effect of the mutant gene is to cripple the wings of any adult not bearing the normal allele *C*. The fertilized egg develops into a normal queen named Madonna. What is the probability that wingless males will be *found in a hive* founded two generations later by one of Madonna's granddaughters?

d.   By one of Madonna's great-great-granddaughters?

Answer: The initial cross is *Ww Rr* × *W r*. Note that since males are haploid, they have only one set of chromosomes. As a consequence, their gametes are only of one kind (e.g., the *W r* male will have only *W r* gametes) and their phenotype can be used to directly infer their genotype.

a. The progeny females will be 1/2 *W– Rr* (black-eyed, wax sealers) and 1/2 *W– rr* (black-eyed, resin sealers).

b. As males arise from unfertilized eggs, they receive chromosomes only from their mother. The progeny males will be 1/4 *W R* (black-eyed, wax sealers), 1/4 *W r* (black-eyed, resin sealers), 1/4 *w r* (white-eyed, resin sealers) and 1/4 *w R* (white-eyed, wax sealers).

c. The egg fertilized by the mutation-bearing sperm results in a *Cc* female. Since fertilization occurs in flight, only males that are *C* contribute genes to the next generation. Hence the first generation arises from the cross *Cc* × *C*. There is a 1/2 chance of obtaining daughters that are *Cc*. Such a daughter can only be fertilized by a *C* male, so that the chance of her having a *Cc* daughter is also 1/2. The chance of having a *Cc* granddaughter is thus 1/2 × 1/2 = 1/4. Such granddaughters will have wingless males if they are prolific. Thus, the probability that wingless males will be found in a hive founded two generations later by one of Madonna's granddaughters is the probability that the granddaughter is *Cc*, or 1/4.

d. (1/2)⁴ = 1/16.

10.26   Consider the following pedigree, in which the allele responsible for the trait (*a*) is recessive to the normal allele (*A*).

a. What is the genotype of the mother?

b. What is the genotype of the father?

c. What are the genotypes of the children?

d. Given the mechanism of inheritance involved, does the ratio of children with the trait to children without the trait match what would be expected?

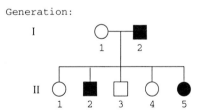

Answer:

a. If the allele responsible for the trait is recessive to the normal allele, then to have affected offspring in generation II, the mother (individual I-1) must be heterozygous (i.e., be *Aa*). If she were homozygous for the normal allele (i.e., *AA*), all the offspring would be *A*–, and be normal. If she were heterozygous, the cross in the first generation would be *Aa* × *aa*, and one would expect about 50 percent affected and 50 percent normal offspring. This is close to what is observed, and so the mother is *Aa*.

b. As the father is affected with a recessive trait, he must be *aa*.

c. Since the father is homozygous for the recessive allele, all the children must have inherited an abnormal allele from their father. If they inherited a normal, dominant allele from their mother, they will not be affected (*Aa*: II-1, II-3, II-4), while if they inherited the abnormal, recessive allele from their mother, they will be affected (*aa*: II-2, II-5).

d. Given that the parents are *Aa* × *aa*, one expects a 1:1 ratio of affected to unaffected children. For the five offspring shown, one sees a ratio of 2:3, which, given the number of offspring, approximates a 1:1 ratio. Remember that each birth is independent of the others, and while, if many progeny are seen, one should see about a 1:1 ratio, for small numbers of progeny, the ratios may be significantly off from what is expected. Indeed, even if the couple were to have more unaffected children, the pedigree would still be consistent with the inheritance of a recessive trait. (Can you show that if the pedigree is taken on its own, *without any information about whether the trait is dominant or recessive*, the pedigree is also consistent with the inheritance of a dominant trait?)

10.27   For the following pedigrees A and B, indicate whether the trait involved in each case could be recessive or dominant. Explain your answer.

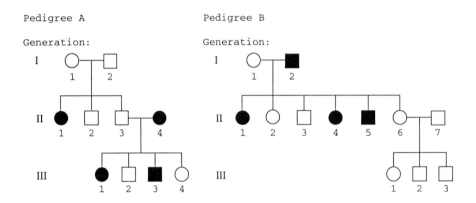

Answer: For pedigree A, parents not showing the trait in generation I have a daughter that exhibits the trait. This is typical of a cross of two heterozygotes giving a homozygous recessive, affected individual: *Aa* × *Aa* (two normal parents) give 3 *A*– (normal):1 *aa* (affected). If this were the case, individuals II-2 and II-3 could be carriers (i.e., be *Aa*). If individual II-3 is a carrier and his spouse is homozygous recessive (*aa*), generation III would arise from the cross *Aa* × *aa*, and the 1:1 ratio of affected to unaffected individuals seen would be expected. Thus, pedigree A is consistent with the trait being recessive.

In pedigree B, the trait is present in half of the individuals in generations I and II, but in none of those of generation III. However, the parents of generation III do not themselves exhibit the trait. This is consistent with the trait being dominant. With this view, individual I-1 would be *aa* and individual I-2 would be *Aa*. Half of their progeny would be expected to show the trait, as is observed. Furthermore, unaffected parents should have unaffected offspring, as is seen in generation III. Notice however, that the pedigree is also consistent with a recessive trait that is not rare. In this case, individual I-1 would be heterozygous, and the cross in generation I would be $Aa \times aa$, giving the 50 percent affected progeny seen in generation II. Although individual II-6 would have to be Aa, if her spouse was AA, all the children would be normal.

10.28   After a few years of marriage, a woman comes to believe that among all of the reasonable relatives in her and her husband's families, her husband, her mother-in-law, and her father have so many similarities in their unreasonableness that they must share a mutation. A friend taking a course in genetics assures her that it is unlikely that this trait has a genetic basis and that even if it did, all of her children would be reasonable. Diagram and analyze the relevant pedigree to evaluate whether this advice is accurate.

Answer: First draw the pedigree. Then try to fit the "unreasonableness" trait to a dominant ($A-$ = affected, aa = unaffected) or recessive character ($A-$ = unaffected, aa = affected), as shown below:

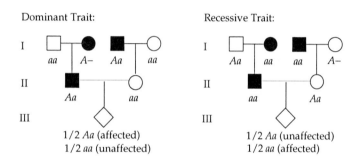

In the diagrams above, the woman is II-2, her husband is II-1, her father is I-3, and her mother-in-law is I-2. If the trait indeed has a genetic basis, it could be modeled as either a dominant or a recessive trait. Notice that one can infer whether an $A-$ individual is AA or Aa based on the offspring that are produced. Independent of whether the trait is dominant or recessive, in this particular situation one expects about half of the woman's children to be "unreasonable."

10.29   Gaucher's disease is caused by a chronic enzyme deficiency that is more common among Ashkenazi Jews than in the general population. A Jewish man has a sister afflicted with the disease. His parents, grandparents, and three siblings are not affected. Discussions with relatives in his wife's family reveal that the disease is not likely to be present in his wife's family, although some relatives recall that the brother of his wife's paternal grandmother suffered from a very similar disease. Diagram and analyze the relevant pedigree to determine (a) the genetic basis for inheriting this trait and (b) the highest probability that if this couple has a child, the child will be affected (i.e., what is the chance of the worst case scenario occurring?).

Answer: An uncertainty exists as to whether the brother of the man's wife's paternal grandmother had Gaucher's disease. If this distant relative had the disease, a disease allele might have been passed on to the man's wife. Therefore, in a "worst case scenario," consider this distant relative to have had the disease. Under this scenario, the pedigree is as shown below:

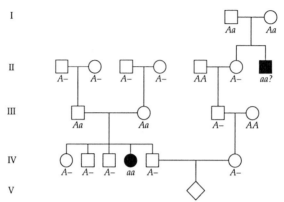

In this pedigree, the man is IV-5, his affected sister is IV-4, his wife is IV-6, and the brother of his wife's paternal grandmother is II-7. Since II-7 is affected but his parents are not, the disease must be a recessive trait and each of his parents must be heterozygous.

To calculate the chance that, if the couple has a child, the child will be affected, one needs to calculate the probability that V-1 can receive an *a* allele from each of its parents. For each parent, this is 1/2 the chance a parent is *Aa*.

Since we know the parents of IV-5 must be *Aa*, and IV-5 is *A–*, there is a 2/3 chance that IV-5 is *Aa*. Thus, there is a $1/2 \times 2/3 = 1/3$ chance that IV-5 will pass the *a* allele to V-1.

The probability that IV-6 is *Aa* is more complex, and is:

  Prob(III-3 was *Aa* <u>and</u> III-3 passed the *a* allele on to IV-6)

  = Prob[(II-6 was *Aa* <u>and</u> II-6 passed *a* to III-3) <u>and</u> III-3 passed *a* to IV-6)]

  = $[(2/3 \times 1/2) \times 1/2] = 1/6$.

Thus, there is a $1/6 \times 1/2 = 1/12$ chance that IV-6 will pass the *a* allele to V-1. In this worst case scenario, the chance that both parents will pass on an *a* allele and have an affected child is $1/12 \times 1/3 = 1/36$.

If the brother of the wife's paternal grandmother did not have the disease, IV-6 would be *AA* and the child would be *A–* and phenotypically normal.

The following four questions include material covered in Chapter 4.

10.30 a^+, b^+, c^+, and d^+ are independently assorting Mendelian genes controlling the production of a black pigment. The alternate alleles that give abnormal functioning of these genes are *a*, *b*, *c*, and *d*. A black individual of genotype $a^+/a^+\ b^+/b^+\ c^+/c^+\ d^+/d^+$ is crossed with a colorless individual of genotype $a/a\ b/b\ c/c\ d/d$ to produce a black F_1. $F_1 \times F_1$ crosses are then done. Assume that a^+, b^+, c^+, and d^+ act in a pathway as follows:

colorless $\xrightarrow{a^+}$ colorless $\xrightarrow{b^+}$ colorless $\xrightarrow{c^+}$ brown $\xrightarrow{d^+}$ black

a. What proportion of the F$_2$ are colorless?

b. What proportion of the F$_2$ are brown?

Answer: The F$_1$ cross is $a^+/a \; b^+/b \; c^+/c \; d^+/d \times a^+/a \; b^+/b \; c^+/c \; d^+/d$.

a. A colorless F$_2$ individual would result if an individual has an a/a, b/b, and/or c/c genotype. This would consist of many possible genotypes. Rather than identify all of these combinations, it is possible to use the fact that [the proportion of colorless individuals] = 1 - [the proportion of pigmented individuals]. The proportion of pigmented individuals ($a^+/- b^+/- c^+/-$) is 3/4 x 3/44 × 3/4 = 27/64. The chance of not obtaining this genotype is 1 - 27/64 = 37/64.

b. A brown individual is $a^+/- b^+/- c^+/- d/d$. The proportion of brown individuals is 3/4 × 3/4 × 3/4 × 1/4 = 27/256.

10.31   Using the genetic information given in Problem 10.30, now assume that a^+, b^+, and c^+ act in a pathway as follows:

Black can be produced only if both red pigments are present; that is, c^+ converts the two red pigments together into a black pigment.

a. What proportion of the F$_2$ are colorless?

b. What proportion of the F$_2$ are red?

c. What proportion of the F$_2$ are black?

Answer:

a. Colorless individuals are $a/a \; b/b \; -/-$. The chance of obtaining such an individual from a cross of $a^+/a \; b^+/b \; c^+/c \times a^+/a \; b^+/b \; c^+/c$ is 1/4 × 1/4 = 1/16.

b. There are two ways to determine the proportion of red individuals. First, notice that red individuals are obtained either when only one of the a^+ or b^+ functions is present (no matter what genotype is at c), or when both a^+ and b^+ functions are present but c^+ is not. Thus, these phenotypes are obtained from the following genotypes: $a^+/- b/b \; -/-$, $a/a \; b^+/- -/-$, or $a^+/- b^+/- c/c$. The probability of obtaining one of these genotypes is

$$(3/4 \times 1/4 \times 1) + (1/4 \times 3/4 \times 1) + (3/4 \times 3/4 \times 1/4) = 33/64.$$

A second way is to use the information from parts a and c. From part c, one has that 27/64 individuals are black, so the remaining 37/64 are either red or colorless. From part a, 1/16 = 4/64 are colorless. Thus there are (37 - 4)/64 = 33/64 that are red.

c. Black individuals are formed only if both red pigments are available and are then converted to black pigment. Thus, an individual must be $a^+/- b^+/- c^+/-$. The chance of obtaining such an individual is $3/4 \times 3/4 \times 3/4 = 27/64$.

10.32 Three genes on different chromosomes are responsible for three enzymes that catalyze the same reaction in corn:

$$\text{colorless compound} \xrightarrow{a^+, b^+, c^+} \text{red compound}$$

The normal functioning of any one of these genes is sufficient to convert the colorless compound to the red compound. The abnormal functioning of these genes is designated by a, b, and c, respectively.

a. A red $a^+/a^+ b^+/b^+ c^+/c^+$ is crossed to a colorless $a/a\, b/b\, c/c$ to give a red F_1, $a^+/a\, b^+/b\, c^+/c$. The F_1 is selfed. What proportion of the F_2 are colorless?

b. It turns out that another step is involved in the pathway. It is controlled by gene d^+, which assorts independently of a^+, b^+, and c^+:

$$\text{colorless compound 1} \xrightarrow{d^+} \text{colorless compound 2} \xrightarrow{a^+, b^+, c^+} \text{red compound}$$

The inability to convert colorless 1 to colorless 2 is designated d. A red $a^+/a^+ b^+/b^+ c^+/c^+ d^+/d^+$ is crossed to a colorless $a/a\, b/b\, c/c\, d/d$. The F_1 are all red. The red F_1's are now selfed. What proportion of the F_2 are colorless?

Answer:

a. Since any of the normal alleles a^+, b^+, or c^+ is sufficient to catalyze the reaction leading to color, in order for color to fail to develop, all three normal alleles must be missing. That is, the colorless F_2 must be $a/a\, b/b\, c/c$. The chance of obtaining such an individual is $1/4 \times 1/4 \times 1/4 = 1/64$.

b. Now, colorless F_2 are obtained if *either* one or both steps of the pathway are blocked. That is, colorless F_2 are obtained in either of the following genotypes: $d/d\, -/-\, -/-\, -/-$ (the first or both steps blocked) or $d^+/-\, a/a\, b/b\, c/c$ (second step blocked). The chance of obtaining such individuals is

$$(1/4 \times 1 \times 1 \times 1) + (3/4 \times 1/4 \times 1/4 \times 1/4) = (64 + 3)/256 = 67/256.$$

10.33 In J. R. R. Tolkien's *The Lord of the Rings*, the Black Riders of Mordor ride steeds with eyes of fire. As a geneticist, you are very interested in the inheritance of the fire-red eye color. You discover that the eyes contain two types of pigments, brown and red, that are usually bound to core granules in the eye. In wild-type steeds, precursors are converted by these granules to the above pigments, but in steeds homozygous for the recessive X-linked gene w (white eye), the granules remain unconverted and a white eye results. The metabolic pathways for the synthesis of the two pigments are shown in figure. Each step of the pathway is controlled by a gene: Mutation v results in vermilion eyes, cn results in cinnabar eyes, st results in scarlet eyes, bw results in brown eyes, and se results in black eyes. All these mutations are recessive to their wild-type alleles, and all are unlinked. For the following genotypes, show the proportion of steed eye phenotypes that would be obtained in the F_1 of the given matings.

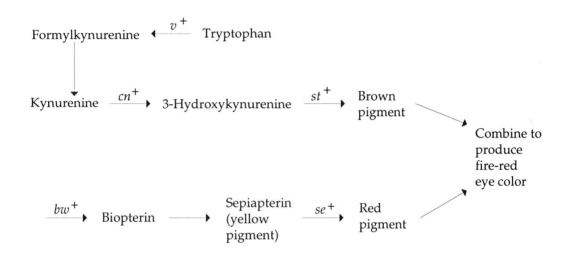

a. $ww\ bw^+bw^+\ stst\ \times\ w^+Y\ bwbw\ st^+st^+$

b. $w^+w^+\ sese\ bwbw\ \times\ wY\ se^+se^+\ bw^+bw^+$

c. $w^+w^+\ v^+v^+\ bwbw\ \times wY\ vv\ bwbw$

d. $w^+w^+\ bw^+bw\ st^+st\ \times\ wY\ bwbw\ stst$

Answer: In this problem, XX individuals are female, and XY individuals are male. As will be seen in the next chapter, genes that show X-linked inheritance show several features that are different than genes that show autosomal inheritance. One of the mother's two Xs is given to each of her gametes, and so she produces X-bearing eggs. The father has an X and Y, so he produces X-bearing and Y-bearing sperm. If a sperm with an X fertilizes an egg, an XX, or female individual is produced. On the other hand, if a sperm with a Y fertilizes an egg, an XY, or male individual is produced. Consequently, sons receive their X only from their mother, while daughters receive an X from each of their mother and father.

a. Since males get a w from their mother (and a Y from their father), they will be wY (white). Females get a w^+ from their father and a w from their mother, so they will be ww^+. The progeny will be 1/2 $ww^+\ bwbw^+\ stst^+$, fire-red-eyed daughters and 1/2 $w/Y\ bwbw^+\ stst^+$, white-eyed sons.

b. $ww^+\ sese^+\ bwbw^+$ and $w^+Y\ sese^+\ bwbw^+$, all fire-red eyes.

    c. $ww^+\ vv^+\ bwbw$ and $w^+Y\ vv^+\ bwbw$, all brown eyes.

    d. $1/4\ w^+w$ or w^+Y, $bwbw^+\ stst^+$, fire-red eyes;

        $1/4\ w^+w$ or w^+Y, $bwbw\ stst^+$, brown eyes;

        $1/4\ w^+w$ or w^+Y, $bwbw^+\ stst$, scarlet eyes;

        $1/4\ w^+w$ or w^+Y, $bwbw\ stst$ (the color of 3-hydroxykynurenine plus the color of the precursor to biopterin, or colorless = white).

11

CHROMOSOMAL BASIS OF INHERITANCE, SEX LINKAGE, AND SEX DETERMINATION

CHAPTER OUTLINE

CHROMOSOME THEORY OF INHERITANCE
Sex Chromosomes

Sex Linkage

Nondisjunction of X Chromosomes

SEX DETERMINATION
Genotypic Sex Determination Systems

Environmental Sex Determination Systems

ANALYSIS OF SEX-LINKED TRAITS IN HUMANS
X-Linked Recessive Inheritance

X-Linked Dominant Inheritance

Y-Linked Inheritance

REVIEW OF KEY TERMS, SYMBOLS, AND CONCEPTS

In your own words, write a brief, precise definition of each term in the groups below. Check your definitions using the text. Then, develop a concept map using the terms in each list.

1	2	3
chromosome theory	genotypic sex determination	wild type
sex chromosome	environmental sex determination	mutant allele
X chromosome	Y chromosome sex determination	Mendelian symbolism
Y chromosome	X chromosome-autosome balance	*Drosophila* symbolism
homogametic sex	system	$A, a, AA, Aa, aa, aY, XaY$
heterogametic sex	disjunction, nondisjunction	a^+, a, Xa^+Y, XaY
sex-linkage	segregation, chromosome pairing	
X-linkage	primary nondisjunction	
hemizygous	secondary nondisjunction	
homozygous	X chromosome nondisjunction	
crisscross inheritance	aneuploidy	
reciprocal cross	karyotype	
X-linked recessive trait	Turner, Klinefelter, XYY syndromes	

1	2	3
X-linked dominant trait	dosage compensation	
Y-linked trait	Barr body	
holandric trait	Lyon hypothesis, lyonization	
	X-inactivation center	
	XIC, Xic, XIST, Xist	
	testis-determining factor gene	
	sex-reversal individual	
	Sex-determining region Y (*SRY*)	
	SRY, Sry genes	
	transgene, transgenic organism	
	hermaphroditic	
	monoecious, dioecious	
	mating type	

THINKING ANALYTICALLY

The problems on mendelian genetics in this chapter are more complicated than those in Chapter 10, and present more of a challenge to your analytical reasoning skills. Review the "Thinking Analytically" hints in Chapter 10 of this guide, and approach the problems analytically and systematically. After you have arrived at a solution, always go back and test it against the data presented in the problem. Try to avoid falling into a trap: Don't look at the answer presented here before you have attempted to solve the problem independently. Being able to understand the answer in this guide is not equivalent to being able to solve the problem independently. You won't have the guide in an exam. By trying to solve problems independently, you will improve your analytical thinking. This will enable you to do better on an exam.

Take care to represent crosses accurately with appropriate symbols. While you can often use Mendelian or normal/abnormal notation (see Box 11.1) equally well, become fluent with both. Geneticists use each type of notation. As you symbolize traits in crosses, consistently use one type of notation, be careful to use a single type of symbol for each gene (e.g., g and g^+ or g and G for green and yellow seed color, not g and Y), and clearly distinguish between X-linked and autosomal traits, as these follow different inheritance patterns. For example, when assigning members of a pedigree symbols for genetic traits, use a notation that reflects whether inheritance is autosomal or X-linked. This will make it easier for you to spot patterns as well as infer expected types of offspring. Use X^aX^a for a female with an X-linked recessive trait, X^AY or $X^{a+}Y$ for a male with an X-linked dominant trait, X^aY for a male with a recessive trait, and Aa or a^+a for an individual with an autosomal trait.

The proof that genes lie on chromosomes came from relating abnormal patterns of trait inheritance of traits to abnormal patterns of chromosome inheritance. Understanding how chromosome behavior during meiosis relates to the segregation and independent assortment of traits in genetic crosses is therefore central to this material. Review the material in Chapter 1 on chromosome pairing and segregation during meiosis and relate it to how autosomal alleles in a heterozygote segregate during the formation of gametes. Then diagram what happens if the alleles are on an X chromosome and there is X-chromosome nondisjunction. Are the normal crisscross inheritance patterns altered? Are the results of testcrosses with the progeny altered?

QUESTIONS FOR PRACTICE

Multiple Choice Questions

1. The chromosome theory of inheritance holds that
   a. chromosomes are inherited.
   b. the chromosomes contain the hereditary material.
   c. the genes are inherited.
   d. the chromosomes are DNA.

2. Proof that genes lie on chromosomes was obtained by
   a. correlating aneuploids resulting from nondisjunction with inheritance patterns.
   b. showing that some genes appear to be sex-linked.
   c. showing that males have an X and a Y, while females have two X's.
   d. showing that in *Drosophila*, males are the heterogametic sex.

3. An individual that produces both ova and sperm
   a. has the XY genotype.
   b. reproduces asexually.
   c. is said to be hermaphroditic.
   d. both b and c, above.

4. What piece of evidence best indicates that two X-chromosomes are required for a normal human female, even though one of the X-chromosomes is inactivated into a Barr body?
   a. Turner females are usually infertile and have morphological abnormalities.
   b. XXY individuals show a Klinefelter syndrome.
   c. 47, XXX individuals are almost completely normal females.
   d. Lyonization occurs in 46, XX individuals.

5. The somatic cells of an individual having the karyotype 48, XXXY would have
   a. four Barr bodies.
   b. three Barr bodies.
   c. two Barr bodies.
   d. no Barr bodies.

6. Pedigrees showing X-linked recessive traits typically have
   a. only females being affected.
   b. all daughters of an affected father being affected.
   c. all sons of an unaffected mother being normal.
   d. the trait appearing more frequently in males.

7. In humans, what can be said about genes on a normal male's X chromosome?
   a. They are hemizygous.
   b. They are inactivated when the male's cells form Barr bodies.

   c. They are inherited as autosomal recessive traits.

   d. They are responsible for male sex-type.

8. During spermatogenesis in a male fly, there is X-chromosome nondisjunction during meiosis I. What types of sperm are produced?

   a. X- and Y-bearing sperm.

   b. XX- and YY-bearing sperm..

   c. XY- and no-sex-chromosome-bearing sperm..

   d. XX-, XY-, X- and Y-bearing sperm..

9. Which of the following is true about organisms where sex-type is determined by an X-chromosome-autosome balance system?

   a. Sex-type is determined by the number of X-chromosomes. Organisms with two X chromosomes are female, organisms with one X chromosome are male, regardless of the number of autosomes.

   b. Sex-type is determined by the ratio of X-chromosomes to autosomes. The Y chromosome plays no role in sex determination.

   c. A key gene called SRY on the Y chromosome determines sex-type.

   d. The number of autosomes determines sex type. Organisms with one set of autosomes are male, while organisms with two sets of autosomes are female.

10. What unusual feature is associated with the *Xist* gene?

   a. It is active on both X chromosomes of a normal female.

   b. It is inactive on both X chromosomes of a normal female.

   c. It is active only on the non-lyonized X chromosome of a normal female.

   d. It is active only on the lyonized X chromosome of a normal female.

11. Which of the following statements is <u>not true</u> about sex determination in mammals?

   a. It is equivalent to testis determination.

   b. In males, it results from the action of testis-determining factor.

   c. Sex reversal occurs when the SRY gene is present in males.

   d. The SRY gene is considered to encode the testis-determining factor.

    Answers: *1b; 2a; 3c; 4a; 5c; 6d; 7a; 8c; 9b; 10d; 11c.*

Thought Questions

1. What is meant by crisscross inheritance, and what clinical significance does it have in pedigree analysis?

2. Develop a flowchart illustrating the decision-making path you would employ to ascertain whether a pedigree showed autosomal dominant, autosomal recessive, X-linked dominant, X-linked recessive, or Y-linked inheritance.

3. Define the term lyonization, give an example of it, and discuss its functional significance.

4. Why do you think that most flowering plants are monoecious, whereas in most animals, the sexes are separate?

5. If all mammals have evolved from a common ancestor, how do you account for the variety of chromosome numbers that they possess? By what mechanism do you think

changes in chromosome number could have occurred? (Consider chromosome number variation resulting from nondisjunction and other accidental changes.)

6. Except for the loci involved with sex determination in mammalian males, there is little clear evidence for genetic loci on the Y chromosome. Why might this be the case and what might this tell you about the Y chromosome in mammals?

7. What are some of the different mechanisms by which sex type can be determined? Do you think it is significant that so many different mechanisms can be employed?

8. Even though X-inactivation occurs in XXY individuals, they do not have the same phenotype as XY males. Similarly, even though X inactivation occurs in XX individuals, they do not have the same phenotype as XO individuals. Why might this be the case?

9. How might structural and functional genomics provide additional insights into the answer to Thought Question 8?

10. An individual who phenotypically appears to have Klinefelter syndrome has a karyotype of XX, 46. An individual who phenotypically appears to have Turner syndrome has a karyotype of XY, 46. What common explanation might underlie each of these anomalies? [Hint: review the text material on sex reversal.]

Thought Questions for Media

After reviewing the media on the *iGenetics* CD-ROM, try to answer these questions.

1. After which division (Meiosis I or Meiosis II) are haploid cells produced? At which point are haploid gametes produced?

2. If nondisjunction occurs in Meiosis I, how many types of abnormal gametes are produced? Are any normal gametes produced?

3. If nondisjunction occurs in Meiosis II, how many types of abnormal gametes are produced? Are any normal gametes produced?

4. The animation illustrates how nondisjunction in either Meiosis I or Meiosis II can lead to the production of monosomic and trisomic zygotes. How might nondisjunction be involved in generating a nullosomic (none of one type of chromosome) or a tetrasomic (four copies of one kind of chromosome) zygote?

5. In one meiosis in an *Aa Bb* individual, four gametes are produced. How many different genotypes are produced?

6. Based on the animation and considering your answer to question 1, how can four equal frequencies of gametes (_ *Ab*, _ *AB*, _ *aB*, _ *ab*) be obtained?

7. At what point during Meiosis does the chromosome behavior that underlies independent assortment occur?

1. a. Why is it important to determine that none of the individuals that have married into Anna's or Jackson's families have a separate family history of deafness?

b. How would your analysis of the pedigree of Jackson's family change if you learned that individuals II-3, II-5, and III-4 have a history of deafness?

c. Since both congenital and progressive hearing loss are relatively uncommon traits, when a pedigree analysis is being performed, can you just assume that individuals marrying into the family have no family history of deafness? If not, how would you proceed?

2. What is the chance that, if Anna and Jackson have two boys and two girls, they will all have normal hearing?

3. Anna may or may not be a carrier for deafness. Suppose Anna and Jackson indeed have two boys and two girls with normal hearing. Can you conclude anything about whether Anna is a carrier for deafness? If so, what? If not, why not?

SOLUTIONS TO TEXT PROBLEMS

11.1 Depict each of the following crosses, first using Mendelian and then using *Drosophila* notation (Box 11.1, p. 288). Give the genotype and phenotype of the F_1 progeny that can be produced.

a. In humans, a mating between two individuals, each heterozygous for the recessive trait phenylketonuria, whose locus is on chromosome 12.

b. In humans, a mating between a female heterozygous for both phenylketonuria and X-linked color blindness and a male with normal color vision and heterozygous for phenylketonuria.

c. In *Drosophila*, a mating between a female with white eyes, curled wings, and normal long bristles and a male that has normal red eyes, normal straight wings, and short, stubble bristles. In these individuals, curled wings result from a heterozygous condition at a gene whose locus is on chromosome 2, whereas the short, stubble bristles result from a heterozygous condition at a gene whose locus is on chromosome 3.

d. In *Drosophila*, a mating between a female from a true-breeding line that has eyes of normal size that are white, black bodies (a recessive trait on chromosome 2), and tiny bristles (a recessive trait called *spineless* on chromosome 3) and a male from a true-breeding line that has normal red eyes, normal grey bodies, normal long bristles, and reduced eye size (a dominant trait called *eyeless* on chromosome 4).

Answer: The crosses and their progeny are tabulated below:

	MENDELIAN NOTATION	*DROSOPHILA* NOTATION LONG VERSION	*DROSOPHILA* NOTATION SHORT VERSION
a.			
Allele symbols:	P = normal	$p+$ = normal	+ = normal
	p = phenylketonuria	p = phenylketonuria	p = phenylketonuria
Cross:	$Pp \times Pp$	$p+p \times p+p$	×
F_1:	$1\,PP{:}2Pp{:}1pp$	$1\,p+p+{:}2\,p+p{:}1pp$	×
F_1 phenotypes:	3/4 normal	1/4 phenylketonuria	

b.			
Allele symbols:	C = normal	$c+$ = normal	+ = normal
	c = color blind	c = color blind	c = color blind
Cross:	$Cc\ Pp \times CY\ Pp$	$c+c\ p+p \times c+Y\ p+p$	$+c\ +p \times +Y\ +p$
F_1:	1/16 $CC\ PP$	1/16 $c+c+\ p+p+$	1/16 ++ ++
	1/8 $CC\ Pp$	1/8 $c+c+\ p+p$	1/8 ++ +p
	1/16 $CC\ pp$	1/16 $c+c+\ pp$	1/16 ++ pp
	1/16 $Cc\ PP$	1/16 $c+c\ p+p+$	1/16 +c ++
	1/8 $Cc\ Pp$	1/8 $c+c\ p+p$	1/8 +c +p
	1/16 $Cc\ pp$	1/16 $c+c\ pp$	1/16 +c pp
	1/16 $CY\ PP$	1/16 $c+Y\ p+p+$	1/16 +Y ++
	1/8 $CY\ Pp$	1/8 $c+Y\ p+p$	1/8 +Y +p
	1/16 $CY\ pp$	1/16 $c+Y\ pp$	1/16 +Y pp
	1/16 $cY\ PP$	1/16 $cY\ p+p+$	1/16 cY ++
	1/8 $cY\ Pp$	1/8 $cY\ p+p$	1/8 cY +p
	1/16 $cY\ pp$	1/16 $cY\ pp$	1/16 cY pp

F_1 phenotypes: 3/8 normal females   1/16 phenylketonuria males

1/8 phenylketonuria females 3/16 color-blind males

3/16 normal males   1/16 color-blind, phenylketonuria males

c.			
Allele symbols:	normal eyes = W	normal eyes = $w+$	normal eyes = +
	white eyes = w	white eyes = w	white eyes = w
	normal wings = c	normal wings = $C+$	normal wings = +
	curled wings = C	curled wings = C	curled wings = C
	normal bristles = s	normal bristles = $S+$	normal bristles = +
	stubble bristles = S	stubble bristles = S	stubble bristles = S

	MENDELIAN NOTATION	DROSOPHILA NOTATION LONG VERSION	DROSOPHILA NOTATION SHORT VERSION
Cross:	*ww Cc s s*	*ww CC+ S+S+*	*ww C+ ++*
	x	x	x
	WY *cc Ss*	*w+Y C+C+ SS+*	+Y ++ S+
F₁ genotypes:	1/8 *Ww Cc Ss*	1/8 *w+w CC+ SS+*	1/8 +*w* C+ S+
	1/8 *Ww Cc ss*	1/8 *w+w CC+ S+S+*	1/8 +*w* C+ ++
	1/8 *Ww cc Ss*	1/8 *w+w C+C+ SS+*	1/8 +*w* ++ S+
	1/8 *Ww cc s s*	1/8 *w+w C+C+ S+S+*	1/8 +*w* ++ ++
	1/8 *wY Cc Ss*	1/8 *wY CC+ SS+*	1/8 *wY* C+ S+
	1/8 *wY Cc ss*	1/8 *wY CC+ S+S+*	1/8 *wY* C+ ++
	1/8 *wY cc Ss*	1/8 *wY C+C+ SS+*	1/8 *wY* ++ S+
	1/8 *wY cc s s*	1/8 *wY C+C+S+S+*	1/8 *wY* ++ ++

F₁ phenotypes: 1/8 stubble, curled females   1/8 white, stubble, curled males
1/8 curled females   1/8 white, curled males
1/8 stubble females   1/8 white, stubble males
1/8 normal females   1/8 white males

d.

Allele symbols:	white eye = *w*	white eye = *w*	white eye = *w*
	red eye = *W*	red eye = *w+*	red eye = +
	black body = *b*	black body = *b*	black body = *b*
	grey body = *B*	grey body = *b+*	grey body = +
	normal bristles = *S*	normal bristles = *s+*	normal bristles = +
	tiny bristles = *s*	tiny bristles = *s*	tiny bristles = *s*
	normal size eye = *e*	normal size eye = *E+*	normal size eye = +
	reduced size eye = *E*	reduced size eye = *E*	reduced size eye = *E*
Cross:	*ww bb ss e e*	*ww bb ss E+E+*	*ww bb ss ++*
	x	x	x
	WY *BB SS EE*	*w+Y b+b+ s+s+ EE*	+Y ++ ++ *EE*
F₁ genotypes:	1/2 *Ww Bb Ss Ee*	1/2 *w+w b+b s+s EE+*	1/2 +*w* +*b* +*s* +*E*
	1/2 *wY Bb Ss Ee*	1/2 *wY b+b s+s EE+*	1/2 *wY* +*b* +*s* +*E*

F₁ phenotypes: 1/2 eyeless females   1/2 white, eyeless males

11.2   In *Drosophila*, white eyes are a sex-linked character. The mutant allele for white eyes (*w*) is recessive to the wild-type allele for brick-red eye color (*w+*). A white-eyed female is crossed with a red-eyed male. An F₁ female from this cross is mated with her father, and an F₁ male is mated with his mother. What will be the eye color of the offspring of these last two crosses?

Answer: The initial cross is *ww* ₓ *w+*Y, so that the F₁ females are *ww+* and the F₁ males are *w*Y. The second set of crosses are therefore *w+w* ₓ *w+*Y and *w*Y ₓ *ww*. The former will give all brick-red females (*w+–*) and half white (*w*Y) and half brick-red (*w+*Y) males. The latter will give only white eyed males and females (*w*Y and *ww*).

11.3   One form of color blindness (*c*) in humans is caused by a sex-linked recessive mutant gene. A woman with normal color vision (*c*+) and whose father was color-blind marries a man of normal vision whose father was also color-blind. What proportion of their offspring will be color-blind? (Give your answer separately for males and females.)

Answer: Since fathers always give their X chromosome to their daughters, the woman must be heterozygous for the color-blindness trait and is *c*+*c*. As her husband received his X chromosome from his mother and has normal color-vision, he is *c*+Y. The cross is therefore *c*+*c* $\times$ *c*+Y. All daughters will receive the paternal X bearing the *c*+ allele and have normal color-vision. As sons will receive the maternal X; half will be *c*Y and be color-blind and half will be *c*+Y and have normal color-vision.

11.4   In humans, red-green color blindness is recessive and X-linked, while albinism is recessive and autosomal. What types of children can be produced as the result of marriages between two homozygous parents: a normal-visioned albino woman and a color-blind, normally pigmented man?

Answer: Let *c* and *c*+ be the color-blind and normal vision alleles, respectively, and let *a* and *a*+ be the albino and normal pigmentation alleles, respectively. Then the cross can be represented as *c*+*c*+ *aa* $\times$ *c*Y *a*+*a*+. As all the offspring will be *a*+*a*, all will have normal pigmentation. The offspring will either be *c*+*c* or *c*+Y, and have normal color vision. The daughters will, however, be carriers for the color-blindness trait.

11.5   In *Drosophila*, vestigial (partially formed) wings (*vg*) are recessive to normal long wings (*vg*+), and the gene for this trait is autosomal. The gene for the white eye trait is on the X chromosome. Suppose a homozygous white-eyed, long-winged female fly is crossed with a homozygous red-eyed, vestigial-winged male.
a.   What will be the genotypes and phenotypes of the F_1?
b.   What will be the genotypes and phenotypes of the F_2?
c.   What will be the genotypes and phenotypes of the offspring of a cross of the F_1 back to each parent?

Answer:
a.   The initial cross is *ww vg*+*vg*+ $\times$ *w*+Y *vgvg*. The F_1 consists of *w*Y *vg*+*vg* (white, normal-winged) males and *ww*+ *vg*+*vg* (red, normal-winged) females.
b.   The F_2 would be produced by crossing *w*Y *vg*+*vg* males and *w*+*w vg*+*vg* females. In both the male and the female progeny, 1/8 will be white and vestigial, 1/8 will be red and vestigial, 3/8 will be white and normal-winged, and 3/8 will be red and normal-winged.

c. If the F_1 males are crossed back to the female parent, the cross is $wY\ vg\!+\!vg$ $\times$ $w\,w$ $vg\!+\!vg\!+$. All the progeny would be white and normal-winged. If the F_1 females are crossed back to the male parent, the cross is $w\,w\!+\ vg\!+\!vg$ $\times$ $w\!+\!Y\ vgvg$. Among the male progeny, there would be 1/4 white, vestigial; 1/4 red, vestigial; 1/4 white, normal-winged; and 1/4 red, normal-winged. Among the female progeny, half would be red and normal-winged and half would be red and vestigial.

11.6   In *Drosophila*, two red-eyed, long-winged flies are bred together and produce the offspring given in the following table:

	FEMALES	MALES
red-eyed, long-winged	3/4	3/8
red-eyed, vestigial-winged	1/4	1/8
white-eyed, long-winged	–	3/8
white-eyed, vestigial-winged	–	1/8

What are the genotypes of the parents?

Answer: From problem 11.5, we know that w is X-linked while vg is autosomal. This can also be determined by considering just one trait at a time, and examining the frequency of progeny phenotypes. The ratio of long-winged to vestigial-winged progeny is 3:1 (3/4 to 1/4) in both sexes, while the ratio of red-eyed to white-eyed progeny is all to none in females and 1:1 in males. This is consistent with vg being autosomal and w being X-linked. The 3:1 ratio of long-winged to vestigial-winged progeny indicates that each parent was heterozygous at the vg locus. Since both parents had red eyes, both had (at least) one $w\!+$ allele. Since half of the sons are white-eyed, the mother must have been heterozygous. Therefore, the parents were $w\!+\!w\ vg\!+\!vg$ $\times$ $w\!+\!Y\ vg\!+\!vg$.

11.7   In chickens, a dominant sex-linked gene (B) produces barred feathers, and the recessive allele (b), when homozygous, produces nonbarred (solid color) feathers. Suppose a nonbarred cock is crossed with a barred hen.
a. What will be the appearance of the F_1 birds?
b. If an F_1 female is mated with her father, what will be the appearance of the offspring?
c. If an F_1 male is mated with his mother, what will be the appearance of the offspring?

Answer:
a. In poultry sex type is determined by a ZZ (male) and ZW (female) system. The cross can be depicted as bb (nonbarred cock) $\times BW$ (barred hen). The F_1 progeny will be bW (nonbarred) hens and Bb (barred) cocks.

b. The cross can be represented as $bW \times bb$. All the progeny will be nonbarred.

c. The cross can be represented as $Bb \times BW$. The progeny will be 1/2 barred cocks ($1/4\,BB$, $1/4\,Bb$), 1/4 barred hens (BW) and 1/4 nonbarred hens (bW).

11.8   A man (A) suffering from defective tooth enamel, which results in brown-colored teeth, marries a normal woman. All their daughters have brown teeth, but the sons are normal. The sons of man A marry normal women, and all their children are normal. The daughters of man A marry normal men, and 50 percent of their children have brown teeth. Explain these facts.

Answer: Notice that the trait is transmitted from the father to his daughters, indicating criss-cross inheritance. This is typical of an X-linked trait. Since man A marries a normal woman and all of their daughters have the trait, the trait must be dominant. Man A's X chromosome bearing the defective tooth enamel allele was inherited by all of his daughters, and none of his sons. All of his daughters would therefore have defective tooth enamel, and be heterozygous for the defective enamel allele. These daughters would transmit the defective enamel allele 50 percent of the time, giving rise to 50 percent of their children being affected.

11.9   In humans, differences in the ability to taste phenylthiourea result from a pair of autosomal alleles. Inability to taste is recessive to ability to taste. A child who is a nontaster is born to a couple who can both taste the substance. What is the probability that their next child will be a taster?

Answer: Since the inability to taste the substance is recessive, the nontaster child must be homozygous for the recessive allele and each of his parents must have given the child a recessive allele. Since both parents can taste, they must also bear a dominant allele. Let T represent the dominant (taster) allele, and t represent the recessive (nontaster) allele (Note: Mendelian notation is used here for convenience, but also because there is no value in assigning a normal (+) and abnormal allele). Then the cross can be written as $Tt \times Tt$. The chance that their next child will be a taster is the chance that the child will be TT or Tt, or 3/4.

11.10   Cystic fibrosis is inherited as an autosomal recessive. Two parents without cystic fibrosis have two children with cystic fibrosis and three children without. The parents come to you for genetic counseling.

a. What is the numerical probability that their next child will have cystic fibrosis?

b. Their unaffected children are concerned about being heterozygous. What is the numerical probability that a given unaffected child in the family is heterozygous?

Answer:

a. Since the disease is autosomal recessive, and unaffected parents have affected offspring, both parents must be heterozygous. Let $c+$ represent the normal allele and *c* represent the disease allele. Then the parental cross can be represented as *c+c* × *c+c*, and there is a 1/4 chance that any conception will produce a *cc* (affected) child.

    b. If a child is not affected, the child is either *c+c+* (*p* = 1/3) or *c+c* (*p* = 2/3). Thus, there is a 2/3 chance that a non-affected child is heterozygous.

11.11   Huntington disease is a human disease inherited as a Mendelian autosomal dominant. The disease results in choreic (uncontrolled) movements, progressive mental deterioration, and eventually death. The disease affects the carriers of the trait any time between 15 and 65 years of age. The American folk singer Woody Guthrie died of Huntington disease, as did one of his parents. Marjorie Mazia, Woody's wife, had no history of this disease in her family. The Guthries have three children. What is the probability that a particular Guthrie child will die of Huntington disease?

Answer: Let *H* represent the disease allele, and let *h* represent the normal allele. Since we are told that one of Woody's parents died of the disease and are not told anything about the other parent, we may assume that only one parent had the disease allele. Thus, Woody must have been *Hh*. His children are the progeny of a cross that can be represented as *Hh* × *hh*. Each will have a 50 percent chance of receiving the *H* allele.

11.12   Suppose gene *A* is on the X chromosome, and genes *B*, *C*, and *D* are on three different autosomes. Thus *A*– signifies the dominant phenotype in the male or female. An equivalent situation holds for *B*–, *C*–, and *D*–. The cross *AA BB CC DD* females × *a*Y *bb cc dd* males is made.

    a. What is the probability of obtaining an *A*– individual in the F_1?

    b. What is the probability of obtaining an *a* male in the F_1?

    c. What is the probability of obtaining an *A*– *B*– *C*– *D*– female in the F_1?

    d. How many different F_1 genotypes will there be?

    e. What proportion of F_2s will be heterozygous for the four genes?

    f. Determine the probabilities of obtaining each of the following types in the F_2: (1) *A*– *bb CC dd* (female); (2) *a*Y *BB Cc Dd* (male), (3) *A*Y *bb CC dd* (male), (4) and *aa bb Cc Dd* (female).

Answer:

    a. Since only a single trait is being followed, consider just part of the cross: *AA* × *a*Y. The progeny will either be *A*Y or *Aa*, and all are *A*–. Thus, the chance of obtaining an *A*– individual in the F_1 is 1.

    b. As shown in (a), there is no chance (*p* = 0) of obtaining an *a*Y individual in the F_1.

    c. The F_1 progeny will be *A*– *Bb Cc Dd*. Half will be female, so *p* = 1/2.

    d. Two, *Aa Bb Cc Dd* (females) and *A*Y *Bb Cc Dd* males.

e. For the X chromosome trait, the F_1 cross is $AY \times Aa$. Half of the female offspring (1/4 of the total) will be heterozygous Aa individuals. For each of the autosomal traits, 1/2 of the offspring will be heterozygous (e.g., $Bb \times Bb$ gives 1/2 Bb individuals). Thus, the chance that an F_2 individual will be heterozygous at all four traits is $1/4 \times 1/2 \times 1/2 \times 1/2 = 1/32$.

f. Before determining the probabilities, consider that at any autosomal gene, there is a 1/4 chance of obtaining either type of homozygote (e.g., BB, bb) and a 1/2 chance of obtaining a heterozygote. At the A gene, the cross is $AY \times Aa$, and so there is a 1/4 chance of obtaining an AY male, a 1/4 chance of obtaining an aY male, a 1/4 chance of obtaining an Aa female and a 1/4 chance of obtaining an AA female (there will be a 1/2 chance of obtaining an $A-$ female). Then the chance of obtaining (1) an $A-$ bb CC dd (female) is $p = (1/2 \times 1/4 \times 1/4 \times 1/4) = 1/128$; (2) an aY BB Cc Dd (male) is $p = (1/4 \times 1/4 \times 1/2 \times 1/2) = 1/64$; (3) an AY bb CC dd (male) is $p = (1/4 \times 1/4 \times 1/4 \times 1/4) = 1/256$; and (4) an aa bb Cc Dd (female) is $p = (0 \times 1/4 \times 1/2 \times 1/2) = 0$.

11.13 As a famous mad scientist, you have cleverly devised a method to isolate *Drosophila* ova that have undergone primary nondisjunction of the sex chromosomes. In one experiment you used females homozygous for the sex-linked recessive mutation causing white eyes (w) as your source of nondisjunction ova. The ova were collected and fertilized with sperm from red-eyed males. The progeny of this "engineered" cross were then backcrossed separately to the two parental strains. What classes of progeny (genotype and phenotype) would you expect to result from these backcrosses? (The genotype of the original parents may be denoted as ww for the females and $w+/Y$ for the males.)

Answer: First consider what kinds of animals will be produced in the "engineered" cross. Primary nondisjunction of sex chromosomes in the meiosis of a female will result in eggs that have either zero or two X chromosomes. Thus, the eggs will either lack the w allele or be ww. Sperm from a red-eyed male will either bear a Y chromosome or bear the $w+$ allele. Upon fertilization then, four classes of embryos will be obtained: Y-only, $w+O$, wwY and $w+ww$. Animals with either zero or three X chromosomes are inviable, and so only $w+$ (red, XO males) and wwY (white, XXY females) animals will be obtained.

Now consider the backcrosses. The "engineered" red males will be sterile, as they lack a Y chromosome needed for male fertility. Hence, the only backcross that will give progeny is the mating between the wwY females and the $w+Y$ males. The sex chromosome constitution of the female's gametes is dependent on the pairing and disjunction of the two X chromosomes and the Y chromosome during meiosis. If there is normal pairing and disjunction of the two X chromosomes and the Y chromosome assorts independently of them, XY (wY) and X (w) eggs will be produced. If, as described in the text, less frequent secondary nondisjunction occurs, XX-bearing (ww) and Y-bearing eggs will be produced. The zygotes produced when these eggs are fertilized by sperm from a w+Y male, are shown in the following Punnett square:

		Gametes of wwY Female			
		Normal Disjunction		Secondary Nondisjunction	
		wY	w	$w\,w$	Y
Gametes of w+Y Male	w+	w+wY (XXY) red female	w+w (XX) red female	w+$w\,w$ (XXX) inviable	w+Y (XY) red male
	Y	wYY (XYY) white male	wY (XY) white male	wwY (XXY) white female	YY inviable

11.14   In *Drosophila*, the bobbed gene (bb+) is located on the X chromosome: bb mutants have shorter, thicker bristles than wild-type flies. Unlike most X-linked genes, however, the Y chromosome also carries a bobbed gene. The mutant allele bb is recessive to bb+. If a wild-type F_1 female that resulted from primary nondisjunction in oogenesis in a cross of bobbed female with a wild-type male is mated to a bobbed male, what will be the phenotypes and their frequencies in the offspring? List males and females separately in your answer. (Hint: Refer to the chapter for information about the frequency of nondisjunction in *Drosophila*, see p. 290.)

Answer: The cross that gave rise to the wild-type F_1 female can be denoted as XbbXbb x Xbb^+Ybb^+. Nondisjunction in meiosis of the XbbXbb female would produce an XbbXbb egg. Fertilization by a Ybb^+-bearing sperm would produce a bb+ (XbbXbbYbb^+) female. We want to know what progeny result when this female is mated to a bb (XbbYbb) male. Normal disjunction (which occurs about 96 percent of the time) in this female will produce XbbYbb^+ and Xbb-bearing eggs. If these eggs are fertilized by sperm from a bb male (i.e., either Xbb or Ybb), half bb+ (XbbXbbYbb^+ and XbbYbb^+Ybb) males and females and half bb (XbbXbb and XbbYbb) males and females will be produced. If secondary nondisjunction occurs (about 4 percent of the time), then XbbXbb and Ybb^+ eggs will be produced. When these eggs are fertilized by sperm from a bb male, the only viable progeny will be bb females (XbbXbbYbb) and bb+ males (XbbYbb^+). This is diagrammed as follows:

		Gametes of $X^{bb}X^{bb}Y^{bb^+}$ Female			
		Normal Disjunction–96%		Secondary Nondisjunction–4%	
		48% $X^{bb}Y^{bb+}$	48% X^{bb}	2% $X^{bb}X^{bb}$	2% Y^{bb^+}
Gametes of $X^{bb}Y^{bb}$ Male	50% X^{bb}	$X^{bb}X^{bb}Y^{bb^+}$ bb^+ female 24%	$X^{bb}X^{bb}$ bb female 24%	$X^{bb}X^{bb}X^{bb}$ inviable 1%	$X^{bb}Y^{bb^+}$ bb^+ male 1%
	50% Y^{bb}	$X^{bb}Y^{bb^+}Y^{bb}$ bb^+ male 24%	$X^{bb}Y^{bb}$ bb male 24%	$X^{bb}X^{bb}Y^{bb}$ bb female 1%	YY inviable 1%

Among the viable progeny there will be 24/98 = 24.5% normal females, 25/98 = 25.5% bobbed females, 25/98 = 25.5% normal males and 24/98 = 24.5% bobbed males.

11.15 A Turner syndrome individual would be expected to have how many Barr bodies in the majority of cells?

a. 0   c. 2
b. 1   d. 3

Answer: a. Turner syndrome individuals have only one X, as they are XO. Consequently, no X is inactivated.

11.16 An XXY Klinefelter syndrome individual would be expected to have how many Barr bodies in the majority of cells?

a. 0   c. 2
b. 1   d. 3

Answer: b. All but one X chromosome is inactivated. An XXY individual, having two X chromosomes, has one inactivated.

11.17 In human genetics, pedigrees are used to analyze inheritance patterns. Females are represented by a circle, and males by a square. The following figure presents three, 2-generation family pedigrees for a trait in humans. Normal individuals are represented by unshaded symbols and people with the trait by shaded symbols. For each pedigree (A, B, and C), state (by answering yes or no in the appropriate blank space) whether transmission of the trait can be accounted for on the basis of each of the listed simple modes of inheritance:

	PEDIGREE A	PEDIGREE B	PEDIGREE C
Autosomal recessive			
Autosomal dominant			
X-linked recessive			
X-linked dominant			

Answer: This problem raises the issue that the precise mode of inheritance of a trait often cannot be determined when a pedigree is small, and the frequency of the trait in a population is unknown. For example, Pedigree A could easily fit an autosomal dominant trait (*AA* and *Aa* = affected): the affected father would be heterozygous for the trait (*Aa*), the mother would be unaffected (*aa*), and half of their offspring would be affected. However, if the trait were autosomal recessive (i.e., *aa* = affected individuals), and the mother were heterozygous (*Aa*) and the father homozygous (*aa*), half of the offspring would still be affected. One could also fit the pedigree to an X-linked recessive trait: the mother would be heterozygous (X^AX^a), the father hemizygous (X^aY), and half of the progeny would be affected (either X^aX^a or X^aY). An X-linked dominant trait would not fit the pedigree, as it would require all the daughters of the affected father to be affected (as they all receive their father's X), and not allow a son to be affected (as he does not receive his father's X). Pedigrees B and C can be solved by similar analytical reasoning.

	PEDIGREE A	PEDIGREE B	PEDIGREE C
Autosomal recessive	Yes	Yes	Yes
Autosomal dominant	Yes	Yes	No
X-linked recessive	Yes	Yes	No
X-linked dominant	No	No	No

11.18 Shaded symbols in the following pedigree represent a trait. Which of the progeny eliminate X-linked recessiveness as a mode of inheritance for the trait?
a. I-1 and I-2
b. II-4
c. II-5
d. II-2 and II-4

Generation:

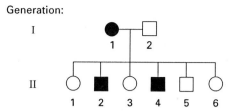

Answer: If the trait were X-linked recessive, then II-5 should be affected, as he would receive his mother's X chromosome. Therefore the correct answer is (c), II-5.

11.19   When constructing human pedigrees, geneticists often refer to particular individuals by a number. The generations are labeled by Roman numerals and the individuals in each generation by Arabic numerals. For example, in the pedigree in the following figure, the female with the asterisk is I-2. Use this means to designate specific individuals in the pedigree. Determine the probable inheritance mode for the trait shown in the affected individuals (the shaded symbols) by answering the following questions. Assume the condition is caused by a single gene.

Generation:

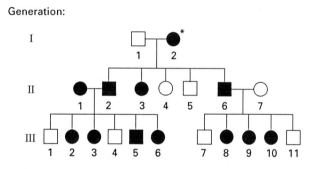

a.   Y-linked inheritance can be excluded at a glance. What two other mechanisms of inheritance can be definitely excluded? Why can these be excluded?

b.   Of the remaining mechanisms of inheritance, which is the most likely? Why?

Answer:

a.   Y-linked inheritance can be excluded because females are affected. X-linked recessive inheritance can also be excluded, as an affected mother (I-2) has a normal son (II-5). Autosomal recessive inheritance can also be excluded, as in such a case, two affected parents such as II-1 and II-2 could only have affected offspring, which they do not.

b.   The two remaining mechanisms of inheritance are X-linked dominant and autosomal dominant. Genotypes can be written to satisfy both mechanisms of inheritance. Of these two, X-linked dominant inheritance may be more likely, as II-6 and II-7 have only affected daughters, indicating criss-cross inheritance. If the trait were autosomal dominant, one would expect half of the daughters and half of the sons to be affected.

11.20   A three-generation pedigree for a particular human trait is shown in the following figure:

Generation:

a. What is the mechanism of inheritance for the trait?
b. Which persons in the pedigree are known to be heterozygous for the trait?
c. What is the probability that III-2 is a carrier (heterozygous)?
d. If III-3 and III-4 marry, what is the probability that their first child will have the trait?

Answer:

a. The trait must be recessive, as unaffected parents (I-1 and I-2, II-1 and II-2) have affected offspring. It also must be autosomal, as affected female daughters are born to unaffected fathers.

b. Given the answer to (a), individuals I-1 and I-2, as well as individuals II-1 and II-2 must be heterozygous. Also, individuals III-4 and III-5 must be heterozygous as they have an affected, homozygous mother.

c. One can denote the parents of III-2 as $Aa \times Aa$. We know individual III-2 is $A-$, so she is either AA ($p = 1/3$) or Aa ($p = 2/3$).

d. By the same reasoning as described in (c), individual III-3 has a 2/3 chance of being Aa. The chance that he will contribute an a allele to his offspring is thus $2/3 \times 1/2 = 1/3$. The chance that individual III-4 will contribute an a allele to her offspring is 1/2, as she is heterozygous. Thus, the chance that progeny of III-3 and III-4 will be affected is $1/3 \times 1/2 = 1/6$.

11.21   For each of the more complex pedigrees shown in Figure 11.B, determine the probable mechanism of inheritance: autosomal recessive, autosomal dominant, X-linked recessive, X-linked dominant, or Y-linked.

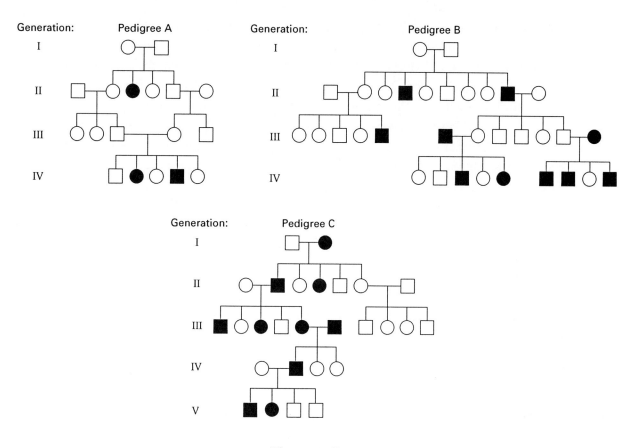

Figure 11.B

Answer: In complex pedigrees, an appropriate strategy is to ask initially whether the trait is Y-linked, then if it is dominant or recessive, and finally whether it is autosomal or X-linked. Proceeding logically through these choices helps limit the options. Before concluding, it is important to verify that the phenotype of every member of the pedigree fits the inferred inheritance pattern. Often, there may be only a single individual that can be used to distinguish one type of inheritance pattern from another.

Pedigree A: Clearly, the trait is not Y-linked, as males are not the sole transmitters of the trait. The most striking aspect of this pedigree is that the trait skips generations, i.e., unaffected parents have affected offspring. This indicates that the trait must be recessive. Now, one is left to determine if it is autosomal or X-linked. It does not fit an X-linked pedigree, as two affected females have normal (albeit heterozygous) fathers. For X-linked recessive pedigrees, both parents must contribute an abnormal allele, so that affected daughters must have affected fathers. The trait is therefore autosomal recessive. (Check by assigning appropriate genotypes to each pedigree member.)

Pedigree B: This pedigree also shows that the trait is not Y-linked, and must be recessive, as twice there are unaffected parents who have affected offspring. The preponderance of affected males suggests that it might be X-linked. To determine this for certain, try to assign genotypes to see if such an inheritance mode fits. It does. Could the trait be autosomal recessive? This would be a possibility if the trait were relatively common, as one would have to suppose that the individuals who married into the family in generation II were heterozygotes. This may be the case, as several homozygotes do marry into the family in generation III. What is the best guess then? X-linked recessive is the most likely, partly because of the frequency of affected males, but mostly because the homozygous female in generation III has three affected male offspring.

Pedigree C: The trait is expressed in every generation, making it a good candidate for a dominant trait. It is expressed equally by males and females, making it a good candidate for an autosomal trait. Indeed, it must be autosomal, for two reasons: First, individuals III-5 and III-6 have unaffected daughters, which would not be possible if the trait were X-linked and dominant, and second, individual IV-2, a male, has an affected male offspring, which would not be possible if the trait were X-linked. Thus, the trait is autosomal dominant.

In 11.22 through 11.24, select the correct answer.

11.22   If a genetic disease is inherited on the basis of an autosomal dominant gene, one would expect to find which of the following?
a.   Affected fathers have only affected children.
b.   Affected mothers never have affected sons.
c.   If both parents are affected, all of their offspring have the disease.
d.   If a child has the disease, one of his or her grandparents also had the disease.

Answer: Answer (a) is untrue because if the affected father was heterozygous, only half of his offspring should be affected. Answer (b) is untrue because, if the mother is heterozygous, half of her offspring, regardless of sex type, should be affected. Answer (c) is untrue as, if the parents are each heterozygous, 1/4 of their offspring should be homozygous recessive and normal. Answer (d) is the most likely. Note, however, that if the mutation was new in either the child or his/her parents, his/her grandparent could have been unaffected.

11.23   If a genetic disease is inherited as an autosomal recessive, one would expect to find which of the following?
a.   Two affected individuals never have an unaffected child.
b.   Two affected individuals have affected male offspring but no affected female children.
c.   If a child has the disease, one of his or her grandparents will have had it.
d.   In a marriage between an affected individual and an unaffected one, all the children are unaffected.

Answer: Answer (a) is true because two affected individuals will always have affected children (*a a* × *a a* can give only *a a* offspring). Answer (b) is untrue, as an autosomal trait is inherited independent of sex type. Answer (c) need not be true, as the trait could be masked by normal dominant alleles through many generations before two heterozygotes marry and produce affected, homozygous offspring. Answer (d) could also be true. If the trait is rare, then it is likely that an unaffected individual marrying into the pedigree is homozygous for a normal allele. Since the trait is recessive, and the children receive the dominant, normal allele from the unaffected parent, the children will be normal. Answer (d) would not be true if the unaffected individual was heterozygous. In this case, half of the children would be affected.

11.24   Which of the following statements is not true for a disease that is inherited as a rare X-linked dominant?
a. All daughters of an affected male will inherit the disease.
b. Sons will inherit the disease only if their mothers have the disease.
c. Both affected males and affected females will pass the trait to half the children.
d. Daughters will inherit the disease only if their father has the disease.

Answer: The only untrue statement is (d). Since daughters receive an X chromosome from each of their parents, they can inherit an X-linked dominant disease from either their mother or father.

11.25   Women who were known to be carriers of the X-linked, recessive, hemophilia gene were studied to determine the amount of time required for the blood clotting reaction. It was found that the time required for clotting was extremely variable from individual to individual. The values obtained ranged from normal clotting time at one extreme, to clinical hemophilia at the other extreme. What is the most probable explanation for these findings?

Answer: Since hemophilia is an X-linked trait, the most likely explanation is that random inactivation of X chromosomes (lyonization) produces individuals with different proportions of cells with a functioning allele. Normal clotting times would be expected in females with a functional $h+$ allele, i.e., females whose X^h chromosome was very frequently inactivated. Clinical hemophilia would be expected in females without a functional $h+$ allele, i.e., females whose X^{h+} chromosome was very frequently inactivated. Intermediate clotting times would be expected to be proportional to the amount of $h+$ function, which is related to the frequency of inactivation of the X^{h+} chromosome.

11.26   Hurler syndrome is a genetically transmitted disorder of mucopolysaccharide metabolism resulting in short stature, mental retardation and various bony malformations. Two specific types are described with extensive pedigrees in the medical genetics literature:

Type I – recessive autosomal

Type II – recessive X-linked

You are a consultant in a hospital ward with several patients with Hurler syndrome who have asked you for advice about their relatives' offspring. Being aware that both types are extremely rare and that afflicted individuals almost never re-produce, what counsel you would give to a woman with Type I Hurler syndrome (whose normal brother's daughter is planning marriage) about the offspring of the proposed marriage? In your answer, state the probabilities of affected offspring and sex differences where relevant.

Answer: Draw out the pedigree of the patient and try to assign genotypes to the relevant individuals. Let h represent the Hurler syndrome Type I allele. Then the patient is hh. Since we are told that Hurler syndrome patients virtually never re-produce, neither of her parents is expected to be hh. Still, in order for the patient to be hh, her parents must have been $Hh \times Hh$. Since her brother is normal, he is $H-$, with a 2/3 chance of being Hh. The brother's daughter has a half-chance of receiving either of the brother's (H or h) alleles. Thus, the chance that the brother's daughter has an h allele is $2/3 \times 1/2 = 1/3$. Since the trait is extremely rare, it is likely she will marry an HH individual, and have $H-$ children. Therefore there is no chance the brother's daughter will have affected children, as her husband most likely will pro-vide a dominant, normal H allele. Since Type I is autosomal, there will be no sex differences.

12

EXTENSIONS OF MENDELIAN GENETIC ANALYSIS

CHAPTER OUTLINE

MULTIPLE ALLELES

ABO Blood Groups

Drosophila Eye Color

Relating Multiple Alleles to Molecular Genetics

MODIFICATIONS OF DOMINANCE RELATIONSHIPS

Incomplete Dominance

Codominance

Molecular Explanations of Incomplete Dominance and Codominance

GENE INTERACTIONS AND MODIFIED MENDELIAN RATIOS

Gene Interactions That Produce New Phenotypes

Epistasis

ESSENTIAL GENES AND LETHAL ALLELES

GENE EXPRESSION AND THE ENVIRONMENT

Penetrance and Expressivity

Effects of the Environment

Nature versus Nurture

REVIEW OF KEY TERMS, SYMBOLS, AND CONCEPTS

In your own words, write a brief, precise definition of each term in the groups below. Check your definitions using the text. Then, develop a concept map using the terms in each list.

1	2	3
mutant	dominance	penetrance
multiple alleles	epistasis, epistatic	expressivity
allelic series	hypostasis, hypostatic	population
diploid	dihybrid cross	individual
wild-type allele	dominant epistasis	phenocopy
complete dominance	recessive epistasis	phenocopying agent
complete recessiveness	duplicate dominant epistasis	hereditary trait
incomplete dominance	duplicate recessive epistasis	nature vs. nurture
partial dominance	duplicate gene interaction	norm of reaction

1	2	3
codominance	complementary gene action	sex-limited trait
essential gene	9:3:3:1	sex-influenced trait
lethal allele	9:6:1	sex-linked gene
recessive lethal allele	9:3:4	autosomal gene
dominant lethal allele	9:7	
ABO blood group	12:3:1	
MN blood group	13:3	
blood-typing	9:6:1	
cellular antigen	15:1	
antibody		
agglutination		
universal donor, recipient		
haplosufficient		

THINKING ANALYTICALLY

While the reasoning methods used in this chapter are not very different from those used in the earlier chapters on mendelian genetics, there is much more information to consider. Phenotypes are now affected by multiple alleles, gene interactions, and environmental influences. To understand how all of these affect or contribute to a phenotype, *analyze one at a time*. First focus on understanding what each factor contributes to a phenotype. Then consider how several jointly affect a phenotype.

As geneticists discover additional factors that affect a phenotype, the phenotype is often described in different, more revealing ways. For example, when a disease is first observed, it may be described only in terms of its inheritance pattern—say, as a dominantly inherited trait. As more is learned about the disease, its phenotype will be reassessed in light of the new knowledge. Consequently, as more is understood, different labels will be applied to the disease phenotype. These labels will indicate the kind and degree of interaction that occurs within a set of alleles at one gene (e.g., the type(s) of dominance relationships), between several alleles at more than one gene (e.g., the type(s) of epistasis), and between genetic and environmental influences (e.g., the level of penetrance and/or expressivity). Although complex, these labels are very useful: They quickly convey a coherent, informative description of the phenotype.

The major message of this chapter is that phenotypes can be affected by many factors. These factors include the set of alleles an organism inherits as well as the environment(s) in which it develops and lives.

QUESTIONS FOR PRACTICE

Multiple Choice Questions

1. In clover leaves, chevron pattern (a light-colored triangular leaf pattern) is controlled by seven different alleles at a single gene. From this information alone, what can be said about this trait?

    a. Alleles at this gene show incomplete dominance.

    b. There is a multiple allelic series with seven alleles that controls chevron pattern.

c. This gene shows epistasis.

d. One allele at this gene must be completely dominant.

2. The phenotype associated with a wild-type allele of a particular gene is

   a. the phenotype that is always found in nature.

   b. a reference phenotype used by geneticists for comparison.

   c. a special mutant phenotype.

   d. the most common phenotype seen.

3. A phenocopy is different from a particular heritable mutation in that

   a. a phenocopy cannot have the same phenotype as the mutation.

   b. the biochemical anomaly in a phenocopy and a mutation must be different.

   c. the phenocopy is always dominant.

   d. a phenocopy is not a heritable trait.

4. Neurofibromatosis is a dominantly inherited disease that can show mild, moderate, or severe symptoms. Every individual that inherits the dominant allele shows at least mild symptoms. This means that the disease allele shows

   a. variable penetrance and complete expressivity.

   b. variable expressivity and complete penetrance.

   c. variable penetrance and variable expressivity.

   d. complete penetrance and complete expressivity.

5. Two alleles at the *white* locus in *Drosophila melanogaster* are $w^{apricot}$, which has orange-colored eyes and w^{coral}, which has pink-colored eyes. This is an example of

   a. codominance.

   b. a multiple allelic series.

   c. penetrance.

   d. epistasis.

6. One difference between epistasis and dominance is that

   a. epistasis occurs between two different genes while dominance occurs between alleles at one gene.

   b. only epistasis is influenced by environmental interactions.

   c. dominant traits are completely penetrant, epistatic interactions may not be.

   d. dominant traits may show variable penetrance, epistatic interactions may not.

For questions 7, 8, 9, and 10, choose the kind of inheritance that best explains the data.

Explain your choices.

   a. recessive lethal allele

   b. dominant lethal allele

   c. incomplete dominance; two allelic pairs

   d. duplicate recessive epistasis; two allelic pairs

   e. dominant epistasis; two allelic pairs

7. When crossed, two pure-breeding varieties of white kernel corn yield progeny with purple kernels. When these purple progeny are selfed, a count of the kernels in the F_2 yields an average of 270 purple kernels : 210 white kernels per ear.

8. When pure-breeding wheat with red kernels is crossed to the pure-breeding white variety, the progeny have pink kernels. One hundred F_2 plants exhibit the following phenotypes: 6 red, 25 dark pink, 38 pink, 25 light pink, 6 white.

9. Yellow mice crossed to pure-breeding agouti mice produce a 50:50 ratio of yellow to agouti offspring. Crosses between yellow mice never produce 100 percent yellow progeny, but rather yield 36 yellow and 15 agouti offspring.

10. At age 52, a man begins to show the symptoms of Huntington disease. Like his mother before him, he eventually dies from the disease. His wife is normal and there is no history of the disease in his wife's family or his father's family. Two of his four children also die from the disease, albeit not until late in their lives.

Answers: 1b; 2b; 3d; 4b; 5b; 6a; 7d; 8c; 9a; 10b.

Thought Questions

1. Distinguish between dominance and epistasis, and between epistasis and multiple alleles.

2. How would you distinguish whether a complex mutant phenotype was caused by one gene or alleles at several genes? (Hint: review independent assortment.)

3. Tay-Sachs disease is fatal due to a lack of the enzyme hexoaminidase A. Phenotypically normal heterozygotes have about half as much enzyme activity as homozygotes for the normal allele. In what sense do alleles at the gene affected in Tay-Sachs disease show incomplete dominance, codominance, and recessive lethality?

4. A sex-linked gene controls coat color in cats. One allele determines black coat color while another allele determines orange coat color. A separate set of genes determines where color is produced (i.e., where white patches are). Use this information to explain why most calico (black, orange and white patched) cats are female. How do rare calico males arise? Do you expect them to be fertile?

5. In a very large natural population, could you ever presume to know all the allelic variants in a multiple allelic series? (Hint: Could new variants appear at any time?)

6. Devise a situation in which a multiple allelic series shows elements of codominance as well as dominant lethality.

7. Could a lethal allele, either dominant or recessive, be incompletely penetrant? (Hint: Consider small variations in the timing of events during development.)

8. Recall from Chapter 9 that SNPs (single nucleotide polymorphisms) are very common, about one per several hundred base pairs of DNA. What does this tell you about the number of alleles that exist at one gene in a population? Do you expect the allelic differences to always show clear patterns of dominance or recessiveness relative to a "wild-type" allele?

9. Some traits are influenced by many genes as well as the environment. How might you use gene chips to identify genes influencing such a trait. How would you then analyze the epistatic relationships between the genes influencing such a trait?

10. What different explanations are there for a trait to be incompletely penetrant? What approaches can be devised to test these explanations?

Thought Questions for Media

After reviewing the media on the *iGenetics* CD-ROM, try to answer these questions.

1. Based on viewing the animation, give an example where neither of two alleles at a gene is dominant or recessive. Using the alleles of your example, write the genotypes of a cross whose progeny show identical genotypic and phenotypic ratios. What type of dominance relationship is shown by these two alleles?
2. Correct the following false statement: "In incomplete dominance, a heterozygous individual exhibits the phenotype of both homozygotes."
3. Based on viewing the animation, give an example of a situation where two dominant alleles are fully expressed at the same time. Using the alleles of your example, write the genotypes of a cross whose progeny show identical genotypic and phenotypic ratios. What type of dominance relationship is shown by these two alleles?
4. Suppose you are able to show that a cross of two heterozygotes gives progeny in 1:2:1 genotypic and phenotypic ratios. What additional information do you need to distinguish between incomplete dominance and codominance?

1. In the modern courtroom, blood type tests can be used to exclude paternity, but it has become more difficult to use them convincingly to demonstrate paternity.
   a. Should the blood-type tests have excluded Charlie Chaplin from paternity of Carol Ann? Why or why not?
   b. Suppose a defendant who is the alleged father takes a blood-type test that does not exclude them from paternity consideration. What arguments might the lawyer of the defendant make in a modern courtroom to support the exclusion of the test results as "compelling" evidence? (Assume the tests are done correctly.)
   c. As mentioned in the iActivity, an individual of type A blood can be either homozygous or heterozygous. Suppose a blood-typing test allowed these two genetic conditions to be distinguished. Based on what you inferred about the ABO blood types of Joan and Carol Ann Berry in the iActivity, and supposing that you could identify their exact blood types, can you now predict the exact blood type of the father?
2. Why is it helpful to use both the M-N and the ABO blood group tests, instead of just one alone? Would a third blood-type test be even more useful, or are two enough?

SOLUTIONS TO TEXT PROBLEMS

12.1   In rabbits, C = agouti coat color, c^{ch} = chinchilla, c^h = Himalayan, and c = albino. The four alleles constitute a multiple allelic series. The agouti C is dominant to the three other alleles, c is recessive to all three other alleles, and chinchilla is dominant to Himalayan. Determine the phenotypes of progeny from the following crosses:
a. $C/C \times c/c$
b. $C/c^{ch} \times C/c$
c. $C/c \times C/c$
d. $C/c^h \times c^h/c$
e. $C/c^h \times c/c$

Answer:
a.   All agouti
b.   3/4 agouti, 1/4 chinchilla
c.   3/4 agouti, 1/4 albino
d.   1/2 agouti, 1/2 Himalayan
e.   1/2 agouti, 1/2 Himalayan

12.2   If a given population of diploid organisms contains only three, alleles of a particular gene (say w, $w1$, and $w2$), how many different diploid genotypes are possible in the populations? List all possible genotypes of diploids (consider only these three alleles).

Answer: Six genotypes are possible: w/w, $w/w1$, $w/w2$, $w1/w1$, $w1/w2$, $w2/w2$.

12.3   The genetic basis of the ABO blood types seems most likely to be:
a.   multiple alleles
b.   polyexpressive hemizygotes
c.   allelically excluded alternates
d.   three independently assorting genes

Answer: a.

12.4   In humans the three alleles I^A, I^B, and i constitute a multiple allelic series that determines the ABO blood group system, as we described in this chapter. For the following problems, state whether the child mentioned can actually be produced from the marriage. Explain your answer.
a.   an O child from the marriage of two A individuals
b.   an O child from the marriage of an A to a B
c.   an AB child from the marriage of an A to an O
d.   an O child from the marriage of an AB to an A
e.   an A child from the marriage of an AB to a B

Answer:

a. Yes, if both parents were $I^A i$.

b. Yes, if the A parent were $I^A i$ and the B parent were $I^B i$.

c. No, as neither parent has an I^B allele.

d. No, as an O child must obtain an i allele from each parent, and one parent is $I^A I^B$.

e. Yes, providing that the B parent is $I^B i$ (and the child is $I^A i$).

12.5   A man is blood type O,M. A woman is blood type A,M, and her child is type A,MN. The man cannot be the father of this child because:

a. O men cannot have type A children.

b. O men cannot have MN children.

c. An O man and an A woman cannot have an A child.

d. An M man and an M woman cannot have an MN child.

Answer: d. If both parents are M, an MN child is impossible because neither has an N allele. An A child is possible if the mother contributes I^A and the father contributes i.

12.6   A woman of blood group AB marries a man of blood group A whose father was group O. What is the probability that

a. their two children will both be group A?

b. one child will be group B and the other group O?

c. the first child will be a son of group AB and the second child a son of group B?

Answer: First determine the genotypes of the parents. The mother is type AB, so must have the genotype $I^A I^B$. The father is type A, so he must have at least one I^A allele. The grandfather was type O, so only had i alleles. Therefore the cross must be $I^A I^B \times I^A i$. The four equally likely genotypes ($I^A I^A$, $I^A i$, $I^B I^A$, $I^B i$) give rise to three phenotypes: A ($p = 1/2$), AB ($p = 1/4$), or B ($p = 1/4$).

a. The chance that two children will both be group A is $1/2 \times 1/2 = 1/4$.

b. There is no chance of producing an O child, so $p = 0$.

c. The chance of a male AB child is $1/2 \times 1/4 = 1/8$. The chance of a male B child is $1/2 \times 1/4 = 1/8$. Therefore the chance of both events happening is $1/8 \times 1/8 = 1/64$. As the first event is independent of the second, this is the chance of the events happening in the order specified.

12.7   If a mother and her child belong to blood group O, what blood group could the father not belong to?

Answer: Since the child is group O, its genotype is ii. Therefore the father must have been able to contribute an i allele. The father could not have been type AB, whose genotype is $I^A I^B$.

12.8   A man of what blood group could not be the father of a child of blood type AB?

Answer: A man who has group O blood, and is genotypically *ii*, could not contribute either the I^A or I^B to an AB individual.

12.9   In snapdragons, red flower color (C^R) is incompletely dominant to white (C^W); the C^R/C^W heterozygotes are pink. A red-flowered snapdragon is crossed with a white-flowered one. Determine the flower color of (a) the F_1, (b) the F_2, (c) the progeny of a cross of the F_1 to the red parent, and (d) the progeny of a cross of the F_1 to the white parent.

Answer:
a.   The cross is $C^R C^R \times C^W C^W$, the F_1 are all $C^R C^W$, and are pink.
b.   The F_2 will be 1 $C^R C^R$:2 $C^R C^W$:1 $C^W C^W$, and be 1 red:2 pink:1 white.
c. $C^R C^W \times C^R C^R$ produces 1/2 $C^R C^R$ (red) and 1/2 $C^R C^W$ (pink) progeny.
d. $C^R C^W \times C^W C^W$ produces 1/2 $C^R C^W$ (pink) and 1/2 $C^W C^W$ (white) progeny.

12.10   In shorthorn cattle, the heterozygous condition of the alleles for red coat color (C^R) and white coat color (C^W) is roan coat color. If two roan cattle are mated, what proportion of the progeny will resemble their parents in coat color?

Answer: A cross between two roan cattle can be denoted as $C^R C^W \times C^R C^W$. The progeny will be 1/4 $C^R C^R$, 1/2 $C^R C^W$, and 1/4 $C^W C^W$. Thus, half will be roan progeny.

12.11   What progeny will a roan shorthorn have if bred to (a) a red, (b) a roan, or (c) a white?

Answer: In Shorthorn cattle, the color roan indicates a heterozygote ($C^R C^W$) because of incomplete dominance of each allele. Hence, the crosses can be represented as (a) $C^R C^W \times C^R C^R$, (b) $C^R C^W \times C^R C^W$, and (c) $C^R C^W \times C^W C^W$. (a) will give 1/2 red and 1/2 roan, (b) will give 1/4 red, 1/2 roan and 1/4 white, and (c) will give 1/2 roan and 1/2 white.

12.12   In peaches, fuzzy skin (F) is completely dominant to smooth (nectarine) skin (f), and the heterozygous conditions of oval glands at the base of the leaves (G^O) and no glands (G^N) give round glands. A homozygous fuzzy, no-gland peach variety is bred to a smooth, oval-gland variety.
a.   What will be the appearance of the F_1?
b.   What will be the appearance of the F_2?
c.   What will be the appearance of the offspring of a cross of the F_1 back to the smooth, oval-glanded parent?

Answer:

a. The parental cross can be written as *FF GNGN* × *ff GOGO*. The F$_1$ will be all *Ff GNGO* and be fuzzy with round leaf glands.

b. As the alleles at the *G* gene show incomplete dominance, there will be a modified 9:3:3:1 ratio in the F$_2$. The progeny will be 3/16 fuzzy, oval-glanded (*F– GOGO*), 6/16 fuzzy, round-glanded (*F– GOGN*), 3/16 fuzzy, no-glanded (*F– GNGN*), 1/16 smooth, oval-glanded (*ff GOGO*), 2/16 smooth, round-glanded (*ff GOGN*), and 1/16 smooth, no-glanded (*ff GNGN*).

c. The cross can be written as *Ff GNGO* × *ff GOGO*. The progeny will be 1/4 fuzzy, oval-glanded (*Ff GOGO*), 1/4 fuzzy, round-glanded (*Ff GNGO*), 1/4 smooth, oval-glanded (*ff GOGO*) and 1/4 smooth, round-glanded (*ff GNGO*).

12.13   In guinea pigs, short hair (*L*) is dominant to long hair (*l*), and the heterozygous conditions of yellow coat (*CY*) and white coat (*CW*) give cream coat. A short-haired, cream guinea pig is bred to a long-haired, white guinea pig, and a long-haired, cream baby guinea pig is produced. When the baby grows up, it is bred back to the short-haired, cream parent. What phenotypic classes and in what proportions are expected among the offspring?

Answer: The initial cross can be diagrammed as *L– CYCW* × *ll CWCW*. As a long-haired, cream baby (*ll CYCW*) is produced, one can infer that the short-haired parent must have been *Ll*. The backcross can be diagrammed as *ll CYCW* × *Ll CYCW*. There will be 1/8 short-haired yellow, 1/4 short-haired cream, 1/8 short-haired white, 1/8 long-haired yellow, 1/4 long-haired cream and 1/8 long-haired white progeny.

12.14   The shape of radishes may be long (*SL/SL*), oval (*SL/SS*), or round (*SS/SS*), and the color of radishes may be red (*CR/CR*), purple (*CR/CW*), or white (*CW/CW*). If a long, red radish plant is crossed with a round, white plant, what will be the appearance of the F$_1$ and the F$_2$?

Answer: The cross can be diagrammed as *SL/SL CR/CR* × *SS/SS CW/CW*. The F$_1$ will be oval and purple (*SL/SS CR/CW*). The F$_2$ consists of 1/16 long red (*SL/SL CR/CR*), 1/8 oval red (*SL/SS CR/CR*), 1/16 round red (*SS/SS CR/CR*), 1/8 long purple (*SL/SL CR/CW*), 1/4 oval purple (*SL/SS CR/CW*), 1/8 round purple (*SS/SS CR/CW*), 1/16 long white (*SL/SL CW/CW*), 1/8 oval white (*SL/SS CW/CW*) and 1/16 round white (*SS/SS CW/CW*).

12.15   In poultry, the dominant alleles for rose comb (*R*) and pea comb (*P*), if present together, give walnut comb. The recessive alleles of each gene, when present together in a homozygous state, give single comb. What will be the comb characters of the offspring of the following crosses?

a. *R/R P/p* × *r/r P/p*
b. *r/rP/P* × *R/rP/p*
c. *R/rp/p* × *r/rP/p*

Answer:

a. 3/4 walnut (*R/rP/−*), 1/4 rose (*R/rp/p*).
b. 1/2 walnut (*R/rP/−*), 1/2 pea (*r/rP/−*).
c. 1/4 walnut (*R/rP/p*), 1/4 rose (*R/rp/p*), 1/4 pea (*r/rP/p*), 1/4 single (*r/rp/p*).

12.16   For the following crosses involving the comb character in poultry, determine the genotypes of the two parents:
a. A walnut crossed with a single produces offspring that are 1/4 walnut, 1/4 rose, 1/4 pea, and 1/4 single.
b. A rose crossed with a walnut produces offspring that are 3/8 walnut, 3/8 rose, 1/8 pea, and 1/8 single.
c. A rose crossed with a pea produces five walnut and six rose offspring.
d. A walnut crossed with a walnut produces one rose, two walnut, and one single offspring.

Answer: To approach solving this problem, first consider the possible genotypes of the parents and their offspring from the phenotypes they present. Then consider the phenotypic ratios in the offspring and determine the precise genotype.

a. *R/rP/p* (walnut) × *r/rp/p/p* (single).
b. *R/rp/p* (rose) × *R/rP/p* (walnut).
c. *R/− p/p* (rose) × *r/rP/p* (pea).
d. *R/r P/p* × *R/r P/p* (note that since a single *r/r p/p* offspring is produced, both parents must have an *r* and a *p* allele).

12.17   In poultry, feathered (*F*) shanks (part of the legs) are dominant to clean (*f*), and white plumage (*I*) of white leghorns is dominant to black (*i*). Comb phenotypes and genotypes are given in Figure 12.5.
a. A feathered-shanked, white, rose-combed bird crossed with a clean-shanked, white, walnut-combed bird produces these offspring: 2 feathered, white, rose; 4 clean, white, walnut; 3 feathered, black, pea; 1 clean, black, single; 1 feathered, white, single; 2 clean, white, rose. What are the genotypes of the parents?
b. A feathered-shanked, white, walnut-combed bird crossed with a clean-shanked, white, pea-combed bird produces a single offspring that is clean-shanked, black, and single-combed. In additional offspring from this cross, what proportion can be expected to resemble each parent?

Answer: Approach this problem by considering each set of traits separately.
a. A cross between a feathered and a clean bird produces 6 feathered:7 clean offspring (approximately 1:1), indicating the parents are *F/f* × *f/f*. A cross between two white birds produces 9 white and 4 black offspring (approximately 3:1), indicating the parents are *I/i* × *I/i*. Since a cross between a rose and a walnut bird produces single-combed (as well as walnut, rose, and pea) offspring, each parent

must have an *r* and a *p* allele. Thus, the parents must have been R/r p/p × R/r P/p. The complete genotypes of the parents were F/f I/i R/r p/p × f/f I/i R/r P/p.

b. The single-combed, clean-shanked, black offspring displays the phenotypes associated with the recessive alleles at the F/f, I/i, R/r and P/p genes. Since its genotype is f/f i/i r/r p/p, each parent was able to give it recessive *f*, *i*, *r*, and *p* alleles. Considering this and the parents' phenotypes, the parents' genotypes must be F/f I/i R/r P/p and f/f I/i r/r P/p. To resemble the feathered-shanked, white, walnut-combed parent, the offspring must be $F/-$ $I/-$ $R/-$ $P/-$. The chance of this is $1/2 \times 3/4 \times 1/2 \times 3/4 = 9/64$. To resemble the clean-shanked, white, pea-combed parent, the offspring must be f/f $I/-$ r/r $P/-$. The chance of this is $1/2 \times 3/4 \times 1/2 \times 3/4 = 9/64$.

12.18 F_2 plants segregate 9/16 colored : 7/16 colorless. If a colored plant from the F_2 is chosen at random and selfed, what is the probability that there will be *no* segregation of the two phenotypes among its progeny?

Answer: Since there is a modified 9:3:3:1 ratio in the F_2, the F_1 cross must have been of the form Aa Bb × Aa Bb. An F_2 colored plant must have the genotype $A-$ $B-$, where *A* and *B* are dominant alleles that must be present for colored pigment to be produced. In order for "no segregation of the two phenotypes" to be observed in its progeny, the colored plant must be true breeding, i.e., AA BB. Thus, the question can be rephrased as: 'What is the chance that if an F_2 colored plant is picked, it is true breeding?' Of *all* the plants in the F_2, only 1/16 are AA BB. Among the 9/16 $A-$ $B-$ plants, $1/9 [= (1/16)/(9/16)]$ are true-breeding plants, so $p = 1/9$.

12.19   In peanuts, the plant may be either "bunch" or "runner." Two different strains of peanut, V4 and G2, in which "bunch" occurred were crossed, with the following results:

V4 bunch × V4 bunch

↓

all bunch

G2 bunch × G2 bunch

↓

all bunch

The two true-breeding strains of bunch were crossed in the following way:

V4 bunch × G2 bunch

↓

F_1 runner

F_1 × F_1

↓

F_2 9 runner : 7 bunch

What is the genetic basis of the inheritance pattern of runner and bunch in the F_2?

Answer: The 9:7 ratio in the F_2 is a modified 9:3:3:1 ratio, where the *A– B–* genotypes are "runner" and the *A– bb, aa B–* and *aa bb* genotypes are "bunch." This is an example of needing dominant alleles at each of two genes to observe a phenotype. When only recessive alleles at either of the two genes are present, they block (are epistatic to) the "runner" phenotype. Thus, this is an example of duplicate recessive epistasis.

12.20   In rabbits, one enzyme (the product of a functional gene *A*) is needed to produce a substance required for hearing. Another enzyme (the product of a functional gene *B*) is needed to produce another substance required for hearing. The genes responsible for the two enzymes are not linked. Individuals homozygous for either one or both of the nonfunctional recessive alleles, *a* or *b*, are deaf.
   a.   If a large number of matings were made between two double heterozygotes, what phenotypic ratio would be expected in the progeny?
   b.   This phenotypic ratio is a result of what well-known phenomenon?
   c.   What phenotypic ratio would be expected if rabbits homozygous recessive for trait A and heterozygous for trait B were mated to rabbits heterozygous for both traits?

   Answer:
   a.   Since individuals homozygous for either one or both recessive alleles are deaf, individuals that are *aa B–, A– bb*, or *aa bb* will be deaf. Only *A– B–* individuals are able to hear. Thus, one will get a 9 hearing: 7 deaf phenotypic ratio.
   b.   This is duplicate recessive epistasis. Homozygous recessive alleles at either of two genes block hearing, and are epistatic to the dominant alleles at the other gene.
   c.   The cross being described can be written as: *aa Bb × Aa Bb*. Use a branch diagram to show that there would be 5/8 deaf progeny (1/8 *Aa bb* + 1/2 *aa* –) and 3/8 hearing (*Aa B–*).

12.21   In Doodlewags (hypothetical creatures), the dominant allele *S* causes solid coat color; the recessive allele *s* results in white spots on a colored background. The black coat color allele *B* is dominant to the brown allele *b*, but these genes are expressed only in the genotype *a/a*. Individuals that are *A/–* are yellow regardless of *B* alleles. Six pups are produced in a mating between a solid yellow male and a solid brown female. Their phenotypes are 2 solid black, 1 spotted yellow, 1 spotted black, and 2 solid brown.
   a.   What are the genotypes of the male and female parents?
   b.   What is the probability that the next pup will be spotted brown?

   Answer: Two characteristics controlled by three genes are described here. Spotted coat (*where* pigment is positioned) is controlled by the *S/s* alleles. The pigmentation color itself (brown, black or yellow) is controlled by the *B/b* and *A/a* genes, where *A–* is epistatic to (i.e., blocks the expression of) alleles at the *B/b* gene. Consider each characteristic separately and remember that when dealing with small numbers of progeny, precise Mendelian ratios are not always obtained.

a. Two solid-colored Doodlewags produce 4 solid and 2 spotted pups. In order for any spotted Doodlewags to be produced, both parents must have been heterozygous, i.e., *Ss*. The yellow male parent can initially be assigned the genotype *A– –*, and the brown female must be *aa bb*. Since both black and brown pups are obtained, the yellow parent must be *Aa Bb*. Thus, the parents are *Ss Aa Bb × Ss aa bb*.

b. A spotted brown pup has the genotype *ss aa bb*.

p (*ss aa bb* pup)

= p(*s* from each parent) x p(*a* from each parent) x p(*b* from each parent)

= $(1/2 \times 1/2) \times (1/2 \times 1) \times (1/2 \times 1)$

= 1/16.

12.22   The allele *l* in *Drosophila* is recessive and sex-linked, and lethal when homozygous or hemizygous (the condition in the male). If a female of genotype *L/l* is crossed with a normal male, what is the probability that the first two surviving progeny will be males?

Answer: The cross can be denoted as $L/l \times L/Y$, where Y is the Y chromosome. The progeny of this cross are 1 L/Y:1 l/Y:1 L/L:1 L/l. Of these, *l/Y* progeny die. Thus, one observes a 1 L/Y male:2 L/– female progeny ratio. The chance of observing a surviving male offspring is 1/3. The chance of observing two males as the first two surviving progeny is $1/3 \times 1/3 = 1/9$.

12.23   A locus in mice is involved with pigment production; when parents heterozygous at this locus are mated, 3/4 of the progeny are colored and 1/4 are albino. Another phenotype concerns coat color; when two yellow mice are mated, 2/3 of the progeny are yellow and 1/3 are agouti. The albino mice cannot express whatever alleles they have at the independently assorting agouti locus.

a. When yellow mice are crossed with albino, they produce an F$_1$ consisting of 1/2 albino, 1/3 yellow, and 1/6 agouti. What are the probable genotypes of the parents?

b. If yellow F$_1$ mice are crossed among themselves, what phenotypic ratio would you expect among the progeny? What proportion of the yellow progeny produced here would be expected to be true breeding?

Answer: Two loci are involved here. The first controls pigment production. From the information that a cross of heterozygous parents gives a 3 colored:1 albino ratio, we can infer that the homozygous recessive condition is that of no pigmentation at all. If we denote this locus as *C/c*, this also means that *C–* is required for pigmentation. Another way to state this is that *cc* blocks the production of pigment.

The second locus determines whether the coat color is yellow or agouti. The 2 yellow:1 agouti progeny ratio seen in a cross between two yellow mice is a modified 3:1 ratio from a monohybrid cross. It indicates recessive lethality. Specifically, it indicates that the yellow allele is dominant for coat color, but that when homozygous, it is lethal. If we denote this locus as Y/y, the YY condition is lethal, Yy individuals are yellow and *yy* individuals are agouti.

Now consider the relationship between the two loci. If *cc* blocks the production of pigment, *cc* is epistatic to Yy and *yy* (*cc* Yy and *cc* *yy* mice will be albino).

a. From the above analysis, the phenotype of a yellow mouse indicates that its genotype must be C– Yy and the phenotype of an albino mouse indicates that its genotype must be *cc* *y*–. To determine what the unknown alleles are, consider the two traits separately by considering color/no color (the C/c locus) and type of color (the Y/y locus). There are half albino and half colored offspring, indicating that the cross must have been $Cc \times cc$. There is a 2:1 ratio of yellow to agouti offspring, indicating that the cross was $Yy \times Yy$. Therefore, the parental genotypes were Cc $Yy \times cc$ Yy.

b. The yellow F_1 mice have the genotype Cc Yy. The progeny that will be obtained from the cross Cc $Yy \times Cc$ Yy are 1/4 albino, 1/2 yellow and 1/4 agouti (remember that the YY progeny are inviable). None of the yellow mice will be true breeding, as they are all Yy.

12.24   In *Drosophila melanogaster*, a recessive autosomal allele, ebony (*e*), produces a black body color when homozygous, and an independently assorting autosomal allele, black (*b*), also produces a black body color when homozygous. Flies with genotypes e/e $b^+/$–, $e^+/$–b/b and e/e b/b are phenotypically identical with respect to body color. Flies with genotype $e^+/$–$b^+/$–have a grey body color. True-breeding e/e b^+/b^+ ebony flies are crossed with true-breeding e^+/e^+ b/b black flies.

a. What will be the phenotype of the F_1 flies?

b. What phenotypes and what proportions would occur in the F_2 generation?

c. What phenotypic ratios would you expect to find in the progeny of these backcrosses: (1) $F_1 \times$ true-breeding ebony and (2) $F_1 \times$ true-breeding black?

Answer:

a. The F_1 flies will be b/b^+ e/e^+ and be wild-type in color (grey).

b. The F_2 will show a 9 $b^+/$–$e^+/$–(grey):3 $b^+/$–e/e (black):3 b/b $e^+/$–(black):1 b/b e/e (black) ratio, i.e., 9/16 grey and 7/16 black.

c. The $F_1 \times$ true-breeding ebony can be denoted b/b^+ $e/e^+ \times b^+/b^+$ e/e, and will give a 1 $b^+/$–e/e:1 $b^+/$–e/e^+ progeny ratio, 1/2 black and 1/2 grey. The $F_1 \times$ true-breeding black can be denoted b^+/b $e/e^+ \times b/b$ e^+/e^+, and will give a 1 b^+/b $e^+/$–:1 b/b $e^+/$–progeny ratio, 1/2 grey and 1/2 black.

12.25   In four-o'clock plants, two genes, Y and R, affect flower color. Neither is completely dominant, and the two interact on each other to produce seven different flower colors:

$Y/Y R/R$ = crimson $Y/y R/R$ = magenta

$Y/Y R/r$ = orange-red $Y/y R/r$ = magenta-rose

$Y/Y r /r$ = yellow $Y/y r /r$ = pale yellow

$y/y R/R$, $y/y R/r$, and $y/y r /r$ = white

a. In a cross of a crimson-flowered plant with a white one ($y/y r/r$), what will be the appearances of the F_1, the F_2, and the offspring of the F_1 backcrossed to the crimson parent?

b. What will be the flower colors in the offspring of a cross of orange-red × pale yellow?

c. What will be the flower colors in the offspring of a cross of a yellow with a $y/y R/r$ white?

Answer:

a. $Y/Y R/R \times y/y r /r$ will give a magenta-rose $Y/y R/r$ F_1, and an F_2 that is 1/16 crimson ($Y/Y R/R$), 1/8 orange-red ($Y/Y R/r$), 1/16 yellow ($Y/Y r/r$), 1/8 magenta ($Y/y R/R$), 1/4 magenta-rose ($Y/y R/r$), 1/8 pale yellow ($Y/y r/r$) and 1/4 white ($y/y -/-$). A backcross of the F_1 to the crimson parent will give 1/4 crimson ($Y/Y R/R$), 1/4 magenta-rose ($Y/y R/r$), 1/4 magenta ($Y/y R/R$) and 1/4 orange-red ($Y/Y R/r$).

b. The cross can be denoted as $Y/Y R/r \times Y/y r /r$. The progeny will be 1/4 orange-red ($Y/Y R/r$), 1/4 magenta-rose ($Y/y R/r$), 1/4 yellow ($Y/Y r /r$) and 1/4 pale yellow ($Y/y r /r$).

c. The cross can be denoted as $Y/Y r /r \times y/y R/r$, and the progeny will be 1/2 $Y/y R/r$ magenta-rose and 1/2 $Y/y r /r$ pale yellow.

12.26   Two four-o'clock plants were crossed and gave the following offspring: 1/8 crimson, 1/8 orange-red, 1/4 magenta, 1/4 magenta-rose, and 1/4 white. Unfortunately, the person who made the crosses was color-blind and could not record the flower colors of the parents. From the results of the cross, deduce the genotypes and flower colors of the two parents.

Answer: First determine the genotypes of the progeny. They are 1/8 $Y/Y R/R$, 1/8 $Y/Y R/r$, 1/4 $Y/y R/R$, 1/4 $Y/y R/r$, and 1/4 $y/y -/-$. Now consider each gene separately. There are 1/4 Y/Y, 1/2 Y/y, and 1/4 y/y progeny, a 1:2:1 ratio, so the parental cross must have been $Y/y \times Y/y$. Among the 3/4 of the progeny whose R/r genotypes can be determined, half are R/R and half are R/r, indicating that the parental genotypes were $R/R \times R/r$. Thus the parental cross was $Y/y R/R$ (magenta) × $Y/y R/r$ (magenta-rose).

12.27   Genes A, B, and C are independently assorting and control production of a black pigment.

a. Assume that A, B, and C act in a pathway as follows:

$$A \quad B \quad C$$

$$\text{colorless} \quad \rightarrow \quad \rightarrow \quad \rightarrow \quad \text{black}$$

The alternative alleles that give abnormal functioning of these genes are designated a, b, and c, respectively. A black $A/A\ B/B\ C/C$ is crossed with a colorless $a/a\ b/b\ c/c$ to give a black F_1. The F_1 is selfed. What proportion of the F_2 is colorless? (Assume that the products of each step except the last are colorless, so only colorless and black phenotypes are observed.)

b. Assume that C produces an inhibitor that prevents the formation of black by destroying the ability of B to carry out its function, as follows:

$$A \quad B$$

$$\text{colorless} \quad \rightarrow \quad \rightarrow \quad \text{black}$$

$$\uparrow$$

$$C \text{ (inhibitor)}$$

A colorless $A/A\ B/B\ C/C$ individual is crossed with a colorless $a/a\ b/b\ c/c$, giving a colorless F_1. The F_1 is selfed to give an F_2. What is the ratio of colorless to black in the F_2? (Only colorless and black phenotypes are observed, as in part [a].)

Answer:

a. In order for an individual to be black, it must have normal function at each step of the pathway. This is provided by the alleles A, B, and C. Thus, $A/-\ B/-\ C/-$ individuals will be black, while all others (those having a/a and/or b/b and/or c/c) will be colorless. The chance of obtaining a black $A/-\ B/-\ C/-$ individual from a cross of $A/a\ B/b\ C/c \times A/a\ B/b\ C/c$ is $3/4 \times 3/4 \times 3/4 = 27/64$. The proportion of the F_2 that is colorless is $1 - 27/64 = 37/64$. There will be a 37 colorless:27 black ratio.

b. With this pathway, an individual is black only if it has the first two steps of the pathway (those provided by A and B) and lacks the inhibitor provided by C, i.e., if it is $A/-\ B/-\ c/c$. The chance of obtaining this genotype from a cross of $A/a\ B/b\ C/c \times A/a\ B/b\ C/c$ is $3/4 \times 3/4 \times 1/4 = 9/64$. The proportion of the F_2 that is colorless is $1 - 9/64 = 55/64$. There will be a 55 colorless:9 black ratio. Thus, the ratio of black to colorless in the F_2 can be used to distinguish between hypotheses concerning these two pathways.

12.28 In cats, two alleles (B, O) at an X-linked gene control whether black or orange pigment is deposited. A dominant allele at an autosomal gene I/i partially inhibits the pigment deposition, lightening the coat color either from black to grey or orange to pale orange. A dominant allele at the autosomal gene T/t determines whether a tabby, or vertically striped, pattern is present. The tabby pattern depends on a dominant agouti (A) allele for expression, with nonagouti (a) epistatic to tabby. The agouti allele also causes a speckled rather than solid color coat. Judy, a stray cat with speckled, tortoiseshell pattern with grey and pale orange spots and no trace of a tabby pattern, gives birth to four kittens. Of the three female offspring, two are solid grey and the third is speckled grey and light orange like her mother but also shows traces of a tabby pattern. The single male offspring is solid grey.

a. Explain how the tortoiseshell pattern arises in cats. That is, how can a cat have distinct patches of fur with different pigment deposits?

b. Cats with a tortoiseshell pattern are usually female. Explain why this is the case and also why, when an unusual male tortoiseshell cat is found, he is atypically large and typically not very swift.

c. What are possible genotype(s) of Judy and her kittens?

d. What phenotype(s) should be considered in assessing the neighborhood males for paternity?

Answer:

a. The tortoiseshell cat has pigment deposited in patches of orange and black, with the pigment color determined by alleles at an X-linked gene. In females, one X chromosome is inactivated, so that only one allele is expressed at a time. The pigment color in each patch depends on which allele is expressed. The color is orange if it is the O allele and black if it is the B allele. Thus, the tortoiseshell black/orange pattern reflects the pattern of X-chromosome inactivation. When the X chromosome bearing the B allele is inactivated, the O allele functions to deposit orange pigment. When the X chromosome bearing the O allele is inactivated, the B allele functions to deposit black pigment.

b. Since the pattern of a tortoiseshell cat results from X-inactivation, a process that occurs in animals with more than one X chromosome. It will normally only occur in XX, female individuals. Thus, tortoiseshell cats are usually female. The exceptional male tortoiseshell cat probably has a sex-chromosome abnormality, and could be an XXY male. In an XXY male, one of the two X chromosomes would be inactivated. If an XXY male were heterozygous for the O and B alleles, he could exhibit a tortoiseshell pattern. By analogy with human XXY (Klinefelter) males, one might expect XXY cats to be larger and less intelligent.

c. Consider one trait at a time, and the phenotypic description of each cat. Judy has both black and orange pigments, and so is X^O/X^B. Her pigment deposition is inhibited, as her tortoiseshell patches appear as grey and pale orange spots, and so she is $I/-$. She shows a speckled pattern, and so is agouti and must be $A/-$. Since some of her offspring are not speckled (e.g., her son is solid, and so is a/a), she must carry an a allele and be A/a. She is not tabby, and so is t/t. She is $X^O/X^B\ I/-A/a\ t/t$.

   Her male offspring is solid grey. Since he is grey, he has the X^B allele (and a Y chromosome) and also $I/-$. Since he is solid colored, he is not agouti, and must be a/a. Since the tabby pattern is dependent on $A/-$ for expression, he may be either t/t or T/t. Since Judy, his mother, was t/t, he cannot be T/T. He is either $X^B Y\ I/-a/a\ t/t$ or $X^B Y\ I/-a/a\ T/t$.

   Two of the female offspring are, like their brother, solid grey. Since they are females, they have two X^B alleles. Using the same logic as for their brother, they are either $X^B/X^B\ I/-a/a\ t/t$ or $X^B/X^B\ I/-a/a\ T/t$.

The third female offspring is speckled, tortoiseshell, light, and tabby. Thus, she is $X^B/X^O\ I/\text{--}\ A/\text{--}\ T/t$.

d. Consider one trait at a time. Since Judy is not tabby, she is t/t and can only contribute t alleles. Since one of the offspring is tabby, the father must have been able to contribute a T allele, and must have been $T/\text{--}$. Since two female offspring are grey and $X^B X^B$, the father must have been X^B. Since Judy is $I/\text{--}$, and was able to give an I allele to each of her offspring, the father was i/i, I/i, or I/I. The father could have been either A/a or a/a (he was not A/A, since some of the progeny are solid colored and a/a), since Judy could have contributed the A allele to her speckled offspring. Thus, the father's genotypes could have been $X^B Y$ ($I/\text{--}$ or i/i) $T/\text{--}$ (A/a or a/a). This means that the father could have been black and tabby ($X^B Y\ i/i\ T/\text{--}\ A/a$), grey and tabby ($X^B Y\ I/\text{--}\ T/\text{--}\ A/a$), solid black ($X^B Y\ i/i\ T/\text{--}\ a/a$), or solid grey ($X^B Y\ I/\text{--}\ T/\text{--}\ a/a$).

12.29   In *Drosophila*, a mutant strain has plum-colored eyes. A cross between a plum-eyed male and a plum-eyed female gives 2/3 plum-eyed and 1/3 red-eyed (wild-type) progeny flies. A second mutant strain of *Drosophila*, called stubble, has short bristles instead of the normal long bristles. A cross between a stubble female and a stubble male gives 2/3 stubble and 1/3 normal-bristled flies in the offspring. Assuming that the plum gene assorts independently from the stubble gene, what will be the phenotypes and their relative proportions in the progeny of a cross between two plum-eyed, stubble-bristled flies? (Both genes are autosomal.)

Answer: For either of the stubble or plum mutants, a cross of two mutant individuals gives a 2 mutant:1 wild-type progeny ratio. This 2:1 ratio is a modified 3:1 ratio from a monohybrid cross, where the 25 percent homozygous mutant individuals die. We can denote the cross (using P/p for plum, S/s for stubble) as $P/p\ S/s \times P/p\ S/s$. Any PP and/or SS progeny will be inviable. The kinds of progeny expected can be diagrammed as follows:

$$2/3\ S/s \begin{cases} 2/3\ P/p \longrightarrow 4/9\ S/s\ P/p\ \text{(stubble, plum)} \\ 1/3\ p/p \longrightarrow 2/9\ S/s\ p/p\ \text{(stubble, red)} \end{cases}$$

$$1/3\ s/s \begin{cases} 2/3\ P/p \longrightarrow 2/9\ s/s\ P/p\ \text{(long, plum)} \\ 1/3\ p/p \longrightarrow 1/9\ s/s\ p/p\ \text{(long, red)} \end{cases}$$

12.30   In *Drosophila*, a recessive, temperature-sensitive mutation at a gene on chromosome 2 called *transformer-2 (tra-2)* causes XX individuals raised at 29°C to be transformed into phenotypic males. At 16°C, these individuals develop as normal females. The sex-type of XY individuals is unaffected by the *tra-2* mutation. Suppose you are given three true-breeding, unlabeled vials containing different strains of *Drosophila* all raised at 16°C. Two of the strains have white eyes and one has red eyes. You are told that one of the white-eyed strains also carries the *tra-2* mutation. Devise two different methods to determine which white-eyed strain has the *tra-2* mutation. Is there a reason to prefer one method over the other?

Answer: Since the *transformer-2* mutation transforms XX individuals into males at the restrictive temperature of 29°C, one way to decide which white-eyed strain carries the *tra-2* mutation is to examine the progeny produced when the strains are raised at the restrictive temperature. The *tra-2* strain should produce only phenotypic males. Transfer adults from each white-eyed strain to a fresh vial, and collect the eggs that are laid. Raise half of the eggs collected from each strain at the permissive temperature of 16°C, and raise the other half at the restrictive temperature of 29°C. The white-eyed strain carrying the *tra-2* mutation will give only male progeny at 29°C, but both male and female progeny at 16°C. The white-eyed strain carrying a *tra-2*$^+$ allele will give male and female progeny at both temperatures. Raising animals at the permissive temperature serves as a control to assess the relative number of males and females normally produced by each strain.

An alternative method is to employ a set of crosses to assess the chromosomal constitution (XX or XY) of an animal independently of its sexual phenotype ("maleness" or "femaleness"). In such a cross, a XX *tra-2/tra-2* animal raised at the restrictive temperature would appear to be a male. Such crosses can be designed using the X-linked white-eyed gene. Consider the following two crosses between a red-eyed *tra-2*$^+$/*tra-2*$^+$ strain and a white-eyed *tra-2/tra-2* strain. Both crosses are done at 16°C, but the progeny of the second cross are raised at 29°C.

I. *w/Y tra-2/tra-2* (white XY male) x *w*$^+$/*w*$^+$ *tra-2*$^+$/*tra-2*$^+$ (red XX female)
    Progeny [raise at 16°C]: 1/2 *w*$^+$/*Y tra-2/tra-2*$^+$ (red XY males)
    1/2 *w*/*w*$^+$ *tra-2/tra-2*$^+$ (red XX females)
II. *w*$^+$/*Y tra-2/tra-2*$^+$ (from cross I) x *w/w tra-2/tra-2* (white XX female)
    Progeny [raise at 29°C]: 1/4 *w*$^+$/*w tra-2/tra-2* (red XX "males")
    1/4 *w*$^+$/*w tra-2/tra-2*$^+$ (red XX females)
    1/4 *w/Y tra-2/tra-2*$^+$ (white XY males)
    1/4 *w/Y tra-2/tra-2* (white XY males)

In the second cross, XX progeny are red eyed, while XY progeny are white eyed. Since the *tra-2/tra-2* mutation transforms XX animals into males at 29°C, red-eyed "males" will be seen. Thus, if this set of crosses is done with each of the white-eyed strains, the white-eyed strain that also has a *tra-2* mutation can be identified.

Both methods work satisfactorily to identify the *tra-2* strain and each has its own advantage. The first method is faster, as it requires only one cross, not two. The second method has an internal control to identify an animal's chromosomal constitution independent of its sexual phenotype.

12.31 Normal *Drosophila* have straight wings and smooth, well-ordered compound eyes. A strain with curly wings and rough eyes has the following properties. Interbreeding its males and females always gives progeny identical to the parents. An outcross of a male from the strain to a normal female gives 45 curly and 49 rough progeny. An outcross of a female from the strain to a normal male gives 53 curly and 47 rough progeny. Crossing a curly F_1 male and female from the first outcross gives 81 curly and 53 straight progeny. The same curly F_1 male mated to a normal female gives 57 curly and 61 normal progeny. Crossing a rough F_1 male and female from the first outcross gives 78 rough and 42 smooth progeny. When the same rough F_1 male is mated to a normal female, 46 rough and 48 normal progeny are recovered. Develop hypotheses to explain these data, and test them using chi-square tests.

Answer: Since interbreeding males and females from the strain gives progeny identical to the parents, an initial hypothesis is that the strain is true breeding. If this is the case, *and* the rough-eyed and curly-winged traits are dominant, outcrossing a male or a female from the strain should give progeny that are all rough and curly. To demonstrate this, let C be the curly allele, and R be the rough allele. The strain is $C/C\,R/R$, and an outcross is $C/C\,R/R \times +/+ \; +/+$, with progeny $C/+ \; R/+$. However, we know that outcrossing does not give all curly and rough progeny. It gives about a 1:1 ratio of curly to rough progeny (outcrossing a male gives 45 rough:49 curly, progeny total = 94, 1:1 expected = 47:47, $\chi^2 = 0.17$, df = 1, $0.5 < P < 0.7$, accept; outcrossing a female gives 53 rough:47 curly, progeny total = 100, 1:1 expected = 50:50, $\chi^2 = 0.36$, df = 1, $0.5 < P < 0.7$, accept). This suggests that while the curly-winged and rough-eyed traits may be dominant, the strain is not true breeding. How then can inbreeding give progeny phenotypes identical to the parents?

Some insights come from analyzing the other crosses. The cross of two curly F_1 animals gives 81 curly and 53 normal progeny, while the cross of two rough F_1 animals gives 78 rough and 42 normal animals. Each of these progeny ratios are closer to 2:1 than 3:1 (For the 81 curly:53 normal progeny, progeny total = 134, 2:1 expected = 89:45, $\chi^2 = 2.14$, df = 1, $0.1 < P < 0.2$, accept; 3:1 expected = 100:34, $\chi^2 = 14.2$, df = 1, $P < 0.001$, reject. For the 78 rough:42 normal, progeny total = 120, 2:1 expected = 80:40, $\chi^2 = 0.15$, df = 1, $P = 0.7$, accept; 3:1 expected = 90:30, $\chi^2 = 6.4$, df = 1, $0.01 < P < 0.05$, reject.). A 2:1 ratio is a modified 1:2:1 ratio, where 1/4 of the progeny die due to recessive lethality. Here, a dominant curly-winged phenotype is seen in about 2/3 of the viable progeny from one cross, and a dominant rough-eyed phenotype is seen in about 2/3 of the progeny from the other cross.

When rough or curly F_1 progeny are crossed to normal animals, a 1 mutant:1 normal progeny ratio is seen (For curly $F_1 \times$ normal female, 57 curly and 61 normal progeny are seen: progeny total = 118, 1:1 expected = 59:59, $\chi^2 = 0.14$, df = 1, $0.70 < P < 0.90$, accept. For rough $F_1 \times$ normal female, 46 rough and 48 normal progeny are seen: progeny total = 94, 1:1 expected = 47:47, $\chi^2 = 0.04$, df = 1, $0.70 < P < 0.90$, accept.). These would be the expectations if these crosses were between heterozygotes for a dominant allele and an animal with normal alleles (e.g., $C/+ \times +/+$ and $R/+ \; \times \; +/+$).

Thus, the subsequent crosses support the hypotheses that the curly-winged and rough-eyed alleles are dominant alleles that are each recessive lethal. To explain how inbreeding the strain produces identical progeny to parents, consider the possibility that the curly-winged and rough-eyed phenotypes are caused by alleles at two different genes, each on different members of the same homologous pair of chromosomes, i.e., the strain is $C\ R^+/C^+\ R$. Then a cross between two members of the strain is $C\ R^+/C^+\ R \times C\ R^+/C^+\ R$ and gives a 1 $C\ R^+/C\ R^+$:2 $C\ R^+/C^+\ R$:1 $C^+\ R/C^+\ R$ progeny ratio. Since R/R and C/C animals are inviable, only $C\ R^+/C^+\ R$ animals are recovered. If a $C\ R^+/C^+\ R$ animal is crossed to a $C^+\ R^+/C^+\ R^+$, a 1 $C\ R^+/C^+\ R^+$:1 $C^+\ R/C^+\ R^+$ (1 C:1 R) progeny ratio is obtained. These predictions are consistent with the observed results and supported by the chi-square tests.

Another possibility is that the C and R alleles are mutations at one gene, and that the different mutations represent pleiotropic affects. In this case, one could write the strain as C/R, and a cross between two members of the strain as $C/R \times C/R$. This would give a 1 C/C:2 C/R:1 R/R progeny ratio. Since R/R and C/C animals are inviable, only C/R animals are recovered. If a C/R animal is crossed to a $+/+$ animal, a 1 $+/C$:1 $+/R$ progeny ratio is obtained. These predictions are also consistent with the observed results and supported by the chi-square tests.

12.32   In sheep, white fleece (W) is dominant over black (w), and horned (H) is dominant over hornless (h) in males but recessive in females. If a homozygous horned white ram is bred to a homozygous hornless black ewe, what will be the appearances of the F_1 and the F_2?

Answer: One can restate the information given in the problem as follows: In males, H/h and H/H result in horned animals, while h/h results in hornless animals. Both the notation and phenotypes are that of a typical dominant trait. In females, the fact that the trait is sex-influenced makes the situation quite different. In females, only H/H animals are horned. H/h and h/h animals are hornless. The white trait shows dominance in both sexes, with $W/-$ animals being white and ww animals being black.

This information allows one to diagram the cross as $H/H\ W/W$ male x $h/h\ w/w$ female. The F_1 genotype will be $H/h\ W/w$. Both sex types will have white fleece, and while males will be horned, females will be hornless. The F_2 genotypes will be 9 $H/-\ W/-$:3 $H/-\ w/w$:3 $h/h\ W/-$:1 $h/h\ w/w$. Because H/h and H/H show the dominant horned trait in males, the males will be 9/16 horned white, 3/16 horned black, 3/16 hornless white and 1/16 hornless black. Female phenotypes can be determined with the following branch diagram:

12.33   A horned black ram bred to a hornless white ewe produces the following offspring: Of the males, 1/4 are horned, white; 1/4 are horned, black; 1/4 are hornless, white; and 1/4 are hornless, black. Of the females, 1/2 are hornless and black, and 1/2 are hornless and white. What are the genotypes of the parents?

Answer: Start by using the symbols of 12.32 to denote what can be inferred about the genotypes of the parents and the offspring. Remember that in males, the horned condition is dominant, while in females, it is recessive. Hence, $H/-$ (= H/H or H/h) denotes the horned condition in males, while $h/-$ (h/h or H/h) denotes the hornless condition in females. Then the parents are $H/-\ w/w$ (male) × $h/-\ W/-$ (female). The male progeny are $1/4\ H/-\ W/-$, $1/4\ H/-\ w/w$, $1/4\ h/h\ W/-$ and $1/4\ h/h\ w/w$. The female progeny are $1/2\ h/-\ w/w$ and $1/2\ h/-\ W/-$. Since homozygous recessive (male) progeny are recovered, we know that each parent must have had (at least) one recessive h and one recessive w allele. Since none of the female progeny are H/H, only one parent had an H allele. Thus, the parents were $H/h\ w/w$ (male) × $h/h\ W/w$ (female).

12.34   A horned white ram is bred to the following four ewes and has one offspring by the first three and two by the fourth: Ewe A is hornless and black; the offspring is a horned white female. Ewe B is hornless and white; the offspring is a hornless black female. Ewe C is horned and black; the offspring is a horned white female. Ewe D is hornless and white; the offspring are one hornless black male and one horned white female. What are the genotypes of the five parents?

Answer: Using the information and symbols of 12.32, start by inferring what you can about genotypes from the phenotypes:

INDIVIDUAL	PHENOTYPE	INITIALLY INFERRED GENOTYPE
Male Parent	horned white male	$H/-\ W/-$
Ewe A	hornless black female	H/h or h/h, w/w
Ewe A offspring	horned white female	$H/H\ W/-$
Ewe B	hornless white female	H/h or h/h, $W/-$
Ewe B offspring	hornless black female	H/h or h/h, w/w
Ewe C	horned black female	$H/H\ w/w$
Ewe C offspring	horned white female	$H/H\ W/-$
Ewe D	hornless white female	H/h or h/h, $W/-$
Ewe D offspring #1	hornless black male	$h/h\ w/w$
Ewe D offspring #2	horned white female	$H/H\ W/-$

Note that Ewe D's male offspring must be homozygous for the recessive *h* and *w* alleles. This means that both parents must have had at least one recessive allele. Hence the male parent must be *H/h W/w* and Ewe D is *H/h* or *h/h W/w*. That Ewe D's female offspring must be *H/H* means that Ewe D must have an *H* allele. Thus Ewe D is *H/h W/w*. Since Ewe A has an offspring that is *H/H*, Ewe A necessarily has an *H* allele. Hence, Ewe A must be *H/h w/w*. Since Ewe B has an offspring that is *w/w*, Ewe B must have a *w* allele. We cannot tell if Ewe B is *H/h* or *h/h*. So Ewe B is *H/h W/w* or *h/h W/w*. From the genotype of Ewe C, we know she is *H/H w/w*.

12.35   Pattern baldness is more frequent in males than in females. This appreciable difference in frequency is assumed to result from
   a. Y-linkage of this trait
   b. X-linked recessive mode of inheritance
   c. sex-influenced autosomal inheritance
   d. excessive beer-drinking in males, consumption of gin being approximately equal between the sexes

   Answer: c.

12.36   King George III, who ruled England during the period of the revolutionary war in the United States, is an ancestor of Queen Elizabeth II (see Figure 11.13 on p.299). Near the end of his life, he exhibited sporadic periods of "madness." In retrospect, it appears that he showed symptoms of porphyria, an autosomal dominant disorder of heme metabolism. In addition to "madness," the symptoms of porphyria, which include a variety of physical ailments that were shown by King George III, are sporadic and variable in severity, can be affected by diet, and, currently, can be treated with medication.
   a. How would you describe this disease in terms of penetrance and expressivity?
   b. If indeed King George III had porphyria, what is the chance that the current Prince of Wales (Charles) carries a disease allele? State all of your assumptions.

   Answer:
   a. Since the disease can be variable in severity in a single individual, it shows variable expressivity. From the description of the disease, it is possible that some individuals in a population would not show the disease at all (e.g., King George III would not have shown the disease had he had a better diet, or had he died before the onset of symptoms.) Therefore, the disease is likely to show reduced penetrance.
   b. As shown in text Figure 11.13, the parents of Prince Charles, Elizabeth II and Prince Philip, are related as third cousins and are also both descendants of George III. Since the chance that an *A*– individual will pass the trait to the next generation is 1/2, and Elizabeth II and Prince Philip are each six generations removed from George III, there is a $(1/2)^6$ chance that they have the disease allele. This assumes that no one else marrying into the lineage contributed a dis-

ease allele and that George III was heterozygous. Thus, there is a $[1 - (1/2)^6]$ chance that either parent of Prince Charles has the normal, a allele. The table below shows the possible genotypes of the cross between Elizabeth II and Prince Philip, the probability of obtaining an A–offspring if each cross occurred, the probability of each cross occurring, and the overall probability of obtaining an A– offspring with a particular cross.

POSSIBLE GENOTYPES OF ELIZABETH II AND PRINCE PHILLIP	PROBABILITY OF CROSS PRODUCING AN A– OFFSPRING	PROBABILITY OF CROSS	PROBABILITY OF A–OFFSPRING WITH SPECIFIED CROSS
$aa \times aa$	0	$[1 - (1/2)^6] \times [1 - (1/2)^6]$	0
$Aa \times aa$	1/2	$(1/2)^6 \times [1 - (1/2)^6]$	$1/2 \times (1/2)^6 \times [1 - (1/2)^6]$
$aa \times Aa$	1/2	$(1/2)^6 \times [1 - (1/2)^6]$	$1/2 \times (1/2)^6 \times [1 - (1/2)^6]$
$Aa \times Aa$	3/4	$(1/2)^6 \times (1/2)^6$	$3/4 \times (1/2)^6 \times (1/2)^6$

The chance that Prince Charles is A– is the sum of the probabilities of obtaining an A– offspring with each possible cross. It is $0 + \{1/2 \times (1/2)^6 \times [1 - (1/2)^6]\} + \{1/2 \times (1/2)^6 \times [1 - (1/2)^6]\} + \{3/4 \times (1/2)^6 \times (1/2)^6\} = (1/2)^6 - (1/2)^{14} = 0.015564$.

12.37 Jasper Rine and his colleagues at the University of California at Berkeley have launched the Dog Genome Initiative to study canine genes and behavior. They mated Pepper, a vocal, highly affectionate, very social Newfoundland female that is not good at fetching tennis balls but loves water, to Gregor, a quiet, less affectionate, less social border collie that is exceptionally good at fetching tennis balls but avoids water. They obtained 7 F_1 and (thus far) 23 F_2 progeny. When the above behavioral traits were analyzed, all the 7 F_1 were very similar, each showing a mixture of the parents' behavioral traits. When the behaviors of the F_2 were analyzed, differences were more evident. In particular, two of the F_2 dogs (Lucy and Saki) shared Pepper's love of water. (For more information, see "California Geneticists Are Going to the Dogs" by Donald McCaig in *Smithsonian*, Vol. 27, 1996, pp. 126–141.)

a. Develop hypotheses to explain these observations and, when appropriate, test them using a chi-square test.

b. What practical value might there be in studying the genes of canines?

Answer:

a. That the F_1 showed a similar mixture of traits suggests that none of the traits appear to be controlled by alleles at a single gene that function in a completely dominant/recessive manner. That more differences are more evident in the F_2 suggests that some of the traits may be controlled by a small number of interacting genes. The behavioral differences seen in the F_2 could result from the segregation of alleles at these genes segregate in the F_2.

For the "water-loving" trait, 2/23 = 8.7 percent of F_2 dogs show the trait associated with Pepper, their grandmother. Analyze this data to model whether one or several genes could "control" the trait.

Hypothesis I: Two alleles at one gene control love/avoidance of water. Let L = love of water, l = avoidance of water. If the parental cross was $LL \times ll$, the F_1 was Ll and the F_2 was 1 LL:2 Ll:1 ll. Given the F_1 phenotype, alleles L and l must show partial dominance. About 6 ($1/4 \times 23 = 5.75$) F_2 dogs would be expected to love water, and about 17 would be expected to avoid or be indifferent to water. Using a chi-square test to evaluate this hypothesis, $\chi^2 = 3.6$, df = 1, $0.05 < P < 0.10$, and so this hypothesis cannot be rejected as being unlikely.

Hypothesis II: Two alleles at each of two genes control love/avoidance of water. For convenience in notation let $a/a\ b/b$ represent Pepper's genotype, and $A/A\,B/B$ represent Gregor's genotype. The F_1 is $A/a\,B/b$. As in hypothesis I, given the F_1 phenotypes, A/a and/or B/b must show partial dominance. The F_2 is 9 $A/-B/-$:3 $A/-\,b/b$:3 $a/a\,B/-$:1 $a/a\,b/b$. Between 1 and 2 ($1/16 \times 23 = 1.44$) dogs would be expected to be $a/a\,b/b$ and love water. This is observed. Using a chi-square test to evaluate this hypothesis, $\chi^2 = 0.23$, df = 1, and $0.50 < P < 0.70$. This hypothesis is accepted as being possible, and more likely than hypothesis I. Though this does not prove that only two genes control this behavior (for example, we do not know that either dog is homozygous for the hypothesized alleles, or anything about the nature of the interactions between alleles at the same or different genes), it does suggest that there may be a small number of genes that are important for this behavior.

b. This approach should lead to an understanding of how many genes are important for these relatively complex behaviors. Coupled with recombinant DNA methods, it will lead to insight into the (biochemical) function of the genes important for these behaviors. Since dogs are mammals, these studies have comparative value for other mammals, including humans. In addition, the Dog Genome Initiative should lead to the identification of genes in canines for other, health-related traits. This should lead to advances in treating illness in canines, and perhaps other mammals. This would be of interest to the relatively large number of pet owners, among others.

12.38 Parkinson disease is a progressive neurological disease that causes slowness of movement, stiffness, and shaking, and eventually leads to disability. Actor, Michael J. Fox has this disease. Parkinson disease affects about two percent of the U.S. adult population over 50 years of age, and most often appears in individuals who are between their fifth and seventh decades. There has been much discussion among scientists as to whether the disease is caused by environmental factors, genetic factors, or both. Support for the environmental hypothesis stems from the observation that the disease appears not to have been reported until after the industrial revolution and from the discovery that some chemicals can cause parkinsonian symptoms. Support for the genetic hypothesis stems from pedigree analysis.

Consider the pedigree in Figure 12.B (modified to protect patient confidentiality), which shows the incidence of parkinsonism in a family of European descent.

The shaded portions of the pedigree indicate family members who reside in the United States. The remaining portions of the pedigree reside in Europe. Members of the U.S. branches of the family have not visited Europe for any extensive period of time since the initial emigration from Europe.

a. If the disease in this family has a genetic basis, what is its basis? Explain your answer.

b. Why might this pedigree be particularly helpful in distinguishing between an environmental and a genetic cause for Parkinson disease?

c. What reservations, if any, do you have about concluding that the disease has a genetic basis in some individuals?

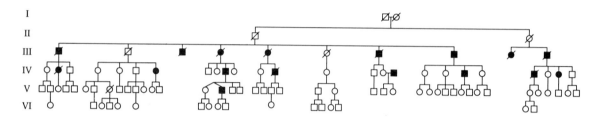

Adapted from K. Markopoulou et al., "A Greek-American Kindred with Autosomal Dominant, Levodopa-responsive Parkinsonism and Anticipation," in *Annals of Neurology* Vol. 38 (1995) 3: 374. Copyright © 1995 by the American Neurological Association. Reprinted by permission of Lippincott-Raven Publishers.

Adapted from K. Markopoulou et al., "A Greek-American Kindred with Autosomal Dominant, Levodopa-responsive Parkinsonism and Anticipation," in *Annals of Neurology* Vol. 38 (1995) 3: 374. Copyright © 1995 by the American Neurological Association. Reprinted by permission of Lippincott-Raven Publishers.

Answer:

a. The disease appears to be inherited as an autosomal dominant trait showing reduced penetrance. The trait is transmitted from father to son in several instances, excluding X-linked inheritance. The trait shows reduced penetrance, as some unaffected members of the pedigree have affected offspring (e.g., III-2 is unaffected, but his daughter, IV-7, is affected). It also shows delayed expressivity, as the disease does not appear to be present in younger individuals in the pedigree (most of generation V and all of generation VI).

b. If the disease were caused by an agent present in a particular environment (e.g., food, water, pesticide, chemical), one would expect the disease not to appear in individuals raised in a completely different environment. That the disease continues to appear in the offspring of pedigree members in generation III who emigrated from Europe is strong evidence that the disease is caused by genetic factors, and not by a particular environmental agent.

c. Given that some chemicals are known to cause the disease, and the relatively high frequency of the disease in adults over 50 years of age, it would be very inappropriate to infer that anyone who has the disease has a mutation (notice that in the pedigree shown, individual IV-17, who marries into the family, has the disease). Such an inference can only be made after carefully evaluating an extended family history for the disease and excluding environmental agents as extended family history for the disease and excluding environmental agents as the primary cause of the disease. The late and variable onset of the disease make such genealogical investigations difficult. It is also difficult to evaluate the potential environmental causes of the disease in just one individual. Since it is currently unknown which environmental factors cause the disease, it is also not known how often disease incidence is related to specific environmental factors. To determine the genetic and environmental contributions to the disease, it is important to study large pedigrees over long periods of time, and undertake epidemiological investigations.

13

GENE MAPPING IN EUKARYOTES

CHAPTER OUTLINE

DISCOVERY OF GENETIC LINKAGE

Morgan's Linkage Experiments with *Drosophila*

GENE RECOMBINATION AND THE ROLE OF CHROMOSOMAL EXCHANGE

Corn Experiments

Drosophila Experiments

Crossing-Over at the Four-Chromatid Stage of Meiosis

CONSTRUCTING GENETIC MAPS

Detecting Linkage Through Testcrosses

Gene Mapping Using Two-Point Testcrosses

Generating a Genetic Map

Gene Mapping Using Three-Point Testcrosses

Calculating Accurate Map Distances

TETRAD ANALYSIS IN CERTAIN HAPLOID EUKARYOTES

Using Random-Spore Analysis to Map Genes in Haploid Eukaryotes

Using Tetrad Analysis to Map Two Linked Genes

Calculating Gene–Centromere Distance in Organisms with Linear Tetrads

MITOTIC RECOMBINATION

Discovery of Mitotic Recombination

Mechanism of Mitotic Crossing-Over

Retinoblastoma, A Human Tumor That Can Be Caused By Mitotic Recombination

REVIEW OF KEY TERMS, SYMBOLS, AND CONCEPTS

In your own words, write a brief, precise definition of each term in the groups below. Check your definitions using the text. Then, develop a concept map using the terms in each list.

1	2	3
linkage, partial linkage	genetic map	tetrad analysis
linked genes	meiotic, mitotic recombination	ordered, unordered tetrads
linkage group	centiMorgan (cM), map unit	linear tetrads
syntenic	recombination frequency	ascus, asci
chromosome	coupling vs. repulsion	*Neurospora crassa*

1	2	3
parental genotypes, classes	two-point testcross	*Saccharomyces cerevisiae*
recombinant genotypes,	three-point testcross	*Chlamydomonas reinhardtii*
classes	two-, three-, four-strand,	ascospore
genetic recombination	double crossovers	vegetative cell
independent assortment	interference	random-spore analysis
crossing-over	coefficient of coincidence	parental ditype, tetrad (PD)
chiasma, chiasmata	mapping function	nonparental-ditype tetrad
cytological markers	mosaic	(NPD)
genetic, gene markers	twin spots	tetratype tetrad (T)
translocation	four-strand stage	first-division segregation
reciprocal exchange	hereditary, sporadic	second-division segregation
four-chromatid stage	retinoblastoma	gene-gene distance
ordered tetrads	bilateral tumors	gene-centromere distance
ascus, asci		

THINKING ANALYTICALLY

When working on a mapping problem, start by systematically organizing the data. This will allow you to extract critical information by inspection. Arrange the data by using symbols to represent the traits, writing out the crosses and their progeny, and tabulating the number of offspring in each progeny class. After organizing the data, inspect two genes at a time. This often allows you to determine if the two genes are linked, and if linked, whether they are sex linked. Any trait appearing in progeny in just one sex type should be checked for sex linkage.

Mapping genes using meiotic recombination and testcrosses. It is essential to remember that two genes that show 50 percent recombination in a test-cross may either be on different chromosomes, or be on the same chromosome, but very far apart. The map distances between two genes can exceed 50 map units, but their recombination frequency cannot exceed 50 percent. If two genes showing 50 percent recombination are each linked to a third, intermediate gene (i.e., they show < 50 percent recombination with the third gene), they will be on the same chromosome, but more than 50 map units apart.

In a three-point testcross, a systematic, methodical approach is essential.

1. Assign gene symbols to the phenotypes that are seen and rewrite the crosses.
2. Reorganize the progeny genotypes according to the frequency of each class.
3. Assign parental, single-crossover, and double-crossover classes — parentals will be most frequent, double crossovers will be least frequent.
4. Infer the gene order by comparing the parental and double-crossover classes.
5. Rewrite the testcross; infer which single-crossover gives rise to which class.
6. Calculate the recombination frequency and map distance for each gene interval.
7. Calculate the coefficient of coincidence and the interference for the region.

When using the chi-square test to check for linkage, remember that this test, like most statistical tests, only serves as a guide for invalidation of a hypothesis. It does not validate or prove a hypothesis. Carefully consider the hypothesis you are testing, and what the values of χ^2 and P mean.

Mapping genes using tetrad analysis and understanding mitotic recombination. Many students find the analysis of tetrads and mitotic recombination quite challenging. Step back for a minute though and ask yourself, "Can I recognize the *principles* behind these methods?" Tetrad analysis is based on the normal events of meiosis in organisms in which all four products of a meiosis remain together. Mitotic recombination is based on the occurrence of a crossover in the context of a normal mitosis. Underlying each of these processes are the fundamental processes of cell division: meiosis and mitosis.

A solid understanding of chromosome behavior during meiosis will enable you to master tetrad analysis and a solid understanding of chromosome behavior during mitosis will enable you to master mitotic recombination. Review how chromosomes behave during meiosis. Consider how T, PD, and NPD type tetrads are produced. Ask yourself what physical basis underlies first- and second-division segregation. Review how sister and nonsister chromatids are distributed to daughter cells during mitosis, and then diagram what happens if a crossover between nonsister chromatids occurs between the centromere and a particular locus. Approaching the material this way will provide you with a solid, *mechanistic* understanding of these processes.

Once you understand how meiosis and mitosis relate to these mapping techniques, you will be able to apply them more readily. Analyzing the results of crosses in which tetrads are produced is in many regards much more straightforward than analyzing the results of crosses in which they are not produced. Try employing the following systematic approach:

1. Assign gene symbols to the traits and write out the cross, considering just two loci at a time.

2. Decide which are parental-type spores and which are recombinant-type spores.

3. If you have unordered asci, calculate the recombination frequency (RF).
   RF = (# recombinant spores/total # spores) × 100%.

4. If you have ordered tetrads, identify PD, T and NPD tetrads.

   a. If PD = NPD (or is close), the genes are not linked.

   b. If PD >> NPD, the genes are linked.

5. RF = [(1/2 T + NPD)/total # asci] ×100%.

6. If you are analyzing linear (ordered) tetrads, consider each locus separately and determine the number of first-division (MI; 2:2 or 4:4) and second-division (MII; 1:1:1:1 or 2:2:2:2) segregation patterns.

7. RF (gene–centromere) = [1/2(MII patterns)/total # asci] ×100%.

8. Draw a map.

In problems involving mitotic recombination, it often helps to remind yourself of one of the basic results of mitosis: Normally, parent cells give rise to identical daughter cells. The following diagram shows the results of normal chromatid segregation in the absence or presence of a mitotic crossover (arrows trace the movement of the centromeres).

No mitotic recombination:

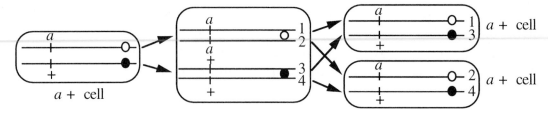

Mitotic recombination between *a* and its
centromere leads to the formation of a twin spot:

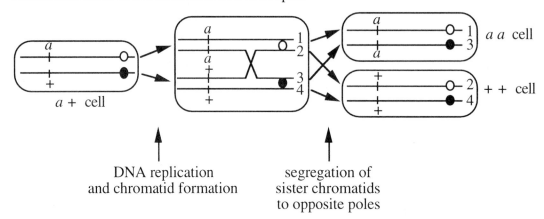

DNA replication
and chromatid formation

segregation of
sister chromatids
to opposite poles

In mitosis, chromatids segregate according to their centromere, not according to the loci attached to that centromere. By following how centromeres normally segregate, one can see how mitotic division normally gives rise to identical cells, and in the presence of mitotic recombination, how it gives rise to twin spots.

In the above example, members of a pair of homologs are identified by white and black centromeres. DNA replication occurs, chromatids form and then, during anaphase of mitosis, the centromeres split and go to opposite poles. The white centromere splits to form new white centromeres 1 and 2 and the black centromere splits to form new black centromeres 3 and 4. Since the centromeres normally move to opposite poles of the cell at anaphase, one possible outcome is that the even-numbered centromeres go to one pole, and the odd-numbered centromeres go to the other pole. This result is shown. (What other possible outcome(s) exist?)

Normally, the movement of chromosomes to opposite poles in mitosis ensures that two identical daughter cells will be produced. A rare mitotic crossover leads to the production of a twin spot in which a cell becomes homozygous at all loci distal to the crossover event. Note that the tissue surrounding the twin spot will remain heterozygous. Since the organism is now composed of tissues having different genotypes, it is referred to as a mosaic.

QUESTIONS FOR PRACTICE

Multiple Choice Questions

1. Evidence that genetic recombination is associated with physical exchange between chromosome homologs was found by

a. observing the existence of chiasmata during meiosis.

b. observing the pairing of homologs.

c. using a combined genetic and cytological approach.

d. showing that genetic recombination was accompanied by an exchange of identifiable chromosomal segments.

e. both c and d.

2. One significant use of ordered tetrads in *Neurospora* was to show that

a. crossing-over occurs at the 2-chromatid stage.

b. crossing-over occurs at the 4-chromatid stage.

c. crossing-over can occur when meiosis does not occur.

d. crossing-over occurs after meiosis has been completed.

3. Alleles are considered to be linked if recombination is less than 50 percent in

a. a $P \times P \rightarrow F_1$ cross.

b. an $F_1 \times F_1 \rightarrow F_2$ cross.

c. an $F_2 \times F_2 \rightarrow F_3$ cross.

d. an $F_1 \times$ homozygous recessive cross.

e. any F_2 progeny $\times$ homozygous recessive cross.

4. If two loci A/a and B/b are 9 map units apart, and an Ab/aB individual is testcrossed,

a. there will be 9 percent $A B$ individuals.

b. there will be 91 percent $A b$ individuals.

c. there will be 4.5 percent $a b$ individuals.

d. there will be 91 percent recombinant individuals.

5. If the genes a and b show 50 percent recombination, genes a and c show 35 percent recombination, and genes b and c show 32 percent recombination,

a. genes a and b are on the same chromosome, and 50 map units apart.

b. genes a and b are on different chromosomes.

c. genes a and b are on the same chromosome, and 67 map units apart.

d. one cannot tell if genes a and b are on the same or different chromosomes from this data.

6. A chi-square test is performed with a hypothesis that two genes are unlinked. A chi-square value of 11.35 is obtained, which in turn gives a value of $P = 0.01$ (i.e., 1 percent). Based on this information, one should

a. accept the hypothesis as being possible and expect that the genes might be unlinked.

b. accept the hypothesis as being proven true, and know that the genes are unlinked.

c. reject the hypothesis as being unlikely and expect that the genes might be linked.

d. reject the hypothesis as being impossible, and know that the genes are linked.

7. In a three-point cross, interference is a measure of

a. how often one chiasma physically impedes the occurrence of a second crossover in a particular region.

b. the accuracy of the map distances between three genes.

c. whether the data are considered reliable.

d. whether the genes are linked.

8. In a region in which interference is 0.85,
   a. there are fewer double crossovers than expected.
   b. there are more double crossovers than expected.
   c. one observed the expected number of double crossovers.
   d. 0.85 percent of testcross progeny show double-crossover phenotypes.

9. If two genes *a* and *b* are 8.3 map units apart, one expects to find
   a. 8.3 percent recombinant gametes from a doubly heterozygous parent.
   b. 91.7 percent recombinant gametes from a doubly heterozygous parent.
   c. A chiasma between the *a* and *b* loci in 8.3% of the meioses.
   d. A chiasma between the *a* and *b* loci in 91.7% of the meioses.

10. Map distances are most accurate when genes are closely linked because as genes become further apart,
   a. they always show independent assortment.
   b. the chance of multiple crossovers increases.
   c. they no longer recombine.
   d. there is chiasma interference.

11. Tetrad analysis is a technique for
   a. determining base sequences in DNA.
   b. measuring the number of chromatids at meiosis.
   c. separating *Neurospora* mycelia.
   d. mapping genes in organisms retaining the four meiotic products in one structure.

12. Ordered tetrads occur in the asci of
   a. Neurospora.
   b. Chlamydomonas.
   c. Saccharomyces.
   d. Drosophila.

13. A single crossover between two gene loci during meiosis in *Neurospora* spore formation produces an ascus with a genetic configuration known as
   a. tetratype.
   b. parental ditype.
   c. nonparental ditype.
   d. double recombinant.

14. The formula (1/2 T + NPD)/(total # of tetrads) ×100% is used to calculate
   a. the length of a chromosome.
   b. the location of the centromere.
   c. the number of crossovers.
   d. the percentage of recombinants.

For questions 15 and 16, refer to the following ordered tetrad resulting from the *Neurospora* cross $a + \times b +$.

$$
\begin{array}{cc}
a & + \\
a & + \\
a & b \\
a & b \\
\end{array}
$$

```
+    b
+    b
+    +
+    +
```

15. What configuration does this represent?
    a. NPD
    b. PD
    c. T
    d. NPD + PD

16. For the *a* locus, what segregation pattern is shown?
    a. equal
    b. random
    c. first-division
    d. second-division

17. In a tetrad in which a single crossover between two loci has occurred, what percentage of the spores will be recombinant types?
    a. 0%
    b. 25%
    c. 50%
    d. 100%

For questions 18-20, refer to the following information. In *Drosophila*, the *y* mutation is recessive and causes a yellow body color and yellow bristles. The y^+ allele results in grey body color and black bristles. The *sn* mutation causes short, twisty bristles while the sn^+ allele results in long, straight bristles. A y^+ *sn* / *y* sn^+ heterozygote is produced by crossing a *y* sn^+/Y male to a y^+ sn / y^+ sn female.

18. What is normally the phenotype of the y^+ *sn* / *y* sn^+ heterozygote?
    a. grey body and black, long bristles.
    b. yellow body and yellow, long, straight bristles.
    c. yellow body and yellow, short, twisty bristles.
    d. grey body and black, short, twisty bristles.

19. On the surface of some animals, twin spots are seen. What phenotype do they have?
    a. one spot has short, twisty, yellow bristles; the other has long, strait yellow bristles.
    b. one spot has short, twisty, black bristles; the other has long, strait yellow bristles.
    c. one spot has short, twisty, black bristles; the other has long, strait black bristles.
    d. one spot has short, twisty, yellow bristles; the other has long, strait black bristles.

20. How did the twin spots arise?
    a. from chiasma interference.
    b. from second-division segregation.
    c. from crossing-over during meiosis.
    d. from crossing-over during mitosis.
    Answers: 1e; 2b; 3d; 4c; 5c; 6c; 7a; 8a; 9a; 10b; 11d; 12a; 13a; 14d; 15c; 16c; 17c; 18a; 19b; 20d.

Thought Questions

1. Do you think that mapping according to the methods described in this chapter will still be useful if the entire DNA sequence of an organism is known? (Hint: Does genetic and/or cytological mapping narrow the field of possibilities?)

2. Why do you think that sex linkage was described before other examples of linkage in animals? (Hint: Is this an example of a correlation of genetic and cytological data?)

3. Why were the correlations made by Creighton and McClintock in their study of the *waxy* and *colorless* loci in corn important? (Hint: What was the value of cytological data to genetic experiments during that time?)

4. Can one make genetic maps of haploid organisms? (Hint: Review *Neurospora* material.)

5. Does the decision to accept or reject a hypothesis at the 0.05 level mean that one is more likely to discard a correct hypothesis or retain an incorrect one?

6. Do all chromosomes have the same length in terms of map distances?

7. Consider two pairs of genes *A* and *B*, and *C* and *D*. The number of base pairs of DNA between *A* and *B* is the same as the number of base pairs of DNA between *C* and *D*. Can you infer from this information alone whether these pairs of genes have the same, or different, map distances between them? Why or why not?

8. In some organisms, correlations have been made between the physical distance between two closely linked loci (i.e., the number of base pairs of DNA) and the map distance between them. If one measures the recombination frequency between two genes in another chromosomal region, can this information be used to infer the physical distance between them as well? (Hint: Consider the basis of interference and the observation that different regions of a chromosome show different amounts of crossing-over.)

9. *Drosophila* normally have deep-red eyes. A large number of alleles at the X-linked *white* locus cause lighter colored eyes, with w^l causing a completely white eye, w^a causing apricot (light orange)-colored eyes, and w^c causing coral (pink)-colored eyes. In females heterozygous for these two *white* alleles, the amount of pigmentation contributed by each allele is additive, so that w^l/w^a females have apricot-colored eyes and w^a/w^c females have reddish eyes. Diagram the appearance of a twin spot that results from a single mitotic crossover between the centromere and the *white* locus in a w^a/w^c *Drosophila* female.

10. How might one use ordered tetrad analysis to show that meiotic recombination occurs at the four-strand stage of meiosis? Hint: Use diagrams to compare the results of a single crossover between *a* and *b* in a cross of *a b* x + + that occur before and after DNA replication.

11. How could you use mitotic recombination to map linked loci relative to each other? Would you expect the map distances obtained from mitotic recombination to be the same as those derived using meiotic recombination?

12. In *Drosophila*, meiotic recombination does not occur during spermatogenesis. Might mitotic recombination occur in *Drosophila* males? For all chromosomes? If the answer is yes, what might this tell you about the "normal" role of mitotic recombination in cells?

13 For the human genome, a recombination distance of 1 map unit (1 cM) corresponds to about 1 megabase. Human chromosome 1 spans a distance of 356.0 cM. Which of the following physical methods would allow you to distinguish the location of two genes that are (a) less than 1 map unit apart, (b) 10 map units apart, (c) 100 map units apart? i. STSs, ii. somatic cell hybrids, iii. FISH. (It may help to review Chapter 9.)

14. Compared to a chromosomal region that shows no interference, in a chromosomal region that shows high levels of interference, would you expect there to be the same, greater, or fewer megabases of DNA per map unit?

Thought Questions for Media

After reviewing the media on the *iGenetics* CD-ROM, try to answer these questions.

1. In Curt Stern's cross between a *car B/car⁺ B⁺* female and a *car B⁺/Y* male, how many cytologically different X chromosomes were used? How could each be distinguished, and why was this important for the success of the experiment?

2. Suppose no crossover occurred between the *car/car⁺* and *B/B⁺* loci in the parental female. What eye-color, eye-shape and cytological phenotypes would be observed? How would your answers differ if a crossover occurred between these two loci?

3. Would the results in the Three-Point Testcross animation be different if the gene order used in the analysis was the one given initially? How?

1. When the initial data generated using testcrosses was analyzed, an hypothesis of "no linkage" was tested.
   a. What was the rationale for testing this hypothesis instead of testing an hypothesis of "inkage"?
   b. Why was this hypothesis not accepted?
   c. Why, in this case, does this suggest that the three genes are linked?

2. When mapping genes using data from trihybrid crosses, it is essential to determine the gene order. This is done by comparing the parental-type and double-crossover-type progeny.
   a. In the trihybrid testcross, how do you know which progeny classes result from double-crossover events?
   b. How does knowing which progeny classes result from a double crossover help you determine the gene order?

3. When mapping the distance between a pair of genes in the trihyrbid crosses, the number of recombinants in one of the intervals is equal to the sum of the number of single crossovers in that interval plus the number of double crossovers. Why does the number of double crossovers need to be added?

4. From the data in this problem alone, although you can determine the relative locations of the *cu* and *m* genes to the *o* gene at map position 55, you can't determine their exact map position. That is, you cannot determine whether the *cu* gene is at position 49 and the *m* gene is at position 71, or the *cu* gene is at position 61 and the *m* gene is at position 39. Suppose you knew the position of a fourth gene at map position 47. What is the easiest way to determine the correct map positions of *cu* and *m*?

SOLUTIONS TO TEXT PROBLEMS

13.1   A cross $a^+a^+ b^+b^+ \times aa\ bb$ results in an F1 of phenotype a+ b+; the following numbers are obtained in the F$_2$ (phenotypes):

$a^+\ b^+$	110
$a^+\ b$	16
$a\ \ b^+$	19
$a\ \ b$	15
Total	160

Are genes at the a and b loci linked or independent? What F2 numbers would otherwise be expected?

Answer: If two genes are unlinked in a dihybrid cross, one expects a 9:3:3:1 ratio in the F2. For 160 progeny, one would expect 90:30:30:10. Testing the hypothesis of no linkage using a chi-square test, one has 2 = [(110 - 90)2/90 + (16 - 30)2/30 + (19 - 30)2/30 + (15 - 10)2/30] = 17.5, df = 3, P < 0.001. This hypothesis is rejected as being unlikely. It is likely that the genes are linked.

13.2   In corn, a dihybrid for the recessives *a* and *b* is testcrossed. The distribution of the phenotypes was as follows:

A	*B*	122
A	*b*	118
a	*B*	81
a	*b*	79

Are the genes assorting independently? Test the hypothesis with a chi-square test. Explain tentatively any deviation from expectation, and tell how you would test your explanation.

Answer: Use the χ^2 test to test the hypothesis that the genes are unlinked. With this hypothesis, one would expect the cross *Aa Bb* $\times$ *aa bb* to produce four equally frequent classes of progeny (i.e., a 1:1:1:1 ratio). With 400 total progeny, one would expect 100 progeny in each phenotypic class. One has:

PHENOTYPE	OBSERVED ($= o$)	EXPECTED ($= e$)	$(o - e)^2/e$
A B	122	100	4.84
A b	118	100	3.24
a B	81	100	3.61
a b	79	100	4.41

$$\chi^2 = 16.1, df = 3$$

From the χ^2 test, $P < 0.01$. That is, there is less than a 1 percent likelihood of observing this much deviation from expected values by chance alone. This indicates that one can reject the hypothesis of "no linkage" as being unlikely. Note that the chi-square test neither proves that the genes are unlinked nor proves that they are linked.

Linkage might seem reasonable until it is realized that the minority classes are not reciprocal classes (both carry the aa phenotype). If the segregation at each locus is considered, however, the $B/-:b/b$ ratio is about 1:1 (203:197), while the $A/-:a/a$ ratio is not (240:160). The departure of the observed from expected values is thus due to a reduced number of a/a individuals. This departure should be confirmed in other crosses that test the segregation at the A/a locus. It would be particularly informative to check if the lack of a/a corn plants is associated with ungerminated seeds or seedlings that die before they are able to mature.

13.3   The F_1 from a cross of $A\ B/A\ B \times a\ b/a\ b$ is testcrossed, resulting in the following phenotypic ratios:

A B	308
A b	190
a b	292
a B	210

What is the frequency of recombination between genes a and b?

Answer: Recombination frequency = (# recombinants/total) × 100%
= [(190 + 210)/(308 + 190 + 292 + 210)] × 100%
= 40%

13.4   In *Drosophila*, the mutant black (b) has a black body, and the wild type has a grey body; the mutant vestigial (vg) has wings that are much shorter and crumpled compared with the long wings of the wild type. In the following cross, the true-breeding parents are given together with the counts of offspring of F_1 females × black and vestigial males:

P   black and normal × grey and vestigial

F$_1$ females × black and vestigial males

Progeny: grey, normal   283

grey, vestigial   1,294

black, normal   1,418

black, vestigial   241

From these data, calculate the map distance between the black and vestigial genes.

Answer: The cross is $b\ vg^+/b\ vg^+ \times b^+\ vg/b^+\ vg$, which gives an F$_1$ that is $b\ vg^+/b^+\ vg$. An F$_1$ female is crossed with a homozygous recessive $b\ vg/b\ vg$. The female is used as the doubly heterozygous parent, as no crossing-over occurs in male *Drosophila*. The classes can be grouped in reciprocal pairs as follows:

Nonrecombinants (parentals):	grey, vestigial	1,294
	black, normal	1,418
Recombinants (nonparentals):	grey, normal	283
	black, vestigial	241
	Total progeny	3,236

Recombination frequency = $[(283 + 241)/3{,}236] \times 100\% = 16.2\%$ There are 16.2 map units between the genes.

13.5   A gene controlling wing size is located on chromosome 2 in *Drosophila*. The recessive allele *vg* results in vestigial wings when homozygous; the vg^+ allele determines long wings. A new eye mutation, which we will call maroonlike, is isolated. Homozygous maroon-like (*m/m*) results in maroon-colored eyes; the m^+ allele is bright red. The location of the *m* gene is unknown, and you are asked to design an experiment to determine whether *m* is located on chromosome 2.
You cross true-breeding virgin maroon females to true-breeding *vg/vg* males and obtain all wild-type F$_1$ progeny. Then you allow the F$_1$ to interbreed. As soon as the F$_2$ start to hatch, you begin to classify the flies, and among the first six newly hatched flies, you find four wild type, one vestigial-winged and red-eyed fly, and one vestigial-winged, maroon-eyed fly. You immediately conclude that (1) maroonlike is not X-linked and (2) maroonlike is not linked to vestigial. Based on this small sample, how could you tell? On what chromosome is *m* located? (Hint: There is no crossing-over in *Drosophila* males.)

Answer: To eliminate the possibility that *m* is X-linked, consider what kinds of progeny you would expect if it were. If *m* were X-linked, one could write the parental cross as: $X^m/X^m\ vg^+/vg^+ \times X^{m^+}/Y\ vg/vg$. The F$_1$ males would necessarily be X^m/Y vg^+/vg, and so be maroon eyed. Since the F$_1$ are all wild type, *m* cannot be X-linked.

To eliminate the possibility that vg is linked to m, consider the kinds of progeny that could be obtained if it were. If vg and m are linked, one could write the crosses as:

$$P \quad \frac{vg^+\ m}{vg^+\ m}\ \text{females}\ \times\ \frac{vg\ m^+}{vg\ m^+}\ \text{males}$$

$$\downarrow$$

$$F_1 \quad \frac{vg^+\ m}{vg\ \ m^+}\ \text{(All wild type)}$$

The $F_1 \times F_1$ cross is $\dfrac{vg^+\ m}{vg\ \ m^+}$ females $\times\ \dfrac{vg^+\ m}{vg\ \ m^+}$ males

Eggs produced by F_1 females may be $vg\ m^+$ (parental), $vg^+\ m$ (parental), $vg\ m$ (recombinant), or $vg^+\ m^+$ (recombinant). Assuming that the two genes are linked, and remembering that there is no crossing-over in *Drosophila* males, the F_1 males' gametes must be $vg\ m^+$ or $vg^+\ m$ (parental types). Note that if the two genes are on the same chromosome, no matter how far apart they are, the F_1 males' gametes must be these parental types. Since none of the F_1 males' gametes are $vg\ m$, it is impossible for the progeny of the F_1 cross to be homozygous $vg\ m/vg\ m$. (Check this by diagramming a Punnett square.) However, since one of the progeny of the F_1 cross is both vestigial winged and maroon eyed, it must have obtained the m and vg alleles from both parents. Given the genotype of the males, this could only occur through independent assortment, i.e., if the two genes are on different chromosomes. Since it is not on the X or chromosome 2, the m gene must be on chromosome 3 or 4.

13.6   Use the following two-point recombination data to map the genes concerned. Show the order and the length of the shortest intervals.

GENE LOCI	% RECOMBINATION
a, b	50
a, c	15
a, d	38
a, e	8
b, c	50
b, d	13
b, e	50
c, d	50
c, e	7
d, e	45

Answer: Because of the effects of double crossovers, larger recombination frequencies are less accurate measures of map distances than smaller recombination frequencies between close neighbors. As a consequence, the map distances that can be derived from this data are not strictly additive (e.g., $a - d = 38$ and $a - e = 8$, but $d - e = 45$). The distances between nearest neighbors can be used to infer the following map.

Remember that although recombination frequency cannot exceed 50 percent, map distances can exceed 50 map units. Thus, the map distance between c and b can be inferred to be 66 map units (= 7 + 8 + 38 + 13), although c and b only show 50 percent recombination.

13.7   Use the following two-point recombination data to map the genes concerned. Show the order and the length of the shortest intervals.

GENE LOCI	% RECOMBINATION	GENE LOCI	% RECOMBINATION
a, b	50	c, d	50
a, c	17	c, e	50
a, d	50	c, f	7
a, e	50	c, g	19
a, f	12	d, e	7
a, g	3	d, f	50
b, c	50	d, g	50
b, d	2	e, f	50
b, e	5	e, g	50
b, f	50	f, g	15
b, g	50		

Answer: As discussed in the solution to problem 13.6, the most accurate map distances are obtained by summing the map distances between nearest neighbors. It is important to remember that while the percent recombination between two genes cannot exceed 50 percent, map distances can exceed 50 map units. When the percent recombination between two genes is 50 percent, either they are far apart on the same chromosome or on different chromosomes.

In some cases, one of these two options can be eliminated: If two genes showing 50 percent recombination both show evidence of linkage to other, intervening loci after sufficient data are gathered, these two genes lie far apart on the same chromosome. The map distances between the two distant loci can be determined by adding up the distances between the intervening loci.

Now consider the other option: The two genes show 50 percent recombination and no data exist to show linkage of each of them to intervening loci. For these genes, it will not be possible to distinguish between the genes lying on different chromosomes and the genes being very far apart on the same chromosome.

Start this problem by constructing a map using the smallest map distances, and then building on it as you check for linkage with other genes. The solution is:

With only the data provided in this problem, it is not possible to tell whether these two linkage groups lie at least 50 map units apart on the same chromosome or on different chromosomes.

13.8   The following data are from Bridges and Morgan's work on the recombination between the genes black (black body color), curved (curved wings), purple (purple eyes), speck (black specks on wings), and vestigial (crumpled wings) in chromosome 2 of *Drosophila*. On the basis of the data, map the chromosome for these five genes as accurately as possible. Remember that determinations for short distances are more accurate than those for long ones.

GENES IN CROSS	TOTAL PROGENY	NUMBER OF RECOMBINANTS
black, curved	62,679	14,237
black, purple	48,931	3,026
black, speck	685	326
black, vestigial	20,153	3,578
curved, purple	51,136	10,205
curved, speck	10,042	3,037
curved, vestigial	1,720	141
purple, speck	11,985	5,474
purple, vestigial	13,601	1,609
speck, vestigial	2,054	738

Answer: Determine recombination frequencies for each pair of genes by dividing the number of recombinants by the total number of progeny for that pair of genes. One obtains:

GENES IN CROSS	PERCENT OF TOTAL PROGENY
black, curved	22.7
black, purple	6.2
black, speck	47.6
black, vestigial	17.8
curved, purple	20.0
curved, speck	30.2
curved, vestigial	8.2
purple, speck	45.7
purple, vestigial	11.8
speck, vestigial	35.9

Now analyze the data to determine the order of the genes. One approach is to consider that the pair with the greatest recombination frequency are the furthest apart, and then order genes from one or the other end. The genes black and speck are furthest apart:

Now fill in the order by finding the sequence of genes that has an increasing order of recombination with black:

Next, assign map distances based on the recombination frequencies of neighboring genes:

Check gene order by choosing one of the genes (e.g., curved) and verifying that the distances between that gene and the others are approximately correct. Because of multiple crossovers, larger recombination frequencies tend to give underestimates of map distance. The most accurate map distances between two genes can be determined by summing the map distances in all intervals between the genes. Thus, the map distance from *bl* to *sp* is most accurately given by 56.4 (= 6.2 + 11.8 + 8.2 + 30.2) map units, and not 47.6 (= RF×100%) map units.

13.9   A corn plant known to be heterozygous at three loci is testcrossed. The progeny phenotypes and frequencies are as follows:

+	+	+	455
a	b	c	470
+	b	c	35
a	+	+	33
+	+	c	37
a	b	+	35
+	b	+	460
a	+	c	475

	Total	2,000

Give the gene arrangement, linkage relations, and map distances.

Answer: First, note that since the offspring result from a testcross, the phenotypes of the offspring reflect the genotypes of the gametes of the heterozygous parent.

Consequently, these phenotypes can be used to determine the gene arrangement in the heterozygous parent.

Second, notice that there are eight genotypic classes that appear in two frequencies. Four of the genotypic classes have about 460 individuals, while the other four have about 35 individuals. This would be expected if two of the genes were linked and the third was not. In this case, the chromosome bearing the two linked genes could undergo crossing-over, and give rise to two frequencies of gametes. Because crossing-over between two closely linked genes is infrequent, gametes with noncrossover chromosomes are more frequent. The third gene assorts independently. The independent assortment of the third gene results in four, and not just two, genotypes present in each of two frequencies.

With this information, one can proceed in either of two ways. First, one can tabulate the data considering only two pairs of genes at one time. This allows one to view this cross as a series of two-point crosses.

a	b	c	# progeny
a	b		$470 + 35 = 505$
$+$	b		$460 + 35 = 495$
a	$+$		$475 + 33 = 508$
$+$	$+$		$455 + 37 = 492$
a		c	$470 + 475 = 945$
$+$		c	$35 + 37 = 72$
a		$+$	$33 + 35 = 68$
$+$		$+$	$455 + 460 = 915$
	b	c	$470 + 35 = 505$
	$+$	c	$475 + 37 = 512$
	b	$+$	$460 + 35 = 495$
	$+$	$+$	$455 + 33 = 488$

Notice that there is a 1:1:1:1 ratio in the offspring when one considers just the a and b genes, or just the b and c genes. This is what one would expect in a dihybrid cross with two independently assorting genes. Thus, a assorts independently of b and b assorts independently of c. This is not the case for a and c, however. Here, there are two frequencies of data indicative of two linked genes showing recombination. The recombination frequency between a and c is RF = $[(72 + 68)/(72 + 68 + 945 + 915)] \times 100\% = 7\%$, and there are 7 map units between a and c.

Alternatively, one can use the reasoning presented above to infer that the four progeny classes with about 460 individuals contain parental types of chromosomes for two linked genes, as well as an independently assorting chromosome with the third gene. By inspection of the most frequent phenotypes, one sees that only a c and $+$ $+$ chromosomes are found, while the $b/+$ gene assorts independently from these noncrossover chromosomes. Thus, the a and c loci are linked, and the b gene is unlinked. The least frequent progeny classes contain a $+$ and $+$ c recombinant chromosomes, so that the percent recombination between a and c is RF = [(35 + 37 + 33 + 35)/2,000] × 100% = 7%. Just as was seen earlier, the map distance between a and c is 7 map units.

One can diagram these results as:

13.10   Genes a and b are linked, with 10 percent recombination. What would be the phenotypes, and the probability of each, among progeny of the following cross?

$$\frac{a\ \ b^+}{a^+\ b} \times \frac{a\ b}{a\ b}$$

Answer: The $a\ b^+/a^+\ b$ parent will give 90 percent parental-type ($a\ b^+$ or $a^+\ b$) gametes and 10 percent recombinant-type gametes ($a\ b$ or $a^+\ b^+$). The genotypes of these gametes will determine the offspring phenotypes, as the $a\ b/a\ b$ parent will give only $a\ b$ gametes. Therefore, there will be 45% $a\ b^+$, 45% $a^+\ b$, 5% $a\ b$, and 5% $a^+\ b^+$ offspring.

13.11   Genes a and b are sex-linked and are located 7 mu apart in the X chromosome of *Drosophila*. A female of genotype $a^+\ b/a\ b^+$ is mated with a wild-type ($a^+\ b^+\ /Y$).
   a.   What is the probability that one of her sons will be either $a^+\ b^+$ or $a\ b^+$ in phenotype?
   b.   What is the probability that one of her daughters will be $a^+\ b^+$ in phenotype?

Answer: Since the genes are 7 mu apart, the female will have 93 percent parental-type gametes (46.5% $a^+\ b$ and 46.5% $a\ b^+$) and 7 percent recombinant-type gametes (3.5% $a\ b$ and 3.5% $a^+\ b^+$). The wild-type male will give either an X chromosome bearing a^+b^+ or a Y chromosome. As the genes are X-linked, the phenotype of the sons will reflect the chromosome they receive from the mother. The phenotype of the daughters will be $a^+\ b^+$, as they receive the $a^+\ b^+$ X chromosome from their father.
   a. $p = 3.5\%\ (a^+\ b^+) + 46.5\%\ (a\ b^+) = 50\%$.
   b. $p = 100\%$.

13.12   In maize the dominant genes A and C are both necessary for colored seeds. Homozygous recessive plants give colorless seed, regardless of the genes at the second locus. Genes A and C show independent segregation, and the recessive mutant gene waxy endosperm (wx) is linked with C (20 percent recombination). The dominant Wx allele results in starchy endosperm.

a. What phenotypic ratios would be expected when a plant of constitution *c Wx /C wx A/ A* is testcrossed?

b. What phenotypic ratios would be expected when a plant of constitution *c Wx /C wx A/ a* is testcrossed?

Answer: Use branch diagrams to assess what kind of gametes will arise from the heterozygous plants.

a.

b.

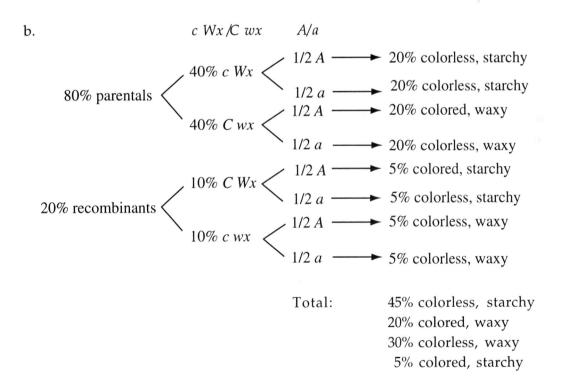

Total: 45% colorless, starchy
20% colored, waxy
30% colorless, waxy
5% colored, starchy

13.13 In tomatoes, tall vine is dominant over dwarf, and spherical fruit shape is dominant over pear shape. Vine height and fruit shape are linked, with a recombinant percentage of 20. A certain tall, spherical-fruited tomato plant is crossed with a dwarf, pear-fruited plant. The progeny are 81 tall, spherical; 79 dwarf, pear; 22 tall, pear; and 17 dwarf, spherical. Another tall and spherical plant crossed with a dwarf and pear plant produces 21 tall, pear; 18 dwarf, spherical; 5 tall, spherical; and 4 dwarf, pear. What are the genotypes of the two tall and spherical plants? If they were crossed, what would their offspring be?

Answer: Let T represent tall vine, t represent dwarf, S represent spherical and s represent pear. Then, the initial tall, spherical × dwarf, pear cross can be represented as $T S /- - \times t s /t s$. Since this is a testcross, the genotypes of the gametes of the (potentially) heterozygous plant can be inferred from the progeny phenotypes:

PHENOTYPE	GAMETE GENOTYPE	First Cross #	First Cross Type	Second Cross #	Second Cross Type
tall, spherical	$T S$	81	parental	5	recombinant
dwarf, pear	$t s$	79	parental	4	recombinant
tall, pear	$T s$	22	recombinant	21	parental
dwarf, spherical	$t S$	17	recombinant	18	parental

In the first cross, the four classes of gametes, their phenotypes and frequencies indicate that the parental genotypes were $T S/t s \times t s/t s$. Similarly, the four classes of progeny and their frequencies in the second cross indicate that it is $T s /t S \times t s /t s$. If the two tall and spherical plants were crossed, one would have $T S /t s \times T s /t S$. One can diagram the expected progeny using a branch diagram:

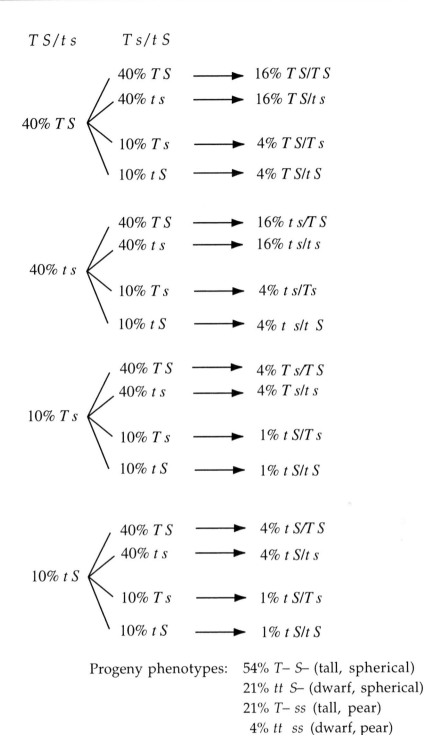

$T S/t s$ $T s/t S$

40% $T S$
 40% $T S$ ⟶ 16% $T S/T S$
 40% $t s$ ⟶ 16% $T S/t s$
 10% $T s$ ⟶ 4% $T S/T s$
 10% $t S$ ⟶ 4% $T S/t S$

40% $t s$
 40% $T S$ ⟶ 16% $t s/T S$
 40% $t s$ ⟶ 16% $t s/t s$
 10% $T s$ ⟶ 4% $t s/Ts$
 10% $t S$ ⟶ 4% $t s/t S$

10% $T s$
 40% $T S$ ⟶ 4% $T s/T S$
 40% $t s$ ⟶ 4% $T s/t s$
 10% $T s$ ⟶ 1% $t S/T s$
 10% $t S$ ⟶ 1% $t S/t S$

10% $t S$
 40% $T S$ ⟶ 4% $t S/T S$
 40% $t s$ ⟶ 4% $t S/t s$
 10% $T s$ ⟶ 1% $t S/T s$
 10% $t S$ ⟶ 1% $t S/t S$

Progeny phenotypes: 54% $T-$ $S-$ (tall, spherical)
         21% tt $S-$ (dwarf, spherical)
         21% $T-$ ss (tall, pear)
         4% tt ss (dwarf, pear)

13.14 Genes a and b are on one chromosome, 20 mu apart; c and d are on another chromosome, 10 mu apart. Genes e and f are on yet another chromosome and are 30 mu apart. Cross a homozygous $A B C D E F$ individual with an $a b c d e f$ one, and cross the F$_1$ back to an $a b c$ $d e f$ individual. What are the chances of getting individuals of the following phenotypes in the progeny?

a. $A B C D E F$
b. $A B C d e f$
c. $A b c D E f$

d. *a B C d e f*

e. *a b c D e F*

Answer: The frequency of recombination between two genes can be inferred from the map distance between them. For example, the 20 mu between *a* and *b* indicate that in an *AB/ab* individual, gametes will have 80 percent parental-type chromosomes (40 percent each of *AB*, *ab*) and 20 percent recombinant-type chromosomes (10 percent each of *Ab*, *aB*). The cross under consideration is *AB/ab; CD/cd; EF/ef* × *ab/ab; cd/cd; ef/ef*.

a. The chance of obtaining the parental-type *AB, CD,* and *EF* chromosomes is $p = 0.40 \times 0.45 \times 0.35 = 0.063$ or 6.3%.

b. The chance of obtaining *AB, Cd,* and *ef* chromosomes is $p = 0.40 \times 0.05 \times 0.35 = 0.007$ or 0.7%.

c. The chance of obtaining *Ab, cD,* and *Ef* chromosomes is $p = 0.10 \times 0.05 \times 0.15 = 0.00075$ or 0.075%.

d. The chance of obtaining *aB, Cd,* and *ef* chromosomes is $p = 0.10 \times 0.05 \times 0.35 = 0.00175$ or 0.175%.

e. The chance of obtaining the *ab, cD,* and *eF* chromosomes is $p = 0.40 \times 0.05 \times 0.15 = 0.003$ or 0.3%.

13.15   Genes *d* and *p* occupy loci 5 mu apart in the same autosomal linkage group. Gene *h* is a separate autosomal linkage group and therefore segregates independently of the other two. What types of offspring are expected, and what is the probability of each, when individuals of the following genotypes are testcrossed:

a. $\dfrac{D\ P}{d\ p}\ \dfrac{h}{h}$ b. $\dfrac{d\ P}{D\ p}\ \dfrac{H}{h}$

Answer:

a. 95% of the progeny will have *D P* or *d p* parental-type chromosomes, and 5% of the progeny will have *D p* or *d P* recombinant-type chromosomes. All of the progeny will be *h*. There will be 47.5% *D P h*, 47.5% *d p h*, 2.5% *D p h*, 2.5% *d P h*.

b. 23.75% *d P H*, 23.75% *d P h*, 23.75% *D p H*, 23.75% *D p h*, 1.25% *D P H*, 1.25% *D P h*, 1.25% *d p H*, 1.25% *d p h*.

13.16   A hairy-winged (*h*) *Drosophila* female is mated with a yellow-bodied (*y*), white-eyed (*w*) male. The F$_1$ are all wild type. The F$_1$ progeny are then crossed, and the F$_2$ that emerge are as follows:

Females:	wild type	757
	hairy	243
Males:	wild type	390
	hairy	130
	yellow	4
	white	3
	hairy, yellow	1
	hairy, white	2
	yellow, white	360
	hairy, yellow, white	110

Give genotypes of the parents and the F_1, and note the linkage relations and distances where possible.

Answer: Careful inspection of the data shows that the F_2 males, but not the F_2 females, show the yellow and white traits. In contrast, the hairy trait is shown in an approximately 3:1 ratio in both the females and males (females = 757 normal:243 hairy; males = 757 normal:243 hairy). This indicates that the yellow and white genes are sex linked, while hairy is not.

The normal phenotype of the F_1 heterozygote indicates that the nonhairy, nonyellow, and nonwhite traits are dominant. Therefore, let h and h^+ represent the hairy and nonhairy traits, respectively, y and y^+ represent the yellow and normal body-color traits, respectively, and w and w^+ represent the white- and red-eyed traits, respectively. Then, given the phenotypes of the parents and F_1, and the sex linkage of y and w, the crosses can be written as:

P: $y^+ w^+ /y^+ w^+ ; h/h$ females $\times y\, w/Y; h^+ /h^+$ males
F_1: $y^+ w^+ /y\, w ; h^+ /h$ females $\times y^+ w^+ /Y; h^+ /h$ males

Now determine the map distance between y and w. This can be inferred from the frequency of recombinants among the F_2 males.

PHENOTYPE OF F_2 MALE	GENOTYPE	X-CHROMOSOME RECOMBINANT?	NUMBER
wild type	$y^+ w^+ /Y; h^+ /-$	no	390
hairy	$y^+ w^+ /Y; h/h$	no	130
yellow	$y\, w^+ /Y; h^+ /-$	yes	4
white	$y^+ w/Y; h^+ /-$	yes	3
hairy, yellow	$y\, w^+ /Y; h/h$	yes	1
hairy, white	$y^+ w/Y; h/h$	yes	2
yellow, white	$y\, w/Y; h^+ /-$	no	360
hairy, yellow, white	$y\, w/Y; h/h$	no	110

The recombination frequency between y and w is $[(4 + 3 + 1 + 2)/1{,}000] \times 100\% = 1\%$, so there is 1 map unit between these genes. Note that, since recombination can only be scored in the F_2 males, the number of recombinants is divided by the number of *male* progeny, and not the total number of progeny.

13.17 In the Maltese bippy, amiable (A) is dominant to nasty (a), benign (B) is dominant to active (b), and crazy (C) is dominant to sane (c). A true-breeding amiable, active, crazy bippy was mated, with some difficulty, to a true-breeding nasty, benign, sane bippy. An F_1 individual from this cross was then used in a testcross (to a nasty, active, sane bippy) and produced, in typical prolific bippy fashion, 4,000 offspring. From an ancient manuscript titled *The Genetics of the Bippy, Maltese and Other*, you discover that all three genes are autosomal, a is linked to b but not to c, and the map distance between a and b is 20 mu.

  a. Predict all the expected phenotypes and the numbers of each type from this cross.
  b. Which phenotypic classes would be missing had a and b shown complete linkage?
  c. Which phenotypic classes would be missing if a and b were unlinked?
  d. Again, assuming a and b to be unlinked, predict all the expected phenotypes of nasty bippies and the frequencies of each type resulting from a self-cross of the F_1.

Answer: The crosses can be denoted as:

   Parental: $A\,b/A\,b$; $C/C \times a\,B/a\,B$; c/c
   F_1 testcross: $A\,b/a\,B$; $C/c \times a\,b/a\,b$; c/c

  a. Since the map distance between a and b is 20 mu, the F_2 will have 20 percent recombinants (classes indicated by an "*") between a and b.

GENOTYPE	PHENOTYPE	PERCENT	NUMBER
$A\,b/a\,b$; C/c	amiable, active, crazy	20	800
$A\,b/a\,b$; $c\,/c$	amiable, active, sane	20	800
$a\,B/a\,b$; C/c	nasty, benign, crazy	20	800
$a\,B/a\,b$; $c\,/c$	nasty, benign, sane	20	800
$a\,b/a\,b$; C/c	nasty, active, crazy	5	200*
$a\,b/a\,b$; $c\,/c$	nasty, active, sane	5	200*
$A\,B/a\,b$; C/c	amiable, benign, crazy	5	200*
$A\,B/a\,b$; $c\,/c$	amiable, benign, sane	5	200*

  b. If a and b had shown complete linkage, the recombinant (*) classes would be missing.
  c. No phenotypic classes would be missing if a and b were unlinked. The frequency of each class would be identical (500, or 12.5 percent), however.
  d. If a and b were unlinked, the results of selfing a triple heterozygote (the F_1) are as described previously for a trihybrid cross. The F_2 will have 8 phenotypic

classes in a ratio of 27:9:9:9:3:3:3:1. The nasty bippies must be aa in genotype, and so their distribution is a subset of these classes. If one is only considering the nasty bippies, the other two pairs of phenotypes will be distributed in the 9:3:3:1 ratio expected from a dihybrid cross. One will see 9 nasty, benign, crazy:3 nasty, benign, sane:3 nasty, active, crazy:1 nasty, active, sane.

13.18   Fill in the blanks in the following table. Continuous bars indicate linkage, and the order of linked genes is correct as shown. If all types of gametes are equally probable, write "none" in the right column headed "Least frequent classes." In the right column, show two gamete genotypes, unless all types are equally frequent, in which case write "none."

PARENT GENOTYPES	NUMBER OF DIFFERENT POSSIBLE GAMETES	LEAST FREQUENT CLASSES	
$\underline{A\,b}\,C$			
$a\,B\quad c$			
$\underline{A\,b\,C}$			
$a\quad B\quad c$			
$\underline{A\,b\,C\,D}$			
$a\quad B\quad c\quad d$			
$\underline{A\,b\,C\,D}\,\underline{Ef}$			
$a\quad B\quad C\,d\quad e\,f$			
$\underline{b\,D}$			
$B\,d$			

Answer: Note that the number of classes of gametes is a function of how many different heterozygous loci are present. If there are n heterozygous loci, there will be 2^n possible gametes.

PARENT GENOTYPES	NUMBER OF DIFFERENT POSSIBLE GAMETES	LEAST FREQUENT CLASSES	
$\underline{A\,b}\,C$			
$a\,B\quad c$	$2^3 = 8$	none	
$\underline{A\,b\,C}$			
$a\quad B\quad c$	$2^3 = 8$	$A\,B\,C$	$a\,b\,c$
$\underline{A\,b\,C\,D}$			
$a\quad B\quad c\quad d$	$2^4 = 16$	$A\,B\,C\,d$	$a\,b\,c\,D$
$\underline{A\,b\,C\,D}\,\underline{Ef}$			
$a\quad B\quad C\,d\quad e\,f$	$2^4 = 16$	$A\,B\,C\,D\,e\,f$	$a\,b\,C\,d\,E\,f$
$\underline{b\,D}$			
$B\,d$	$2^2 = 4$	$b\,d$	$B\,D$

13.19 Genes at loci f, m, and w are linked, but their order is unknown. The F_1 heterozygotes from a cross of *FF MM WW* $\times$ *ff mm ww* are testcrossed. The most frequent phenotypes in testcross progeny will be *F M W* and *f m w* regardless of what the gene order turns out to be.

a. What classes of testcross progeny (phenotypes) would be least frequent if locus *m* is in the middle?

b. What classes would be least frequent if locus *f* is in the middle?

c. What classes would be least frequent if locus *w* is in the middle?

Answer: The double-crossover class will always be the least frequent.

a. *FmW, fMw*

b. *MfW, mFw*

c. *FwM, fWm*

13.20 The following numbers were obtained for testcross progeny in *Drosophila* (phenotypes):

+	*m*	+	218
w	+	*f*	236
+	+	*f*	168
w	*m*	+	178
+	*m*	*f*	95
w	+	+	101
+	+	+	3
w	*m*	*f*	1
		Total	1,000

Construct a genetic map.

Answer: Notice that among the eight phenotypic classes, there are four frequencies of progeny. This would be expected if the three genes were linked, and a triply heterozygous parent were testcrossed. Since crossovers between closely linked genes occur less often than no crossovers, the most frequent classes of progeny will be those having nonrecombinant, or parental-type, chromosomes. Thus, the + *m* + and *w* + *f* chromosomes are parental-type chromosomes and indicate that the triply heterozygous parent was obtained as follows:

P: *w* + *f* /*w* + *f* x + *m* +/+ *m* +

F_1:   *w* + *f* /+ *m* + x *w m f* /*w m f*

Since recombination between closely linked genes is infrequent, the least frequent classes result from crossovers between each of the genes in the triple heterozygote, i.e., double crossovers (+ + +, *w m f*). The remaining classes will have resulted from single crossovers.

To help you determine which gene is in the middle in this an in subsequent problems, consider the example shown below, which shows a double crossover between two nonsister chromatids having the gene order $B/b - A/a - C/c$. Relative to the parental-type chromosomes, the recombinant chromosomes have the middle A/a alleles switched:

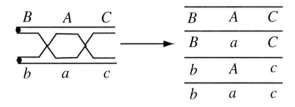

In three-point crosses, comparison of one of the double-crossover classes (the least frequent classes) with one of the parental classes (the most frequent classes) can allow you to infer which gene is in the middle. Depending on how they are chosen, one of two scenarios will be found. In one scenario, alleles at two genes will be identical, while alleles at the third gene will be different. In another scenario, alleles at two genes will be different, while alleles at the third gene will be identical. In each case, the third gene is the gene in the middle. The middle gene is unlike the other two because its alleles have been "switched."

Use this strategy and compare one of the parental-type chromosomes and one of the double-crossover chromosomes. This indicates that the m gene is in the middle:

One parental-type chromosome:	w	$+$	f
One double-crossover chromosome:	w	m	f
Comparison of alleles:	same	different	same

As m is unlike the other two, it is in the middle. While the genes are written in the correct order in this problem, this may not always be the case. (Always determine the correct order before proceeding.)

Now, diagram the crossovers in the triple heterozygote to infer the progeny classes that are associated with each crossover type:

Single crossover between *w, m:*

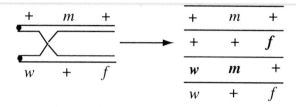

Single crossover between *m, f:*

Double crossover:

With this information, one can re-evaluate the progeny, and determine how much recombination occurred in each gene interval:

+	*m*	+	218	parental
w	+	*f*	236	parental
+	+	*f*	168	single crossover between *w, m*
w	*m*	+	178	single crossover between *w, m*
+	*m*	*f*	95	single crossover between *m, f*
w	+	+	101	single crossover between *m, f*
+	+	+	3	crossover between *w, m,* and between *m, f*
w	*m*	*f*	1	crossover between *w, m,* and between *m, f*
	Total		1,000	

Number of recombinants in *w, m* interval: $168 + 178 + 3 + 1 = 350$
Recombination frequency between *w, m* $= (350/1,000) \times 100\% = 35\%$

Number of recombinants in *m, f* interval: $95 + 101 + 3 + 1 = 200$
Recombination frequency between *m, f* $= (200/1,000) \times 100\% = 20\%$

This information can be represented in the following map:

13.21 Three of the many recessive mutations in *Drosophila melanogaster* that affect body color, wing shape, or bristle morphology are black (*b*) body versus grey in the wild type; dumpy (*dp*), obliquely truncated wings versus long wings in the wild type; and hooked (*hk*) bristles at the tip versus not hooked in the wild type. From a cross of a dumpy female with a black, hooked male, all the F₁ were wild type for all three characters. The testcross of an F₁ female with a dumpy, black, hooked male gave the following results:

wild type	169
black	19
black, hooked	301
dumpy, hooked	21
hooked	8
hooked, dumpy, black	172
dumpy, black	6
dumpy	305
Total	1,001

a. Construct a genetic map of the linkage group (or groups) these genes occupy. If applicable, show the order and give the map distances between the genes.
b. Determine the coefficient of coincidence for the portion of the chromosome involved in the cross. How much interference is there?

Answer:

a. First, use the symbols for the genes to write out the crosses that were done. It does not matter, at this point, what order you assign to the genes. Just be consistent in the order you choose so that you don't get confused.

P: + + dp /+ + dp (female) × b hk +/b hk + (male)
F₁ testcross: + + dp /b hk + (female) × b hk dp /b hk dp (male)

Now rewrite the data to reflect parental-type, single-crossover (SCO) and double-crossover (DCO) classes (based on frequency of each class).

PHENOTYPE	GAMETE GENOTYPE			NUMBER	CLASS
dumpy	+	+	*dp*	305	parental
black, hooked	*b*	*hk*	+	301	parental
hooked, dumpy, black	*b*	*hk*	*dp*	172	SCO
wild type	+	+	+	169	SCO
dumpy, hooked	+	*hk*	*dp*	21	SCO
black	*b*	+	+	19	SCO
hooked	+	*hk*	+	8	DCO
dumpy, black	*b*	+	*dp*	6	DCO

Now determine the gene order by comparing one of the double crossovers to one of the parental types (see solution to Problem 13.20, above):

parental-type genotype: +   +   *dp*

DCO genotype: +   *hk*   +

same different different

The *b* gene is unlike the other two, so it is in the middle. The correct gene order is *dp* – *b* – *hk*. Continue to use this gene order. The F_1 female that was test-crossed was *dp* + +/+ *b hk*. Consequently, the *dp b hk* and + + + progeny are single crossovers between *dp* and *b*, while the *dp* + *hk* and + *b* + progeny are single crossovers between *b* and *hk*. Recombination frequencies (RF) can be calculated as:

$$RF(dp - b) = [(172 + 169 + 6 + 8)/1{,}001] \times 100\% = 35.5\%$$
$$RF(b - hk) = [(21 + 19 + 6 + 8)/1{,}001] \times 100\% = 5.4\%$$

(Remember to include the double crossovers in this calculation, as each double crossover has a crossover in the interval being considered.) The map distance between *dp* and *b* is 35.5 mu and the map distance between *b* and *hk* is 5.4 mu. The map distance between *dp* and *hk* is 35.5 + 5.4 = 40.9 mu.

b. The coefficient of coincidence (c.o.c.) is

$$c.o.c. = frequency\ observed\ doubles/frequency\ expected\ doubles$$
$$= (14/1{,}001)/(0.355 \times 0.054)$$
$$= 0.014/0.01917$$
$$= 0.73$$

$$Interference = 1 - c.o.c.$$
$$= 1 - 0.73$$
$$= 0.27$$

13.22 The frequencies of gametes of different genotypes, determined by testcrossing a triple heterozygote, are as shown:

GAMETE GENOTYPE	%
+ + +	12.9
a b c	13.5
+ + c	6.9
a b +	6.5
+ b c	26.4
a + +	27.2
a + c	3.1
+ b +	3.5
Total	100.0

a. Which gametes are known to have been involved in double crossovers?
b. Which gamete types have not been involved in any exchanges?
c. The order shown is not necessarily correct. Which gene locus is in the middle?

Answer:

a. $a + c$ and $+ b +$ (least frequent).
b. $+ b c$ and $a + +$ (most frequent).
c. locus c (see solution to Problem 13.20, above, for determining the middle locus).

13.23 Two normal-looking *Drosophila* are crossed and yield the following phenotypes among the progeny:

Females:	+ + +	2,000
Sons:	+ + +	3
	a b c	1
	+ b c	839
	a + +	825
	a b +	86
	+ + c	90
	a + c	81
	+ b +	75
	Total	4,000

Give parental genotypes, gene arrangement in the female parent, map distances, and the coefficient of coincidence.

Answer: The differential appearance of the traits in males and females indicates that the traits are sex linked, i.e., they are X-linked. The female progeny are normal, since they received their father's X chromosome, which was + + +/Y. As they are phenotypically normal, they are not helpful in a mapping analysis. The male progeny received an X chromosome from the mother, and therefore can be used to analyze the results of recombination in the mother.

The most frequent progeny classes in the males are + *b c* and *a* + +. These are the parental-type chromosomes. The least frequent classes (the double-crossover classes) are + + + and *a b c*. Comparison of these two classes indicates that gene *a* is in the middle, and the correct order is *b* – *a* – *c* (or *c* – *a* – *b*) (see solution to Problem 13.20, above, for determining the middle locus). The parental genotypes (with the correct gene order) were *c* + *b* /+ *a* + (female) x + + +/Y (male). Now analyze the data to determine which progeny classes result from crossing-over in each gene interval and calculate the recombination frequencies in each interval. (SCO = single crossover; DCO = double crossover).

GAMETE GENOTYPE	NUMBER	CLASS
c + *b*	839	parental
+ *a* +	825	parental
+ *a b*	86	SCO (*a* – *b*)
c + +	90	SCO (*a* – *b*)
c a +	81	SCO (*c* – *a*)
+ + *b*	75	SCO (*c* – *a*)
c a b	1	DCO (*a* – *b*, *c* – *a*)
+ + +	3	DCO (*a* – *b*, *c* – *a*)

Total 2,000

Note that, since recombination cannot be scored in the female progeny, and only the 2,000 male progeny are being considered, the total that is used as the divisor in the calculation of recombination frequency (RF) is 2,000.

$$\text{RF } (a - b) = [(86 + 90 + 1 + 3)/2{,}000] \times 100\% = 9.0\%$$
$$\text{RF } (c - a) = [(81 + 75 + 1 + 3)/2{,}000] \times 100\% = 8.0\%$$

With this information, draw the following map:

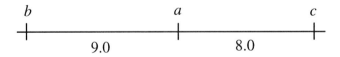

To calculate the coefficient of coincidence (c.o.c.), compare the frequency of actual double crossovers to that expected based on the crossover frequency observed in each interval.

$$\text{c.o.c.} = \text{observed DCO frequency/expected DCO frequency}$$
$$= [(3 + 1)/2{,}000]/(0.09 \times 0.08)$$
$$= 0.002/0.0072$$
$$= 0.28$$

13.24   The following questions make use of this genetic map:

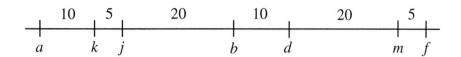

Calculate:

a. the frequency of *j b* gametes from a *J B/j b* genotype
b. the frequency of *A M* gametes from an *a M/A m* genotype
c. the frequency of *J B D* gametes from a *j B d/J b D* genotype
d. the frequency of *J B d* gametes from a *j B d/J b D* genotype
e. the frequency of *j b d/j b d* genotypes in a *j B d/J b D* × *j B d/J b D* mating
f. the frequency of *A k F* gametes from an *A K F/a k f* genotype

Answer:

a. There are 20 map units between *j* and *b*, so there will be 20 percent recombinant-type and 80 percent parental-type gametes. In a *J B/j b* parent, *j b* gametes are half of the parental-type gametes, or 40 percent of the total gametes.

b. There are 65 map units between *A* and *M*, so these loci will show independent assortment, as the frequency of recombinant-type gametes cannot exceed 50 percent. In an *a M/A m* parent, the *A M* gametes are half of the recombinant-type gametes. There will be 25 percent *A M* gametes.

c. In a *j B d/J b D* individual, *J B D* gametes are produced by a double crossover: a crossover in the interval *j – b*, and a crossover in the interval *b – d*. As there are 20 map units between *j* and *b*, and 10 map units between *b* and *d*, the frequency of double crossovers is expected to be $0.20 \times 0.10 \times 100\% = 2\%$. *J B D* gametes are half of the double crossovers produced, so will be seen 1 percent of the time.

d. In a *j B d /J b D* individual, *J B d* gametes are one-half of the gametes produced by a single crossover in the interval *j – b*. Since there are 20 map units between these genes, 10 percent of the gametes will be *J B d*.

e. By the reasoning in (c), *j b d* gametes will be seen 1 percent of the time in a *j B d/J b D* individual. To obtain a *j b d/j b d* genotype, one must obtain such gametes from both parents. The frequency of this is $(0.01 \times 0.01) \times 100\% = 0.01\%$.

f. Based on the map distances, one expects 10 percent recombination between *a* and *k* and 50 percent recombination between *k* and *f*. (Again, note that even though *k* and *f* are more than 50 map units apart, one observes only 50 percent recombination between these two genes.) In an *A K F/a k f* individual, an *A k F* gamete results from a double crossover: one crossover between *a* and *k* (10 percent chance) and one crossover between *k* and *f* (50 percent chance). The chance of both crossovers occurring simultaneously is $0.10 \times 0.50 = 0.05$, or 5%. Since *A k F* gametes are half of the double crossovers produced, they will be 2.5% of the total.

13.25 A female *Drosophila* carries the recessive mutations *a* and *b* in repulsion on the X chromosome (she is heterozygous for both). She is also heterozygous for an X-linked recessive lethal allele, *l*. When she is mated to a true-breeding, normal male, she yields the following progeny:

Females: 1,000   + +

Males: 405   *a* +
                  44   + *b*
                  48   + +
                   2   *a* *b*

Draw a chromosome map of the three genes in the proper order and with map distances as nearly as you can calculate them.

Answer: First, consider what happens when a female that is heterozygous for an X-linked lethal is crossed to a normal male. One can diagram such a cross as:

P: *l*/+ female ×+/*Y* male
F_1:   females: *l* /+ and +/ + (phenotypically normal)
          males: +/*Y* (normal) and *l* /*Y* (dead, not recovered)

In such a cross, one-half of the male progeny are not recovered due to the presence of the lethal allele. Only progeny bearing the + allele are recovered. Thus, the 499 males that are recovered in this cross are half of the expected male progeny.

Second, consider that the lethal-bearing chromosome can be recovered in the female progeny. Since the lethal allele is a recessive mutation, it is "rescued" by the normal + allele contributed to the female progeny by the father's X chromosome. However, as the father's X chromosome bears the + alleles of each gene, the females are phenotypically normal and are not helpful in a recombination analysis.

Now, analyze the phenotypes of the male progeny that are recovered to infer map distances and the gene order. Since one-half of the male progeny are not recovered, each of the four classes seen represents one of the two reciprocal classes of progeny recovered in a three-point cross. Include the third (*l*/+) locus and assign each genotype to a progeny class based on its frequency:

Male progeny: 405   *a*   +   +   parental type
                 44   +   *b*   +   single crossover
                 48   +   +   +   single crossover
                  2   *a*   *b*   +   double crossover

Comparison of the parental and double-crossover classes indicates that *b* is in the middle, and the correct order is *a* – *b* – *l* (see solution to Problem 13.20, above, for determining the middle locus). Since one of the parental-type chromosomes was *a* + +, the other must have been + *b* *l*, the reciprocal. The heterozygous female was therefore *a* + +/+ *b* *l*.

The 44 + *b* + progeny are obtained from gametes arising from single crossovers between *b* and *l*. They are half of the total single crossovers in that interval. The other half were not recovered, as they bore the *l* allele. Similarly, the 48 + + + progeny are half of the single crossovers in the interval *a* – *b*. This information can be used to calculate recombination frequencies (RF) and draw a map.

$$RF\ (a - b) = [(48 + 2)/499] \times 100\% = 10\%$$
$$RF\ (b - l) = [(44 + 2)/499] \times 100\% = 9.2\%$$

13.26   The following *Drosophila* cross is done:

$$\frac{a + b}{+ c +} \times \frac{a\ c\ b}{\underline{\quad}\underline{\quad}}$$

Predict the numbers of phenotypes of male and female progeny that will emerge if the gene arrangement is as shown, the distance between *a* and *c* is 14 mu, the distance between *c* and *b* is 12 mu, the coefficient of coincidence is 0.3, and the number of progeny is 2,000.

Answer: Since the male parent is triply recessive, the phenotypes associated with the female parent's gametes will be evident equally in males and females. The map distances between the loci give the frequency of recombinants (i.e., crossovers) in each gene interval. There will be 14 percent recombinants in the *a – c* interval (7% each of *a c* and + +), and 12 percent recombinants in the *c – b* interval (6% each of + + and *c b*). These recombinants will be distributed between both single- and double-crossover classes.

The coefficient of coincidence gives the percentage of expected double crossovers that are observed. The expected double crossovers can be calculated based on the recombination frequency in each of the two gene intervals, and is $(0.12 \times 0.14) \times 100\% = 1.68\%$. Since the coefficient of coincidence is 0.3, only 30 percent of the expected double crossovers are observed, or $1.68\% \times 30\% = 0.50\%$ (0.25% each of *a c b* and + + +).

The remaining recombinants will be single-crossover classes. This can be calculated by considering that some of the crossovers in each gene interval contribute to the double-crossover classes, and each double crossover has a crossover in each gene interval. This means the frequency of single crossovers in each gene interval is equal to the difference between the frequency of crossovers in that interval and the frequency of double crossovers. Consequently, there will be 14% – 0.5% = 13.5% single crossovers in the *a – c* interval (6.75% each *a c* + and + + *b*), and 12% – 0.5% = 11.5% single crossovers in the *c – b* interval (5.75% each *a* + + and + *c b*).

The remaining progeny [100% – (13.5% + 11.5% + 0.5%) = 74.5%] will be parental types (37.25% *a* + *b* and 37.25% + *c* +). The types or progeny are therefore:

GENOTYPE	PERCENT	NUMBER
a + b	37.25	745
+ c +	37.25	745
a c +	6.75	135
+ + b	6.75	135
a + +	5.75	115
+ b c	5.75	115
a c b	0.25	5
+ + +	0.25	5

13.27   A farmer who raises rabbits wants to break into the Easter market. He has stocks of two true-breeding lines. One is hollow and long-eared but not chocolate, and the second is solid, short-eared and chocolate. Hollow (*h*), long ears (*le*), and chocolate (*ch*) are all recessive, autosomal, and linked as in the following map:

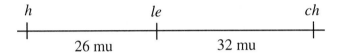

The farmer can generate a trihybrid by crossing his two lines and at great expense he is able to obtain the services of a male homozygous recessive at all three loci to cross with his F₁ females.

The farmer has buyers for both solid and hollow bunnies; however, all must be chocolate and long eared. Assuming that interference is zero, if he needs 25 percent of the progeny of the desired phenotypes to be profitable, should he continue with his breeding? Calculate the percent of the total progeny that will be the desired phenotypes.

Answer: The crosses under consideration are:

P: *h le Ch /h le Ch × H Le ch /H Le ch*
F₁: *h le Ch /H Le ch × h le ch /h le ch*

To be profitable, the farmer needs 25 percent of the progeny to be either *h le ch /h le ch* or *H le ch /h le ch*. Hence, he is concerned with the probability of obtaining a h le ch or a H le ch gamete from an *h le Ch /H Le ch* individual. Gametes that are *h le ch* arise from a single crossover between *le* and *ch*. Since there are 32 mu between *le* and *ch*, there will be 16 percent *h le ch* individuals (one-half of the recombinants between *le* and *ch*). Gametes that are *H le ch* arise from a crossover in each interval. Since there is no interference, their frequency will be half of the expected double-crossover frequency, or (0.5 × 0.32 × 0.26) × 100% = 4.16%. The expected frequency of *h le ch* and *H le ch* gametes is 4.16% + 16% = 20.16%. The farmer should stop breeding and cut his losses.

13.28   Three different semidominant mutations affect the tail of mice. They are linked genes, and all three are lethal in the embryo when homozygous. Fused-tail (*Fu*) and kinky-tail (*Ki*) mice have kinky-appearing tails, while brachyury (*T*) mice have short tails. A fourth gene, histocompatibility-2 (*H-2*), is linked to the three tail genes and is concerned with tissue transplantation. Mice that are *H-2*/+ will accept tissue grafts, whereas +/+ mice will not. In the following crosses the normal allele is represented by +. The phenotypes of the progeny are given for four crosses.

(1) $\dfrac{Fu\ +}{+\ Ki}$ × $\dfrac{+\ +}{+\ +}$

Fused tail	106
Kinky tail	92
Normal tail	1
Fused-kinky tail	1

(2) $\dfrac{Fu\ H\text{-}2}{+\ +}$ × $\dfrac{+\ +}{+\ +}$

Fused tail, accepts graft	88
Normal tail, rejects graft	104
Normal tail, accepts graft	5
Fused tail, rejects graft	3

(3) $\dfrac{T\ H\text{-}2}{+\ +}$ × $\dfrac{+\ +}{+\ +}$

Brachy tail, accepts graft	1048
Normal tail, rejects graft	1152
Brachy tail, rejects graft	138
Normal tail, accepts graft	162

(4) $\dfrac{Fu\ +}{+\ T}$ × $\dfrac{+\ +}{+\ +}$

Fused tail	146
Brachy tail	130
Normal tail	14
Fused-brachy tail	10

Make a map of the four genes involved in these crosses, giving gene order and map distances between the genes.

Answer: Since all of the genes have a dominant phenotype, and crosses are made to a homozygous recessive strain, the data can be analyzed as a series of two-point testcrosses as follows:

CROSS	GENES INVOLVED	# RECOMBINANTS TOTAL	RECOMBINATION FREQUENCY (%)	APPARENT MAP DISTANCE
1	*Fu, Ki*	2/200	1	1 mu
2	*Fu, H-2*	8/200	4	4 mu
3	*T, H-2*	300/2,500	12	12 mu
4	*Fu, T*	24/300	8	8 mu

Two maps are consistent with these data.

13.29   The cross in *Drosophila* of

$$\frac{a^+\,b^+\,c\;\;d\;\;e}{a\;\;b\;\;c^+\,d^+\,e^+}\quad X\quad\frac{a\;b\;c\;d\;e}{a\;b\;c\;d\;e}$$

gave 1,000 progeny of the following 16 phenotypes:

	GENOTYPE					NUMBER
(1)	a^+	b^+	c	d	e	220
(2)	a^+	b^+	c	d	e^+	230
(3)	a	b	c^+	d^+	e	210
(4)	a	b	c^+	d^+	e^+	215
(5)	a	b^+	c^+	d^+	e	12
(6)	a	b^+	c^+	d^+	e^+	13
(7)	a^+	b	c	d	e^+	16
(8)	a^+	b	c	d	e	14
(9)	a	b^+	c^+	d	e^+	14
(10)	a	b^+	c^+	d	e	13
(11)	a^+	b	c	d^+	e^+	8
(12)	a^+	b	c	d^+	e	8
(13)	a^+	b^+	c^+	d	e^+	7
(14)	a^+	b^+	c^+	d	e	7
(15)	a	b	c	d^+	e^+	6
(16)	a	b	c	d^+	e	7

a. Draw a genetic map of the chromosome, indicating the linkage of the five genes and the number of map units separating each.

b. From the single-crossover frequencies, what would be the expected frequency of $a^+\,b^+\,c^+\,d^+\,e^+$ flies?

Answer:

a. Approach this problem by considering two genes at a time. Then one has:

GENE PAIR	# PARENTAL-TYPE PROGENY	# RECOMBINANT-TYPE PROGENY	RECOMBINATION FREQUENCY (%)	LINKED?
a, b	902	98	9.8	yes
a, c	973	27	2.7	yes
a, d	957	43	4.3	yes
a, e	497	503	50.0	no
b, c	875	125	12.5	yes
b, d	945	55	5.5	yes
b, e	497	503	50.0	no
c, d	930	70	7.0	yes
c, e	498	502	50.0	no
d, e	496	504	50.0	no

The genes *a*, *b*, *c*, and *d* are linked, while *e* is unlinked to the other four genes. Use the smallest distances as the most accurate map distances. One has:

b. Rewrite the parental cross using the correct gene order:

$$\frac{b^+\ d\ a^+\ c}{b\ d^+\ a\ c^+}\ \frac{e}{e^+}\ \times\ \frac{b\ d\ a\ c}{b\ d\ a\ c}\ \frac{e}{e}$$

To obtain a $b^+\ d^+\ a^+\ c^+$ fly, there must be crossovers between *b* and *d*, *d* and *a*, and *a* and *c*. Two reciprocal crossovers will be found: one-half of the progeny will be $b^+\ d^+\ a^+\ c^+$ and one-half of the progeny will be *b d a c*. Among these progeny, one-half will be e^+ and one-half will be *e*.

$$p(b^+\ d^+\ a^+\ c^+\ e^+) = p(\text{triple crossover}) \times 1/2 \times 1/2$$
$$= (0.055 \times 0.043 \times 0.027) \times 0.25$$
$$= 1.6 \times 10^{-5}.$$

13.30 In *Drosophila*, many different mutations have been isolated that affect a normally brick-red eye color caused by the deposition of brown and bright-red pigments. Two X-linked recessive mutations are *w* (white eyes, map position 1.5) and *cho* (chocolate-brown eyes, map position 13.0), with *w* epistatic to *cho*.

a. A white-eyed female is crossed to a chocolate-eyed male, and the normal, red-eyed F_1 females are crossed to either wild-type or white-eyed males. Determine the frequency of the progeny types produced in each cross.

b. The recessive mutation *st* causes scarlet (bright-red) eyes, and maps to the third chromosome at position 44. Mutant flies with only *st* and *cho* alleles have white eyes, and *w* is epistatic to *st*. Suppose a true-breeding *w* male is crossed to a true-breeding *cho, st* female. Determine the frequency of the progeny types you would expect if the F$_1$ females are crossed to true-breeding scarlet-eyed males.

Answer:

a. The cross is *w +/w* + (white female) × + *cho*/Y (chocolate male), and the F$_1$ females are *w +/+ cho* (red). Since the *w* and *cho* genes are 11.5 map units apart, the F$_1$ females will have 11.5 percent recombinant-type gametes (5.75% each ++ and *w cho*) and 88.5 percent parental-type gametes (44.25% each *w +* and + *cho*). When these gametes are combined with those of wild-type (50% each + + and Y) or white-eyed (50% each *w* + and Y) males, one obtains the progeny shown in the following branch diagrams.

Cross: *w + /+ cho* x + + /Y

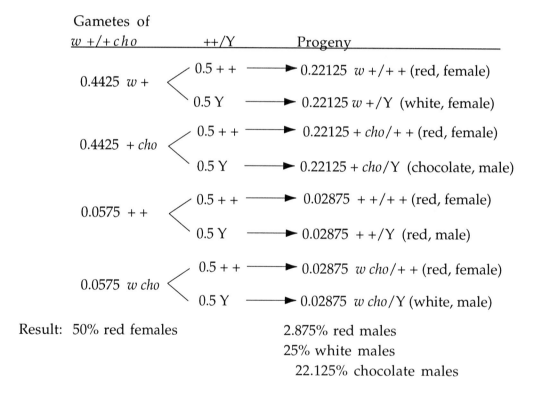

Gametes of

w +/+ cho	++/Y	Progeny

0.4425 *w +*
  0.5 + + → 0.22125 *w +/+* + (red, female)
  0.5 Y → 0.22125 *w +*/Y (white, female)

0.4425 + *cho*
  0.5 + + → 0.22125 + *cho*/+ + (red, female)
  0.5 Y → 0.22125 + *cho*/Y (chocolate, male)

0.0575 + +
  0.5 + + → 0.02875 + +/+ + (red, female)
  0.5 Y → 0.02875 + +/Y (red, male)

0.0575 *w cho*
  0.5 + + → 0.02875 *w cho*/+ + (red, female)
  0.5 Y → 0.02875 *w cho*/Y (white, male)

Result: 50% red females

2.875% red males
25% white males
22.125% chocolate males

Gametes of

$w +/+ cho$	$w +/Y$	Progeny
0.4425 $w +$	0.5 + +	0.22125 $w +/w +$ (white, female)
	0.5 Y	0.22125 $w +/Y$ (white, male)
0.4425 $+ cho$	0.5 $w +$	0.22125 $+ cho/w +$ (red, female)
	0.5 Y	0.22125 $+ cho/Y$ (chocolate, male)
0.0575 $+ +$	0.5 + +	0.02875 $+ +/w +$ (red, female)
	0.5 Y	0.02875 $+ +/Y$ (red, male)
0.0575 $w cho$	0.5 $w +$	0.02875 $w cho/w +$ (white, female)
	0.5 Y	0.02875 $w cho/Y$ (white, male)

Result: 25% red females   2.875% red males
          25% white females   25% white males
                                 22.125% chocolate males

b. The initial cross is $\{w +/Y; +/+\} \times \{+ cho/+ cho; st/st\}$ with F_1 females being $\{w +/+ cho; +/st\}$. These trihybrid females will have eight types of gametes: 88.5 percent will be parental types (22.125% each of $\{w +; +\}$, $\{w +; st\}$, $\{+ cho; +\}$, $\{+ cho; st\}$), and 11.5 percent will be recombinants between w and cho (2.875% each of $\{+ +; +\}$, $\{+ +; st\}$, $\{w cho; +\}$, $\{w cho; st\}$). The results obtained when the F_1 female is crossed to a true-breeding scarlet male (with $\{+ +; st\}$ and $\{Y; st\}$ gametes) are shown in the following branch diagrams:

Cross: $w +/+ cho; st/+ \times + +/Y; st/s t$

Gametes of

w +/+ cho; st/+   ++/Y; st/s t   Progeny

0.2215 w +

0.5 + +; st ⟶ 0.110625 w +/+ +; +/st (red female)

0.5 Y; st ⟶ 0.110625 w +/Y; +/st (white male)

0.2215 + cho

0.5 w +; st ⟶ 0.110625 w +/+ +; st/st (scarlet female)

0.5 Y; st ⟶ 0.110625 w +/Y; st/st (white male)

0.2215 + +

0.5 + +; st ⟶ 0.110625 + cho/+ + ; +/st (red female)

0.5 Y; st ⟶ 0.110625 + cho/Y; +/st (chocolate male)

0.2215 w cho

0.5 w +; st ⟶ 0.110625 + cho/+ +; st/st (scarlet female)

0.5 Y; st ⟶ 0.110625 + cho/Y; st/st (white male)

0.02875 w +

0.5 + +; st ⟶ 0.014375 + +/+ +; +/st (red female)

0.5 Y; st ⟶ 0.014375 + +/Y; +/st (red male)

0.02875 + cho

0.5 w +; st ⟶ 0.014375 + +/w +; st/st (scarlet female)

0.5 Y; st ⟶ 0.014375 + +/Y; st/st (scarlet male)

0.02875 + +

0.5 + +; st ⟶ 0.014375 w cho/+ +; +/st (red female)

0.5 Y; st ⟶ 0.014375 w cho/Y; +/st (white male)

0.02875 w cho

0.5 w +; st ⟶ 0.014375 w cho/+ +; st/st (scarlet female)

0.5 Y; st ⟶ 0.014375 w cho/Y; st/st (white male)

Result: 25% red females
        25% scarlet females

1.4375% red males
1.4375% scarlet males
36.0625% white males
11.0625% chocolate males

13.31   Breeders of thoroughbred horses used for racing keep extensive pedigree information. Such information can be useful to determine simple inheritance patterns (e.g.,
chestnut coat color has been determined to be recessive to bay coat color) and to
speculate whether race horses that win very competitive races ("classy" horses)
share genetic traits. Sharpen Up was a chestnut stallion who was only somewhat
successful as a race horse. He was retired from horse-racing at the age of four and
put out to stud. His progeny were very successful: of 367 foals fathered in the
United States, 43 were prize-winners in very competitive races, and of 200 foals fathered in England, 40 were prize-winners in very competitive races. A commentator
who analyzed Sharpen Up's progeny (and that of other chestnut prize-winners) has
suggested that whatever gene combinations produced class (winning horses) were

tied to chestnut coat. Indeed, of the 83 progeny that have shown class (won very competitive races), about 45 were also chestnut in color. Use a chi-square test to assess whether there is any reason to believe that if there is a gene (or genes) for class, it is linked to the gene for chestnut coat color. Examine this issue using two different assumptions: (1) Sharpen Up was mated equally frequently to homozygous bay, heterozygous bay/chestnut, and homozygous chestnut mares; (2) Sharpen Up was mated equally frequently to heterozygous bay/chestnut and homozygous chestnut mares. Carefully state any additional assumptions and your hypothesis.

Answer: First, use the chi-square test to evaluate the hypothesis that there is no relationship between chestnut coat color and "class." If, by using the chi-square test, we are able to reject this hypothesis, further investigation into the potential linkage of the coat color gene and a "class" gene would be warranted. In the statement of the problem, two assumptions are stated concerning the mates of Sharpen Up. In the initial chi-square test proposed here, these are the major assumptions. Other needed assumptions follow from the hypothesis of the chi-square test. However, evaluation of linkage of the chestnut gene and a "class" gene require a number of additional assumptions. These will be discussed below.

Given a hypothesis that there is no relationship between "class" and chestnut coat color, then the likelihood of obtaining a "classy" horse in a mating with Sharpen Up is uniform with regard to coat color. Then, since 83 "classy" horses were produced from a total of $367 + 260 = 627$ progeny, the chance of obtaining a "classy" horse from a mating with Sharpen Up is $83/627 = 0.1324 = 13.24\%$, independent of coat color. To perform the chi-square test, we need to determine the expected number of "classy" chestnut and "classy" bay horses, and compare this to the observed number of "classy" chestnut and "classy" bay horses.

Assumption I: Sharpen up is mated equally frequently to homozygous bay, heterozygous bay/chestnut and homozygous chestnut mares. Chestnut is recessive to bay, so let chestnut be represented by c and bay by C. Since Sharpen Up is chestnut, the three types of crosses occurring equally frequently are $cc \times CC$, $cc \times Cc$, and $cc \times cc$. The first cross will produce no cc progeny; the second will produce 50% cc progeny; the third cross will produce 100% cc progeny. If each crosses occurs equally frequently, $[(0 \times 1/3) + (1/2 \times 1/3) + (1/3)] = 1/2$, or $1/2 \times 627 = 314$ of the progeny were chestnut. [In this answer, fractions of a horse will be rounded up or down to the nearest "whole" horse.] The remaining $627 - 314 = 313$ progeny were bay.

Using the assumption that the frequency of "classy" horses is uniform, the frequency of "classy" horses is 13.24 percent. Then, under assumption I, the expected number of "classy" chestnut progeny = $314 \times 0.1324 = 42$ and the expected number of "classy" bay progeny = $313 \times 0.1324 = 41$. The observed numbers of "classy" horses were 45 chestnut and 38 bay. For these values, $\chi^2 = [(45 - 42)^2/42 + (38 - 41)^2/41] = 0.43$, df = 1, $0.50 < P < 0.70$. Under assumption I then, the hypothesis that chestnut coat color and "class" are unrelated is accepted as possible.

Assumption II: Sharpen up is mated equally frequently to heterozygous bay/chestnut and chestnut mares. The first cross, $Cc \times cc$, will produce 50 percent cc

(chestnut) progeny and the *cc x cc* cross will produce 100 percent *cc* (chestnut) progeny. Thus, if both types of crosses occur equally frequently, 75 percent, or $0.75 \times 627 = 470$, of the progeny were chestnut under assumption II. The remaining $627 - 470 = 157$ progeny were bay.

If the frequency of "classy" horses is 13.24 percent, then under assumption II we would expect $470 \times 0.1324 = 62$ chestnut, "classy" progeny and 21 bay, "classy" progeny. The observed numbers of "classy" horses were 45 chestnut and 38 bay. For these values, $\chi^2 = [(45 - 62)^2/62 + (38 - 21)^2/21] = 18.4$, df $= 1$, $P < 0.001$. Under assumption II then, we would reject the hypothesis that the chestnut coat color gene and "class" are unrelated as being unlikely. It would be reasonable to consider the hypothesis that a gene closely linked to chestnut might contribute to "class."

Notice that the evidence for a relationship between chestnut coat and "class" hinges on knowing what alleles at the chestnut/bay gene were present in the mares bred to Sharpen Up. This information is available (although not in this problem). It would be a valuable exercise to consider what additional assumptions would be required to specifically test for linkage to a "class" gene. The following might be necessary: assumptions about the number of alleles in the population of horses, the dominance relationship(s) between them, and whether they are in repulsion or in coupling with the chestnut allele. Needless to say, this is a complex endeavor.

13.32   A cross was made between a pantothenate-requiring (*pan*) strain and a lysine-requiring (*lys*) strain of *Neurospora crassa*, and 750 random ascospores were analyzed for their ability to grow on a minimal medium (a medium lacking pantothenate and lysine). Thirty colonies subsequently grew. Map the *pan* and *lys* loci.

Answer: First, write out the strains that were crossed and the kinds of progeny that are possible.

pan +	x	+ *lys*	→	*pan*	+	parental-type spore
				+	*lys*	parental-type spore
				pan	*lys*	recombinant-type spore
				+	+	recombinant-type spore

Notice that, since spores that are *pan* or *lys* require supplements to grow, the only spores that can grow on minimal medium are wild-type, or + + spores. All parental-type spores and half of the recombinants cannot grow. Thus, the 30 spores that grew are half of the recombinants. Therefore, there were a total of 60 recombinants in 750 progeny tested, giving a map distance of $(60/750) \times 100\% = 8$ mu.

13.33   Four different albino strains of *Neurospora* were each crossed to the wild type. All crosses resulted in half wild-type and half albino progeny. Crosses were made between the first strain and the other three with the following results:

1×2:   975 albino, 25 wild type

1×3:   1000 albino

1×4:   750 albino, 250 wild type

Which mutations represent different genes, and which genes are linked? How did you arrive at your conclusions?

Answer: First, consider the results of the set of crosses to the wild type.

$$\text{albino} \times + \rightarrow 50\% \text{ albino}, 50\% +$$

The observation of equal frequencies of parental-type spores in the progeny indicates that the albino strains have an allele that behaves in a Mendelian fashion. That is, for each of the four strains, the albino and + alleles segregate from each other as would be expected of alleles at one gene. The question now becomes whether each of the albino strains results from a mutation in the same or a different gene. This issue can be resolved by considering the second set of crosses and the possibility that the different strains are mutant at different genes. If different strains have mutations at different genes, the wild-type spores that are found represent half of the recombinant types of spores, as shown below:

$$1 \times 2: \quad a^1 + \quad \times \quad + a^2 \quad \rightarrow \quad 975 \text{ albino } (a^1 a^2, a^1 + \text{ or } + a^2)$$
$$25 \text{ wild type } (+ +)$$

$$1 \times 3: \quad a^1 + \quad \times \quad + a^3 \quad \rightarrow \quad 1{,}000 \text{ albino } (a^1 a^3, a^1 + \text{ or } + a^3)$$
$$0 \text{ wild type } (+ +)$$

$$1 \times 4: \quad a^1 + \quad \times \quad + a^4 \quad \rightarrow \quad 750 \text{ albino } (a^1 a^4, a^1 + \text{ or } + a^4)$$
$$250 \text{ wild type } (+ +)$$

In the cross of 1×2, the appearance of 25 wild-type spores indicates that there are a total of 50 recombinant spores (5%). Hence, genes 1 and 2 are linked, and 5 map units apart. In the cross of 1×3, there are no recombinant spores, and so these albino alleles appear to be at the same gene, and may be identical. In the cross of 1×4, there are a total of 500 recombinant spores (50%) and so genes 1 and 4 appear to be unlinked. There are therefore three different genes, with genes 1 (= 3) and 2 being linked.

13.34 Genes *met* and *thi* are linked in *Neurospora crassa*; we want to locate *arg* with respect to *met* and *thi*. From the cross *arg* + + $\times$ + *thi met*, the following random ascospore isolates were obtained. Map these three genes.

arg	*thi*	*met*	26	*arg*	+	+	51
arg	*thi*	+	17	+	*thi*	+	4
arg	+	*met*	3	+	+	*met*	14
+	*thi*	*met*	56	+	+	+	29

Answer: Notice that there are 8 classes of progeny which appear in four frequencies, reminiscent of a three-point cross with three linked loci. Therefore, treat this as you would a three-point cross. Comparison of one of the parental types (+ *thi met*) to one of the double recombinants (*arg* + *met*) tells us that *met* is in the middle, between *arg* and *thi*. Rewrite the progeny types as (SCO = single crossover):

parental	+	*met*	*thi*	56
parental	*arg*	+	+	51
SCO between *arg – met*	*arg*	*met*	*thi*	26
SCO between *arg – met*	+	+	+	29
SCO between *met – thi*	*arg*	+	*thi*	17
SCO between *met – thi*	+	*met*	+	14
double crossover	*arg*	*met*	+	3
double crossover	+	+	*thi*	4
				200

The map distance between *arg* and *met* is [(26 + 29 + 3 + 4)/200] × 100% = 31 mu, and the map distance between *met* and *thi* is (17 + 14 + 3 + 4)/200 = 19 mu. Therefore, we have the following map:

13.35 Double exchanges between two loci can be of several types, called two-strand, three-strand, and four-strand doubles.

a. Four recombination gametes would be produced from a tetrad in which the first of two exchanges is depicted in the following figure. Draw in the second exchange.

b. In the following figure, draw in the second exchange so that four nonrecombination gametes would result.

Answer: A solution to parts (a) and (b) can follow from trying to diagram a number of different crossovers and their resolution (by following a chromosome "through" the crossover from left to right). It is also possible to reason through these as follows: In part (a), four recombinant gametes are needed. The crossover shown occurs between two nonsister chromatids, and gives two of these. A crossover between the remaining two nonsister chromatids would give two more, making a total of four. In part (b), four nonrecombinant gametes are needed. The crossover shown gives two recombinant gametes, and so a second crossover must be drawn between these same two nonsister chromatids to change them back to nonrecombinant-type chromosomes. Shown below is a diagram of a four-strand double crossover, the solution to (a), and a two-strand double crossover, the solution to (b), with resolution for the crossover events. Note that the diagram shown in (b) is equivalent to a two-strand double crossover between any two nonsister chromatids.

a.

b.

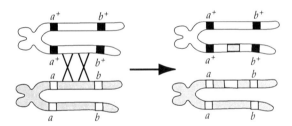

13.36 A cross between a pink (p^-) yeast strain of mating type **a** and a cream strain (p^+) of mating type α produced the following tetrads:

18	p^+ **a**	p^+ **a**	p^- α	p^- α
8	p^+ **a**	p^- **a**	p^+ α	p^- α
20	p^+ α	p^+ α	p^- **a**	p^- **a**

On the basis of these results, are the p and mating type genes on separate chromosomes?

Answer: As the initial cross is p^- **a** x p^+ α, there are 20 PD tetrads, 18 NPD tetrads, and 8 T tetrads. Since the number of PD and NPD tetrads is approximately equal, these two genes assort independently and therefore are on different chromosomes. (Note that once tetrad types are assigned, determination of linkage is much easier than in nontetrad analysis. Simply ask if PD = NPD!)

13.37   The following asci were obtained from the cross *leu + × + rib* in yeast. Draw the linkage map and determine the map distance.

110	45	6	39
leu +	*leu rib*	+ +	*leu* +
+ *rib*	*leu* +	*leu rib*	+ *rib*
leu +	+ +	*leu rib*	+ +
+ *rib*	+ *rib*	+ +	*leu rib*

Answer: Categorizing these unordered asci shows that there are 110 PD, 6 NPD, and 45 + 39 = 84 T tetrads. Since PD >> NPD, the loci are linked. The percent recombination between them is given by:

$$RF = [(1/2\ T + NPD)/(total\ \#\ asci)] \times 100\%$$
$$= [[(1/2 \times 84) + 6]/(110 + 6 + 45 + 39)] \times 100\%$$
$$= (48/200) \times 100\%$$
$$= 24\%$$

The map distance between *leu* and *rib* is 24 mu.

13.38   The genes *a*, *b*, and *c* are on the same chromosome arm in *Neurospora crassa*. The following ordered asci were obtained from the cross *a b + × + + c*:

45	5	146	1	10	20	15	58
a b +	*a b* +	*a b* +	*a b* +	*a b* +	*a b* +	*a b* +	*a b* +
+ *b c*	*a* + +	*a b* +	+ + +	*a* + *c*	+ + *c*	*a b c*	+ *b* +
a + +	+ *b c*	+ + *c*	*a b c*	+ *b* +	*a b* +	+ + +	*a* + *c*
+ + *c*	+ + *c*	+ + *c*	+ + *c*	+ + *c*	+ + *c*	+ + *c*	+ + *c*

a. Determine the correct gene order.
b. Determine all gene–gene and gene–centromere distances.

Answer: To solve this problem, consider only one pair of loci at a time, determine the gene–gene and gene–centromere distances for that pair, and then relate the findings for both pairs of loci. For the *a* and *b* loci, one can assign the type of tetrad and the segregation pattern (MI = alleles segregated during meiosis I, MII = alleles segregated during meiosis II) as shown below:

45	5	146	1	10	20	15	58
T	T	PD	PD	T	PD	PD	T
a b	*a b*	*a b*	*a b*	*a b*	*a b*	*a b*	*a b*
+ *b*	*a* +	*a b*	+ +	*a* +	+ +	*a b*	+ *b*
a +	+ *b*	+ +	*a b*	+ *b*	*a b*	+ +	*a* +
+ +	+ +	+ +	+ +	+ +	+ +	+ +	+ +
MII MI	MI MII	MI MI	MII MII	MI MII	MII MII	MI MI	MII MI

For the cross $a\ b \times +\ +$ then, there are $(146 + 1 + 20 + 15) = 182$ PD, $(45 + 5 + 10 + 58) = 118$ T, and 0 NPD tetrads. Since PD >> NPD, the loci are linked. The recombination frequency between them is given by:

$$\begin{aligned} RF &= [(1/2\,T + NPD)/\text{total \# asci}] \times 100\% \\ &= [(1/2 \times 118)/300] \times 100\% \\ &= 19.7\% \end{aligned}$$

The recombination frequency of a and b with the centromere is given by:

$$\begin{aligned} RF\ (\text{gene–centromere}) &= (1/2\ \text{MII type patterns/total}) \times 100\% \\ RF\ (a\text{–centromere}) &= [1/2(45 + 1 + 20 + 58)/300] \times 100\% \\ &= 20.7\% \\ RF\ (b\text{–centromere}) &= [1/2(5 + 1 + 10 + 20)/300] \times 100\% \\ &= 6\% \end{aligned}$$

For the cross $b\ + \times +\ c$, we have:

45	5	146	1	10	20	15	58
T	T	PD	T	PD	PD	T	PD
b +	b +	b +	b +	b +	b +	b +	b +
b c	+ +	b +	+ +	+ c	+ c	b c	b +
+ +	b c	+ c	b c	b +	b +	+ +	+ c
+ c	+ c	+ c	+ c	+ c	+ c	+ c	+ c
MI MII	MII MI	MI MI	MII MI	MII MII	MII MII	MI MII	MI MI

There are $(146 + 10 + 20 + 58) = 234$ PD, $(45 + 5 + 1 + 15) = 66$ T and 0 NPD tetrads. Since PD >> NPD, b and c are linked. The recombination frequency between them is given by:

$$\begin{aligned} RF &= [(1/2 \times 66)/300] \times 100\% \\ &= 11\% \end{aligned}$$

The recombination frequency of c with the centromere is given by:

$$\begin{aligned} RF\ (c\text{–centromere}) &= [1/2(45 + 10 + 20 + 15)/300] \times 100\% \\ &= 15\% \end{aligned}$$

For the cross $a\ + \times +\ c$, we have:

45	5	146	1	10	20	15	58
PD	PD	PD	T	T	PD	T	T
a +	a +	a +	a +	a +	a +	a +	a +
+ c	a +	a +	+ +	a c	+ c	a c	+ +
a +	+ c	+ c	a c	+ +	a +	+ +	a c
+ c	+ c	+ c	+ c	+ c	+ c	+ c	+ c

There are (45 + 5 + 146 + 20) = 216 PD, (1 + 10 + 15 + 58) = 84 T and 0 NPD tetrads. Since PD >> NPD, *a* and *c* are linked. The recombination frequency between them is given by:

$$RF = [(1/2 \times 84)/300] \times 100\%$$
$$= 14\%$$

Using the calculations above, $a - b$ is 19.7 map units, $a - c$ is 14 map units, $b - c$ is 11 map units, and $b -$ centromere is 6 map units. Thus, the gene order is centromere $- b$ $- c - a$, and one has the following map (taking into consideration that, due to increasing numbers of multiple crossovers, more accurate RFs are obtained over smaller intervals):

(13.39) The frequency of mitotic recombination in experimental organisms can be increased by exposing them to low levels of ionizing radiation (such as X rays) during development. Hans Becker used this method to examine the patterns of clones produced by mitotic recombination in the *Drosophila* retina. (*Drosophila* has a compound eye consisting of many individual units called ommatidia.) What type of spots would be produced in the *Drosophila* retina if you irradiated a developing *Drosophila* female obtained from crossing a white-eyed male with a cherry-eyed female? (See Table 12.2 for a description of the *w* and *w*ch alleles.)

Answer: The cross is *w*/Y (white male) × *w*ch/*w*ch (cherry female), and so the female progeny are heterozygous at the white gene and are *w*/*w*ch. As shown in the diagram in the "Thinking Analytically" section of this chapter, when a single mitotic crossover occurs between a gene and its centromere in a heterozygote, the two daughter cells produced are each homozygous for a different allele. That is, this type of mitotic recombination event in an *a*/+ heterozygote will produce *a a* and ++ daughter cells in an *a*/+ background. By analogy to this event (draw it out), if mitotic recombination occurred in a *w*/*w*ch individual during the development of the eye, and crossovers occurred between the white gene and the centromere (which is most of the X chromosome), *w*/*w* and *w*ch/*w*ch cells would be produced in a *w*/*w*ch background.

The alleles at the white gene control the amount of pigment deposited in cells of the eye and show partial dominance. In phenotypically white *w*/*w* homozygotes, 0.44% of wild-type pigment levels are found, while in cherry-colored *w*ch/*w*ch homozygotes, 4.1% of wild-type pigment levels are found. It is reasonable to expect that *w*/*w*ch heterozygotes will have pink eyes, and have about 2.0% of wild-type pigment levels. If mitotic recombination occurs, twin spots will be seen: In a pink background (*w*/*w*ch), one will see neighboring white (*w*/*w*) and cherry (*w*ch/*w*ch) twin spots. These cells in the spots have descended from a cell in which there was a mitotic recombination event.

13.40   From a cross of *y1 y2⁺* x *y1⁺ y2*, where *y1* and *y2* are both alleles of the same gene in yeast, the following tetrad type occurs at very low frequencies:

$$
\begin{array}{ll}
y1^+ & y2 \\
y1 & y2 \\
y1 & y2 \\
y1 & y2^+
\end{array}
$$

Explain the origin of this tetrad at the molecular level. (*Hint:* See Box 13.2.)

Answer: The tetrad is not a PD, NPD or T tetrad. The tetrad shows evidence of gene conversion of both alleles: The wild-type *y1⁺* allele has undergone conversion to *y1*, and the wild-type *y2⁺* allele has undergone conversion to *y2*. When a heteroduplex is formed that contains a mismatch needing repair, the mismatch can be repaired to either the wild-type or the mutant allele. If strand exchange occurred and subsequent branch migration through the *y* gene generated mismatches at both the *y1* and *y2* sites, the strands could have been repaired to cause the indicated gene conversion events.

14

GENE MAPPING IN BACTERIA AND BACTERIOPHAGES

CHAPTER OUTLINE

GENETIC ANALYSIS OF BACTERIA

GENETIC MAPPING IN BACTERIA BY CONJUGATION

Discovery of Conjugation in *E. coli*

The Sex Factor *F*

High-Frequency Recombination Strains of *E. coli*

F' Factors

Using Conjugation To Map Bacterial Genes

Circularity of the *E. coli* Map

GENETIC MAPPING IN BACTERIA BY TRANSFORMATION

GENETIC MAPPING IN BACTERIA BY TRANSDUCTION

Bacteriophages: An Introduction

Transduction Mapping of Bacterial Chromosomes

MAPPING GENES OF BACTERIOPHAGES

FINE-STRUCTURE ANALYSIS OF A BACTERIOPHAGE GENE

Recombination Analysis of *rII* Mutants

Deletion Mapping

Defining Genes by Complementation (*Cis-Trans*) Tests

REVIEW OF KEY TERMS, SYMBOLS, AND CONCEPTS

In your own words, write a brief, precise definition of each term in the groups below. Check your definitions using the text. Then, develop a concept map using the terms in each list.

1	2	3
transfer of genetic material	transfer of genetic material	bacteriophage cross
conjugation	transduction, cotransduction	turbid, clear plaques
plating	phage vectors	permissive host
colony	transductants	nonpermissive host
titer	phage lysate	bacterial lawn
minimal medium	virulent vs. temperate phage	host range property
complete medium	lysogenic pathway	intergenic mapping
auxotroph	prophage	"beads on a string" view
prototroph	lysogeny	intragenic mapping

1	2	3
replica plating	lytic cycle	fine-structure mapping
transconjugants, exconjugant	generalized transduction	homoallelic mutations
sex factor	specialized transduction	heteroallelic mutations
F^-, F', Hfr, F^+ strains	transducing phage	deletion mapping
plasmid, episome	selected, unselected marker	point, deletion, revertant
F–duction (sexduction)	transformation	mutations
merodiploid	competent cells	hot spot
interrupted mating	natural, engineered	cis-trans test
donor vs. recipient	transformation	complementation test
F–pili (sex–pili)	electroporation	cistron
F factor origin	heteroduplex DNA	gene as a unit of function
	cotransformation	

THINKING ANALYTICALLY

While this chapter focuses on the genetics of bacteria and bacteriophages, many of the core concepts introduced here are used throughout the study of genetics. Of particular importance are the genetic principles that underlie selection, recombination and complementation. These have had a major impact on how we think about gene structure and function: geneticists working in many different research areas are concerned with how to *select* for or against specific phenotypes; analysis of recombination within a gene (*intragenic* recombination) formed a foundation for our current understanding of gene structure; the concept of a gene as a unit of function was developed by using complementation tests to measure whether two mutants affect the same function. It is therefore essential to thoroughly understand these genetic principles as they are developed using bacterial and phage systems in this chapter.

Having stressed the importance of the concepts presented in this chapter, it is also important to be forewarned that much of the material used to develop these concepts is complicated, and will not necessarily be intuitive. For example, there are many refinements of bacteria and phage types and special characteristics that are associated with one or another aspect of bacterial or phage growth and mating. Carefully read the chapter sections that describe these characteristics until you thoroughly understand them. The names are quite descriptive, and once you use them a few times in solving problems, you will become adept at using them. Approach using the terms with more than rote memorization: Use them in context until you fix upon what is practically a visual image of them.

As with the proceeding chapters, carefully read the statements and conditions of a particular problem so that you gain a clear understanding of what it asks, and what data it gives you to work with. Then organize and reorganize the data, and sometimes, reorganize again, using scratch paper and pencil until you can see how to use the data to solve the problem. If you still get stuck, try representing the processes that are used in the problem with diagrams, and ask yourself how the data fit into the biological process you've drawn out.

The problems in this chapter are especially well-organized to help you build up your understanding of the material. Work through each of them sequentially to fully develop your understanding and analytical skills.

QUESTIONS FOR PRACTICE

Multiple Choice Questions

1. A strain, such as a strain of *E. coli*, that requires nutritional or other kinds of supplements for growth and/or survival is known as
    a. a prototroph.
    b. a heterotroph.
    c. a pleiotroph.
    d. an auxotroph.

2. A conjugating bacterial cell that typically transfers only part of its *F* factor and some chromosomal genes is
    a. *F+*.
    b. *F'*.
    c. *Hfr*.
    d. *F–*.

3. The process by which cells take up genetic material from the extracellular environment and incorporate it into their genetic complement is called
    a. transduction.
    b. transformation.
    c. translocation.
    d. DNA transfusion.

4. In bacteria, conjugation involves
    a. the union of two bacterial genomes.
    b. the fusion of two cells of opposite mating types.
    c. a virus-mediated exchange of DNA.
    d. the transfer of DNA from one cell into another.

5. A self-replicating genetic element found in the cytoplasm of bacteria is a
    a. sex pilus.
    b. plasmid.
    c. viral capsid.
    d. cotransductant.

6. Which of the following is true about cells having *F* factors?
    a. In both *F+* and *Hfr* cells, fertility genes are transferred first.
    b. In both *F+* and *Hfr* cells, genes are transferred through sex pili.
    c. In *Hfr* cells, bacterial genes closest to the origin are transferred first.
    In *F'* cells, only *F* factor genes are transferred.

7. Phage that can grow using either a lytic or lysogenic pathway is called
    a. virulent.

b. temperate.

c. intemperate.

d. transductant.

8. Recombination that occurs between two alleles at one gene is
   a. unheard of.
   b. intergenic recombination.
   c. intragenic recombination.
   d. more frequent that recombination between two closely linked genes.

9. A complementation test measures
   a. whether two mutants undergo intergenic recombination.
   b. whether two mutants undergo intragenic recombination.
   c. whether two mutants are linked.
   d. whether two mutants affect the same function.

10. *E. coli K12(λ)* cells will only support the growth of T4 phage that are *r+*. If two different mutant *rII* phage coinfect an *E. coli K12(λ)* cell and lysis occurs,
    a. intragenic recombination must have occurred.
    b. complementation must have occurred.
    c. the two *rII* phage must have mutations in different cistrons.
    d. both a and b are true.
    e. both b and c are true.
    f. a, b, and c are true.

11. How can you distinguish between a point mutation and a deletion mutation?
    a. Point mutations can't be seen cytologically; deletion mutations can be seen.
    b. Point mutations can be reverted; deletion mutations can't be reverted.
    c. A deletion mutation will complement a point mutation in the same gene.
    d. Point mutations can be transduced; deletion mutations can't be transduced.

12. Which of the statements accurately describe an episome and a plasmid?
    a. An episome is a plasmid that can integrate into the host chromosome.
    b. A plasmid is a circular extrachromosomal element.
    c. An *F* factors is a plasmid that is also an episome.
    d. All episomes are *F* factors, but not all *F* factors are plasmids.
    e. a, b, and c, but not d, are accurate.
    f. a, b, c, and d are accurate.

Answers: 1d; 2c; 3b; 4d; 5b; 6c; 7b; 8c; 9d; 10e; 11b; 12d.

Thought Questions

1. Explain why two genes that are close together on a chromosome show a high frequency of cotransduction and cotransformation.

2. Compare the life cycles of T4, P1 and λ. Which is (are) temperate? Which is (are) virulent? Which can undergo lysogeny?

3. Contrast the features and/or conditions of generalized transduction and specialized transduction.

4. What is the significance of bacterial transformation and conjugation in relation to the rapidity with which certain infectious organisms adapt to changing environmental conditions or factors, such as antibiotics? (Hint: Sexual reproduction promotes genetic variability. How do parasexual systems compare?)

5. Explain how intragenic recombination is different from complementation.

6. Deletion mapping as used by Benzer in T4 was important in defining the location of point mutations at the *rII* locus. What might it mean for recessive mutations to be "uncovered" by deletions in eukaryotes. Diagram how you might use a set of nested deletions to localize a *Drosophila* point mutant. (*Drosophila* have polytene chromosomes in which deletion breakpoints can be mapped cytologically).

7. Consider how we may select for prototrophic and drug-resistant bacterial strains. Can you think of clever (or even not so clever) ways to attempt to select for (a) a pesticide-resistant strain of beetles, (b) bacteria that are able to degrade a toxic chemical, (c) very sweet sweet-corn, and (d) a strain of cats that doesn't respond to catnip?

8. When two true-breeding white-flowered sweet peas are crossed, a purple F_1 is produced. When the F_1 is selfed, the F_2 is 9 purple : 7 white. As described in Chapter 12, the 9:7 ratio is characteristic of duplicate recessive epistasis. Why is duplicate recessive epistasis also called complementary gene action?

9. Suppose a linear piece of DNA with genes (in order) *a+ b+* and *c+* enters a bacterial cell that is *a– b–* and *c–*. How many crossovers are required to convert the bacterial cell to (a) *a+ b+ c+*, (b) *a+ b+ c–*, (c) *a+ b– c+*, (d) *a– b+ c–*? How would your answers change if the DNA was circular? In each case, which would be the most frequent, and the least frequent event?

10. P1 and λ phage have been modified to serve as cloning vectors by removing selected genes (thereby making room for DNA inserts) and introducing specific mutations to remove some functions. Carefully consider their life cycles, and speculate what features of their life cycles it might be useful to retain in a cloning vector, and what features it might be necessary to remove?

Thought Questions for Media

After reviewing the media on the *iGenetics* CD-ROM, try to answer these questions.

1. The *Mapping Bacterial Genes by Conjugation* animation shows that the *leu+* and *thr+* genes are transferred about eight minutes after conjugation begins, but that we can't tell which one is transferred first. What does this tell you about the limits of resolution of mapping by using the interrupted mating technique?

2. What are the units used to relate the distance between two bacterial genes mapped by interrupted mating? Do you expect these units to be proportional to the number of DNA base pairs between the two loci?

3. Could you perform an interrupted mating experiment between an F^+ strain and an F^- strain? Why or why not?

4. Why is it necessary to use diploids to perform a complementation test?

5. Suppose you had two tree-breeding mutant lines of deaf rabbits. How would you determine if the cause of deafness in each line was the same?

6. To assess if two genes complement each other, is it important to obtain recombinants between them?

1. Suppose that, in the initial cross between the prototrophic strain to the F^- strain that was *leu$^-$, arg$^-$, his$^-$, and trp$^-$*, the media used for selection of *leu$^+$* recombinants was prepared incorrectly. On plate A, streptomycin was mistakenly left out of the medium, and only supplemental arginine, histidine and tryptophan were added. On plate B, streptomycin was added, but leucine was mistakenly added along with the other supplements (arginine, histidine, and tryptophan). Compared to all of the other plates used to select for recombinants at the other loci, you observe a much larger number of colonies on plates A and B.

   a. Why are there so many more colonies on plates A and B, compared to the others?

   b. Suppose you picked several dozen individual colonies from each of plates A and B. Would you expect the genotypes of all of the colonies from both plates to be the same? Would you expect the genotypes of all of the colonies from just one of the plates to be the same?

   c. Could any of the colonies on plates A and B be recombinants?

   d. What would you expect their genotype(s) to be?

   e. How could you experimentally address your answers to **c** and **d**?

2. As presented in the iActivity, multiple *Hfr* strains are used to map the relative location of genes distributed throughout the *E. coli* chromosome.

   a. Does each *Hfr* strain have one or more than one F factor inserted in its *E. coli* chromosome?

   b. If, in an *Hfr* strain, a bacterial gene is far from the F factor site of insertion, will it be transferred frequently to an F^- strain?

   c. Why are multiple *Hfr* strains needed to map genes distributed throughout the *E. coli* chromosome?

   d. When maps are being constructed, why doesn't it matter if the F factors in the different *Hfr* strains are inserted in opposite directions (relative to each other) in the *E. coli* chromosome?

SOLUTIONS TO TEXT PROBLEMS

14.1   In $F+ \times F-$ crosses, the $F-$ recipient is converted to a donor with very high frequency. However, it is rare for a recipient to become a donor in *Hfr* $\times$ $F-$ crosses. Explain why.

Answer: The frequency with which a recipient is converted to a donor reflects the frequency with which a complete *F* factor is transferred. In *F+* x *F-* crosses, only the *F* factor is transferred, and this occurs relatively quickly. In *Hfr* x *F-* crosses, transfer starts at the origin within the *F* element, and then must proceed through the bacterial chromosome before reaching the *F* factor. In order for the entire *F* factor to be transferred, the whole chromosome would have to be transferred. This would take about 100 minutes, and usually, the conjugal unions break apart before then.

14.2   With the technique of interrupted mating, four *Hfr* strains were tested for the order in which they transmitted a number of different genes to an *F-* strain. Each *Hfr* strain was found to transmit its genes in a unique order, as shown in the accompanying table (only the first six genes transmitted were scored for each strain).

ORDER OF TRANSMISSION	*Hfr* STRAIN			
	1	2	3	4
First	*O*	*R*	*E*	*O*
	F	*H*	*M*	*G*
	B	*M*	*H*	*X*
	A	*E*	*R*	*C*
	E	*A*	*C*	*R*
Last	*M*	*B*	*X*	*H*

What is the gene order in the original strain from which these *Hfr* strains derive? Indicate on your diagram the origin and polarity of each of the four *Hfrs*.

Answer: The diagram below shows the gene sequence in the original *F+* strain, and the locations of the four different *F* factor insertions. (Note that only one insertion exists in a particular *Hfr* strain.)

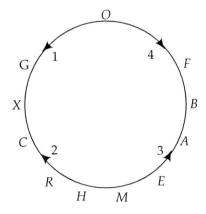

14.3   At time zero an *Hfr* strain (strain 1) was mixed with an *F-* strain, and at various times after mixing, samples were removed and agitated to separate conjugating cells. The cross may be written as:

| Hfr 1: | a+ | b+ | c+ | d+ | e+ | f+ | g+ | h+ | strs |
| F-: | a | b | c | d | e | f | g | h | strr |

(No order is implied in listing the markers.)

The samples were then plated onto selective media to measure the frequency of *h+ strR* recombinants that had received certain genes from the *Hfr* cell. The graph of the number of recombinants against time is shown in the accompanying figure.

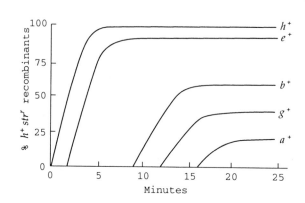

a. Indicate whether each of the following statements is true or false.

i. All *F+* cells that received *a+* from the *Hfr* in the chromosome transfer process must also have received *b+*.

ii. The order of gene transfer from *Hfr* to *F+* was *a+* (first), then *g+*, then *b+*, then *e+*, then *h+*.

iii. Most *e+ strR* recombinants are likely to be *Hfr* cells.

iv.   None of the *b+ strR* recombinants plated at 15 minutes are also *a+*.

b. Draw a linear map of the *Hfr* chromosome indicating the

i. point of nicking (the origin) and direction of DNA transfer

ii. order of the genes *a+*, *b+*, *e+*, *g+*, and *h+*

iii.   shortest distance between consecutive genes on the chromosomes

Answer:

a.

i. True. The graph indicates that *a+* is transferred last, starting about 16 minutes after conjugal pairing. The genes are transferred linearly in the order *h+* (starting at 0 minutes), *e+* (starting at 2 minutes), *b+* (starting at 9 minutes), *g+* (starting at 12 minutes) and then *a+*.

ii. False. The data show that *a+* took the longest time to be transferred and so was the last gene to be received. The correct order of gene transfer was *h+* (first), *e+*, *b+*, *g+*, and *a+* (last).

iii. False. In order for the recipient cell to be transformed to *F+* or *Hfr*, it must receive a complete copy of the *F* factor. Since only part of the *F* factor is transferred at the beginning of conjugation, and *e+* is transferred quite quickly after conjugal pairing, most *e+ strr* recombinants will have only a small part of the donor chromosome. The remaining part of the *F* factor is only transferred after the entire bacterial chromosome is transferred. Because of turbulence, the conjugal pairing is almost always disrupted before transfer of an entire chromosome is completed. Hence, the chance that complete transfer will occur is quite remote.

iv. True. The graph shows that *a+* is not transferred until after about 16 minutes has elapsed.

b.

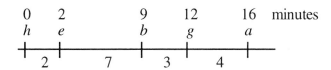

14.4   If an *E. coli* auxotroph *A* could grow only on a medium containing thymine, and an auxotroph *B* could grow only on a medium containing leucine, how would you test whether DNA from *A* could transform *B*?

Answer: Strain *A* is *thy– leu+*, while strain *B* is *thy+ leu–*. To test if DNA from *A* can transform *B*, one is interested in whether one can transform the *leu–* allele of *B* to *leu+*. To do this, add DNA from strain *A* to a leucine–fortified culture of *B*. Incubate long enough for transformation to occur, then plate out these potentially transformed *B* cells on minimal medium or on medium supplemented only with thymine. As shown in the table below, one can select for transformants by plating on such media, as growth on such media requires *leu+*.

| | | MEDIUM TYPE | | |
STRAIN	MINIMAL	PLUS LEUCINE	PLUS THYMINE	PLUS THYMINE & LEUCINE
leu+ thy+	+	+	+	+
leu+ thy–	–	–	+	+
leu– thy+	–	+	–	+
leu– thy–	–	–	–	+

14.5   Three different prototrophic strains (1, 2 and 3) that are all sensitive to the antibiotic streptomycin are isolated. Each is individually mixed with an auxotrophic F– strain that is *a b c d e f g h* (and therefore requires compounds A, B, C, D, E, F, G, and H to grow) and resistant to the antibiotic streptomycin. At one-minute intervals after the initial mixing, a sample of the mixture is removed, shaken violently, and plated on media to select for *c+ str*R recombinants. Recombinants are then tested for the presence of other genes. The following results are obtained:

Strain 1 × F–: No *c+* recombinants are ever obtained, even after 25 minutes.

Strain 2 × F–: *c+* recombinants are obtained at 6 minutes, *g+* at 8 minutes, *h+* at 11 minutes, *a+* at 14 minutes, *b+* at 16 minutes. No *d+, e+,* and *f+* recombinants are obtained.

Strain $3 \times F-$: $c+$ recombinants are obtained at the 1-minute time point and $c+ g+$ recombinants are obtained on or after the 3-minute time point. No $a+$, $b+$, $d+$, $e+$, $f+$ or $h+$ recombinants are obtained.

If $c+$ recombinants obtained at the 16-minute time point from the cross involving strain 2 are mixed with an amp^R (ampicillin-resistant) $F-$ strain, no $c+$ amp^R recombinants are ever recovered. However, if $c+$ recombinants obtained at the 16-minute time point from the cross involving strain 3 are mixed with an amp^R $F-$ strain, amp^R $c+$ recombinants can be recovered after 1 minute of mating.

a. How was the initial selection for $c+ str^R$ recombinants done? How were the subsequent selections done?

b. Use these data to ascertain, as best you can, whether each strain is $F-$, Hfr, $F+$, or F'. If these data do not allow you to make an unambiguous determination, indicate the possibilities.

c. To the extent you can, draw a map of the possible chromosome(s) present in each of strains 1, 2, and 3. Indicate the location and distance between genes $a+$, $b+$, $d+$, $e+$, $f+$ and $h+$ as best you can.

Answer:

a. To initially select for $c+ str^R$ recombinants, plate the progeny on minimal medium without compound C, but supplemented with streptomycin and compounds A, B, D, E, F, G, and H. To assess the complete genotype of the $c+ str^R$ recombinants, replica plate them onto different minimal media supplemented with streptomycin and all but two of the compounds (compound C and one other). For example, to test if a $c+ str^R$ colony was also $a+$, replica plate it onto a medium that lacked compound A, but was supplemented with streptomycin and B, D, E, F, G, and H. If the colony were able to grow on this medium, it would be $a+ c+ str^R$. If it were unable to grow, it would be $a\ c+ str^R$.

b. Strain #1: Since no $c+$ recombinants are ever obtained, strain #1 is unable to transfer $c+$. This means it is either (1) $F-$; (2) Hfr, but with the F factor inserted either far from $c+$, or close to it but in an orientation so that genes are transferred in a direction opposite to $c+$; (3) F', with $c+$ in the bacterial chromosome. It should not be $F+$, as then, at a very low frequency, some $c+$ recombinants would be obtained.

Strain #2: Since $c+$ recombinants are obtained at 6 min., and $g+$, $h+$, $a+$ and $b+$ recombinants are obtained at subsequent time intervals, strain #2 is Hfr. The genes are transferred in the following order: $c+$, $g+$, $h+$, $a+$ and $b+$. From the times of their transfer, the map position of the genes is: origin $(0) - c+ (6) - g+ (8) - h+$ $(11) - a+ (14) - b+ (16)$. The location of genes $d+$, $e+$, and $f+$ cannot be precisely determined; since they are not transferred in an $Hfr \times F-$ cross, they are either far away from the F factor insertion site, or close to it but near the fertility genes, which are only rarely transferred by an Hfr strain. When the recombinants obtained from the strain #2 $\times F-$ mating at the 16-minute time period are crossed to an amp^R $F-$ strain, $c+$ is not transferred. If these recombinants cannot conjugate with *F*–, this indicates that although strain #2 is fertile, it did not transfer a complete *F* factor. It therefore must be *Hfr*.

Strain #3: Strain #3 transfers *c*+ within 1 minute and *g*+ by three minutes. From analysis of the strain #2 ₓ *F*– cross, we knew that these genes are 2 minutes apart. This data supports this conclusion. Since no other recombinants are obtained, no other genes are transferred. This suggests that strain #3 is *F'*, and that the segment of DNA containing *c*+ and *g*+ is in the *F'* factor. If this is the case, the complete *F* factor will be transferred in a strain #3 × *F*– cross if the mating is allowed to proceed long enough. This is observed: *c*+ recombinants from the strain #3 × *F*– cross obtained at 16 minutes are able to transfer *c*+ to an *F*– *amp*R strain. Therefore, strain #3 is *F'*.

c. Information known with certainty is diagrammed below. The location of genes in strains #1 and #3 is inferred from crosses with strain #2. The location of genes *d*+, *e*+, and *f*+ is unknown.

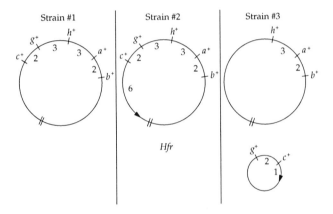

14.6   You are given a prototrophic *str*R (streptomycin-resistant) *Hfr* strain and an *amp*R (ampicillin-resistant) *F*– auxotrophic strain that requires leucine (*leu*), arginine (*arg*), lysine (*lys*), purine (*pur*), and biotin (*bio*).

a. Devise a strategy to determine quickly which gene (*leu*+, *arg*+, *lys*+, *pur*+, or *bio*+) lies closest to the *F*–factor origin of replication.

b. Even when the prototrophic *Hfr* strain is mixed with the *F*– strain for very long periods of time, streptomycin resistance is not transferred. State two hypotheses that explain this finding.

Answer:

a. Prepare a set of bacterial plates with five different media, each containing minimal media supplemented with ampicillin and all but one of leucine, arginine, lysine, purine and biotin. Mix the *Hfr* strain with the *F*– strain. After, say, 2 min. and 5 min., remove some of the bacteria from the mating, violently shake them, and plate them on each of the media. This will select for growth of *amp*R recombinants that are able to grow in the absence of one supplement. For example, plating on medium with ampicillin, leucine, arginine, lysine and purine will select for *bio*+ *amp*R recombinants. Incubate the plates to let colonies grow, and identify the plate that has the most colonies after the shortest mating interval.

This will identify the prototrophic gene transferred first, and so identify the gene closest to the origin of replication of the *F* factor. If, say, only plates lacking leucine have growth after 2 min., then *leu+* is closest to the *F*–factor origin of replication.

b. The *str*R gene could be far from the origin of replication of the *F* factor in the *Hfr* chromosome. Alternatively, the *str*R gene might be on a separate plasmid unable to be transferred to the *F*- cell (perhaps it is a defective *F* factor).

14.7   Indicate whether each of the following occurs or is a characteristic of

    Generalized Transduction   (GT)
    Specialized Transduction   (ST)
    Occurs in Both   (B)
    Occurs in Neither   (N)

a. Phage carries DNA of bacterial or viral DNA origin, never both.
b. Phage carries viral DNA covalently linked to bacterial DNA.
c. Phage integrates into a specific site on the host chromosome.
d. Phage integrates at a random site on the host chromosome.
e. "Headful" of bacterial DNA is packaged into phage.
f. Host is lysogenized.
g. Prophage state exists.
h. Temperate phage is involved.
i. Virulent phage is involved.

Answer:
a. GT
b. ST
c. ST
d. GT
e. GT
f. B
g. B
h. B
i. N

14.8   Consider the following transduction data:

DONOR	RECIPIENT	SELECTED MARKER	UNSELECTED MARKER	%
aceF+ dhl	*aceF dhl+*	*aceF+*	DHL	88
aceF+ leu	*aceF leu+*	*aceF+*	*leu*	34

Is *dhl* or *leu* closer to *aceF*?

Answer: The notation *aceF* represents a specific insertion site for an *F* factor. This table shows that cells selected for transduction of *F*+ were isolated and then tested for the cotransduction of *dhl* or *leu*. It shows that in one experiment, of the *aceF*+ transductants that were isolated, 88 percent were also transduced with the *dhl* marker. In another experiment, of the *aceF*+ transductants that were isolated, only 34 percent were also transduced with the *leu* marker.

In order to obtain a transductant, a double crossover must occur between the transduced, donor DNA and the host chromosome. The closer two loci are together on the same chromosome, the greater the probability that they will both be included within the limits of a double crossover. Therefore, two loci that are closer together will show a greater frequency of cotransduction: *dhl* is closer to *aceF*+ than *leu*.

14.9   Consider the following data with P1 transduction:

DONOR	RECIPIENT	SELECTED MARKER	UNSELECTED MARKER	%
aroA pyrD+	*aroA*+ *pyrD*	*pryD*+	AROA	5
aroA+ *cmlB*	*aroA cmlB*+	*aroA*+	CMLB	26
cmlB pyrD+	*cmlB*+ *pyrD*	*pyrD*+	CMLB	54

Choose the correct order:
a. *aroA – cmlB – pyrD*
b. *aroA – pyrD – cmlB*
c. *cmlB – aroA – pyrD*

Answer: The frequency of cotransduction gives an indication of the closeness of each pair of genes: the higher their cotransduction frequency, the closer the two genes. The *pryD* and *cmlB* genes show the highest cotransduction frequency, and are the closest together. This eliminates (c) as a possibility. The genes *aroA* and *pyrD* show the lowest cotransduction frequency, and so, they are the furthest apart. This eliminates (b) as a possibility. The *aroA* and *cmlB* genes show an intermediate cotransduction frequency, as would be expected if *cmlB* were between *aroA* and *pyrD*. Thus, the correct answer is (a).

14.10   Order the mutants *trp, pyrF*, and *qts* on the basis of the following three-factor transduction cross:

Donor	*trp*+ *pyr*+ *qts*
Recipient	*trp py rqts*+
Selected Marker	*trp*+

UNSELECTED MARKERS	NUMBER
pyr+ *qts*+	22
pyr+ *qts*	10
pyr qts+	68
pyr qts	0

Answer: Notice that in this cross, by selecting for *trp+*, one selects for recombinants. The frequency of the different classes of recombinants can be affected by two factors: the distance between genes and the number of crossovers that are needed to obtain a particular genotype. Since the bacterial chromosome is circular, recombinants are only obtained by either two, or some multiple of two, crossovers. Obtaining four crossovers will be less common than obtaining two crossovers, and so a genotype that requires four crossovers to be produced is likely to be the least common. In this case, with the parents being *trp+ pyr+ qts* and *trp pyr qts+*, the gene order that requires a quadruple crossover to produce the least frequent *trp+ pyr qts* class is *trp – pyr – qts*. The other three transductant classes can be generated by double crossovers. Try drawing this out.

14.11 Order *cheA, cheB, eda,* and *supD* from the following data:

MARKERS	% COTRANSDUCTION
cheA – eda	15
cheA – supD	5
cheB – eda	28
cheB – supD	2.7
eda – supD	0

Answer: The higher the frequency of cotransduction, the closer the loci. Thus, the relative proximity of the loci to each other is:

cheB – eda	closest together
cheA – eda	↓
cheA – supD	↓
cheB – supD	↓
eda – supD	furthest apart

A gene order that is consistent with these relationships is *eda – cheB – cheA – supD*.

14.12 Wild-type phage T4 grows on both *E. coli* B and *E. coli* K12(λ), producing turbid plaques. The *rII* mutants of T4 grow on *E. coli* B, producing clear plaques, but do not grow on *E. coli* K12(λ). This host range property permits the detection of a very low number of *r+* phages among a large number of *rII* phages. With this sensitive system it is possible to determine the genetic distance between two mutations within the same gene, in this case the *rII* locus. Suppose *E. coli* B is mixedly infected with *rIIx* and *rIIy*, two separate mutants in the *rII* locus. Suitable dilutions of progeny phages are plated on *E. coli* B and *E. coli* K12(λ). A 0.1-ml sample of a thousandfold dilution plated on *E. coli* B produced 672 plaques. A 0.2-ml sample of undiluted phage plated on *E. coli* K12(λ) produced 470 turbid plaques. What is the genetic distance between the two *rII* mutations?

Answer: The plaques produced on *E. coli* K12(λ) are *r+*, while those on *E. coli* B may be either *r+* or *r−*. Thus, the total number of progeny can be inferred from the number of plaques formed on *E. coli* B. Since *E. coli* B is coinfected with *rIIx* and *rIIy*, the only way to obtain an *r+* progeny phage is to have a crossover within the *rII* locus. The progeny resulting from a crossover would be 1/2 *r+* and 1/2 *rIIxy* recombinants. The number of recombinant phage is twice the number of *r+* phage, which can be assayed for by growth on *E. coli* K12(λ).

recombinant progeny in 1 mL = 2 × (number of *r+* phage/mL)
$$= 2 \times (470/0.2)$$
$$= 4,700/mL.$$

total # of progeny in 1 mL = (dilution factor) × (# progeny phage/mL)
$$= 1,000 \times (672/0.1)$$
$$= 6.72 \times 10^6 /mL.$$

RF $= [4,700/(6.72 \times 10^6)] \times 100\%$
$= 0.07\%.$

The map distance between *rIIx* and *rIIy* is 0.07 mu.

14.13   Construct a map from the following two-factor phage cross data (show map distance):

CROSS	% RECOMBINATION
r1 × *r2*	0.10
r1 × *r3*	0.05
r1 × *r4*	0.19
r2 × *r3*	0.15
r2 × *r4*	0.10
r3 × *r4*	0.23

Answer: Recall that, as discussed in Chapter 13, the most accurate map distances are those obtained over the shortest intervals.

14.14   The following two-factor crosses were made to analyze the genetic linkage between four genes in phage χ: *c, mi, s,* a6nd *co*.

PARENTS	PROGENY
c + × + mi	1,213 *c +*, 1,205 *+ mi*, 84 *+ +*, 75 *c mi*
c + × + s	566 *c +*, 808 *+ s*, 19 *+ +*, 20 *c s*
co + × + mi	5,162 *co +*, 6,510 *+ mi*, 311 *+ +*, 341 *co mi*
mi + × + s	502 *mi +*, 647 *+ s*, 65 *+ +*, 56 *mi s*

Construct a genetic map of the four genes.

Answer: Analyze the data as you would a set of two-factor crosses:

CROSS	NUMBER OF PROGENY	# RECOMBINANTS	MU
c + × + mi	2,577	159	6.2
c + × + s	1,413	39	2.8
co + × + mi	12,324	652	5.3
mi + × + s	1,270	121	9.5

Two maps are compatible with these data:

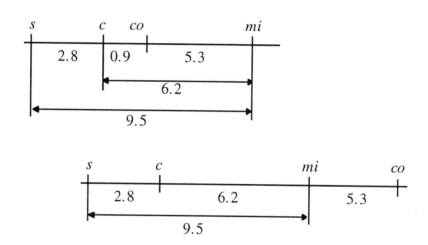

14.15   Wild-type (*r+*) strains of T4 produce turbid plaques, whereas *rII* mutant strains produce larger, clearer plaques. Five *rII* mutations (*a* − *e*) in the *A* cistron of the *rII* region of T4 give the following percentages of wild-type recombinants in two-point crosses:

CROSS	% OF WILD-TYPE RECOMBINANTS
a × b	0.2 percent
a × c	0.9 percent
a × d	0.4 percent
b × c	0.7 percent
e × a	0.3 percent
e × d	0.7 percent
e × c	1.2 percent
e × b	0.5 percent
b × d	0.2 percent
d × c	0.5 percent

What is the order of the mutational sites, and what are the map distances between the sites?

Answer: Between any two *rII* mutants *rIIx and rIIy* there are two products of intragenic recombination: *rII++* and *rIIxy*. Thus, the frequency of wild-type recombinants is half the total recombinant frequency. These data give the following map:

14.16   Given the following map with point mutants and given the data in the following table, draw a topological representation of deletion mutants *r21*, *r22*, *r23*, *r24*, and *r25*. (Be sure to show the endpoints of the deletions; + = *r+* recombinants are obtained, 0 = *r+* recombinants are not obtained.)

Map:

r12   r16   r11   r15   r13   r14   r17

DELETION MUTANTS	POINT MUTANTS						
	r11	*r12*	*r13*	*r14*	*r15*	*r16*	*r17*
r21	0	+	0	+	0	+	+
r22	+	+	0	0	+	+	0
r23	0	0	0	+	0	0	+
r24	+	+	0	0	+	+	+
r25	+	+	0	0	0	+	+

Answer: If no *r+* recombinants are obtained, the deletion removes the site of the point mutant. If *r+* recombinants are obtained, the site of the point mutation is not within the boundaries of the deletion. To determine the deleted region then, define the region that includes all of the point mutations unable to recombine with the deletion. Check your answer by verifying that all of the point mutations outside of this region do recombine with the deletion.

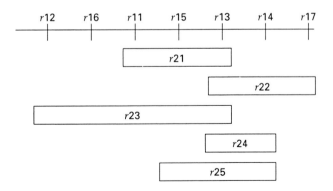

14.17   Given the following deletion map with deletions *r31*, *r32*, *r33*, *r34*, *r35* and *r36*, place the point mutants *r41*, *r42*, etc., on the map. Be sure you show where they lie with respect to end points of the deletions.

Deletion map (r31, r32, r33, r34, r35, r36)

	DELETION MUTANTS (+ = RECOMBINANTS PRODUCED; 0 = NO R$^+$ RECOMBINANTS PRODUCED)					
POINT MUTANTS	r31	r32	r33	r34	r35	r36
r41	0	0	0	0	+	0
r42	0	0	0	+	0	+
r43	0	0	+	+	+	0
r44	0	0	0	0	+	+
r45	0	+	0	+	+	+
r46	0	0	+	0	+	0

Show the dividing line between the *A* cistron and the *B* cistron on your map above from the following data [+ = growth on strain *K12(λ)*, 0 = no growth on strain *K12(λ)*]:

MUTANT	COMPLEMENTATION WITH	
	rIIA	rIIB
R31	0	0
r32	0	0
r33	0	+
r34	0	0
r35	0	+
r36	0	0
r41	0	+
r42	0	+
r43	+	0
r44	0	+
r45	0	+
r46	0	+

Answer: First define where the point mutants lie using a systematic approach that utilizes two facts: (1) if a point mutant is *able* to recombine with a deletion mutant, it must lie *outside* of the deleted region and (2) if a point mutant is *unable* to recombine with a deletion mutant, it must lie *within* the deleted region. This means that a point mutant must lie within a region remaining intact in each of the deletions with which it does recombine, and conversely, it must lie in a deleted region that is shared by each of the deletions with which it does not recombine. Employ both of these inferences to define the region in which the point mutant lies.

Then determine the positions of the *A* and *B* cistrons. Use the fact that if two mutants are unable to grow on *E. coli K12(λ)* ("0"), the mutants cannot together provide the functions to complete the *rII* pathway. Either the *rIIA* or *rIIB* function is missing. Consequently, both mutants must be defective in the same function. In other words, the mutants do not complement each other. For example, if a mutant does not complement a known *rIIA* mutant (i.e., there is no growth on *E. coli K12(λ)*, ("0"), then the mutation is in the *A* cistron. Note that deletions can affect both the *A* and *B* cistrons, while point mutations can only affect one or the other cistron.

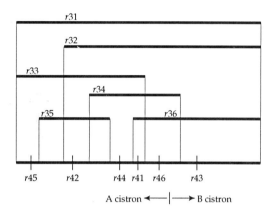

14.18 Some adenine-requiring mutants of yeast are pink because of the intracellular accumulation of a red pigment. Diploid strains were made by mating haploid mutant strains. The diploids exhibited the following phenotypes:

CROSS	DIPLOID PHENOTYPES
1 × 2	pink, adenine-requiring
1 × 3	white, prototrophic
1 × 4	white, prototrophic
3 × 4	pink, adenine-requiring

How many genes are defined by the four different mutants? Explain.

Answer: When two haploid strains mate to form a diploid cell, each contributes its genome. Consequently, there are two sets of genes in a diploid cell, and complementation between two mutants can be observed. If two mutations are in the same unit of function (i.e., the same gene), then they will not complement when together in a diploid cell and the mutant phenotype will be exhibited. If two mutations are in different genes, they will complement each other in a diploid cell and the wild-type phenotype will result.

In the data presented here, mutations 1 and 3, and mutations 1 and 4 complement each other, indicating that mutations 1 and 3 are in different genes, and mutations 1 and 4 are in different genes. On the other hand, mutations 1 and 2, and mutations 3 and 4 fail to complement each other. Thus, mutations 1 and 2 are in one gene, while mutations 3 and 4 are in a different gene. There are two genes.

14.19   In *Drosophila*, mutants A, B, C, D, E, F, and G all have the same phenotype: the absence of red pigment in the eyes. In pairwise combinations in complementation tests the following results were produced, where + = complementation and − = no complementation.

	A	B	C	D	E	F	G
G	+	−	+	+	+	+	−
F	−	+	+	−	+	−	
E	+	+	−	+	−		
D	−	+	+	−			
C	+	+	−				
B	+	−					
A	−						

   a. How many genes are present?
   b. Which mutants have defects in the same gene?

Answer: Mutants that fail to complement each other are in the same gene. Mutants G and B fail to complement each other, mutants C and E fail to complement each other, and mutants A, F and D fail to complement each other. Therefore there are three genes, with mutants G and B in one, mutants A, F, and D in a second, and mutants C and E in a third.

14.20   A homozygous white-eyed Martian fly (w_1/w_1) is crossed to a homozygous white-eyed fly from a different stock (w_2/w_2). It is well known that wild-type Martian flies have red eyes. This cross produces all white-eyed progeny. State whether the following are true or false. Explain your answer.
   a. w_1 and w_2 are allelic genes.
   b. w_1 and w_2 are nonallelic.
   c. w_1 and w_2 affect the same function.
   d. The cross was a complementation test.
   e. The cross was a cis-trans test.
   f. w_1 and w_2 are allelic by terms of the functional test.

The F_1 white-eyed flies were allowed to interbreed, and when you classified the F_1 you found 20,000 white-eyed flies and 10 red-eyed progeny. Concerned about contamination, you repeat the experiment and get exactly the same results. How can you best account for the presence of the red-eyed progeny? As part of your explanation give the genotypes of the F_1 and F_2 generation flies.

Answer:

a. True. In the cross $w_1/w_1 \times w_2/w_2$, the offspring are $w_1 w_2$. That they are white eyed indicates that w_1 and w_2 are mutations in the same function, i.e., the same gene. Thus, w_1 and w_2 are allelic genes.

b. False. If the genes were nonallelic, each mutation would be in a different function. The two mutations would each be in different steps of a pathway, with each mutant retaining the function of a different step. Since the progeny obtain a set of genes from each mutant parent, they would have the function of both steps, and have red eyes. Since they have white eyes, this statement is false.

c. True.

d. True. A complementation test examines whether two mutations affect the same function.

e. True. The F_1 is a trans-heterozygote.

f. True. If two genes affect the same function, they are allelic.

The complementation test indicates that the two mutations affect the same function, and are therefore alleles at the same gene. However, it does not indicate whether they are *identical* alleles or not. To evaluate if two allelic mutations lie in exactly the same position in a gene, one needs to assess whether recombination can occur between them. If two alleles are identical, and lie in the same site, *intragenic* recombination between them cannot occur. If they lie in different sites, *intragenic* recombination can occur, giving rise to wild-type recombinant chromosomes. The appearance of wild-type F_2 progeny results from intragenic recombination, as illustrated below.

If w_1 and w_2 lie in different sites in the same gene, the cross and the F_1 progeny can be written as

$$P: \qquad \frac{W_1 \ +}{W_1 \ +} \times \frac{+ \ W_2}{+ \ W_2} \qquad\qquad F_1: \quad \frac{W_1 \ +}{+ \ W_2}$$

A rare *intragenic* crossover between the two mutant sites can be diagrammed as follows:

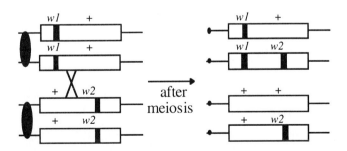

This crossover gives rise to gametes that are $w_1 \ w_2$ and $+ \ +$. The $w_1 \ w_2$ gamete would not be detected ($w_1 \ w_2/w_1 \ +$ and $w_1 \ w_2/+w_2$ flies are white eyed, as are their noncrossover siblings), but a $+ \ +$ gamete would give rise to a red-eyed offspring that has a genotype of $++/w_1+$ or $++/+w_2$. It is interesting to note that from the frequency of the white-eyed progeny, one can determine the recombination frequency (RF) between the two point mutants, just as in Benzer's cis-trans tests in the *rII* region of T4.

RF $(w_1, w_2) = [(2 \times 10)/20,010] \times 100\% = 0.1\%$. The w_1 and w_2 mutation sites are 0.1 mu apart.

14.21   Propose a genetic explanation for the ugly duckling phenomenon: Two white parents have a rare black offspring amidst a prolific number of white offspring.

Answer: First think about why the parents might be white and have mostly white offspring. Presumably, the parents are white because they lack a functional gene that makes a product (an enzyme perhaps) that produces black pigment. If the parents were white because they lacked the function of two *different* genes needed for black pigment production, a cross between them would produce black, and not white offspring. Since most of their offspring are white, it is likely that they each lack an identical function needed for black pigment production. Consider the options for how this could occur, and then consider how a black offspring might arise under each option.

Option 1: Each parent is homoallelic at a gene that results in white, and not black pigmentation. If this is the case, one can denote the cross as *a1/a1* x *a2/a2*, and all progeny are *a1/a2*. Since the parents are homoallelic, no intragenic recombination will occur. In this case, an *a+* allele could arise by a rare, new mutation (a reversion mutation), which would restore the function of the gene in the black pigment pathway. The offspring would be *a++/(a1* or *a2)*, and be black.

Option 2: At least one parent is heteroallelic at a gene that results in white, and not black pigmentation. In this case, one can denote the cross as *a1/a* x *a–/a–*, where *a–* represents any mutant, nonfunctional allele at this gene (the two *a–* alleles need not be identical). In the heteroallelic parent *a1/a2*, a rare intragenic crossover between the sites of the *a1* and *a2* mutations will result in *a+* and *a1,2* alleles, so that an *a+/a–* offspring will be produced. This offspring will have *a+* gene function, and so will be black.

14.22   Both *trpA* and *trpB* mutants of *E. coli* lack tryptophan synthetase activity. All *trpA* mutants complement all *trpB* mutants.
   a. Explain how two different complementing mutants (*trpA* and *trpB*) can affect the activity of the same enzyme.
   b. (This part of the question integrates material from Chapter 4). How will two such mutants be related in terms of their position within a metabolic pathway?

Answer:
   a. There are at least two options. First, the enzyme could be composed of multiple polypeptide subunits. The mutants are at different genes, each of which encodes

a polypeptide that is part of the multimeric enzyme. Second, the enzyme is composed of just one type of polypeptide, but the polypeptide is modified before it becomes active as an enzyme. One mutant is at a gene that encodes the polypeptide that will be modified to become the enzyme; the second mutant is at a gene that encodes a protein that modifies the enzymatic polypeptide and which is required to make it functional (e.g., it could be a protease that cleaves a pro-enzyme, making it active as an enzyme; it could be a kinase that phosphorylates a non-active form of the enzyme, making it active.)

b. Under the first option in (a), the two mutants will lie at the same position in the metabolic pathway, as they affect the same enzymatic step. Under the second option in (a), this may appear to be the case as well, depending on how the pathway is experimentally established. If the two mutants are positioned in the pathway by testing for growth after supplemental nutrients are added and by the accumulation of precursor compounds, the two mutants will appear to lie at the same step. However, the second mutant, at the gene which normally encodes a product to activate the enzyme, is actually positioned before the gene for the enzyme. It would not sit in the linear pathway that depicts the enzymes involved in biosynthesis of tryptophan, but rather as a branch leading to the production of the enzyme it activates.

14.23　A large number of mutations in *Drosophila* alter the normal brick-red eye color. As we discussed in Chapter 12, even alleles at one gene (*white, w*) can display a variety of phenotypes.

You are given a wild-type, deep-red strain and six independently isolated, true-breeding mutant strains that have varying shades of brown eyes, with the assurance that each mutant strain has only a single mutation. How would you determine:

a. whether the mutation in each strain is dominant or recessive?

b. how many different genes are affected in the six mutant strains?

c. which mutants, if any, are allelic?

d. whether any of these mutants are alleles at genes already known to affect eye color?

Answer:

a. Cross each mutation to the wild-type, deep-red strain and observe the phenotypes of the progeny. A dominant mutation, by definition, is one that appears in a heterozygote. If the progeny show deep-red eyes, the mutation must be recessive. If the progeny show brownish eyes, the mutation is dominant.

b. Set up pairs of crosses between the mutants to perform complementation tests. Mutations that affect the same gene function will produce brown-eyed progeny when crossed and belong to the same complementation group. Mutations that affect different functions will produce deep-red-eyed progeny when crossed and belong to different complementation groups. Counting the number of different complementation groups will give the number of genes that are affected.

c. Allelic mutations are those that are members of the same complementation group, as determined in (b).

d. One could assess if a particular mutant is allelic to a known eye-color gene by performing complementation tests between it and mutants at all known eye-color genes. This would involve crossing the mutant to mutants from a collection of strains with known eye-color mutations and observing the progeny of each cross. If the progeny have a mutant eye color, one would infer that the mutations carried in the two strains are allelic. However, this would be a tremendous amount of work. There are many eye-color mutations and this would require a large number of crosses. It would be faster to first determine which of the six mutations are allelic, and then choose a representative allele from each complementation group and identify its chromosomal location using a set of two- and/or three-point mapping crosses. Once this is done, examine published genetic maps of the *Drosophila* genome (e.g., at http://www.flybase.org) and ask if any known eye-color mutations lie in the same region. Then, obtain strains with these eye-color mutations and perform complementation tests between these mutant strains and a representative mutant from each complementation group identified with the new eye-color mutations.

15

NON-MENDELIAN INHERITANCE

CHAPTER OUTLINE

ORIGIN OF MITOCHONDRIA AND CHLOROPLASTS
ORGANIZATION OF EXTRANUCLEAR GENOMES
Mitochondrial Genome

Chloroplast Genome
RULES OF NON-MENDELIAN INHERITANCE
EXAMPLES OF NON-MENDELIAN INHERITANCE
Shoot Variegation in the Four O'Clock

The [*poky*] Mutant of *Neurospora*

Yeast *petite* Mutants

Non-Mendelian Inheritance in *Chlamydomonas*

Human Genetic Diseases and Mitochondrial DNA Defects

Exceptions to Maternal Inheritance

Infectious Heredity: Killer Yeast
CONTRASTS TO EXTRANUCLEAR INHERITANCE
Maternal Effect

Genomic Imprinting

REVIEW OF KEY TERMS, SYMBOLS, AND CONCEPTS

In your own words, write a brief, precise definition of each term in the groups below. Check your definitions using the text. Then, develop a concept map using the terms in each list.

1	2	3
extranuclear inheritance/gene	mitochondria	chloroplast
non-Mendelian inheritance/ gene	nucleoid region	nucleoid region
uniparental inheritance	H, L strands	SSC, LSC, IRA, IRB regions
maternal inheritance	D loop	23S, 5S, 4.5S, 16S rRNAs
biparental inheritance	continuous replication	cycloheximide
cytohet	ORF, URF	ribulose bisphosphate decarboxylase
maternal effect	12S, 16S rRNAs	shoot variegation in four o'clocks
nuclear genotype	mitochondrial genetic code	leukoplast
maternal effect gene	mitochondrial DNA	
genomic (parental) imprinting	[*poky*] in *Neurospor a*	
	petite, grande in yeast	

1	2	3
infectious inheritance	nuclear, neutral, suppressive	
endosymbiont hypothesis	*petite*	
cyanobacterium	protoperithecia	
purple nonsulfer	controlled cross	
photosynthetic bacterium	heteroplasmy	
erythromycin resistance in	Leber's hereditary optic	
Chlamydomanas	neuropathy	
killer yeast	Kearns-Sayre syndrome	
L, M viruses	myoclonic epilepsy and	
shell coiling direction in	ragged-red fiber disease	
Limnaea peregra		
PWS, Angelman syndrome		

THINKING ANALYTICALLY

After developing skills to analyze nuclear inheritance patterns, non-Mendelian patterns of inheritance are quite a twist at first. However, since non-Mendelian inheritance patterns are usually due to the extranuclear inheritance of mitochondrial or chloroplast genomes, the patterns seen are well defined. In general, they follow from the cytoplasmic contributions of one (female) parent to the offspring.

Consideration of the variation in inheritance patterns and the variation in the structure and function of the mitochondrial and chloroplast genomes provides a valuable perspective on nuclear inheritance patterns and nuclear genome structure and function. After organizing the factual information that is present in this chapter, take the time to compare and contrast the organization, replication, and expression of mitochondrial and chloroplast genes with nuclear genes. The salient features of an important biological process can often be better understood by examining variations in it.

Unlike extranuclear inheritance patterns that are controlled by extranuclear genes, maternal effects and genomic imprinting are controlled by nuclear genes. Keep this distinction clear. In considering maternal effects, it will help to diagram the generations of a cross, and illustrate how contributions from the parental generation are important for the development of the progeny. Carefully read the material in the chapter and do the problems to discover how to distinguish a maternal effect from an extranuclear, maternally inherited trait.

QUESTIONS FOR PRACTICE

Multiple Choice Questions

1. DNA is found in
    a. the nucleus of eukaryotes.
    b. mitochondria.
    c. chloroplasts.
    d. all subcellular organelles.
    e. all of the above except d.

2. In general, extranuclear genes show
   a. maternal inheritance.
   b. Mendelian inheritance.
   c. maternal effects.
   d. dominance.

3. Mitochondrial DNA is
   a. typically single stranded and coiled in nucleosomes.
   b. uniform in size in all species.
   c. uniformly double stranded, supercoiled, and circular.
   d. found only in animals and fungi.

4. In the D loop model of replication of mitochondrial DNA, replication
   a. is synchronous with nuclear DNA replication.
   b. originates at distinct locations on the H and L strands and is continuous.
   c. originates on both strands in the D loop and is semidiscontinuous.
   d. only occurs in the maternal cytoplasm.

5. The ribosomal proteins of mitochondrial ribosomes are
   a. coded for in the nucleoid region.
   b. coded for in the nuclear genome, and are the same as those used in cytoplasmic ribosomes.
   c. coded for in the nuclear genome, and are different from those used in cytoplasmic ribosomes.
   d. encoded on genes in between mitochondrial rRNA genes.

6. Which of the following is not a consequence of the differences in the genetic code used by most mitochondrial and nuclear genes?
   a. Fewer tRNAs are needed in the mitochondria.
   b. Fewer amino acids are used in mitochondrial proteins.
   c. Wobble is used more extensively.
   d. Some nonsense codons in mitochondrial genes are sense codons in nuclear genes, and vice versa.

7. Which of the following is true about both mitochondrial and chloroplast genomes?
   a. Both have double-stranded, circular, supercoiled genomes that typically exist in multiple copies per organelle.
   b. Both are small in size, typically only 16–18 kb.
   c. Both have only one copy of rRNA genes.
   d. Both have a similar density in a CsCl density gradient.

8. Which of the following is not a typical characteristic of extranuclear traits?
   a. They show uniparental inheritance.
   b. They cannot be mapped relative to nuclear genes.
   c. They show non-Mendelian segregation in crosses.
   d. They are affected by substitution of a nucleus with a different genotype.

9. Two brothers have a hereditary disease associated with a particular lesion in mitochondrial DNA. One brother is more severely affected than the other. Which of the following is *not* a plausible explanation for this observation?

a. The brothers have different degrees of heteroplasmy.

b. The brothers have different proportions of two mitochondrial types.

c. The brothers do not have identical nuclear genomes.

d. Different mitochondrial genes are affected in the two brothers.

10. Which of the following is *not* true about genomic imprinting?

a. It is an example of extranuclear inheritance.

b. Expression patterns of imprinted genes can vary depending on their parental source.

c. Expression patterns of imprinted genes are correlated with their methylation states.

d. Genomic imprinting can affect the severity of disease symptoms.

Answers: 1e; 2a; 3c; 4b; 5c; 6b; 7a; 8d; 9d; 10a.

Thought Questions

1. What are the tenets of the endosymbiont hypothesis? What arguments can you marshal to support, or detract from, this hypothesis?

2. Speculate on the evolutionary origin of plant chloroplasts, compared to the presumed origin of mitochondria.

3. Is there any evidence that there are paternal contributions to mtDNA inheritance? What, if any, significance might these contributions have?

4. How might molecular methods be employed to analyze a maternal line of descent? How might this be useful to trace movements of populations over time? Do any significant complications arise because of paternal contributions to mtDNA inheritance?

5. Distinguish between biparental and uniparental inheritance. Which organisms have organelles that show biparental inheritance?

6. One often thinks of non-Mendelian inheritance being associated with genes in mitochondrial or chloroplast DNA. What other examples of non-Mendelian inheritance exist? What is the significance of the examples you cite?

7. In what ways does cpDNA differ from nuclear and mitochondrial DNA?

8. The mtDNAs of most organisms contain similar coding information. Given this, speculate why animal mtDNAs are always relatively small (<20 kb), while mtDNAs of some other organisms can be quite large. (Put another way, what advantages do small extranuclear mtDNA genomes confer?) Why should genes be retained in mtDNA at all, since at least some proteins (e.g., ribosomal proteins) are able to be imported into the mitochondria?

9. Recall that environmental factors, as well as other genetic factors, were used to explain variable expressivity. What role might genomic imprinting play?

10. How do you account for the maternal effect in shell-coiling in the snail, *Limnaea peregra*? What features of this phenomenon indicate that it is controlled via a maternal effect, and not via extranuclear inheritance?

Thought Questions for Media

After reviewing the media on the *iGenetics* CD-ROM, try to answer these questions.

1. A four o'clock plant shows variegation. That is, part of the plant has only green leaves, part has only white leaves and part has mixed green and white leaves. Suppose you fertilized flowers in the green-only region of the plant with pollen from flowers in the white-only part of the plant. Based on the animation, what outcomes would you expect?

2. What is the difference between a leukoplast and a chloroplast?

3. In the Maternal Effect animation, dextral (right-handed) coiling is dominant to sinistral (left-handed) coiling, but the coiling pattern is determined by the maternal contribution, not the genotype of the zygote. Suppose you had a population of *Dd* dextral snails.

   a. What crosses would you do to obtain a *Dd* sinistral snail? (Remember that you can only tell the progeny's coiling phenotype and must infer the genotype by testcrossing or selfing!)

   b. What crosses would you do to obtain a *dd* sinistral snail?

   c. Could you ever obtain a *DD* sinistral snail?

4. How does maternal effect differ from maternal inheritance, since both involve cytoplasmic contributions from the mother?

1. The iActivity provided data indicating that individuals with MERFF show one or more symptoms that can include hearing loss, dementia, muscle jumps, seizures, unsteadiness, vision problems, or loss of cognitive skills.

   a. How would you characterize MERFF in terms of penetrance, expressivity and pleiotrophy?

   b. Based on what you know about the mode of inheritance of MERFF, what hypotheses might you form to explain its symptomatic variability?

   c. How might you use methods similar to those presented in the iActivity to test your hypotheses

2. The iActivity presented data that allowed you to distinguish between heteroplasmic maternal inheritance and autosomal dominant inheritance with variable expressivity.

   a. What methods were used in the iActivity to distinguish between these modes of inheritance?

   b. Would it ever be possible to distinguish between these modes of inheritance based on pedigree analysis alone?

   c. What challenges do mitochondrial inheritance present for the analyses of pedigrees?

3. Suppose a MERFF-like disorder was caused by a mutation in a nuclear gene whose product was imported into the mitochondrion. What types of inheritance might be associated with this disorder?

SOLUTIONS TO TEXT PROBLEMS

15.1   Compare the structure of the nuclear genome, the mitochondrial genome, and the chloroplast genome.

Answer: The nuclear genome is organized into linear chromosomes that are long double-stranded DNA molecules packaged by histone and nonhistone chromosomal proteins. Both mitochondrial and chloroplast genomes are circular, supercoiled, double-stranded DNA molecules and are not complexed with packaging proteins. While there is some variation in the size of chloroplast genomes (80 to 600 kb) and mitochondrial genomes (<20 kb in animals, 80 kb in yeast, 100 to 2,000 kb in plants), these extracellular genomes are not nearly as large as most eukaryotic chromosomes. Unlike nuclear chromosomes that contain diverse genes and noncoding sequences, mitochondria contain similar, unique genes, with larger mitochondrial genomes containing more noncoding sequences. Diploid, mitotically active eukaryotic cells have two copies of each chromosomal homolog that divide in an exquisitely organized mitosis. On the other hand, extranuclear genomes can exist in a variable number of copies per cell and can replicate independently in many phases of the cell cycle. A single yeast mitochondrion, for example, can have 10–30 nucleoid regions, each containing four to five mitochondrial DNA genomes.

15.2   Imagine that you have discovered a new genus of yeast. In your studies on this organism, you isolate DNA and subject it to CsCl density gradient centrifugation. In addition to a major peak, you observe a minor peak of lighter density. How could you determine whether the minor peak represents organellar (presumably mitochondrial) DNA as opposed to AT-rich repeated sequence in the nuclear genome?

Answer: In addition to being relatively AT-rich, mitochondrial DNA is circular, supercoiled, and has a fixed size. Its sequence is partially or completely known in a number of organisms, including yeast. There are several alternative approaches to determine if the minor peak fraction contains mitochondrial DNA. A first approach is to compare the properties of DNA in the minor peak fraction to DNA obtained from isolated mitochondria. Separate mitochondria from nuclei by differential centrifugation or by using sucrose density gradients. Then isolate and characterize the DNA from these two organellar fractions. Assess the density of the DNAs in CsCl density gradients and visualize the DNAs using electron microscopy. DNA associated with the mitochondrial fraction should be circular. DNA associated with the nuclear fraction will not be circular. If the minor peak is from mitochondria, purified DNA from mitochondria, separated in a CsCl density gradient, should have an identical density to that of the minor peak.

A second approach is to grow the yeast in the presence of an intercalating agent such as acridine, and see whether this treatment causes the minor peak species to disappear. If it does, the minor peak is organellar in origin.

A third approach is to isolate the minor peak, label it with 3H, and hybridize this labeled DNA to DNA within suitably prepared yeast cells. Then, using autoradiography and the electron microscope, determine whether the label is found over the nucleus or the mitochondria.

A fourth approach is to isolate DNA from the minor peak and study its homology to that of other yeast mitochondria (for example, perform a comparative DNA sequence analysis).

15.3   What genes are present in the human mitochondrial genome?

Answer: Human mitochondrial DNA contains the genes for the 12S and 16S mitochondrial rRNAs; 22 tRNAs; cytochrome b; and some of the polypeptide subunits of cytochrome c oxidase (COI, COII, COIII), NADH-dehydrogenase (ND1-6), and ATPase (ATPase 6 and 8). See Figure 15.3.

15.4   What conclusions can you draw from the fact that most nuclear-encoded mRNAs and all mitochondrial mRNAs have a poly(A) tail at the 3' end?

Answer: That most nuclear and mitochondrial mRNAs are polyadenylated suggests that polyadenylation serves some function that is basic and very likely important, perhaps related to mRNA stability or translation. However, the features unique to polyadenylation of mitochondrial transcripts give little insight into a general function. For example, polyadenylation is necessary in some mitochondrial mRNAs to complete a missing part of a UAA stop codon, but this function is not required for nuclear mRNAs. Since mitochondrial mRNAs do not exit the mitochondrion, the 3' poly(A) tail is presumably not needed for transport between cellular compartments. Experiments in which *Xenopus* oocytes were injected with globin mRNA with and without a poly(A) tail have suggested that one more general function of the tail is to confer stability on eukaryotic mRNAs. This view has been supported by investigations that have shown that shortening of the poly(A) tail plays a significant part in the control of mRNA degradation. Additional insights into the function of poly(A) tails have come from observations on the control of translation of maternally deposited mRNAs that are stored in oocytes. Here, the length of the poly(A) tail is regulated cytoplasmically, and stored mRNAs have shorter poly(A) tails than actively translated mRNAs. A longer poly(A) tail is able to promote the initiation of translation.

15.5   A substantial body of evidence indicates that defects in mitochondrial energy production may contribute to the neuronal cell death seen in a number of late-onset neurodegenerative diseases, including Alzheimer disease, Parkinson disease, Huntington disease, and amyotrophic lateral sclerosis (ALS, or Lou Gehrig disease). Some of these diseases have been associated with mutations in the nuclear genome. One experimental system that has been developed to evaluate the contributions of the mitochondrial genome to these diseases uses a cytoplasmic hybrid known as a cybid. Cybids are made by repopulating a tissueculture cell line that has been made mitochondria deficient with mitochondria from the cytoplasm of a human platelet cell. The cybids thus have nuclear DNA from the tissue culture cell and mitochondrial DNA from the human platelet cell.

The mitochondrial protein cytochrome oxidase has subunits encoded by both nuclear and mitochondrial genes. Patients with Alzheimer disease have been reported to have lower levels of cytochrome oxidase than age-matched controls.

a. What is the evidence that cytochrome oxidase has subunits encoded by both nuclear and mitochondrial genes?

b. Given the means to assay cytochrome oxidase activity, how would you investigate whether the decreased levels of cytochrome oxidase activity in patients with Alzheimer disease could be ascribed to nuclear or mitochondrial genetic defects? What controls would you create?

c. If you can to demonstrate that the mitochondrial contribution to cytochrome oxidase is responsible for lowered cytochrome oxidase activity, can you conclude that each mitochondrion of an affected individual has an identical defect?

Answer:

a. Mitochondrial ribosomes are sensitive to most inhibitors of bacterial ribosome function, such as chloramphenicol. However, they are generally insensitive to antibiotics to which cytoplasmic ribosomes are sensitive, such as cycloheximide. Selective use of antibiotics that inhibit translation by mitochondrial vs. cytoplasmic ribosomes has shown that components 2, 5, and 6 of cytochrome oxidase are synthesized on mitochondrial ribosomes, while components 1, 3, 4, and 7 are synthesized on cytoplasmic ribosomes. See Figure 15.4.

b. Studies on the role of the mitochondrial genome in Alzheimer's disease can be made by comparative analysis of cytochrome oxidase activity in cybids made with platelets from diseased individuals and in cybids made with platelets from age-matched control individuals. It is important to assess a number of different enzyme activities associated with mitochondrial proteins to ensure that the deficits in cytochrome oxidase were specific.

c. As discussed in the text, the cells of individuals with diseases resulting from mitochondrial DNA defects have a mixture of mutant and normal mitochondria—that is, they show heteroplasmy. Thus, assays in cybids are measurements of the enzyme activity present in a population of mitochondria in a cell. It would be unlikely that each of the mitochondria of an affected individual has an identical defect.

15.6   Discuss the differences between the universal genetic code of the nuclear genes of most eukaryotes and the code found in human mitochondria. Is there any advantage to the mitochondrial code?

Answer: While plant mitochondria use the universal nuclear genetic code, mitochondria from other organisms, including humans, utilize a code that differs in codon designation. In addition, the mitochondrial code typically has more extensive wobble, so that many fewer tRNAs are needed to read all possible sense codons. In humans, only 22 mitochondrial tRNAs are needed, as opposed to the 32 required for nuclear mRNAs. [There is some variability between mitochondrial codes of different organisms, as well as between the nuclear codes of different organisms (e.g., ciliated protozoa do not use the universal nuclear code).] Fewer mitochondrial tRNAs confer the advantage that fewer tRNA genes are needed in the mitochondria, allowing for a smaller mitochondrial genome.

15.7   Compare and contrast the cytoplasmic, mitochondrial, and chloroplast protein-synthesizing systems.

Answer: Compare these protein-synthesizing systems from three perspectives: the ribosomes used in translation, the mechanisms of translation initiation, elongation and termination, and the nature of the genetic code.

Mitochondrial and chloroplast ribosomes are different from each other as well as from cytoplasmic ribosomes. Cytoplasmic ribosomes are 80S, with 60S and 40S subunits. Human mitochondrial ribosomes are 60S, with 45S and 35S subunits. Chloroplast ribosomes are 70S, with 50S and 30S subunits, and are similar in size to prokaryotic ribosomes. Mitochondrial ribosomes lack the 5S and 5.8S rRNA components of cytoplasmic ribosomes, and have a 16S rRNA and 12S rRNA in the large and small subunits, respectively. Chloroplast ribosomes have a 23S, 5S, and 4.5S rRNA in the large subunit, and a 16S rRNA in the small subunit. The number of ribosomal proteins found in the chloroplast and mitochondrial ribosomes is not well defined. With a few exceptions (*Neurospora*, yeast), the proteins of mitochondrial ribosomes are distinct from those in cytoplasmic ribosomes. It is known that most mitochondrial ribosomal proteins are encoded by nuclear genes, and chloroplast ribosomal proteins are encoded by both nuclear and chloroplast genes.

Translation initiation in mitochondria (except for plant and yeast mitochondria) is quite different from initiation in the cytoplasm. Animal mitochondrial mRNAs lack a 5' cap and have virtually no 5' leader sequence. Therefore mitochondrial ribosomes bind to mitochondrial mRNAs and orient translation initiation differently than cytoplasmic ribosomes. Initiation in plant and yeast mitochondria is more like cytoplasmic translation initiation: Although there is no 5' cap, there is a 5' leader and translation initiation may be at the first AUG. In chloroplasts, translation initiation is much like in bacteria. A formylmethionyl tRNA is used to initiate all proteins, and the formylation reaction is catalyzed by a transformylase in the chloroplast. Both mitochondria and chloroplasts use their own translation initiation factors, elongation factors, and release factors that are distinct from those used in the cytoplasm. In some ways, translation in both chloroplasts and mitochondria is similar to translation in prokaryotes. Chloroplast and mitochondrial ribosomes are both insensitive to cycloheximide, an inhibitor of cytoplasmic ribosomes, but sensitive to nearly all antibiotics that inhibit prokaryotic translation.

The genetic code used by both chloroplast and cytoplasmic ribosomes is the universal code, while the code used by mitochondria is different. Mitochondria have fewer tRNAs, and there is considerably more wobble.

15.8   What features of non-Mendelian inheritance distinguish it from the inheritance of nuclear genes?

Answer: Non-Mendelian inheritance due to extranuclear genes can be distinguished from nuclear inheritance by four characteristics. First, reciprocal crosses of extranuclear genes give different results because uniparental inheritance is typically seen. These results are distinct from the results of reciprocal crosses of sex-linked nuclear genes, and from the results of reciprocal crosses of autosomal nuclear genes (which give the same results regardless of sex type). Second, extranuclear genes cannot be mapped to chromosomes in the nucleus. New extranuclear mutations do not show linkage to any known nuclear linkage group. Third, ratios typical of Mendelian segregation are not found. Fourth, extranuclear inheritance is indifferent to nuclear substitution.

15.9   Distinguish between maternal effect and non-Mendelian inheritance.

Answer: Maternal effect is the determination of gene-controlled characters by the maternal genotype prior to the fertilization of the egg cell. A maternal effect is seen when nuclear genes of the mother function to specify some characteristic of the zygote. For example, a maternal effect could result from a maternally transcribed gene whose product was localized at one pole of the embryo and was responsible for the polarity of the developing embryo.

In contrast to nuclear genes that can function in the mother, the genes involved in non-Mendelian inheritance are extranuclear and are found in mitochondria and chloroplasts. If the mitochondria are inherited with transmission of the mother's cytoplasm, mitochondrial genes will show maternal inheritance, a type of extranuclear inheritance.

15.10   Reciprocal crosses between two types of the evening primrose, *Oenothera hookeri* and *Oenothera muricata*, produce the following effects on the plastids:

O. *hookeri* female × 0. *muricata* male → Yellow plastids

O. *muricata* female × 0. *hookeri* male → Green plastids

Explain the difference between these results, noting that the chromosome constitution is the same in both types.

Answer: Both offspring have the same hybrid nuclear constitution, but differ in the maternal cytoplasm they inherited. Thus, factors in the cytoplasm are likely to be the cause of the phenotypic difference that is seen. The two possible types of cytoplasmic factors are those that would cause a maternal effect and those that are inherited maternally. If the difference in phenotype is due to a maternal effect, the difference is due to the deposition in the oocyte of gene products from the mother's nuclear genome. For these results to be explained by a maternal effect, one would have to hypothesize (1) that a such a maternally contributed gene product affected plastid color, and (2) that this product was different in O. *hookeri* and O. *muricata*. If the difference in phenotype is due to maternal inheritance, the plastids contributed by one female parent would have to be different from the plastids contributed by the other. Specifically, yellow plastids would have been contributed by the *O. hookeri* female and green plastids would have been contributed by the *O. muricata* female.

It is noteworthy that in most angiosperms (flowering plants), the plastids are inherited only from the maternal parent. Thus, maternal inheritance of plastids would explain the results presented in this problem. However, in the genus *Oenothera*, biparental inheritance (inheritance from both the male and the female parent) of plastids has been reported (see text). If biparental inheritance does not occur all of the time (i.e., maternal inheritance occurs some of the time), many progeny would be just as described in the results presented here. When plastids are contributed biparentally, and the plastids contributed by the male and female parent segregate to different daughter cells during mitosis, a green patch of tissue would be seen in the yellow progeny from the cross *O. hookeri* female × *O. muricata* male, and a yellow patch of tissue would be seen in the green progeny from the cross *O. muricata* female × *O. hookeri* male.

15.11   A series of crosses are performed with a recessive mutation in *Drosophila* called *tudor*. Homozygous *tudor* animals appear normal and can be generated from the cross of two heterozygotes, but a true-breeding *tudor* strain cannot be maintained. When homozygous *tudor* males are crossed to homozygous *tudor* females, both of which appear to be phenotypically normal, a normal-appearing F_1 is produced. However, when F_1 males are crossed to wild-type females, or when F_1 females are crossed to wild-type males, no progeny are produced. The same results are seen in the F_1 progeny of homozygous *tudor* females crossed to wild-type males. The F_1 progeny of homozygous *tudor* males crossed to wild-type females appear normal, and they are capable of issuing progeny when mated either with each other or with wild-type animals.
   a. How would you classify the *tudor* mutation? Why?
   b. What might cause the *tudor* phenotype?

Answer:
   a. The *tudor* mutation is a maternal effect mutation. Homozygous *tudor* mothers give rise to sterile progeny, regardless of their mate.
   b. The "grandchildless" phenotype results from the absence of some maternally packaged component in the egg needed for the development of the F_1's germ line.

15.12   A form of male sterility in corn is maternally inherited. Plants of a male-sterile line crossed with normal pollen give male-sterile plants. Some lines of corn carry a dominant, so-called restorer (*Rf*) gene that restores pollen fertility in male-sterile lines.
   a. If a male-sterile plant is crossed with pollen from a plant homozygous for gene *Rf*, what will be the genotype and phenotype of the F_1?

b. If the F_1 plants of part (a) are used as females in a testcross with pollen from a normal plant (*rf/rf*), what would be the result? Give genotypes and phenotypes and designate the type of cytoplasm.

Answer:

a. Let the normal cytoplasm be denoted by [*N*], and the male-sterile cytoplasm be denoted by [*Ms*]. The cross can be written as [*Ms*] *rf/rf* female × [*N*] *Rf/Rf* male. The F_1 would be [*Ms*] *Rf/rf*, and be male-fertile.

b. The cross is [*Ms*] *Rf/rf* female × [*N*] *rf/rf* male. Half of the progeny would be [*Ms*] *Rf/rf* and half would be [*Ms*] *rf/rf*. Thus, half of the progeny will be male-fertile and half will be male-sterile.

15.13   In *Neurospora* a chromosomal gene *F* suppresses the slow-growth characteristic of the [*poky*] phenotype and makes a [*poky*] culture into a *fast*-[*poky*] culture, which still has abnormal cytochromes. Gene *F* in combination with normal cytoplasm has no detectable effect. (Hint: Since both nuclear and extranuclear genes are considered, it is convenient to use symbols to distinguish the two. Thus cytoplasmic genes are designated in square brackets, e.g., [*N*] for normal cytoplasm, [*poky*] for poky.)

a. A cross in which *fast*-[*poky*] is used as the female (protoperithecial) parent and a normal wild-type strain is used as the male parent gives half [*poky*] and half *fast*-[*poky*] progeny ascospores. What is the genetic interpretation of these results?

b. What would be the result of the reciprocal cross of the cross described in part (a), that is, normal female × *fast*-[*poky*] male?

Answer:

a. The phenotypic results indicate that half of the progeny are [*poky*] and half are *fast*-[*poky*]. This means that all of the progeny have the [*poky*] mitochondrial phenotype (by maternal inheritance) and that the *F* gene must be a nuclear gene segregating according to Mendelian principles. Using the symbolism given above, the cross can be written as *F* [*poky*] female × + [*N*] male, and is expected to give half *F* [*poky*] and half + [*poky*] progeny. Considering the phenotypes, the [*poky*] progeny are + [*poky*] and the *fast*-[*poky*] progeny are *F* [*poky*].

b. The cross could be written as + [*N*] female × *F* [*poky*] male. The progeny will be half + [*N*] and half *F* [*N*]. These two genotypes are both normal, and have indistinguishable phenotypes.

15.14   Distinguish between nuclear (segregational), neutral, and suppressive *petite* mutants of yeast.

Answer: Petites are a class of mutations that affect mitochondrial function. *Neutral petites* are able to grow on a medium that will support fermentation, but cannot grow on a medium that supports only aerobic respiration because they lack nearly all of their mitochondrial DNA. *Nuclear petites* result from a nuclear mutation that affects mitochondrial function (e.g., in a nuclear gene that encodes a subunit of a mitochondrial protein). These mutations, if crossed to a wild-type (*grande*) strain, will show a typical 2:2 Mendelian segregation pattern. *Neutral* and *suppressive petites* result from mutations in the mitochondrial genome. They show uniparental inheritance (but not maternal inheritance): When crossed to a normal cell, and (*grande*) diploids go through meiosis, a 0:4 ratio of *petite:grande* is seen. *Suppressive petites*, unlike *neutral petites*, do have an effect on the wild type. A diploid formed from a *suppressive petite* and a normal cell will have respiratory properties intermediate between the *petite* and normal. Mitosis in this diploid results in mostly *petites* (up to 99%) with a respiratory-deficient phenotype, and meiosis results in a 4:0 ratio of *petite:grande*. At a molecular level, the *suppressive petite* mutations result from partial deletions of the mitochondrial DNA.

15.15   In yeast a haploid *nuclear* (segregational) *petite* is crossed with a *neutral petite*. Assuming that both strains have no other abnormal phenotypes, what proportion of the progeny ascospores are expected to be *petite* in phenotype if the diploid zygote undergoes meiosis?

Answer: Nuclear genes will show Mendelian segregation, so that +/*petite* should show 2:2 segregation. One should see 1/2 *petite* and 1/2 wild-type (*grande*) progeny.

15.16   When grown on a medium containing acriflavin, a yeast culture produces a large number of very small (*tiny*) cells that grow very slowly. How would you determine whether the slow-growth phenotype was the result of a cytoplasmic factor or a nuclear gene?

Answer: This problem is formally very similar to determining the mode of inheritance for yeast *petite* mutants. Acriflavin intercalates between base pairs, and might be used to introduce *petite*-like mutations. If the *tiny* phenotypes are due to a nuclear gene, then meiosis in cells formed from a cross of *tiny* × wild type should result in a 2:2 segregation of *tiny*:wild-type ascospores. If, in contrast, an extranuclear gene is involved, one would expect a 0:4 or 4:0 ratio, and see only wild-type or *tiny* progeny.

15.17   *Drosophila melanogaster* has a sex-linked, recessive, mutant gene called *maroon-like* (*ma-l*). Homozygous *ma-l* females or hemizygous *ma-l* males have light-colored eyes because of the absence of the active enzyme xanthine dehydrogenase, which is involved in the synthesis of eye pigments. When heterozygous *ma-l+/ma-l* females are crossed with *ma-l* males, all the offspring are phenotypically wild type. However, half the female offspring from this cross, when crossed back to *ma-l* males, give all *ma-l* progeny. The other half of the females, when crossed to *ma-l* males, give all phenotypically wild-type progeny. What is the explanation for these results?

Answer: Since *ma-l* is sex linked, we know it is nuclearly inherited. One can therefore diagram the crosses and the results. In the first cross, *ma-l+/ma-l* × *ma-l/Y* gives 1/4 *ma-l/ma-l* females, 1/4 *ma-l+/ma-l* females, 1/4 *ma-l+/Y* males, and 1/4 *ma-l/Y* males. To explain why the half of the total F_1 progeny that are *ma-l* hemizygotes or homozygotes do not have light-colored eyes, consider the possibility of a maternal effect. The parental female was *ma-l+/ma-l*, and so could have provided normal xanthine dehydrogenase (or stable, normal xanthine dehydrogenase mRNA, or the biochemical product of the xanthine dehydrogenase reaction) to the embryo. The results of the crosses indicate that this maternally transmitted product is sufficient for the F_1 progeny to have a normal phenotype. When the F_1 females are backcrossed to the *ma-l* males, two different crosses are possible. One is *ma-l+/ma-l* × *ma-l/Y*. Just like the initial cross, this will give all wild-type progeny. The other cross is *ma-l/ma-l* × *ma-l/Y*, which will give all *maroon-like* progeny (as the mother can no longer supply the *ma-l+* product to her progeny).

15.18   When females of a particular mutant strain of *Drosophila melanogaster* are crossed to wild-type males, all the viable progeny flies are females. Hypothetically, this result could be the consequence of either a sex-linked, male-specific lethal mutation or a maternally inherited factor that is lethal to males. What crosses would you perform to distinguish between these alternatives?

Answer: If the mutation is a sex-linked, male-lethal mutation, the first cross can be diagrammed as *L/L* × *+/Y*, giving *L/+* (females) and *L/Y* (dead males). If the F_1 females are crossed to normal males, the cross is *L/+* × *+/Y*. The progeny are 1/4 *L/+* (normal females), 1/4 *+/+* (normal females), 1/4 *+/Y* (normal males), and 1/4 *L/Y* (dead males), a 2:1 ratio of females to males. If the male lethality was associated with a maternally inherited factor lethal to males, the F_1 females should possess this factor (as they received cytoplasm from their mother). Consequently, just like their mother, the F_1 females should have no male offspring when mated to wild-type males.

15.19   Reciprocal crosses between two *Drosophila* species, *D. melanogaster* and *D. simulans*, produce the following results:

D. melanogaster female × *D. simulans* male → Females only

D. simulans female × *D. melanogaster* male → Males, with few or no females

Propose a possible explanation for these results.

Answer: When *melanogaster* females are crossed with *simulans* males, *melanogaster* cytoplasm is given to the offspring. Female progeny will have an X from the *melanogaster* as well as the *simulans* parent, while male progeny will have an X from the *melanogaster* parent but only a Y (with few structural genes) from the *simulans* parent. Female progeny survive selectively because of nuclear gene products provided on the *simulans* X needed for hybrid survival in *melanogaster* cytoplasm. When a *simulans* female is crossed with a *melanogaster* male, *simulans* cytoplasm is given to the offspring. Female progeny will have a *melanogaster* as well as a *simulans* X, while male progeny will have a *simulans* X and a *melanogaster* Y. Since few or no females are recovered, it appears that the *melanogaster* X encodes products that (generally) cause lethality in the *simulans* cytoplasm.

15.20 Some *Drosophila* are very sensitive to carbon dioxide; administering it to them anesthetizes them. The sensitive flies have a cytoplasmic particle called *sigma* that has many properties of a virus. Resistant flies lack *sigma*. The sensitivity to carbon dioxide shows strictly maternal inheritance. What would be the outcome of the following two crosses: (a) sensitive female × resistant male and (b) sensitive male × resistant female?

Answer: In part (a), all of the progeny would inherit the *sigma* factor from the (sensitive) female parent. Consequently, all the progeny will be sensitive. In part (b), the resistant female parent lacks the *sigma* factor. All of the progeny will also lack the factor, and so be resistant.

15.21 A few years ago the political situation in Chile was such that very many young adults were kidnapped, tortured, and killed by government agents. When abducted young women had young children or were pregnant, the children were taken and given to government supporters to raise as their own. Now that the political situation has changed, grandparents of stolen children are trying to locate and reclaim their grandchildren. Imagine that you are a judge in a trial centering on the custody of a child. Mr. and Mrs. Escobar believe Carlos Mendoza is the son of their abducted, murdered daughter. If this is true, then Mr. and Mrs. Sanchez are the paternal grandparents of the child because their son (also abducted and murdered) was the husband of the Escobars' daughter. Mr. and Mrs. Mendoza claim that Carlos is their natural child. The attorney for the Escobar and Sanchez couples informs you that scientists have discovered a series of RFLPs in human mitochondrial DNA. He tells you that his clients are eager to be tested and asks that you order that Mr. and Mrs. Mendoza and Carlos be tested also.
  a. Can mitochondrial RFLP data be helpful in this case? In what way?
  b. Do all seven parties need to be tested? If not, who actually needs to be tested in this case? Explain your choices.
  c. Assume that the critical people have been tested and you have received the results. How would the results resolve the question of Carlos' parentage?

Answer:
  a. Mitochondrial RFLP data can be helpful to trace the maternal line of descent. If Carlos is the son of Mr. and Mrs. Mendoza, then Carlos and Mrs. Mendoza should have identical (or at least highly similar) RFLPs. If, on the other hand, Carlos is the son of Mrs. Escobar's murdered daughter, then Carlos and Mrs.

Escobar should have identical (or at least highly similar) mitochondrial RFLPs. If Mrs. Escobar and Mrs. Mendoza have different mitochondrial RFLPs, it can be determined which of them contributed mitochondria to Carlos.

b. Only Carlos, Mrs. Escobar and Mrs. Mendoza need to be tested. The potential grandfathers need not be tested, as they will not have given any of their mitochondria to Carlos. In addition, Mrs. Sanchez need not be tested, as her son, even if he was Carlos' father, would not have given him mitochondria (see, however, the text for exceptions to maternal inheritance). Only individuals who might have contributed mitochondria maternally need to be tested. If the DNA markers were nuclear, then anyone claiming to be related to Carlos should be tested.

c. If Mrs. Mendoza and Mrs. Escobar do not differ in mitochondria RFLPs, the data will not be helpful. This could be because the RFLPs are not very polymorphic, and many individuals share the same RFLPs. In this case, it would be helpful to use nuclear markers and test all the "relatives." If the mitochondrial RFLPs do differ, and Carlos matches Mrs. Mendoza, the case should be dismissed. If Carlos matches Mrs. Escobar, then the Escobar and Sanchez couples are indeed the grandparents, and the Mendozas have claimed a stolen child.

15.22 The analysis of mitochondrial DNA has been very useful in assessing the history of specific human populations. For example, a 9-bp deletion in the small intergenic region between the genes for cytochrome oxidase subunit II and tRNA.Lys (see Figure 15.3) has been a very informative marker to trace the origins of Polynesians. The deletion is widely distributed across southeast Asia and the Pacific and is present in 80 to 100 percent of individuals in the different populations within Polynesia. One of the most polymorphic regions of the mitochondrial genome is found in the region between the genes for tRNA.Phe and tRNA.Thr. In Asians with the 9-bp deletion, a specific set of DNA sequence polymorphisms in this region is found. Using the 9-bp deletion and the DNA sequence polymorphisms as markers, comparative analysis of Asian populations has found a genetic trail of mitochondrial DNA variation. The trail begins in Taiwan, winds through the Philippines and Indonesia, proceeds along the coast of New Guinea, and then moves into Polynesia. Based on an estimated rate of mutation in the tRNA.Phe to tRNA.Thr region, this expansion of mitochondrial DNA variants is thought to be about 6,000 years old. This is consistent with linguistic and archeological evidence that associates Polynesian origins with the spread of the Austronesian language family out of Taiwan between 6,000 and 8,000 years ago.

a. Why are these types of mitochondrial DNA polymorphisms such good markers for tracing human migration patterns?

b. Why is it important to correlate findings from mitochondrial DNA polymorphisms with other (non-DNA) assessment methods?

c. Why might sequences in the tRNA.Phe to tRNA.Thr region be more polymorphic than other sequences in the mitochondrial genome?

d. The 9-bp deletion has also been found in human populations in Africa. What different explanations are possible for this, and how might these explanations be evaluated?

Answer:

a. The analysis of mitochondrial DNA is a powerful tool in analyzing maternal lineages in humans. By following the inheritance of a set of polymorphisms linked to mitochondrial DNA, maternal lineages can be followed.

b. In cases such as this one, it is important to relate these findings to independent assessment methods (language, archeological evidence). This is because DNA polymorphisms can arise at multiple points in a maternal lineage, and taken alone, are not proof of a historical relationship.

c. This region lacks coding sequences, and is used to regulate mitochondrial DNA replication. Thus, it may have fewer constraints that force conservation of its DNA sequence.

d. There are at least three explanations: a single origin of the deletion in Asia, with migration to Africa; a single origin in Africa, with migration to Asia; or independent, identical mutations in both Africa and Asia. If either of the first two explanations were correct, then DNA in the tRNA.Phe to tRNA.Thr region would be relatively similar in sequence in those African and Asian populations with the deletion. If the third explanation were correct, then DNA in the tRNA.Phe to tRNA.Thr region would be relatively dissimilar in those African and Asian populations with the deletion. (The latter is seen.)

15.23   The pedigree in the following figure shows a family in which an inherited disease called Leber hereditary optic atrophy is segregating. This condition causes blindness in adulthood. Studies have recently shown that the mutant gene causing Leber hereditary optic atrophy is located in the mitochondrial genome.

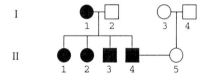

a. Assuming II-4 marries a normal person, what proportion of his offspring should inherit Leber's hereditary optic atrophy?

b. What proportion of the sons of II-2 should be affected?

c. What proportion of the daughters of II-2 should be affected?

Answer:

a. Since II-4 is a male, he will not contribute any of his mutant mitochondria to his offspring. All of his offspring will have normal mitochondria from their mother, and be normal.

b. Since II-2 is a female, all of her progeny will obtain her mutant mitochondria, and hence all will be affected. All of her sons will be affected.

c. All of the daughters will be affected, as all will have mutant mitochondria from their mother.

15.24   The inheritance of the shell-coiling direction in the snail *Limnaea peregra* has been studied extensively. A snail produced by a cross between two individuals has a shell with a right-hand twist (dextral-coiling). This snail produces only left-hand (sinistral) progeny on selfing. What are the genotypes of the F_1 snail and its parents?

Answer: If the coil direction were controlled by an extranuclear gene, then the progeny would always exhibit the phenotype of the mother, owing to maternal inheritance. If the trait were determined by a nuclear gene that did not show a maternal effect, then one would expect a "true-breeding" individual to give rise to individuals just like itself. Since neither of these are observed, these data are best explained by considering a nuclear gene that shows a maternal effect. In this case, the shell-coiling phenotype is determined by the genotype of the mother. One can infer the maternal genotype from the progeny phenotype. If dextral is *D*, and sinistral is *d*, the F_1 genotype must have been *dd*, as it only gives sinistral offspring. Since the F_1 itself has a dextral pattern, its maternal parent must have had a *D* allele. To give the F_1 a *d* allele, the maternal parent must have been *Dd*. The paternal parent must have had a *d* allele, and could have been either *dd* or *Dd*.

15.25   Beckwith-Wiedemann syndrome (BWS) is characterized by fetal malformation and cancer. BWS has been mapped to chromosome region 11p15.5 by its association with balanced chromosomal rearrangements. This region contains an embryonic tumor suppressor gene and a number of other genes, including *KVLQT1*. Mutations in *KVLQT1* cause a dominantly inherited heart defect that results in cardiac arrhythmia and sudden death. When a wide variety of childhood and adult tumors are examined for gene expression in region 11p15.5, a preferential loss of expression of the paternal alleles is seen. Most normal fetal tissues only express the maternal allele, but heart tissue typically expresses maternal and paternal alleles of *KVLQT1*.

   a. What evidence would be necessary to show that genomic imprinting may play a role in the Beckwith-Wiedemann syndrome? From the previous description, does such evidence exist?
   b. What is the molecular basis for imprinting? How is it detected?
   c. What kind of evidence would be necessary to show that imprinting is involved with the dominantly inherited heart defect associated with the *KVLQT1* gene?
   d. What similarities, if any, do you see in the imprinting of genes in this region with imprinting for the Prader-Willi and Angelman syndromes discussed in this chapter?

Answer:
   a. It would be necessary to show that individuals with BWS have the loss of expression of a parental allele that contributes to the onset of BWS. From what is described in the question, there is a tumor suppressor gene (tumor suppressor genes function to suppress cell division and inhibit tumor growth) that if not

expressed, could result in tumor formation. In addition, the region appears to be subject to imprinting because of the expression pattern of genes in the region in tumors, and the expression pattern of *KVLQT1* in some tissues of normal individuals. It could be that the loss of expression of one tumor suppressor allele would give rise to tumor formation due to the sole expression of a mutant allele. This hypothesis would need to be evaluated, however.

b. The molecular basis for imprinting is a decrease in the expression of a specific allele due to the heritable methylation of that allele in one parent. To demonstrate imprinting, it is necessary to identify which of a paternally or maternally inherited allele is transcribed. This can be done if the parental alleles are polymorphic, and the differences between them can be detected by analysis of their mRNA or protein products.

c. It would be necessary to demonstrate that only one of the two parental alleles is expressed in the heart of diseased individuals. For example, if the mutation caused imprinting to occur abnormally, the levels of mRNA for the *KVLQT1* gene could be lowered, and this might lead to the disease state. It would be important to distinguish between decreased levels of expression of the *KVLQT1* gene due to abnormal imprinting of one allele, and decreased levels of expression due to some other reason (e.g., a mutation affecting transcriptional control).

d. In both situations, a region of a chromosome appears to be subject to imprinting, as the alleles of multiple genes in the region contributed by one parent are not expressed.

16

REGULATION OF GENE EXPRESSION IN BACTERIA AND BACTERIOPHAGES

CHAPTER OUTLINE

THE *lac* OPERON OF *E. coli*

    Lactose as a Carbon Source for *E. coli*

    Experimental Evidence for the Regulation of *lac* Genes

    Jacob and Monod's Operon Model for the Regulation of *lac* Genes

    Positive Control of the *lac* Operon

    Molecular Details of *lac* Operon Regulation

THE *trp* OPERON OF *E. coli*

    Gene Organization of the Tryptophan Biosynthesis Genes

    Regulation of the *trp* Operon

REGULATION OF GENE EXPRESSION IN PHAGE LAMBDA

    Early Transcription Events

    The Lysogenic Pathway

    The Lytic Pathway

REVIEW OF KEY TERMS, SYMBOLS, AND CONCEPTS

In your own words, write a brief, precise definition of each term in the groups below. Check your definitions using the text. Then, develop a concept map using the terms in each list.

1	2	3
regulated genes	*lac, trp* operons	lambda (λ) phage
constitutive genes	*lacA, -Z, -Y, -I* genes	lytic pathway
inducible genes	negative, positive control	lysogenic pathway
inducers and effectors	allolactose	genetic switch
controlling site	partial diploids	lambda repressor
housekeeping genes	cis-dominance	*cro* gene
induction	trans-dominance	*recA* gene
coordinate induction	O^c, I^-, I^s, I^{-d} mutations	antiterminator
operon	superrepressor	P_R, P_{RE}, P_{RM}, P_L, P_I
polycistronic mRNA	allosteric shift	O_R, O_L
polygenic mRNA	catabolite repression	antitermination

1	2	3
effector molecule	glucose effect	readthrough transcription
operator	CAP-cAMP complex	integrase
repressor molecule	CAP site	*cI, cII, cIII* genes
promoter	effector	Q, Cro proteins
polarity	aporepressor	
polar effects	attenuation	
polar mutations	attenuator site	
	pause signal	
	antitermination	
	feedback inhibition	
	allosteric shift	
	inducible, repressible operon	

THINKING ANALYTICALLY

This chapter presents how the expression of bacterial and bacteriophage genes is regulated. While the regulation of a particular set of genes can be complex, it is invariably based on a general paradigm. This is that the structural organization of a set of genes is related to both their induction by effector molecules and subsequent expression (as diagrammed in Figure 16.1). As you study the regulation of each set of genes, keep this general principle in site. Reconsider it with each of the operons – analyze how it is used and elaborated upon.

Once you have a solid understanding of the general principle underlying prokaryotic gene expression, the challenge is to understand and retain the complex details of the regulatory circuitry. It will help to first study the text figures and then diagram (eventually, from memory) the structure of each operon and the role of regulatory factors within it. This is especially valuable when considering the regulation of genes in phage λ. This will take time, as it requires repeated practice and comparative review!

You can strengthen your understanding of the principles underlying prokaryotic gene expression and your detailed knowledge of the regulatory circuitry of operons by examining the consequences of mutations in different operon elements. First, address why mutations in regulatory elements such as the promoter or operator will be cis-dominant. Second, address why some mutations in the genes for diffusible regulatory factors *can* be trans-dominant. Third, consider how the properties of different mutations in a specific operon can provide you with a basis to develop a model of its structure. Finally, relate the regulation of the operon to how it functions within a biochemical or growth pathway.

QUESTIONS FOR PRACTICE

Multiple Choice Questions

1. Genes that respond to the needs of a cell or organism in a controlled manner are known as
   a. inducer genes.
   b. effector genes.

c. regulated genes.

d. constitutive genes.

2. A mutation that causes a gene always to be expressed, irrespective of what the environmental conditions may be, is known as a(n)

a. inducer mutation.

b. effector mutation.

c. regulator mutation.

d. constitutive mutation.

3. A gene that is stimulated to undergo transcription in response to a particular molecular event that occurs at a controlling site near that gene is said to be

a. inducible.

b. constitutive.

c. a promoter.

d. an inducer.

4. An operon which is inducible may be under

a. positive control only.

b. negative control only.

c. constitutive control only.

d. both positive and negative control.

5. The effector molecule which induces the *lac* protein-coding genes is

a. lactose.

b. allolactose.

c. glucose.

b-galactosidase.

6. Before transcription of the *lac* operon can occur, RNA polymerase must bind strongly to the promoter. This happens when

a. CAP binds to the CAP site in the promoter.

b. a CAP-cAMP complex binds to the CAP site in the promoter.

c. catabolite repression occurs.

d. lacI+ is mutated to *lacI$^-$*.

7. Which of the following is an example of an effector molecule acting via positive control?

a. lactose inducing the lac operon

b. glucose causing catabolite repression

c. tryptophan attenuating the trp operon

d. the lambda cI gene product, at a certain cellular level, favoring the lysogenic pathway

8. Bacterial operons containing protein-coding genes for the synthesis of amino acids, such as the tryptophan operon, are customarily classified as

a. negatively controlled.

b. positively controlled.

c. repressible operons.

d. inducible operons.

9. Ultraviolet light induces integrated phage λ to enter the lytic pathway by
   a. cleaving repressor monomers.
   b. initiating transcription of the cro gene.
   c. converting the RecA protein to a protease.
   d. all of the above, directly or indirectly.

10. Which of the following is not critical to the genetic switch controlling the choice between the lysogenic and lytic pathways in phage λ?
   a. the competition between the products of the cI gene and the cro gene.
   b. transcription of the genes, J, K, L, and M.
   c. the concentration of λ repressor protein dimers
   d. whether RNA polymerase binds to P_{RM} or P_R

   Answers: 1c; 2d; 3a; 4d; 5b; 6b; 7b; 8c; 9d; 10b.

Thought Questions

1. What three proteins are synthesized when lactose is the sole carbon source in *E. coli*? What does each do?

2. What are the roles of *lacA, lacI, lacO, lacY*, and *lacZ* in *E. coli* carbohydrate metabolism? In what order are they arranged in the DNA molecule?

3. Describe the sequence of events that occurs in the *lac* operon when *E. coli* is grown in the presence of both glucose and lactose.

4. Distinguish between cis-dominant mutations and trans-dominant mutations. Why is *lacO*^{c} cis-dominant but *lacI*^{s} trans-dominant? Would a mutation that led to constitutive expression of the *cI* gene be cis- or trans-dominant?

5. How is attenuation related to the coupling of transcription and translation in prokaryotes?

6. What are the fundamental differences between the *lac* and *trp* operons in *E. coli*?

7. How do structural changes in DNA or RNA conformation play a role in:
   a. catabolite repression by glucose and CAP-cAMP?
   b. antitermination and termination in attenuation of the *trp* operon?

8. What is catabolite repression?

9. In what different or similar ways are allosteric shifts used in the regulation of inducible and repressible operons?

10. Speculate as to what phenotype each of the following λ mutations would have: (a) A mutation in the *cI* gene that resulted in repressor molecules that bound O_L and O_R less well. (b) A mutation in the *cro* gene that resulted in no Cro protein being produced. (c) A mutation in O_R that resulted in decreased affinity for repressor molecules.

Thought Questions for Media

After reviewing the media on the *iGenetics* CD-ROM, try to answer these questions.

1. In the *lac* operon, is the operator wholly within, wholly outside of, or partially within the promoter?
2. How could you distinguish between promoter and operator mutations?
3. An operon is defined as a cluster of genes along with an adjacent promoter and operator that controls the transcription of those genes.
   a. Must all operons be polycistronic?
   b. Must all of the genes in one operon be transcribed together?
4. How does lactose mediate de-repression of the *lac* operon? Does it act directly?
5. Which type of mutation in the *lac* operon causes the production of β-galactosidase whether or not lactose is present?
6. Why does it make sense for E. coli to transcribe the *lac* operon at a very slow rate in the presence of glucose? (Consider the products of β-galactosidase enzymatic activity.)
7. What phenotype would you expect of a mutation in the CAP site in the *lac* promoter?

1. In the iActivity, the strain containing the O^c mutation ($I^+ O^c Z^+$) showed constitutive expression both by itself and as a merozygote of the form $I^+O^cZ^+/F'$ $I^+O^+Z^+$. Would the phenotype be different if the merozygote had a genotype that was either $I^+O^cZ^+/F'$ $I^+O^+Z^-$ or $I^+O^cZ^+/F'$ $I^-O^+Z^+$? For each case, why or why not?
2. In the iActivity, the strain containing the I^s mutation ($I^s O^+ Z^+$) showed repressed expression both by itself and as a merozygote of the form $I^s O^+Z^+/F'$ $I^+O^+Z^+$. Would the phenotype be different if the merozygote had a genotype that was either $I^s O^+ Z^+/F'$ $I^+O^+Z^-$ or $I^s O^+ Z^+/F'$ $I^-O^+Z^+$? For each case, why or why not?
3. In the iActivity, you analyzed data showing that the *lac* operon was inducible and under negative control.
   a. In theory, if you can experimentally demonstrate that an operon is inducible, must it also be under negative control?
   b. Can an inducible operon be under both negative and positive control?
   c. Can an inducible operon be under only positive control?

SOLUTIONS TO TEXT PROBLEMS

16.1   How does lactose bring about the induction of synthesis of β-galactosidase, permease, and transacetylase? Why does this event not occur when glucose is also in the medium?

Answer: The addition of lactose to *E. coli* cells brings about a rapid synthesis of these three enzymes by the induction of a single promoter that lies upstream of the genes for these three enzymes. The three genes are part of a *lac* operon that is transcribed as a single unit. When lactose is added, it is metabolized (isomerized) to allolactose, which binds to a repressor protein. Without bound allolactose, the repressor protein blocks transcription from the *lac* promoter. Hence, the *lac* operon is normally under a negative control mechanism. When allolactose is bound, the repressor protein is inactivated and is unable to bind to the operator site to block transcription. As a result, RNA polymerase binds to the promoter and initiates transcription of a single mRNA that encodes all three proteins.

One of the enzymes that is synthesized, β-galactosidase, cleaves lactose to produce glucose and galactose (which is converted to glucose in a subsequent enzymatic step). Consequently, if glucose is present in the medium, it is redundant to induce the *lac* operon. Glucose blocks induction of the *lac* operon by utilizing a positive control mechanism. In this catabolite repression, glucose causes a great reduction in the amount of cAMP in the cell. For normal induction of the *lac* operon, cAMP must complex with a CAP (catabolite gene activator protein) that, in turn, binds to a CAP site upstream of the *lac* promoter and activates transcription. In the absence of cAMP, the cAMP-CAP complex is absent, and so transcription cannot be activated.

16.2   Operons produce polygenic mRNA when they are active. What is a polygenic mRNA? What advantages, if any, does it confer in terms of the cell's function?

Answer: Polygenic mRNAs contain coding information for more than one protein. These mRNAs are transcribed from operons that contain several genes encoding related functions such as catalyzing steps of a biosynthetic pathway. One advantage conferred by utilizing such mRNAs is that cells can regulate all of the steps of a pathway coordinately. By using a polygenic mRNA, the synthesis of each of a set of enzymes acting in one pathway can be produced by a single regulatory signal.

16.3   If an *E. coli* mutant strain synthesizes β-galactosidase whether or not the inducer is present, what genetic defect(s) might be responsible for this phenotype?

Answer: One possibility is that the repressor protein bound by the inducer cannot bind to the operator (i.e., the repressor is nonfunctional and the strain is I^-), so that its presence or absence makes no difference. Another possibility is that there are base-pair alterations in the operator region that make it unrecognizable by the repressor protein (i.e., the operon is constitutively expressed and the strain is O^c).

16.4   Distinguish the effects you would expect from (a) a missense mutation and (b) a nonsense mutation in the *lacZ* (β-galactosidase) gene of the *lac* operon.

Answer:

a. A missense mutation results in partial or complete loss of β-galactosidase activity, but no loss of permease and transacetylase activities. A nonsense mutation is likely to have polar effects unless the mutation is very close to the normal chain-terminating codon for β-galactosidase. If the nonsense mutation in the DNA occurred near the terminus of the *lacZ* gene, the ribosome would continue to slide along the polygenic mRNA toward the *lacY* gene. However, it would typically dissociate before reaching the start codon for permease because of the greater distance. Thus, few ribosomes would be translating the genes lying downstream of the *lacZ* gene, leading to decreased permease and transacetylase production.

16.5   Elucidation of the regulatory mechanisms associated with the enzymes of lactose utilization in *E. coli* was a landmark in our understanding of regulatory processes in microorganisms. In formulating the operon hypothesis as applied to the lactose system, Jacob and Monod found that results from particular partial diploid strains were invaluable. Specifically, in terms of the operon hypothesis, what information did the partial diploids provide that the haploids could not?

Answer: The use of partial diploids allowed observation of the consequences of placing sequences in *trans* and in *cis*. Partial diploids were used to show that some regulatory sequences must lie in *cis* to *lacZ* (the *lacO* region upstream of the *lacZ* gene) to exert a regulatory effect. For example, O^c mutations are cis-acting: they cause constitutive activation of the *lac* promoter they lie upstream from, but do not activate any other promoter. Partial diploids also were used to show that the *lacI* gene encoded a *trans*-acting factor (a diffusible product that could bind to the *lacO* region) and that promoter function did not require a diffusible substance. For example, a *lacI*$^+$ gene on a plasmid could function in *trans* to regulate a *lac* promoter in *cis* to a *lacI*$^-$ gene.

16.6   For the *E. coli lac* operon, write the partial diploid genotype for a strain that will produce β-galactosidase constitutively and permease by induction.

16.7

Answer: In order to observe such a phenotype, there are three requirements: (1) a functional *lacZ* and a nonfunctional *lacY* gene must both lie downstream of a functional operator and promoter, (2) a nonfunctional *lacZ* and a functional *lacY* gene must lie downstream of an inducible (i.e., O^+) promoter, and (3) a functional repressor gene must be present in the cell (I^+). A genotype that satisfies these requirements is the partial diploid *lacI*$^+$ *lacO*^{c} *lacP*$^+$ *lacZ*$^+$ *lacY*$^-$/*lacI*$^+$ *lacO*$^+$ *lacP*$^+$ *lacZ*$^-$ *lacY*$^+$. Only one *lacI*$^+$ gene is required, so one may be *lacI*$^-$.

16.7   Mutants were instrumental in elaborating the model for regulation of the *lac* operon.

   a. Discuss why *lacO^c* mutants are cis-dominant but not trans-dominant.

   b. Explain why *lacI^s* mutants are trans-dominant to the wild-type *lacI^+* allele but *lacI^-* mutants are recessive.

d. Discuss the consequences of mutations in the repressor gene promoter as compared with mutations in the structural gene promoter.

Answer:

   a. *lacO^c* mutants are mutants in the operator region that is normally bound by the repressor protein. *lacO^c* mutants result from a DNA alteration that precludes the repressor protein from binding the operator. Since the repressor normally blocks transcription initiation from a downstream promoter, *lacO^c* mutants result in constitutive transcription at that promoter. Since the operator acts only on an adjacent, and not any other, promoter, mutations in the operator are only cis-dominant. The *lacO^c* has no effect on other lactose operons in the same cell because *lacO^c* does not code for a product that could diffuse through the cell and affect other DNA sequences.

   b. In wild-type strains, *lacI* encodes a repressor that can block transcription at the *lac* operon by binding to an operator region. By binding the operator, the repressor blocks RNA polymerase from binding to the promoter. This activity of the repressor can be altered if allolactose is present, which binds to the repressor and inhibits it from binding the operator. The superrepressor (*lacI^s*) mutation results in a repressor protein that can bind the operator, but cannot bind allolactose. Once it binds to the operator, it cannot leave the operator, and transcription is always blocked. This results in a dominant mutation, since even if normal repressor molecules (made by *lacI^+*) are present, the superrepressor molecules do not vacate the operator region, and the operon cannot be induced. On the other hand, *lacI^-* mutants either do not make repressor protein, or make repressor that is unable to bind to the operator. In a partial diploid that has both *lacI^-* and *lacI^+* genes, repressor proteins are made (by *lacI^+*) and are capable of diffusing to any *lac* operator region to regulate a *lac* operon. Hence, *lacI^-* is recessive to *lacI^+* because the defect caused by the absence of the repressor proteins in *lacI^-* mutants can be overcome by the synthesis of diffusible repressor protein from the *lacI^+* gene.

   c. The *lacI* gene is constitutively expressed at a low level. Mutations in the repressor gene promoter result in either an increase or a decrease in the level of expression of the repressor gene. They will not affect the structure of repressor molecule, but will affect its cellular concentration. If the mutation causes a complete loss of expression of the repressor protein, it would have the same phenotype as an *I^-* mutant, since no functional repressor would be produced. These mutants would result in constitutive expression of *lacZ*, *lacY*, and *lacA*, and be recessive to *I^+* in partial diploids. If the promoter mutation only partially decreases transcription below normal levels, there will be increased expression of *lacZ*, *lacY*, and *lacA* in the absence of inducer. If the promoter mutation increases transcription above normal levels (the *lacI^Q* and *lacI^{SQ}* mutations presented in the text) a large number of repressor molecules will be produced. Such mutants will reduce the efficiency of induction of the *lac* operon by allolactose, and will be trans-dominant.

16.8   This question involves the *lac* operon of *E. coli* where I = *lacI* (the repressor gene), P = P_{lac} (the promoter), O = *lacO* (the operator), Z = *lacZ* (the β-galactosidase gene), and Y = *lacY* (the permease gene). Complete Table 16.A, using "+" to indicate that the enzyme in question will be synthesized and "−" to indicate that the enzyme will not be synthesized.

Table 16.A

	GENOTYPE	INDUCER ABSENT: β-galactosidase	Permease	INDUCER PRESENT: β-galactosidase	Permease
a.	$I^+ P^+ O^+ Z^+ Y^+$				
b.	$I^+ P^+ O^+ Z^- Y^+$				
c.	$I^+ P^+ O^+ Z^+ Y^-$				
d.	$I^- P^+ O^+ Z^+ Y^+$				
e.	$I^s P^+ O^+ Z^+ Y^+$				
f.	$I^+ P^+ O^c Z^+ Y^+$				
g.	$I^s P^+ O^c Z^+ Y^+$				
h.	$I^+ P^+ O^c Z^+ Y^-$				
i.	$I^{-d} P^+ O^+ Z^+ Y^+$				
j.	$I^- P^+ O^+ Z^+ Y^+$ $I^+ P^+ O^+ Z^- Y^-$				
k.	$I^- P^+ O^+ Z^+ Y^-$ $I^+ P^+ O^+ Z^- Y^+$				
l.	$I^s P^+ O^+ Z^+ Y^-$ $I^+ P^+ O^+ Z^- Y^+$				
m.	$I^+ P^+ O^c Z^- Y^+$ $I^+ P^+ O^+ Z^+ Y^-$				
n.	$I^- P^+ O^c Z^+ Y^-$ $I^+ P^+ O^+ Z^- Y^+$				
o.	$I^s P^+ O^+ Z^+ Y^+$ $I^+ P^+ O^c Z^+ Y^+$				
p.	$I^{-d} P^+ O^+ Z^+ Y^-$ $I^+ P^+ O^+ Z^- Y^+$				
q.	$I^+ P^- O^c Z^+ Y^-$ $I^+ P^+ O^+ Z^- Y^+$				

Table 16.A *(continued)*

GENOTYPE	INDUCER ABSENT:		INDUCER PRESENT:	
	β-galactosidase	Permease	β-galactosidase	Permease
r. $I^+ P^- O^+ Z^+ Y^-$				
$I^+ P^+ O^c Z^- Y^+$				
s. $I^- P^- O^+ Z^+ Y^+$				
$I^+ P^+ O^+ Z^- Y^-$				
t. $I^- P^+ O^+ Z^+ Y^-$				
$I^+ P^- O^+ Z^- Y^+$				

Answer:

GENOTYPE	INDUCER ABSENT:		INDUCER PRESENT:	
	β-galactosidase	Permease	β-galactosidase	Permease
a. $I^+ P^+ O^+ Z^+ Y^+$	−	−	+	+
b. $I^+ P^+ O^+ Z^- Y^+$	−	−	−	+
c. $I^+ P^+ O^+ Z^+ Y^-$	−	−	+	−
d. $I^- P^+ O^+ Z^+ Y^+$	+	+	+	+
e. $I^s P^+ O^+ Z^+ Y^+$	−	−	−	−
f. $I^+ P^+ O^c Z^+ Y^+$	+	+	+	+
g. $I^s P^+ O^c Z^+ Y^+$	+	+	+	+
h. $I^+ P^+ O^c Z^+ Y^-$	+	−	+	−
i. $I^{-d} P^+ O^+ Z^+ Y^+$	+	+	+	+
j. $I^- P^+ O^+ Z^+ Y^+$	−	−	+	+
$I^+ P^+ O^+ Z^- Y^-$				
k. $I^- P^+ O^+ Z^+ Y^-$	−	−	+	+
$I^+ P^+ O^+ Z^- Y^+$				
l. $I^s P^+ O^+ Z^+ Y^-$	−	−	−	−
$I^+ P^+ O^+ Z^- Y^+$				
m. $I^+ P^+ O^c Z^- Y^+$	−	+	+	+
$I^+ P^+ O^+ Z^+ Y^-$				
n. $I^- P^+ O^c Z^+ Y^-$	+	−	+	+
$I^+ P^+ O^+ Z^- Y^+$				
o. $I^s P^+ O^+ Z^+ Y^+$	+	+	+	+
$I^+ P^+ O^c Z^+ Y^+$				

	Genotype				
p.	$I^{-d}\,P^+\,O^+\,Z^+\,Y^-$ / $I^+\,P^+\,O^+\,Z^-\,Y^+$	+	+	+	+
q.	$I^+\,P^-\,O^c\,Z^+\,Y^-$ / $I^+\,P^+\,O^+\,Z^-\,Y^+$	−	−	−	+
r.	$I^+\,P^-\,O^+\,Z^+\,Y^-$ / $I^+\,P^+\,O^c\,Z^-\,Y^+$	−	+	−	+
s.	$I^-\,P^-\,O^+\,Z^+\,Y^+$ / $I^+\,P^+\,O^+\,Z^-\,Y^-$	−	−	−	−
t.	$I^-\,P^+\,O^+\,Z^+\,Y^-$ / $I^+\,P^-\,O^+\,Z^-\,Y^+$	−	−	+	−

16.9 A new sugar, sugarose, induces the synthesis of two enzymes from the *sug* operon of *E. coli*. Some properties of deletion mutations affecting the appearance of these enzymes are as follows (here, "+" = enzyme induced normally, i.e., synthesized only in the presence of the inducer; C = enzyme synthesized constitutively; 0 = enzyme cannot be detected):

MUTATION OF	ENZYME 1	ENZYME 2
Gene *A*	+	0
Gene *B*	0	+
Gene *C*	0	0
Gene *D*	C	C

a. The genes are adjacent in the order *ABCD*. Which gene is most likely to be the structural gene for enzyme 1?

b. Complementation studies using partial diploid (F') strains were made. The extrachromosomal element (F') and chromosome each carried one set of *sug* genes. The results were as follows (symbols are the same as in previous table):

GENOTYPE OF F'	CHROMOSOME	ENZYME 1	ENZYME 2
$A^+\,B^-\,C^+\,D^+$	$A^-\,B^+\,C^+\,D^+$	+	+
$A^+\,B^-\,C^-\,D^+$	$A^-\,B^+\,C^+\,D^+$	+	0
$A^-\,B^+\,C^-\,D^+$	$A^+\,B^-\,C^+\,D^+$	0	+
$A^-\,B^+\,C^+\,D^+$	$A^+\,B^-\,C^+\,D^-$	+	+

From all the evidence given, determine whether the following statements are true or false:

1. It is possible that gene *D* is a structural gene for one of the two enzymes.
2. It is possible that gene *D* produces a repressor.

3. It is possible that gene *D* produces a cytoplasmic product required to induce genes *A* and *B*.

4. It is possible that gene *D* is an operator locus for the *sug* operon.

5. The evidence is also consistent with the possibility that gene *C* could be a gene that produces a cytoplasmic product required to induce genes *A* and *B*.

6. The evidence is also consistent with the possibility that gene *C* could be the controlling end of the *sug* operon (the end from which mRNA synthesis presumably commences).

Answer: First consider the data in general terms. Mutations in genes *A* or *B* result in a loss of one, but not both enzyme activities. These are likely to be structural genes for the enzymes (*B* = enzyme 1, *A* = enzyme 2). The mutations in genes *C* and *D* result in loss of both enzyme activities, suggesting that these genes or regions regulate or affect both genes.

a. Gene *B* is likely to be the gene for enzyme 1, since only a mutation in gene *B* produced a loss of enzyme 1 activity with no effect on enzyme 2 activity. (By similar logic, gene *A* codes for enzyme 2.)

b. 1. False. A mutation in *D* leads to the constitutive synthesis of both enzymes 1 and 2, so *D* cannot be a structural gene for either enzyme.

   2. True. *D* could encode a repressor. Suppose the repressor acted as the *lac* repressor does in the *lac* operon. If mutations in *D* inactivated the repressor, then an absence of repressor would lead to constitutive activation of the operon. In this model, D^- mutants would be recessive to D^+ mutants, which is seen in the analysis of partial diploids ($A^- B^+ C^+ D^+ / A^+ B^- C^+ D^-$ shows inducible activity of both A^+ and B^+).

   3. False. If *D* was needed to induce the *sug* operon, D^- mutants should produce no enzymes. This is not observed.

   4. False. One does see that D^- mutants are constitutive, as would be expected if a D^- operator region could not be bound by a repressor to repress transcription. However, not all of the results support this view. If *D* was an operator, consider what phenotype would be expected in the partial diploid $A^- B^+ C^+ D^+ / A^+ B^- C^+ D^-$. If D^- was a defective operator, this partial diploid would express the A^+ gene (enzyme 2) constitutively, in a cis-dominant manner, and not in an inducible manner. This is not seen. What is seen is a trans-dominant effect where the A^+ gene is inducible. Thus, *D* is not an operator.

   5. False. Since the products of genes *A* and *B* are not inducible in C^- mutants, one might speculate that gene *C* produced a cytoplasmic product that was required to induce genes *A* and *B*. However, consider the partial diploid data. In two of the partial diploids ($A^+ B^- C^- D^+ / A^- B^+ C^+ D^+$ and $A^- B^+ C^- D^+ / A^+ B^- C^+ D^+$), the wild-type genes on the C^- chromosome are not expressed, even though a C^+ gene is on another chromosome. This indicates that *C* shows cis-dominance, and not trans-dominance. If C^+ encoded a cytoplasmic factor, it would diffuse and be capable of acting in a trans-

dominant fashion. Since it does not, C does not encode a cytoplasmic, trans-acting factor.

6. True. The cis-dominant effects that C^- mutants show in partial diploids could be explained if the mutations were in the controlling end of the *sug* operon, in a region such as the promoter.

16.10 Four different polar mutations, *1, 2, 3,* and *4,* in the *lacZ* gene of the *lac* operon were isolated after mutagenesis of *E. coli*. Each caused total loss of β-galactosidase activity. Two revertant mutants, due to suppressor mutations in genes unlinked to the *lac* operon, were isolated from each of the four strains: Suppressor mutations of polar mutation *1* are *1A* and *1B*, those of polar mutation *2* are *2A* and *2B*, and so on. Each of the eight suppressor mutations was then tested, by appropriate crosses, for its ability to suppress each of the four polar mutations; the test involved examining the ability of a strain carrying the polar mutation and the suppressor mutation to grow with lactose as the sole carbon source. The results follow (+ = growth on lactose and − = no growth):

POLAR MUTATION	SUPPRESSOR MUTATION							
	1A	1B	2A	2B	3A	3B	4A	4B
1	+	+	+	+	+	+	+	+
2	+	−	+	+	+	+	−	−
3	+	−	+	−	+	+	−	−
4	+	+	+	+	+	+	+	+

A mutation to a UAG codon is called an amber nonsense mutation, and a mutation to a UAA codon is called an ochre nonsense mutation. Suppressor mutations allowing reading of UAG and UAA are called amber and ochre suppressors, respectively.

a. Which of the polar mutations are probably amber? Which are probably ochre?

b. Which of the suppressor mutations are probably amber suppressors? Which are probably ochre suppressors?

c. How would you explain the anomalous failure of suppressor *2B* to permit growth with polar mutation *3*? How could you test your explanation most easily?

d. Explain precisely why ochre suppressors suppress amber mutants but amber suppressors do not suppress ochre mutants.

Answer:

a. An ochre suppressor mutation will allow reading of the UAA codon, and have a 3'-AUU-5' anticodon. Because the 5'-U in the anticodon can wobble base pair with either a 3'-A or 3'-G in a codon, the ochre suppressor will also allow reading of the UAG codon, and be an amber mutant suppressor. An amber suppressor mutation will allow reading of a UAG codon, and will have a 3'-AUC-5' anticodon. It will be able to suppress only amber mutants. Thus, amber mutants will be those suppressible by all given suppressors, while ochre mutants will be those suppressible by only a subset of suppressors. Mutants *1* and *4* appear to be amber mutants, while mutants *2* and *3* appear to be ochre mutants.

b. An ochre suppressor will allow growth of all four polar mutations, while an amber suppressor will allow growth of only *1* and *4*. Therefore, *1B*, *4A*, and *4B* are amber suppressors, while *1A*, *2A*, *3A* and *3B* are ochre suppressors. *2B* is unlike either of these two groups, and will be discussed in part **c**.

c. Since *2B* suppresses *1*, *2*, and *4*, it is probably an ochre suppressor. *3* might not be suppressed because of the mechanism of suppression. Any of a number of tRNA molecules could have been mutated to have an anticodon that will base pair with an ochre triplet (UAA). It is likely that this tRNA will bring an amino acid to the ochre triplet that is different from that coded by the wild-type message. In some cases, this could result in a nonfunctional β-galactosidase enzyme. In turn, this would lead to the cell being unable to grow on lactose as a sole carbon source, so that suppression would not be seen. The hypothesis that nonfunctional β-galactosidase protein would be made can be tested. One can generate antibodies to wild-type β-galactosidase protein, and use them to immunoprecipitate β-galactosidase protein from mutant cells. The hypothesis would be supported if protein can be precipitated, even though no enzyme activity can be detected.

d. The fact that ochre suppressors suppress amber mutants but amber suppressors do not suppress ochre mutants can be explained by the wobble hypothesis (see pp. 428–429 and Figure 14.11). A 5'-U in the tRNA anticodon can pair with either a 3'-A or 3'-G in the codon. Thus, a 5'-UAG-3' amber mutant codon and a 5'-UAA-3' ochre mutant codon can both be read by a 3'-AUU-5' ochre suppressor anticodon. This allows ochre suppressors to suppress both ochre and amber nonsense mutants. On the other hand, 5'-C in the tRNA anticodon can only pair with a 3'-G in the codon. Thus, a 3'-AUC-5' amber suppressor anticodon can only pair with a 5'-UAG-3' amber mutant codon.

16.11   What consequences would a mutation in the catabolite activator protein (*CAP*) gene of *E. coli* have for the expression of a wild-type *lac* operon?

Answer: The CAP, in a complex with cAMP, is required to facilitate RNA polymerase binding to the *lac* promoter. The RNA polymerase binding occurs only in the absence of glucose, and only if the operator is not occupied by repressor (i.e., lactose is also absent). Suppose the *CAP* gene is mutated so that it could no longer bind to the CAP site. In this case, RNA polymerase would not be able to recognize and bind to the promoter, and the operon would not be expressed. Such a mutation could be distinguished from other mutations that eliminate operon expression (e.g., *I*^{s}, *P*$^-$) by several means. First, it should be recessive to a normal allele in partial diploids, and not show cis- or trans-dominance. Second, it should map to a location other than the *lac* operon.

16.12   The *lac* operon is an inducible operon, whereas the *trp* operon is a repressible operon. Discuss the differences between these two types of operons.

Answer: Both inducible and repressible operons allow sensitive control of transcription. They differ from each other in the details of how such control is achieved. In the *lac* operon, a repressor protein bound to an operator blocks transcription unless lactose is present. Thus, if lactose is absent, the system is OFF. When lactose is added, it is converted to allolactose and acts as an effector molecule to release the repressor from the operator, so that RNA polymerase can transcribe the operon. In the *trp* operon, the control strategy is the opposite. When tryptophan is abundant in the medium, the operon is turned off, as it is unnecessary to synthesize the enzymes needed to build tryptophan. Tryptophan also acts as an effector molecule. It binds to an aporepressor protein and converts it into an active repressor. This repressor is capable of binding the *trp* operator to reduce transcription of the *trp* operon protein-coding genes by RNA polymerase. Transcription of the *trp* operon is reduced by about 70 percent in the presence of tryptophan, while the aporepressor has no affinity for the operator in the absence of tryptophan.

The *trp* operon also can be regulated by attenuation, a mechanism that controls the ratio of the transcripts that include the five structural genes to those that are terminated before the structural genes. Under conditions where some tryptophan is present in the medium, short 140-bp transcripts are produced, and transcription is attenuated. Under conditions of tryptophan starvation or limitation, full-length transcripts are produced. A model for how attenuation occurs is described in text Figures 16.16, 16.17, and 16.18.

16.13   In the presence of high intracellular concentrations of tryptophan, only short transcripts of the *trp* operon are synthesized because of attenuation of transcription 5' to the structural genes. This is mediated by the recognition of two Trp codons in the leader sequence. If these codons were mutated to UAG stop codons, what effect would this have on the regulation of the operon in the presence or absence of tryptophan? Explain.

Answer: For a wild-type *trp* operon, the absence of tryptophan results in antitermination; that is, the structural genes are transcribed and the tryptophan biosynthetic enzymes are made. This occurs because a lack of tryptophan results in the absence of, or at least a very low level of, Trp-tRNA.Trp. In turn, this causes the ribosome translating the leader sequence to stall at the Trp codons (see Figure 16.17a). When the ribosome is stalled at the Trp codons, the RNA being synthesized just ahead of the ribosome by RNA polymerase assumes a particular secondary structure. This favors continued transcription of the structural genes by the polymerase. If the two Trp codons were mutated to stop codons, then the mutant operon would function constitutively in the same way as the wild-type operon in the absence of tryptophan. The ribosome would stall in the same place, and antitermination would result in transcription of the structural genes.

For a wild-type *trp* operon, the presence of tryptophan turns off transcription of the structural genes. This occurs because the presence of tryptophan leads to the accumulation of Trp-tRNA.Trp, which allows the ribosome to read the two Trp codons and stall at the normal stop codon for the leader sequence. When stalled in that position, the antitermination signal cannot form in the RNA being synthesized; instead, a termination signal is formed, resulting in the termination of transcription. In a mutant *trp* operon with two stop codons instead of the Trp codons, the stop codons cause the ribosome to stall, even though tryptophan and Trp-tRNA.Trp are present. This results in an antitermination signal and transcription of the structural genes.

In sum, in both the presence and the absence of tryptophan, the mutant *trp* operon will not show attenuation. The structural genes will be transcribed in both cases and the tryptophan biosynthetic enzymes will be synthesized. Only if an amber suppressor mutation were present in the cell would attenuation be restored. An amber suppressor mutation results when a tRNA has a mutant anticodon that recognizes the amber (UAG) nonsense codon. In this case, the operon will be attenuated under the control of the amino acid that binds the suppressor tRNA.

16.14 In the bacterium *Salmonella typhimurium*, seven of the genes coding for histidine biosynthetic enzymes are located adjacent to one another in the chromosome. If excess histidine is present in the medium, the synthesis in all seven enzymes is coordinately repressed, whereas in the absence of histidine all seven genes are coordinately expressed. Most mutations in this region of the chromosome result in the loss of activity of only one of the enzymes. However, mutations mapping to one end of the gene cluster result in the loss of all seven enzymes, even though none of the structural genes have been lost. What is the counterpart of these mutations in the *lac* operon system?

Answer: Mutations that cause the loss of activity in just one enzyme are mutations in structural genes, similar to *lacZ* and *lacY* mutations. Mutations that cause loss of all seven enzymes could be mutations in the promoter, similar to P_{lac-} mutations.

16.15 On infecting an *E. coli* cell, bacteriophage λ has a choice between the lytic and lysogenic pathways. Discuss the molecular events that determine which pathway is taken.

Answer: When λ infects a cell and its genome circularizes, phage growth begins when RNA polymerase binds the lambda early operon promoters P_L and P_R and transcribes mRNA for the *N* and *cro* genes, respectively. *N* acts as a transcription antiterminator, and extends RNA synthesis to other genes that include the gene *cII*. The cII protein turns on *cI*, the gene for the lambda repressor, as well as genes *O* and *P*, whose products are needed for DNA replication, and gene *Q*, whose product is needed for transcription of the late genes used in lysis and to produce phage particle proteins. Once the lambda repressor and Cro are produced, there is competition between them to set a genetic switch that determines whether a lysogenic or a lytic pathway will be taken. A lysogenic pathway is taken if the lambda repressor dominates, while a lytic pathway is taken if Cro dominates. The events that occur under Cro or repressor domination are diagrammed in text Figure 16.21.

In a cell that will undergo lysogeny, the cII protein (stabilized by the cIII protein) will stimulate transcription of mRNA from P_{RE} and from P_I. This results in synthesis of repressor and of integrase. Lambda repressor binds to two operators: O_R and O_L. This binding blocks transcription from P_R and P_L and so blocks production of Cro and N. It also stimulates transcription from P_{RM} and the production of additional lambda repressor molecules. The stable repression of transcription from P_R together with the integrase-catalyzed integration of the lambda chromosome into the E. coli host chromosome leads to the establishment of lysogeny. If the lambda repressor is not present in high enough concentration, or is cleaved and inactivated, the absence of repressor at O_R leads to the binding of RNA polymerase at P_R and transcription of the cro gene. When the Cro protein is produced in increasing amounts, it acts to decrease transcription from P_R and P_L, which reduces synthesis of the cII protein, and block synthesis of repressor from P_{RM}. By this means, an increase in Cro protein blocks production of the lambda repressor. It allows enough transcription from P_R for Q proteins to accumulate and stimulate the late gene transcription that is needed for starting the lytic pathway. In this way, the competition between the Cro and lambda repressor proteins for the operator sites determines how the genetic switch is set.

16.16   How do the lambda repressor protein and the Cro protein regulate their own synthesis?

Answer: The lambda repressor binds to the operator O_R. When the lambda repressor is bound, it stimulates synthesis of more repressor mRNA from the promoter P_{RM}. Eventually however, at very high concentrations of lambda repressor, O_R will be bound by lambda repressor in a way that blocks further transcription from the promoter P_{RM}. This maintains repressor concentrations in the cell. In the absence of repressor binding to O_R, RNA polymerase transcribes cro mRNA from the promoter P_R. As the concentration of Cro protein produced from this mRNA increases, Cro binds to the operator O_R, and decreases synthesis from P_R and P_L. Not only does this serve to block synthesis of lambda repressor mRNA from P_{RM}, it will eventually block synthesis of cro mRNA as well. Thus, just as the lambda repressor regulates the ability of RNA polymerase to transcribe its own cI gene from P_{RM}, Cro regulates the ability of RNA polymerase to transcribe cro from P_R. See Figure 16.21.

16.17   If a mutation in the phage lambda cI gene results in a nonfunctional cI gene product, what phenotype would you expect the phage to exhibit?

Answer: The *cI* gene product is a repressor protein that acts to keep the lytic functions of the phage repressed when lambda is in the lysogenic state. A *cI* mutant strain would lack the repressor and be unable to repress lysis, so that the phage would always follow a lytic pathway.

16.18 Bacteriophage λ can form a stable association with the bacterial chromosome because the virus manufactures a repressor. This repressor prevents the virus from replicating its DNA and making lysozyme and all the other tools used to destroy the bacterium. When you induce the virus with UV light, you destroy the repressor, and the virus goes through its normal lytic cycle. The repressor is the product of a gene called the *cI* gene and is a part of the wild-type viral genome. A bacterium that is lysogenic for λ⁺ is full of repressor protein, which confers immunity against any λ virus added to these bacteria. Added viruses can inject their DNA, but the repressor from the resident virus prevents replication, presumably by binding to an operator on the incoming virus. Thus, this system has many elements analogous to the *lac* operon. We could diagram a virus as shown in the figure. Several mutations of the *cI* gene are known. The c_i mutation results in an inactive repressor.

a. If you inject *E. coli* with λ containing a c_i mutation, can it lysogenize (form a stable association with the bacterial chromosome)? Why or why not?
b. If you infect a bacterium simultaneously with a wild-type c^+ and a c_i mutant of λ, can you obtain stable lysogeny? Why or why not?
c. Another class of mutants called c^{IN} makes a repressor that is insensitive to UV destruction. Will you be able to induce a bacterium lysogenic for c^{IN} with UV light? Why or why not?

Answer:
a. No. The repressor is necessary to keep the lytic function of the phage repressed, and allow the phage to enter lysogeny. In the presence of a c_i mutation, only the lytic pathway can be taken.
b. Yes. A normal repressor will be made from the wild-type c^+ gene. This repressor is diffusible, and will act in a trans-dominant manner to repress lytic growth.
c. No. UV irradiation of lysogenic bacteria destroys repressor function, which in turn leads to induction, including excision of lambda and lytic growth. In a c^{IN} mutant, the repressor would not be destroyed following UV irradiation, so that the prophage would not be excised and lysogeny would be retained.

17

REGULATION OF GENE EXPRESSION AND DEVELOPMENT IN EUKARYOTES

CHAPTER OUTLINE

LEVELS OF CONTROL OF GENE EXPRESSION IN EUKARYOTES
   Transcriptional Control
   RNA Processing Control
   Transport Control
   mRNA Translation Control
   mRNA Degradation Control
   Protein Degradation Control

GENE REGULATION IN DEVELOPMENT AND DIFFERENTIATION
   Genomic Activity in Higher Eukaryotes
   Constancy of DNA in the Genome During Development
   Differential Gene Activity Among Tissues and During Development
   Immunogenetics and Chromosome Rearrangements During Development

GENETIC REGULATION OF DEVELOPMENT IN *DROSOPHILA*
   Drosophila Developmental Stages
   Embryonic Development
   Imaginal Discs
   Homeotic Genes

REVIEW OF KEY TERMS, SYMBOLS, AND CONCEPTS

In your own words, write a brief, precise definition of each term in the groups below. Check your definitions using the text. Then, develop a concept map using the terms in each list.

1	2	3
transcriptional control	short-term gene regulation	RNA processing control
positive, negative regulatory element/protein	upstream activator sequence	alternative poly(A) sites
promoter, enhancer, silencer	promoter	cleavage stimulation factor
combinatorial gene regulation	positive regulator, activator	alternative splice sites
	UAS_G, GAL4, GAL1, GAL10, GAL7	regulation cascade model

1	2	3
DNA-binding protein, domain structural motif	steroid hormone	transport control
helix-turn-helix, zinc-finger, leucine-zipper motif	steroid hormone receptor, response element	spliceosome retention
transcription initiation	chaperone	snRNPs
DNase I-sensitive region	second messenger	hnRNA
DNase I-hypersensitive site	polypeptide hormone	mRNA translation control
DNase I-hypersensitive region	heat shock response, gene	adenylate/uridylate (AU)-rich element (ARE)
erythroblast	heat shock response element	mRNA degradation control
globin, ovalbumin genes	heat shock transcription control	deadenylation-dependent, deadenylation-Independent decay
histones, nucleosomes	plant hormones	decapping
histone acetylation, phosphorylation	gibberellins, auxins, cytokinins, ethylene, abscisic acid	protein degradation control
transcription repression	SHR, HRE, GRE	proteolysis
DNA methylation		ubiquitin
triplet repeat		N-end rule
FMR-1 gene		

4	5
development	development
differentiation	*Drosophila*
totipotency	*Caenorhabditis elegans*
regeneration	cell lineage
cloning	*Arabidopsis thaliana*
differential gene activity	polar cytoplasm
α-, β-, γ-, δ-, ε-globin genes	syncytium
pseudogene	syncytial, cellular blastoderm
polytene chromosomes	molecular gradient
endoreduplication	parasegment, segment
chromomeres, chromocenter	maternal effect genes
band, interband, puff	segmentation genes
ecdysone	homeotic genes
immune system	gap genes
DNA rearrangement	pair rule genes
antigen	segment polarity genes
antibody	imaginal discs
immunoglobin	serial transplantation
clonal selection	transdetermination
H, L chains	homeobox
C, V, J, D segments	helix-turn-helix motif
somatic recombination	homeodomain
antibody diversity	colinearity rule

THINKING ANALYTICALLY

The complexity of eukaryotic gene regulation has several roots. First, eukaryotic genes and chromosomes are organized differently than their prokaryotic counterparts. Second, the transfer of information from DNA to protein is more complicated in eukaryotes than in prokaryotes, as mRNAs and proteins are processed in additional ways. Third, eukaryotic organisms are capable of substantially more development and differentiation, and the different cell types in a multicellular organism have diverse patterns of gene expression. As you approach this material, keep these roots in mind.

While eukaryotic gene regulation is more complex than in prokaryotes, many of the fundamental principles of gene regulation in bacteria and viruses are retained. For example, the principles of gene regulation used by λ phage to choose between a lytic and lysogenic pathway are similar to many used to control transcription of eukaryotic genes. The genetic switch utilized by lambda has parallels in similar genetic switches utilized by eukaryotes to choose between different cell fates and which sets of genes are expressed. It will be helpful to think about how a principle is retained in prokaryotes and eukaryotes while analyzing the differences between them.

The multiple levels in which eukaryotic gene expression is controlled require you to pay very close attention to detail. Consider each level separately, and refer frequently to the text figures, redrawing them to solidify your understanding. In instances where control is at the level of transcription, it will help you to relate the level of control to the organization of the gene or the chromosome. In instances where control is at the level of mRNA processing, translation, and mRNA stability, it will help you to relate the level of control to the stage where information is being transferred from DNA into protein. In instances where control is at the level of post-translational processing and protein degradation, it will help you to relate the level of control to the fate and function of a protein after it is synthesized.

Once you have understood the levels at which eukaryotic gene expression can be controlled, you will have a foundation to consider how gene expression can be controlled in a temporal and spatial context during development. When genetic pathways and bacterial gene expression was discussed, one considered fairly short timelines in defined situations. In eukaryotic development, timelines are much longer, and the spatial dimension—how do different cell types and tissues differentiate from a common precursor cell—is added. It is essential to place these dimensions in the perspective to the developing organism. Therefore, when you consider the regulation of gene expression during development, be sure you have a thorough understanding of the "biology" of the system that is developing. First understand how the organism (e.g., *Drosophila*) or population of cells (e.g., the immune system) develops, and then consider how genes are regulated in this context. It will be helpful to construct diagrams that illustrate how genes are regulated along a timeline or developmental pathway.

QUESTIONS FOR PRACTICE

Multiple Choice Questions

1. In eukaryotes, cell- and tissue-specific gene expression is achieved via
   a. the use of operons.

b. using a cell- and tissue-specific set of activators and repressors.

c. DNase I sensitivity.

d. selective deletion of genes not active in differentiated cells.

2. Transcription in eukaryotes is activated if positive regulatory proteins are bound at

   a. the enhancer element.

   b. the promoter element.

   c. the operator.

   d. both a and b.

3. Histones act in eukaryotic gene regulation primarily as

   a. enhancers of gene expression.

   b. repressors of gene expression.

   c. promoters.

   d. proteins preventing DNase I digestion.

4. A gene lying in chromatin that is actively transcribed by RNA polymerase II is likely to

   a. have DNase I-hypersensitive sites upstream of the protein coding region.

   b. have DNase I-hypersensitive sites within the protein coding region.

   c. be relatively insensitive to DNase I.

   d. be heavily methylated.

5. The receptors for steroid hormones

   a. lie on the cell surface and act via second messengers.

   b. lie on the cell surface and when bound by hormone, are transported into the nucleus and bind response elements to activate transcription.

   c. lie in the cytoplasm and act via second messengers.

   d. lie in the cytoplasm and when bound by hormone, are transported into the nucleus and bind response elements to activate transcription.

6. Receptors bound by polypeptide hormones can alter gene expression by

   a. acting through a second messenger such as cAMP.

   b. directly binding DNA sequences in the 5′ end of genes.

   c. directly binding DNA sequences in the 3′ end of genes.

   d. affecting a kinase cascade.

   e. both a and d.

   f. both b and c.

7. Sex type in *Drosophila* is controlled by

   a. the ratio of X chromosomes to autosomes.

   b. a cascade of regulated, alternative RNA splicing.

   c. sex-specific selection of polyadenylation sites.

   d. sex-specific transport control.

   e. all of the above.

   f. a and b only.

8. A wide diversity of immunoglobulin molecules is obtained via

   a. new gene synthesis.

   b. combinatorial gene regulation.

   c. alternative RNA splicing.

   d. somatic recombination of DNA.

9. Evidence for the totipotency of nuclei in eukaryotic cells is provided by

   a. the existence of homeotic mutations.

   b. nuclear transplantation experiments.

   c. transdetermination of imaginal discs after serial transplantation.

   d. the transcription of fetal globin genes (γ-globin) only during fetal development and not during adult life.

   e. the finding that nuclei in different adult tissues have the same amount of DNA.

10. In *Drosophila*, maternal effect genes are genes that

   a. are expressed in the mother during oogenesis, and whose products will specify spatial organization in the developing embryo.

   b. cause females to lay eggs.

   c. affect the number or polarity of body segments.

   d. affect the identity of a segment.

11. The homeotic mutations of *Drosophila*

   a. cause transformation of one segment to another.

   b. alter the function of proteins that are regulators of transcription.

   c. alter highly conserved functions found in nearly all organisms.

   d. do all of the above.

Answers: 1b; 2d; 3b; 4a; 5d; 6f; 7f; 8d; 9b; 10a; 11d.

Thought Questions

1. Suppose you have cloned gene X. (a) Design an experiment to determine if gene X *is available for transcription* in liver and in brain tissue. (b) Now design an experiment to determine if gene X *is transcribed* in liver and/or in brain tissue. How do these experiments differ?

2. Present evidence that argues for or against the following statement: "Histone and non-histone proteins function as repressors of gene expression in eukaryotic cells."

3. What is the evidence that methylation plays a role in transcriptional control in some eukaryotes? What evidence is there that methylation does not entirely determine the transcriptional activity of some genes?

4. Consider the cascade of alternative splicing events that are used to regulate sex type in *Drosophila*. From an evolutionary perspective, what advantages might there be to having a cascade of events to regulate such an important process? (Hint: Consider the nature of the initial signal for sex type, the X:A ratio (a ratio of either 1/2 or 2/2), and how a splicing cascade "amplifies" this signal.)

5. Consider how hormones act. (a) Since hormones are diffusible, why are certain cells, but not others, targets of a particular hormonal signal? (b) How is the response of a cell to a peptide hormone fundamentally different from the response of a cell to a steroid hormone? (c) Propose a hypothesis to explain why it is that steroid hormone re-

ceptors are located inside the target cells, whereas the receptors for peptide hormones are located on the surfaces of target cells.

6. Suppose Gurdon's experiments on totipotency were repeated using differentiated B lymphocytes as the source of nuclei for transplantation. To what extent would you expect these nuclei to be totipotent? If mature organisms developed from cells with transplanted B cell nuclei, what would be the nature of their immune system?

7. In *Drosophila*, the polar cytoplasm contains factors determining that the nuclei migrating into this region will become germ-line cells. (a) Design an experiment to gather evidence supporting this conclusion. (b) What phenotype would be associated with mutants lacking these factors? (c) Would the mutants from part b identify maternal genes?

8. What are homeoboxes and what is their role in the regulation of development in eukaryotes?

9. In vertebrates, including mammals such as humans, homeotic gene complexes have been identified using homologous probes. Curiously, the gene complexes show similar structural organization, even though vertebrates are not segmented in the same way as invertebrates. What significance might this finding have? How might analyzing mutations in these genes in vertebrates help demonstrate the function of these genes, and test this significance?

10. A number of organisms have been studied intensely with the aim of understanding the genetic control of development. Describe the features of *Drosophila*, *Caenorhabditis*, and *Arabidopsis* that make them useful for such analysis. Why is it important to study more than one model organism?

11. The primary transcripts of many genes undergo tissue-specific alternative mRNA splicing. Indeed, about 15% of human disease mutations are associated with mRNA splicing alterations. (a) For genes that are alternatively spliced, do you expect the proteins that are produced to have identical functions? Why or why not? (b) How might spliceosomes process primary mRNAs differently in different tissues to achieve alternative mRNA processing? [Hint: Consider the alternative mRNA splicing cascade associated with sex-determination in *Drosophila*. Are their tissue-specific (i.e., sex-specific) splicing factors?]

12. Dolly is the lamb that was generated by fusing adult mammary epithelial cells with enucleated oocytes. (a) How does this experiment demonstrate totipotency? (b) How could you use molecular methods to experimentally demonstrate that Dolly had the same genotype as the adult mammary epithelial cells? (c) Suppose you sampled Dolly's DNA at one year of age. Do you expect Dolly's simple telomeric repeats to be the same length as other sheep that were one year old? (d) What impact might imprinting have on our ability to successfully clone eukaryotic organisms?

Thought Questions for Media

After reviewing the media on the *iGenetics* CD-ROM, try to answer these questions.

1. In neuronal cells, the calcitonin/CGRP transcript is cleaved and polyadenylation occurs at the site called pA_2, producing a pre-mRNA with exons 1, 2, 3, 4, and 5. In the thyroid gland, a transcript with exons 1, 2, 3, and 4 is produced and calcitonin, a functional peptide hormone encoded by exon 4 is produced. Why is calcitonin not produced in neurons?

1. In the iActivity, microarrays were used to identify genes that were differentially expressed between differentiating tissues (mesoderm and endoderm) and stem cells. Suppose two genes, *A* and *B*, are upregulated in differentiating mesoderm relative to stem cells. Gene A is expressed 13-fold more and Gene *B* is expressed 2.5-fold more. Neither gene is upregulated in differentiating endoderm.
    a. From this data alone, can you infer anything about the *relative* importance of these genes' expression for mesodermal differentiation?
    b. Suppose mutants were available that caused the rate of each gene's transcription to be halved. Can you predict which mutation might have a more severe effect on mesodermal differentiation?
    c. Based on the results of the microarray analyses, can you infer which gene produces more mRNA copies (the total number of transcripts per gene) in differentiating mesodermal cells?
2. What is meant by a gene that can *serve as a marker* for endoderm differentiation? What features must such a gene have?
3. A gene that encodes a transcription factor is expressed at high levels in differentiating endoderm and differentiating mesoderm, but not in stem cells. What types of genes might be targets of this transcription factor? Would it invariably act through positive regulation of these targets?
4. A gene that encodes a transcription factor is expressed at stem cells, but not in differentiating cells. What role might this gene play in keeping stem cells from differentiating? Would it invariably act through negative regulation of target genes?

SOLUTIONS TO TEXT PROBLEMS

17.1   Promoters, enhancers, transcription factors, and regulatory proteins that are active for one gene typically share structural similarities with these elements in other genes. Nonetheless, the transcriptional control of a gene can be exquisitely specific: It will be specifically transcribed in some tissues at very defined times. Explore how this specificity arises by addressing the following questions.
    a. Distinguish between the functions of promoters and enhancers in transcriptional regulation.
    b. What structural features are found in proteins that bind these DNA elements?
    c. Can an enhancer element bound by a regulatory protein stimulate as well as suppress transcription? If so, how?

d. Given that several different genes may contain the same types of promoter and enhancer elements, and a number of transcription factors contain the same structural features, how is transcriptional specificity generated?

Answer:

a. Promoter and enhancer elements bind specific regulatory proteins. The proteins that bind to promoter elements are crucial for determining whether transcription can occur, while those that bind enhancer elements determine whether transcription will be at a minimal or a maximal level.
b. Structural motifs important for DNA binding include the helix-turn-helix, the zinc finger, the leucine zipper, and the helix-loop-helix.
c. When a protein is bound to an enhancer element, its effect on transcription is dependent in part on the regulatory proteins bound at other enhancer and promoter elements in the region. A negative regulatory protein can bind to an enhancer element and silence transcription. However, if a negative regulatory protein is bound to an enhancer element, and a positive regulatory protein is bound to a promoter element, the net result will depend on their interaction. Either the effect of one protein may modulate the effect of the other, or their interaction may result in an effect that neither alone can cause.
d. Transcriptional specificity is generated through the combinatorial use of a set of transcription factors. Some factors are common to many cells, while others have a more restricted spatial and/or temporal distribution. The transcription of defined arrays of genes in different cells at different times is controlled by the subset of regulatory proteins present in a eukaryotic cell at a particular time.

17.2   Eukaryotic organisms have a large number of copies (usually more than a hundred) of the genes that code for ribosomal RNA, yet they have only one copy of each gene that codes for each ribosomal protein. Disucss the reasons this disparity can work for these organisms.

Answer: Eukaryotic organisms need to make enormous numbers of ribosomes. Since the "final product" of an rDNA gene is an rRNA molecule, one means of making a large quantity of rRNA is to transcribe many rDNA templates. Given a fixed transcription rate, an increase by a factor of n rDNA templates will increase the number of final products by a factor of n. Unlike the rRNAs, the ribosomal proteins are made by translating mRNAs. Since the ribosomal protein genes can be transcribed into *stable* mRNAs that can be translated over and over again, it is unnecessary to have multiple copies of these genes. Synthesis of multiple stable mRNA copies of a ribosomal-protein gene allows production of enough template to ensure adequate ribosomal protein synthesis. Put another way, since the final product is a protein, it is sufficient to amplify the mRNA template, and translate it repeatedly.

17.3   The human α, β, γ, δ, ϵ and ζ globin genes are transcriptionally active at various stages of development. Fill in the following table, indicating whether the globin gene in question is sensitive (S) or resistant (R) to DNase I digestion at the developmental stages listed.

GLOBIN GENE	TISSUE		
	EMBRYONIC YOLK SAC	FETAL SPLEEN	ADULT BONE MARROW
α			
β			
γ			
δ			
ζ			
ε			

Answer: Transcriptionally active chromatin has a looser structure than transcriptionally inactive chromatin. Thus, DNase I sensitivity can identify chromatin that is transcriptionally active. Considering when and where the protein products appear, the following patterns of DNase I sensitivity are expected.

GLOBIN GENE	TISSUE		
	EMBRYONIC YOLK SAC	FETAL SPLEEN	ADULT BONE MARROW
α	R	S	S
β	R	R	S
γ	R	S	R
δ	R	R	S
ζ	S	R	R
ε	S	R	R

17.4   In *Drosophila*, mutations at four genes known as the *male-specific lethals (msls)* cause male-specific lethality during the larval stages. Analysis has shown that male-specific lethality is caused by defects in the process of dosage compensation (the process by which the single X chromosome of a male is transcribed at twice the rate of either of a female's two X chromosomes; see Chapter 11). Examination of polytene chromosomes in normal males and females shows that the X chromosome is less tightly condensed in males than in females, that the X chromosome of a male is enriched in an acetylated form of histone H4, and that the protein products of each of the four *msl* loci are primarily associated with the X chromosome of the male, but not that of the female. Examination of polytene chromosomes in each of the four types of mutant *msl* males reveals that their X chromosome remains about as tightly condensed as an X chromosome in females, and that the absence of any single MSL-protein in a male results in the other three MSL-proteins not associating with the X chromosome.

a. Based on your understanding of the relationship between chromatin structure and gene transcription, how might a decrease in chromatin condensation be associated with dosage compensation?

b. Based on the data presented above, what potential roles might the protein products of the *msl* loci play in dosage compensation?

    d. What evidence is there to suggest that the protein products of the *msl* loci act as a complex?

Answer:

a. The acetylation of histones can destabilize higher-order chromatin structure. As the DNA associated with nucleosomes becomes more accessible to transcription factors, the generally repressive action of histones on transcription is overcome and the rate of transcription is increased. In this case, the four MSL-proteins and an acetylated histone H4 appear to be necessary to decondense the chromatin structure of the X chromosome of the male. This leads to an increase in the rate of transcription of genes on the single X chromosome of the male to a level equal to the rate of transcription of genes on the two X chromosomes of a female.

b. The protein products of the *msl* loci may be involved in maintaining the looser chromatin structure and/or in increasing the rate of transcription once the chromatin has been decondensed.

c. Since mutations at any of the *msl* genes cause the remaining MSL-proteins not to bind the X chromosome of the male, it would appear that each is required for the binding of the others. This suggests that the four genes produce proteins that act together as one complex.

17.5   A cloned DNA sequence was used to probe a Southern blot. There were two DNA samples on the blot, one from white blood cells and the other from a liver biopsy of the same individual. Both samples had been digested with *Hpa*II. The probe bound to a single 2.2 kb band in the white blood cell DNA, but bound to two bands (1.5 and 0.7 kb) in the liver DNA.

a. Is this difference likely to be due to a somatic mutation in a *Hpa*II site? Explain.

b. How would it affect your answer if you knew that white blood cell and liver DNA from this individual both showed the 2-band pattern when digested with *Msp*I?

Answer:

a. A somatic mutation is rather unlikely. Since humans are diploid, the single 2.2 kb band in the white blood cell DNA indicates that both chromosomes have the same restriction sites. The liver cells have two bands whose sizes add up to the size of the band in white blood cells. Thus, it would appear that the liver has an additional site on *both* chromosomes, not just one chromosome (heterozygous cells would have three bands). For this to occur by a mutational mechanism, two different somatic mutations would have had to occur in the same site, in a cell that gave rise to all cells of the tissue being examined (or in all cells of the tissue), an unlikely event.

b. *Msp*I recognizes the same CCGG sequence as *Hpa*II, but unlike *Hpa*II, it will cleave the methylated sequence C^mCGG as well as the unmethylated CCGG. That both liver cells and white blood cells show the same 2-band pattern when digested with *Msp*I, but not *Hpa*II, indicates that there is a central methylated site in white blood cells, but not in liver. Increased DNA methylation has, in some instances, been correlated with a decrease in transcriptional activity. However, not all methylated DNA is transcriptionally silent.

17.6   Both fragile X syndrome and Huntington disease are caused by trinucleotide repeat expansion. Individuals with fragile X syndrome have at least 200 CGG repeats at the 5'-end of the *FMR-1* gene. Individuals with Huntington disease have at least 36 CAG repeats within the protein-coding region of the huntingtin gene.
   a. How is gene expression affected by these repeat expansions?
   b. Based on your answer to (a), why is the fragile X syndrome recessive, while Huntington disease is dominant?
   c. Why is the number of trinucleotide repeats needed to cause the phenotype different for each disease?

Answer:
   a. In fragile X syndrome, the expanded CGG repeat results in hypermethylation and transcriptional silencing. In Huntington disease, the expanded CAG repeat results in the inclusion of a polyglutamine stretch within the huntingtin protein, which causes it to have a novel, abnormal function.
   b. A heterozygote with a CGG repeat expansion near one copy of the *FMR-1* gene will still have one normal copy of the *FMR-1* gene. The normal gene can produce a normal product, even if the other is silenced. (The actual situation is made somewhat more complex by the process of X-inactivation in females, but in general, one would expect that a mutation that caused transcriptional silencing of one allele would not affect a normal allele on a homolog.) In contrast, a novel, abnormal protein is produced by the CAG expansion in the disease allele in Huntington disease. Since the disease phenotype is due to the presence of the abnormal protein, the disease trait is dominant.
   c. Transcriptional silencing may require significant amounts of hypermethylation, and so require more CGG repeats for an effect to be seen. In contrast, protein function may be altered by a relatively smaller sized polyglutamine expansion.

17.7   Both peptide and steroid hormones can affect gene regulation of a targeted population of cells.
   a. What is a hormone?

b. Distinguish between the mechanisms by which a peptide and a steroid hormone affect gene expression.

c. What role do each of the following have in a physiological response to a peptide or a steroid hormone?

   i. steroid hormone receptor (SHR)

   ii. steroid hormone response element (HRE)

   iii. second messenger

   iv. cAMP and adenylate cyclase

Answer:

a. A hormone is typically a low-molecular-weight chemical messenger synthesized in low concentrations in one tissue or cell and transmitted in body fluids to another part of the organism. Hormones act as effector molecules to produce specific effects after binding to a receptor in target cells that may be remote from the hormone's point of origin. Hormones function to regulate gene activity, physiology, growth, differentiation, or behavior.

b. and c. Steroid hormones and peptide hormones employ two fundamentally different mechanisms to regulate gene expression. Steroid hormones traverse the cell membrane and bind to a cytoplasmic steroid hormone receptor (SHR). The complex of the hormone and receptor protein then acts directly to regulate gene expression. The complex binds to specific steroid hormone response elements (HREs) near genes to regulate their transcription. The stability of a gene's mRNA and the processing of precursor mRNAs can be affected as well.

    Polypeptide hormones, such as insulin and certain growth factors, bind to receptors that reside on cell surfaces. The activated, bound receptor then transduces a signal via a second-messenger system inside the cell. Some activated receptors increase the activity of the membrane-bound enzyme adenylate cyclase, which results in an increase in cAMP levels. Increased intracellular levels of cAMP send an intracellular signal (a second messenger) to activate other cellular processes that ultimately lead to an alteration in patterns of gene expression.

17.8   The following figure shows the effect of the hormone estrogen on ovalbumin synthesis in the oviduct of 4-day-old chicks. Chicks were given daily injections of estrogen ("Primary Stimulation") and then after 10 days the injections were stopped. Two weeks after withdrawal (25 days), the injections were resumed ("Secondary Stimulation").

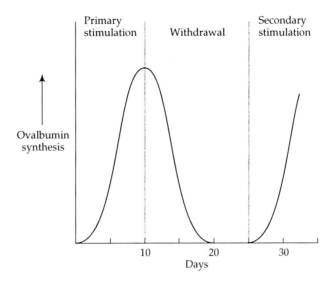

Provide possible explanations of these data.

Answer: The data indicate that the synthesis of ovalbumin is dependent upon the presence of the hormone estrogen. These data do not address the mechanism by which estrogen achieves its effects. Theoretically, it could act (1) to increase transcription of the ovalbumin gene by binding to an intracellular receptor that, as an activated complex, stimulates transcription at the ovalbumin gene; (2) to stabilize the ovalbumin precursor mRNA; (3) to increase the processing of the precursor ovalbumin mRNA; (4) to increase the transport of the processed ovalbumin mRNA out of the nucleus; (5) to stabilize the mature ovalbumin mRNA once it has been transported into the cytoplasm; (6) to stimulate translation of the ovalbumin mRNA in the cytoplasm; and/or (7) to stabilize (or process) the newly synthesized ovalbumin protein. Experiments in which the levels of ovalbumin mRNA were measured have shown that the production of ovalbumin mRNA is primarily regulated at the level of transcription.

17.9   Although the primary transcript of a gene may be identical in two different cell types, the translated mRNAs can be quite different. Consequently, in different tissues, distinct protein products can be produced from the same gene. Discuss two different mechanisms by which the production of mature mRNAs can be regulated to this end; give a specific example for each mechanism.

Answer: Two mechanisms are those controlling choice of poly(A) site and choice of splice site. An example of regulation by choice between alternative poly(A) sites is the production of IgM in B lymphocytes. In two different developmental stages of B lymphocytes, two different poly(A) sites are used, leading to IgM molecules that are either secreted or membrane bound. This results from the developmental repression of one component (CstF-64) of the three-polypeptide CstF (cleavage stimulation factor) complex that functions in poly(A) addition. Its repression causes the formation of a CstF complex with a lower affinity for one poly(A) site, and the use of an alternative site.

An example of gene regulation by differential mRNA splicing is the regulation cascade that governs sex determination in *Drosophila*. Here, an X:A ratio of 1.0 leads to female development as a result of a cascade of alternative female-specific pre-mRNA splicing at a set of regulatory genes that includes *Sxl*, *tra*, and *dsx*. An X:A ratio of 0.5 leads to male development when a male-specific pattern of splicing occurs at these genes.

17.10   Although many mRNAs are present in the cytoplasm of unfertilized vertebrate and invertebrate embryos, the rate of protein synthesis is very low. After fertilization, the rate of protein synthesis increases dramatically without new mRNA transcription.

   a. What differences are seen in the length of poly(A) tails between inactive, stored mRNAs and actively translated mRNAs?
   b. What role does *cytoplasmic* polyadenylation have in this process?
   c. What signals are present in mRNAs that control polyadenylation and deadenylation?
   d. In what way is deadenylation also important for controlling mRNA degradation?

   Answer:
   a. Mature mRNAs that are to be stored in the cytoplasm for future translation are rapidly deadenylated after nuclear pre-mRNA processing and transport into the cytoplasm. They have short poly(A) tails that are 40–60 As long. Actively translated mRNAs typically have longer poly(A) tails that are about 200 As long.
   b. When a stored mRNA is activated, a cytoplasmic polyadenylation enzyme recognizes an adenylate/uridylate (AU)-rich element (ARE; consensus sequence UUUUUAU) in the 3' untranslated region of the mRNA upstream of the AAUAAA polyadenylation sequence and adds about 150 As.
   c. The ARE discussed in part (b) is used as a signal for both deadenylation and cytoplasmic polyadenylation, and so controls mRNA translatability at different times and in opposite ways.
   d. There are two major mRNA decay pathways, one of which is deadenylation dependent and one of which is deadenylation independent. In the former pathway, the poly(A) tails are deadenylated by a poly(A) nuclease until the tails are too short (5-15 As) to bind to the poly(A) binding protein (PAB). Once the tail is almost removed, the 5' cap structure is removed by a decapping enzyme, and the mRNA is degraded from the 5' end by a 5'-to-3' exonuclease.

17.11   Although eukaryotes lack operons like those found in prokaryotes, the exceptional conserved organization of the *ChAT/VAChT* locus is reminiscent of a prokaryotic operon. *ChAT* is the gene for the enzyme choline acetyltransferase, which synthesizes acetylcholine, a neurotransmitter released by one neuron in order to signal another neuron. *VAChT* is the gene for the vesicular acetylcholine transporter protein, which packages acetylcholine into vesicles prior to its release from a neuron. Both *ChAT* and *VAChT* are expressed in the same neuron.

Part of the *VAChT* gene is nested within the first intron of the *ChAT* gene, and the two genes share a common regulatory region and a first exon. The structure of a primary mRNA and two processed mRNA transcripts produced by this locus are diagrammed below. The common regulatory region important for transcription of the locus in neurons is shown in the DNA, and black rectangles represent exons, lines connecting the exons represent spliced intronic regions, and AUG indicates the translation start codons within the *ChAT* and *VAChT* mRNAs. Polyadenylation sites are not shown.

a. In what ways is the organization of the *VAChT/ChAT* locus reminiscent of a bacterial operon?
b. Why is the organization of this locus not structurally equivalent to a bacterial operon?
c. Based on the transcript structures that are shown, what modes of regulation might be used to obtain two different protein products from the single primary mRNA?

Answer:

a. In bacterial operons, a common regulatory region controls the production of single mRNA from which multiple protein products are translated. These products function in a related biochemical pathway. Here, two proteins that are involved in the synthesis and packaging of acetylcholine are both produced from a common primary mRNA transcript.
b. Unlike the proteins translated from an mRNA synthesized from a bacterial operon, the protein products produced at the *VAChT/ChAT* locus are not translated sequentially from the same mRNA. Here, the primary mRNA appears to be alternatively processed to produce two distinct mature mRNAs. These mRNAs are translated starting at different points, producing different proteins.
c. At least two mechanisms are involved in the production of the different ChAT and VAChT proteins: alternative mRNA processing and alternative translation initiation. After the first exon, an alternative 3' splice site is used in the two different mRNAs. In addition, different AUG start codons are also employed.

17.12   Distinguish between the terms *development* and *differentiation*.

Answer: Development is a process of regulated growth and cellular change. It results from the interaction of the genome with the cytoplasm and external environment. It involves a programmed sequence of phenotypic changes that are typically irreversible. Differentiation refers to an aspect of cellular change in development and involves the formation of distinct types of cells, tissues, and organs through the regulation of gene expression. Differentiation is thus a part of development and leads to cells that have characteristic structural and functional properties.

17.13   What is totipotency? Give an example of the evidence for the existence of this phenomenon.

Answer: Totipotency refers to the capacity of a nucleus to direct a cell through all of the stages of development. A nucleus taken from the cell of a differentiated tissue is said to be totipotent if, when it is injected into an enucleated egg, it can direct the development of the organism to the adult stage. If the egg is able to develop into an adult, the differentiated nucleus must have retained all of the genetic information needed to direct development again from the start. In 1975, Gurdon demonstrated that the nucleus of a skin cell of an adult frog was at least partly totipotent. When injected into an enucleated egg, such a nucleus could direct development to the tadpole stage. More recently, Wilmut and his colleagues demonstrated that a mammalian nucleus was totipotent. They showed that the nucleus of a mammary epithelium-derived cell could direct the development of a sheep to the adult stage.

17.14   In Woody Allen's 1973 film *Sleeper*, the aging leader of a futuristic totalitarian society has been dismembered in a bomb attack. The government wishes to clone the leader from his only remaining intact body part, a nose. The characters Miles and Luna thwart the cloning by abducting the nose and flattening it under a steam roller.
   a. In light of the 1996 cloning of the sheep Dolly, how should the cloning have proceeded, if Miles and Luna had not intervened?
   b. If methods akin to those used for Dolly had been successful, in what *genetic* ways would the cloned leader be unlike the original?
   c. Suppose that, instead of a nose, only mature B cells (B lymphocytes of the immune system) were available. What *genetic* deficits would you expect in the "new leader"?
   d. In the set of experiments used to clone Dolly, six additional live lambs were obtained. Why is the production of Dolly more significant than the production of the other lambs?
   e. If the cloning of the leader had succeeded, can you make any prediction about whether the "cloned leader" would be interested in perpetuating the totalitarian state?

Answer:

a. Based on the work of Wilmut and his colleagues, the nose cells would first be dissociated and grown in tissue culture. The cells would be induced into a quiescent state (the G_0 phase of the cell cycle) by reducing the concentration of growth serum in the media. Then, they would be fused with enucleated oocytes from a donor female, and allowed to grow and divide by mitosis to produce embryos. The embryos would be implanted into a surrogate female. After the establishment of pregnancy, its progression would need to be maintained.

b. While the nuclear genome would generally be identical to that in the original nose cell, cytoplasmic organelles would presumably derive from those in the enucleated oocyte. Hence, the mitochondrial DNA would not derive from the original leader. In addition, since telomeres in an older individual are "shorter," one might expect the telomeres in the cloned leader to be those of an older individual.

c. In mature B cells, DNA rearrangements at the heavy- and light-chain immunoglobulin genes have occurred. One would expect the cloned leader to be immunocompromised, as he would be unable to make the wide spectrum of antibodies present in a normal individual.

d. The production of Dolly was significant because it demonstrated the apparent complete totipotency of a nucleus from a mature mammary epithelium cell. The other six lambs developed from the transplanted nuclei of embryonic or fetal cells, which one might expect to be less determined and have a higher degree of totipotency due to their younger developmental age.

e. There is no way to predict the psychological profile of the cloned leader based on his genetic identity. Even identical twins, who are genetically more identical than such a clone, do not always share behavioral traits.

17.15 Discuss some of the evidence for differential gene activity during development.

Answer: The evidence for differential gene activity during development is vast. Classic lines of evidence stem from (1) studies on the differential expression of the α, β, γ, δ, ζ, and ε classes of globin genes during development, (2) differential puffing patterns in the polytene chromosomes in Dipteran insects, and (3) the studies on genes that are expressed in a temporal and spatially specific manner during the development of *Drosophila*. See text.

17.16 The enzyme lactate dehydrogenase (LDH) consists of four polypeptides (a tetramer). Two genes are known to specify two polypeptides, A and B, which combine in all possible ways (A_4, A_3B, A_2B_2, AB_3, and B_4) to produce five LDH isozymes. If, instead, LDH consisted of three polypeptides (i.e., it was a trimer), how many possible isozymes would be produced by various combinations of polypeptides A and B?

Answer: If LDH were a trimer that could be composed of two different polypeptides, four kinds of molecules could be produced: A_3, A_2B, AB_2, and B_3.

17.17   Discuss the expression of human hemoglobin genes during development.

Answer: Distinct genes code for α-like and β-like globin polypeptides which form different types of hemoglobin at different times during human development. In the embryo, hemoglobin is initially made in the yolk sac and consists of two ζ polypeptides and two ε polypeptides. ζ polypeptides are α-like, while ε polypeptides are β-like. At about three months of gestation, hemoglobin synthesis switches to the fetal liver and spleen. Here, hemoglobin is made that consists of two α polypeptides and two β-like polypeptides, either two γA polypeptides or two γG polypeptides. Just before birth, hemoglobin synthesis switches to the bone marrow, were α polypeptides and β polypeptides are predominantly made, along with some β-like δ polypeptides.

17.18   Discuss the organization of the hemoglobin genes in the human genome. Is there any correlation with the temporal expression of the genes during development?

Answer: All of the α-like genes (the ζ, α genes and three pseudogenes) are located in a gene cluster on chromosome 16, while all of the β-like genes (ε, γG, γA, δ, β genes and one pseudogene) are located in a gene cluster on chromosome 11. At a very general level, the organization of the two gene clusters is somewhat similar. Both sets of genes are arranged in the chromosome in an order that exactly parallels the time genes are transcribed during human development. In both gene clusters, the genes transcribed in the embryo are at the left end of the cluster; the genes transcribed in the fetus are to the right of these; and the genes transcribed in the adult are farthest to the right. This is intriguing since the genes are also transcribed in different tissues.

17.19   In humans, β-thalassemia is a disease caused by failure to produce sufficient β-globin chains. In many cases, the mutation causing the disease is a deletion of all or part of the β-globin structural gene. Individuals homozygous for certain of the β-thalassemia mutations are able to survive because their bone marrow cells produce γ-globin chains. The γ-globin chains combine with α-globin chains to produce fetal hemoglobin. In these people, fetal hemoglobin is produced by the bone marrow cells throughout life, whereas normally it is produced in the fetal liver. Use your knowledge about gene regulation during development to suggest a mechanism by which this expression of γ-globin might occur in β-thalassemia.

Answer: There are a number of possibilities. One is that the γ-globin genes in bone marrow are under negative regulation by β-globin (or some metabolite of it). When β-globin is not formed, the γ-globin gene is derepressed.

17.20   What are the polytene chromosomes? Discuss the molecular nature of the puffs that occur in polytene chromosomes during development.

Answer: Polytene chromosomes occur in Dipteran insects, such as *Drosophila*. Polytene chromosomes are formed by endoreduplication, in which repeated cycles of chromosome duplication occur without nuclear division or chromosome segregation. Since they can be 1,000 times as thick as the corresponding chromosomes in meiosis or in the nuclei of normal cells, they can be stained and viewed at the light microscope level. Distinct bands, or chromomeres, are visible, and genes are located both in bands and in interband regions. A puff results when a gene in a band or interband region is expressed at very high levels in a particular developmental stage. Puffs are accompanied by a loosening of the chromatin structure that allows for efficient transcription of a particular DNA region. When increased transcriptional activity at the gene ceases at a later developmental stage, the puff disappears, and the chromosome resumes its compact configuration. In this way, the appearance and disappearance of puffs provides a visual representation of differential gene activity.

17.21   Puffs of regions of the polytene chromosomes in salivary glands of *Drosophila* are surrounded by RNA molecules. How would you show that this RNA is single-stranded and not double-stranded?

Answer: That RNA molecules are present in puffs can be demonstrated by feeding or injecting *Drosophila* larvae with radioactive uridine, an RNA precursor. After this treatment, salivary glands are dissected from larvae and a spread of the polytene chromosomes is subjected to autoradiography to detect the location of the incorporated uridine. Silver grains are evident over puffed regions, indicating that they contain RNA. Evidence that the RNA is single-stranded might be obtained by treating such spreads with an RNase that was capable of digesting only single-stranded RNA. The radiolabel should be recovered in the solution, and not remain bound to the salivary gland chromosome. A lack of signal on puffs following autoradiographic detection (compared to controls) would provide evidence that the RNA in puffs is single-stranded.

17.22   In experiment A, ^{3}H-thymidine (a radioactive precursor of DNA) is injected into larvae of *Chironomus*, and the polytene chromosomes of the salivary glands are later examined by autoradiography. The radioactivity is seen to be distributed evenly throughout the polytene chromosomes. In experiment B, ^{3}H-uridine (a radioactive precursor of RNA) is injected into the larvae, and the polytene chromosomes are examined. The radioactivity is first found only around puffs; later, radioactivity is also found in the cytoplasm. In experiment C, actinomycin D (an inhibitor of transcription) is injected into larvae and then ^{3}H-uridine is injected. No radioactivity is found associated with the polytene chromosomes, and few puffs are seen. Those puffs that are present are much smaller than the puffs found in experiments A and B. Interpret these results.

Answer: Experiment A results in all of the DNA becoming radioactively labeled. The distribution of radioactive label throughout the polytene chromosomes indicates that DNA is a fundamental and major component of these chromosomes. The even distribution of label suggests that each region of the chromosome has been replicated to the same extent. This provides support for the contention that band and interband regions are the result of different types of packaging, not different amounts of DNA replication.

Experiment B results in the radioactive labeling of RNA molecules. The finding that label is found first in puffs indicates that these are sites of transcriptional activity, and arises from molecules that are in the process of being synthesized. The later appearance of label in the cytoplasm reflects the completed RNA molecules that have been processed and transported into the cytoplasm where they will be translated.

Experiment C provides additional support for the hypothesis that transcriptional activity is associated with puffs. The inhibition of RNA transcription by actinomycin D blocks the appearance of signal over puffs, indicating that it blocks the incorporation of ^{3}H-uridine into RNA in puffed regions. The fact that the puffs are much smaller indicates that the puffing process itself is associated with the onset of transcriptional activity for the gene(s) in a specific region of the chromosome.

17.23   The following figure shows the percentage of ribosomes found in polysomes in unfertilized sea urchin oocytes (0 h) and at various times after fertilization:

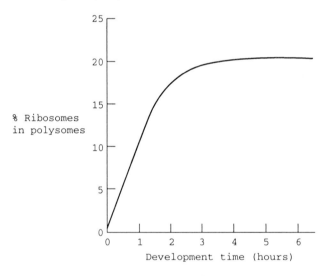

In the unfertilized egg, less than 1 percent of ribosomes are present in polysomes, while at 2 h post-fertilization, about 20 percent of ribosomes are present in polysomes. It is known that no new mRNA is made during the time period shown. How may the data be interpreted?

Answer: Since no new mRNA is synthesized during this time period, preexisting, maternally packaged mRNAs that have been stored in the oocyte must be recruited into polysomes as development begins following fertilization.

17.24   The mammalian genome contains about 10^5 genes. Mammals can produce about 10^6 to 10^8 different antibodies. Explain how it is possible for both of the above sentences to be true.

Answer: The ability to make 10^6 to 10^8 different antibodies arises from the combinatorial way in which antibody genes are generated in different antibody-producing cells during their development, and not the existence of this many separate antibody genes in each and every mammalian cell. A template that exists in germ-line cells is processed differently during the development of different antibody-producing cells to generate antibody diversity.

Antibody molecules consist of two light (L) chains and two heavy (H) chains. The amino acid sequence of one domain of each type of chain is variable, and generates antibody diversity. In the germ-line DNA of mammals, coding regions for these immunoglobulin chains exist in tandem arrays of gene segments. For light chains, there are many variable (V) region gene segments, a few joining (J) segments and one constant (C) gene segment. Somatic recombination during development results in the production of a recombinant V-J-C DNA molecule which, when transcribed, produces a unique, functional L chain. From a particular gene in one cell, only one L chain is produced. A large number of L chains are obtained by recombining the gene segments in many different ways. Diversity in these L chains results from variability in the sequences of the multiple V segments, variability in the sequences of the four J segments and variability in the number of nucleotide pairs deleted at the V-J joints. H chains are similar, except that several D (diversity) segments can be used between the V and J segments, increasing the possible diversity of recombinant H chain genes. The type of C gene segment chosen for the constant domains of the H chain determines whether the antibody is IgM, IgD, IgG, IgE, or IgA.

17.25   Antibody molecules (Ig) are composed of four polypeptide chains (two of one light chain type and two of one heavy chain type) held together by disulfide bonds.
   a. If for the light chain there were 300 different V_K and 4 J_K segments, how many different light chain combinations would be possible?
   b. If for the heavy chain there were 200 V_H segments, 12 D segments, and 4 J_H segments, how many heavy chain combinations would be possible?
   c. Given the information in parts (a) and (b), what would be the number of possible types of IgG molecules (L + H chain combinations)?

Answer:
   a. Not considering the variability in the number of nucleotide pairs deleted at the V_K-J_K joint, there are 300 (V_K segments) $\times$ 4 (J_K segments) = 1,200 different light chain combinations. This number is a lower bound for an estimate, since significantly more variability can be obtained by using imprecise V-J joining.
   b. Not considering the imprecise joining of gene segments that comprise the chain's variable region, there are 200 (V_H segments) $\times$ 12 (D segments) $\times$ 4 (J_H segments) = 9,600 different heavy chain combinations for each of the eight types of Ig (IgM, IgD, IgG_3, IgG_1, IgG_{2b}, IgG_{2a}, IgE, or IgA; see p. 566). If all possible

types of Ig are considered, there are 9,600 x 8 (C_H segments) = 76,800 heavy chain combinations. As in part (a), this is a lower bound for an estimate of heavy chain variability.

c. IgG has four C segments (γ_3, γ_1, γ_{2b}, γ_{2a}; see p. 566). An estimate of the minimal number of combinations for IgG molecules would be $1200 \times 9{,}600 \times 4 = 4.608 \times 10^7$.

17.26   Define *imaginal disc, homeotic mutant*, and *transdetermination*.

Answer: An imaginal disc is a larval structure in *Drosophila* and other insects that undergo a metamorphic transformation from a larva to an adult. During metamorphosis in the pupal period, it will differentiate into an adult structure. It is essentially a sac of cells, a disc, that is set aside early in embryonic development. The disc increases in cell number by mitosis, but remains undifferentiated during larval growth. Although the disc remains undifferentiated up until the time hormonal signals activate the differentiation of adult structures during the pupal period, its fate is *determined* very early in development. Thus, separate imaginal discs are destined to differentiate into different adult structures, such as legs, eyes, antennae, and wings.

Homeotic mutants alter the identity of particular segments, transforming them into copies of other segments. Homeotic mutations thus affect the determination, or fate of a disc. Mutations in the *Antennapedia* gene complex can, for example, transform the fate of cells of the antenna disc so that a leg is formed where an antenna should be. The general inference from such observations is that homeotic genes normally play a pivotal role in establishing the segmental identity of an undifferentiated cell.

Transdetermination is a phenomenon seen in disc transplantation studies. When a disc is transplanted from a larva to an adult abdomen, it can grow and be 'incubated' without differentiating. It can be repeatedly transplanted to new abdomens for incubation, and remain undifferentiated. If it is later transplanted back to a larva that is allowed to undergo metamorphosis, it will differentiate into an adult structure. In rare instances, the determined fate of the disc is altered so that the disc differentiates to another fate. The disc does not totally de-differentiate, and its fate is not totally random. Rather, it takes on another determined fate. For example, a leg disc may become an antennal structure, or a wing structure, but not a genital structure. This process of selective switching of fate is referred to as transdetermination.

17.27   Imagine that you observed the following mutants (*a–e*) in *Drosophila*. Based on the characteristics given, assign each of the mutants to one of the following categories: maternal gene, segmentation gene, or homeotic gene.

a. Mutant *a*: In homozygotes phenotype is normal, except wings are oriented backward.

b. Mutant *b*: Homozygous females are normal but produce larvae that have a head at each end and no distal ends. Homozygous males produce normal offspring (assuming the mate is not a homozygous female).

c. Mutant *c*: Homozygotes have very short abdomens, which are missing segments A2 through A4.

d. Mutant *d*: Affected flies have wings growing out of their heads in place of eyes.

e. Mutant *e*: Homozygotes have shortened thoracic regions and lack the second and third pair of legs.

Answer:

a. As the *polarity* of an individual, differentiated structure is altered, *a* is likely to be a segmentation gene. In particular, it is likely to be a member of the subclass of segmentation genes known as segment polarity genes.

b. The abnormal appearance of progeny of homozygous mothers, but not homozygous fathers, suggests that homozygous mothers produce abnormal oocytes. This view is bolstered by the phenotype of the abnormal progeny. Progeny with defect(s) at one end could arise if a maternally produced gradient in the oocyte was abnormal. Thus, *b* is likely to be a maternal effect gene.

c. The absence of a set of segments is characteristic of the phenotypes of gap gene mutants, a subclass of segmentation gene mutants.

d. It would appear that the fate of the eye disc has been changed to that of a wing disc. The segmental *identity* of cells is controlled by homeotic genes, and so *d* is likely to be a homeotic mutation.

e. In mutant *e*, a set of segments is missing (T2 and T3). Thus, like *c*, *e* is likely to be a mutant in a gap gene, a subclass of segmentation gene mutants.

17.28   If actinomycin D, an antibiotic that inhibits RNA synthesis, is added to newly fertilized frog eggs, there is no significant effect on protein synthesis in the eggs. Similar experiments have shown that actinomycin D has little effect on protein synthesis in embryos up until the gastrula stage. After the gastrula stage, however, protein synthesis is significantly inhibited by actinomycin D, and the embryo does not develop any further. Interpret these results.

Answer: Preexisting mRNA that was made by the mother and packaged into the oocyte prior to fertilization is translated up to the gastrula stage. After gastrulation, new mRNA synthesis is necessary for the production of proteins needed for subsequent embryonic development.

17.29   It is possible to excise small pieces of early embryos of the frog, transplant them to older embryos, and follow the course of development of the transplanted material as the older embryo develops. A piece of tissue is excised from a region of the late blastula or early gastrula that would later develop into an eye and is transplanted to three different regions of an older embryo host (see part a of Figure 17.A). If the tissue is transplanted to the head region of the host, it will form eye, brain, and other material characteristic of the head region. If the tissue is transplanted to other regions of the host, it will form organs and tissues characteristic of those regions in normal development (e.g., ear, kidney, etc.). In contrast, if tissue destined to be an eye is excised from a neurula and transplanted into an older embryo host to exactly the same places as used for the blastula/gastrula transplants, in every case the transplanted tissue differentiates into an eye (see part **b** of Figure 17.A). Explain these results.

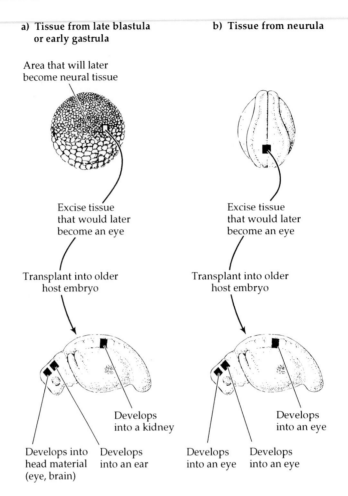

a) Tissue from late blastula or early gastrula

Area that will later become neural tissue

Excise tissue that would later become an eye

Transplant into older host embryo

Develops into head material (eye, brain)

Develops into an ear

Develops into a kidney

b) Tissue from neurula

Excise tissue that would later become an eye

Transplant into older host embryo

Develops into an eye

Develops into an eye

Develops into an eye

Answer: This experiment demonstrates the phenomenon of *determination* and when it occurs during development. The tissue taken from the blastula/gastrula has not yet been committed to its final differentiated state in terms of its genetic programming; that is, it has not yet been *determined*. Thus, when the tissue is transplanted into the host, it adopts the fate of nearby tissues, and differentiates in the same way as they do. Presumably, cues from the tissue surrounding the transplant determine its fate.

In contrast, tissues in the neurula stage are stably determined. By the time the neurula developmental stage has been reached, a developmental program has been set. In other words, the fate of neurula tissue transplants is *determined*. Upon transplantation, they will differentiate according to their own set genetic program. Tissue transplanted from a neurula to an older embryo cannot be influenced by the surrounding tissues. It will develop into the tissue type for which it has been determined; in this case, an eye.

18

GENETICS OF CANCER

CHAPTER OUTLINE

RELATIONSHIP OF THE CELL CYCLE TO CANCER
THE TWO-HIT MUTATION MODEL FOR CANCER
GENES AND CANCER
      Oncogenes
      Tumor Suppressor Genes
      Mutator Genes
THE MULTISTEP NATURE OF CANCER
CHEMICALS AND RADIATION AS CARCINOGENS
      Chemical Carcinogens
      Radiation

REVIEW OF KEY TERMS, SYMBOLS, AND CONCEPTS

In your own words, write a brief, precise definition of each term in the groups below. Check your definitions using the text. Then, develop a concept map using the terms in each list.

1	2	3
tumor	tumor virus	multistep nature of cancer
neoplasm	oncogene	cell cycle
transformation	DNA vs. RNA tumor virus	pRB
benign	sarcoma	G_0 phase
malignant	retrovirus	cyclin
cancer	*RSV, FLV, MMTV, HIV-1*	Cdk complex
metastasis	*gag, pol, env, src, tat* genes	phosphorylation
oncogenesis	nononcogenic retrovirus	p53
terminal differentiation	insertional mutagenesis	p21
stem cell	AIDS	cyclin
germ-line cell	CD4 receptor	Cdk complex
somatic cell	helper T cell	apoptosis
growth factor	gp120 glycoprotein	cell cycle arrest
growth-inhibiting factor	transducing retrovirus	mutator gene
cell cycle	nontransducing retrovirus	tumor suppressor

1	2	3
dedifferentiation	replication-competent	oncogene
two-hit model	transformation-competent	mismatch repair
familial cancer	viral oncogene, v-*onc*	HNPCC, hereditary FAP
sporadic cancer	proto-oncogene	*hMSH2, hMLH1, hPMS1,*
tumor suppressor gene	cellular oncogene, c-*onc*	*hPMS2, mutS, mutL*
oncogene, proto-oncogene	growth factor	genes
mutator gene	protein kinase	carcinogen
multistep nature of cancer	proviral DNA	direct-acting carcinogen
sporadic vs. hereditary	tumor suppressor gene	ultimate carcinogen
retinoblastoma		procarcinogen
loss of heterozygosity		UVA
bilateral tumor		UVB
		SPF
		ionizing radiation

THINKING ANALYTICALLY

Although cancer genetics is complex, focusing on two key issues should help put the topics of this chapter in perspective. Since cancer results from unconstrained cellular growth, the first key issue is to understand how each of the processes discussed in this chapter affects cellular growth. It will be helpful to review how cells proceed through a cell cycle. As you read the text, pay particular attention to how progression through the cell cycle is controlled. Notice how mutations in oncogenes and tumor suppressor genes, both of which relate to growth control, can result in cancer through different mechanisms.

A second key issue is that cancer typically occurs in somatic cells, and so it is important to consider the effect of accumulating mutations in somatic cells and not only germ-line cells. To understand the relationship between hereditary and sporadic forms of cancer, it will help to review the relationship between somatic and germ-line cells. To understand how mutations accumulate in cancerous cells, it is necessary to consider the role of DNA repair within the cell cycle, the consequences of errors in DNA repair, and the effects of carcinogens and ionizing radiation.

QUESTIONS FOR PRACTICE

Multiple Choice Questions

1. About what percentage of breast cancer is hereditary?
    a. 1%
    b. 5%
    c. 10%
    d. 50%

2. Familial retinoblastoma appears to be inherited as a dominant trait. What factor(s) account(s) for this?

    a. A dominant mutation is transmitted through the germ line.

    b. Somatic mutation occurs after a recessive mutation is transmitted through the germ line.

    c. Heterozygous individuals are infected with a retrovirus.

    d. About half of the homozygous, normal individuals in an affected family are infected with a retrovirus at birth.

3. RNA tumor viruses cause cancer
    a. by the same mechanism as DNA tumor viruses.
    b. only if their proviral DNA integrates near a proto-oncogene.
    c. if they carry an oncogene.
    d. if they infect helper T cells.

4. Which of the following is not a feature of a viral oncogene?
    a. It lacks introns.
    b. Its expression is regulated identically to the corresponding cellular proto-oncogene.
    c. Its structure and location in the viral genome varies.
    d. It is not conserved between viral strains.

5. Which of the following is untrue about the product of the *p53* gene?
    a. It is a transcription factor.
    b. It is a tumor suppressor.
    c. It can induce cell death.
    d. When present, it activates the cell cycle from G_1 to S.

6. What is the cellular function of the unphosphorylated product of the *RB* gene, pRB?
    a. pRB binds to transcription factors E2F and DP1 to maintain cells in G_1 or G_0.
    b. pRB binds to p53, to stimulate apoptosis.
    c. pRB is a growth factor, stimulating cellular proliferation.
    d. pRB is involved in DNA mismatch repair.

7. Which protein phosphorylates the product of the *RB* gene, pRB?
    a. A receptor kinase
    b. Phosphorylase
    c. Cyclin/cyclin-dependent kinase
    d. p53

8. What is the relationship between a proto-oncogene and its corresponding viral oncogene?
    a. Only the viral oncogene contains introns.
    b. If the viral oncogene encodes a transcription factor, the corresponding proto-oncogene will encode a growth factor.
    c. The proto-oncogene encodes a product essential to the normal development and function of the organism. The viral oncogene encodes an altered product that has aberrant function.
    d. Usually, the proto-oncogene product is produced in greater amounts. The viral oncogene, being under the control of the retroviral promoter, enhancer, and poly(A) signals, produces smaller amounts of a product.

9. What is apoptosis?
   a. The process by which cancerous cells extend cellular processes in an amoeba-like manner.
   b. The process of uncontrollable cellular growth caused by overexpression of an oncogene.
   c. Cell death that results from the multiple mutations that accumulate in a cancerous cell.
   d. The process of programmed cell death.

10. A genetic predisposition to hereditary nonpolyposis colon cancer (HNPCC) can result from mutations in any of the four genes *hMSH2, hMLH1, hPMS1,* and *hPMS2.* All of these genes are homologous to *E. coli* and yeast genes known to be involved in DNA repair. From this information, one might speculate that HNPCC is caused by a mutation
    a. in a mutator gene.
    b. in an oncogene.
    c. in a proto-oncogene.
    d. in a tumor suppressor gene.

Answers: 1b; 2b; 3c; 4b; 5d; 6a; 7c; 8c; 9d; 10a.

Thought Questions

1. What is the relationship of the cell cycle to cancer?

2. What is the two-hit mutation model for cancer? How is it related to the multistep nature of cancer?

3. In all retroviral RNA genomes, specific sequences are found at the left (R and U_5) and right (R and U_3) ends. In proviral DNA, long terminal repeats (LTRs) are found at each end. How are the LTRs produced?

4. What is meant by a nononcogenic retrovirus? Can infection by a nononcogenic retrovirus lead to increased susceptibility to cancer? Give an example.

5. Distinguish between a viral oncogene, a cellular oncogene, and a proto-oncogene. Are each of these always associated with a transducing retrovirus?

6. There are at least six functional classes of oncogene products. What are these functional classes? How can alteration in such diverse functions lead to a similar oncogenic phenotype?

7. Describe the structure of the HIV virus and viral genome. How does the virus specifically target the immune system? Does the HIV virus itself have viral oncogenes? Why are individuals infected with HIV more susceptible to cancer and infection?

8. What information would you want to know about the UV lights used in tanning salons? Do you think they can be safe?

9. In what ways is programmed cell death a normal process?

10. What is the most lethal, common carcinogen you know of?

11. Cancers are staged according to how far they have progressed towards metastasis. This is illustrated in text Figure 18.15 for the development of hereditary adenomatous polyposis, a colorectal cancer. What genetic changes are associated with the staged progression of tumors? Is there a specific order of changes that *always* occurs? Once a tumor has progressed to a certain stage, can it revert to an earlier stage?

Thought Questions for Media

After reviewing the media on the *iGenetics* CD-ROM, try to answer these questions.

1. How do growth stimulating factors and growth inhibitory factors differ, if at all, in terms of being able to
   a. turn on pathways?
   b. bind to specific cell membrane receptors?
   c. transduce signals to the nucleus?
   d. trigger the expression of a gene or genes for a protein or proteins that stimulate cell division?
2. Many growth stimulating and growth inhibiting factors have been identified. Is it the presence or absence of specific factors, the shear number of stimulating or inhibiting factors, or the balance between factors that determines whether a normal, healthy cell in the G1 phase of the cell cycle is triggered to proceed into S, G_2 and M phases?
3. After DNA damage occurs, how are the levels of p53 protein altered?
4. What is the immediate consequence of altering the level of p53 protein?
5. Why do normal cells undergo apoptosis after extensive DNA damage? Why don't cells with mutations in each of their p53 genes undergo apoptosis?
6. How is a cyclin-CDK complex involved in controlling the ability of a cell to proceed from G_1 into S phase? What is the role of the p21 protein in regulating this process?
7. Why are cells that proceed into S phase with unrepaired DNA damage more likely to become cancerous?
8. The animation illustrated how the p53 protein, following DNA damage, triggers a cellular pathway with inhibitory and stimulatory events.
   a. Which cellular events are inhibited by p53?
   b. Which cellular events are stimulated by p53?
   c. How are these inhibitory and stimulatory events connected?

SOLUTIONS TO TEXT PROBLEMS

18.1   What is the difference between a hereditary and a sporadic cancer?

Answer: Hereditary cancer is associated with the inheritance of a germ-line mutation, sporadic cancer is not. Consequently, hereditary cancer "runs" in families. For some cancers, both hereditary and sporadic forms exist, with the hereditary form being much less frequent. For example, retinoblastoma occurs when both normal alleles of the tumor suppressor gene *RB* are inactivated. In hereditary retinoblastoma, a mutated, inactive allele is transmitted via the germ line. Retinoblastoma occurs in cells of an *RB/+* heterozygote when an additional somatic mutation occurs. In the sporadic form of the disease, retinoblastoma occurs when both alleles are inactivated somatically.

18.2   Individuals with hereditary retinoblastoma are heterozygous for a mutation in the *RB* gene; however, their cancerous cells often have two identically mutated *RB* alleles. Describe three different mechanisms by which the normal *RB* allele can be lost. Illustrate your answer with diagrams.

Answer: Two identical mutated alleles can arise by chromosome nondisjunction during mitosis (this is similar in mechanism to nondisjunction during meiosis II, illustrated in Figure 11.5; mitotic recombination, illustrated in Figures 13.23 and 13.25; or gene conversion by mismatch repair, illustrated in Box Figure 13.2.

18.3   Distinguish between a transducing retrovirus and a nontransducing retrovirus.

Answer: Retroviruses are viruses that have two copies of an RNA genome within a protein core surrounded by a membranous envelope. Transducing retroviruses carry an oncogene from a host cell, while nontransducing retroviruses do not. Consequently, transducing retroviruses may be capable of transforming cells to a cancerous state.

18.4   In what ways is the mechanism of cell transformation by transducing retroviruses fundamentally different from transformation by DNA tumor viruses? Even though the mechanisms are different, how are both able to cause neoplastic growth?

Answer: Tumor growth induced by transforming retroviruses results either from the activity of a single viral oncogene or from the activation of a proto-oncogene due to the nearby integration of the proviral DNA. The oncogene can cause abnormal cellular proliferation via the variety of mechanisms discussed in the text. The expression of a proto-oncogene, normally tightly regulated during cell growth and development, can be altered if it comes under the control of the promoter and enhancer sequences in the retroviral LTR.

Although DNA tumor viruses do not carry oncogenes, they are capable of transforming cells through the action of a gene or genes within their genomes. For example, in a rare event, the DNA virus can be integrated into the host genome, and the DNA replication of the host cell may be stimulated by a viral protein that activates viral DNA replication. This would cause the cell to move from the G_0 to the S phase of the cell cycle.

For both transducing retroviruses and DNA tumor viruses, an abnormally expressed protein(s) leads to the activation of the cell from G_0 to S, and abnormal cell growth.

18.5   Although there has been a substantial increase in our understanding of the genetic basis for cancer, the vast majority of cases of many types of cancer are not hereditary.
   a. How might studying a hereditary form of a cancer provide insight into a similar, more frequent sporadic form?
   b. The incidence of cancer in several members of an extended family might reasonably raise concern as to whether there is a genetic predisposition for cancer in the family. What does the term *genetic predisposition* mean? What might be the basis of a genetic predisposition to a cancer that appears as a dominant trait? What issues must be addressed before concluding that a genetic predisposition for a specific type of cancer exists in a particular family?

   Answer:
   a. Studies of hereditary forms of cancer have led to insights into the fundamental cellular processes affected by cancer. For example, substantial insights into the important role of DNA repair and the relationship between the control of the cell cycle and DNA repair have come from analyses of the genes responsible for hereditary forms of human colorectal cancer. For breast cancer, studying the normal functions of the *BRCA1* and *BRCA2* genes promises to provide substantial insights into breast and ovarian cancer.
   b. Genetic predisposition for cancer refers to the presence of an inherited mutation that, with additional somatic mutations during the individual's lifespan, can lead to cancer. For diseases such as retinoblastoma, a genetic predisposition has been associated with the inheritance of a recessive allele of the *RB* tumor suppressor gene. Retinoblastoma occurs in *RB/+* individuals when the normal allele is mutated in somatic cells and the pRB protein no longer functions. Because somatic mutation is likely, the disease appears dominant in pedigrees.

   Though there is a substantial understanding of the genetic basis for cancer and the genetic abnormalities present in somatic cancerous cells, there are also substantial environmental risk factors for specific cancers. Environmental risk factors must be investigated thoroughly when a pedigree is evaluated for showing a genetic predisposition for cancer.

18.6   Cellular proto-oncogenes and viral oncogenes are related in sequence, but they are not identical. What is the fundamental difference between the two?

   Answer: Cellular proto-oncogenes have important roles in regulating normal cellular processes such as cell division and differentiation. Viral oncogenes are mutated, abnormally expressed forms of proto-oncogenes that cause neoplastic growth. Viral oncogenes lack introns and, as shown in Figure 18.10, are often fused to viral genes.

18.7   Material that has been biopsied from tumors is useful for discerning both the type of tumor and the stage to which a tumor has progressed. It has been known for a long time that biopsied tissues with more differentiated cellular phenotypes are associated with less advanced tumors. Explain this finding in terms of the multistep nature of cancer.

Answer: Tumors result from multiple mutational events that typically involve both the activation of oncogenes and the inactivation of tumor suppressor genes. The analysis of hereditary adenomatous polyposis, an inherited form of colorectal cancer, has shown that the more differentiated cells found in benign, early-stage tumors are associated with fewer mutational events, while the less differentiated cells found in malignant and metastatic tumors are associated with more mutational events. Although the path by which mutations accumulate varies between tumors, additional mutations that activate oncogenes and inactivate tumor suppressor genes generally result in dedifferentiation and increased cellular proliferation.

18.8   An autopsy of a cat that died from feline sarcoma revealed neoplastic cells in the muscle and bone marrow, but not in the brain, liver, or kidney. To gather evidence for the hypothesis that the virus FeSV (Figure 18.9c) contributed to the cancer, Southern blot analysis (see Chapter 7) was performed on DNA isolated from these tissues and on a cDNA clone of the FeSV viral genome. The DNA was digested with the enzyme *Hin*dIII, separated by size on an agarose gel, and transferred to a membrane. The resulting Southern blot was hybridized with a ^{32}P-labeled probe made from a 1.0-kb *Hin*dIII fragment of the feline *fes* proto-oncogene cDNA. The autoradiogram revealed a 3.4-kb band in each lane, with an additional 1.2-kb band in the lanes with muscle and bone marrow DNA. Only a 1.2-kb band was seen in the lane loaded with *Hin*dIII-cut FeSV cDNA. Explain these results, including the size of the bands seen. Do these results support the hypothesis?

Answer: If FeSV contributed to the feline sarcoma, evidence of the presence of FeSV should be found in the neoplastic tissues (muscle and bone marrow). The Southern blot provides this evidence, as a 1.2-kb DNA fragment hybridizes to the *fes* cDNA probe in the lanes with DNA from muscle and bone marrow as well as in the control lane with FeSV cDNA. The difference in size of the 1.2-kb hybridizing fragment and the size of the 1.0-kb *fes* proto-oncogene *Hin*dIII-cut cDNA probe reflects their different origins. The *fes* proto-oncogene is found normally in a cat, while the FeSV *fes* oncogene is found in a retrovirus. The size of the fragment in the retrovirus may reflect a polymorphic *Hin*dIII site and/or a gene rearrangement. Clues to the origin of the 3.4-kb DNA fragment come from observing that it is found in all of the cat tissues and the realization that the *fes* proto-oncogene functions normally in the cat, and so its DNA should also be present in all tissues. Thus, the 3.4-kb DNA fragment is most likely a genomic sequence present in all tissues. Since the *fes* proto-oncogene has a 1.0-kb *Hind*III fragment, the mRNA of this gene is very likely spliced to remove an intronic region(s), 2.4 kb in size.

18.9   The sequences of proto-oncogenes are highly conserved among a large number of animal species. Based on this fact, what hypothesis can you make about the functions of the proto-oncogenes?

Answer: The high degree of conservation of proto-oncogenes suggests that they function in normal, essential, conserved cellular processes. Given the relationship between oncogenes and proto-oncogenes, it also suggests that cancer occurs when these processes are not correctly regulated.

18.10   Explain why HIV-1, the causative agent of AIDS, is considered a nononcogenic retrovirus even though numerous types of cancers are frequently seen in patients with AIDS.

Answer: HIV-1 is a retrovirus that infects, and then kills cells of the immune system, particularly helper T cells. This leads to disabling of the immune response and an increase in susceptibility to certain types of cancer. In contrast to the mechanism by which cancer occurs following infection with HIV-1, an oncogenic retrovirus transforms the growth properties of infected cells to neoplastic growth.

18.11   Give two ways in which cancer can be induced by a retrovirus.

Answer: One mechanism by which a transducing retrovirus causes cancer is for the viral oncogene it carries to be expressed under the control of retroviral promoters. A second mechanism involves insertional mutagenesis that results when the proviral DNA of a retrovirus integrates near a proto-oncogene. In this event, the expression of the proto-oncogene can be controlled by the promoter and enhancer sequences in the retroviral LTR. As these sequences do not respond to the environmental signals that normally regulate proto-oncogene expression, overexpression of the proto-oncogene is induced.

18.12   Proto-oncogenes produce a diverse set of gene products.
   a. What types of gene products are made by proto-oncogenes? Do these gene products share any features?
   b. Which of the following mutations might result in an oncogene?
      i.   a deletion of the entire coding region of a proto-oncogene
      ii.   a deletion of a silencer that lies 5' to the coding region
      iii. a deletion of an enhancer that lies 3' to the coding region
      iv.   a deletion of a 3' splice-site acceptor region
      v.   the introduction of a premature stop codon
      vi.   a point mutation

vii. a translocation that places the coding region near a constitutively transcribed gene

viii. a translocation that places the gene near constitutive heterochromatin

Answer:

a. Proto-oncogenes encode a diverse set of gene products that include growth factors, receptor and non-receptor protein kinases, receptors lacking protein kinase activity, membrane-associated GTP-binding proteins, cytoplasmic regulators involved in intracellular signaling, and nuclear transcription factors. These gene products all function in intercellular and intracellular circuits that regulate cell division and differentiation.

b. In general, mutations that activate a proto-oncogene convert it into an oncogene. Since (i), (iii), and (viii) cause a decrease in gene expression, they are unlikely to result in an oncogene. Since (ii) and (vii) could activate gene expression, they could result in an oncogene. Mutations (iv), (v), and (vi) cannot be predicted with certainty. The deletion of a 3' splice-site acceptor would alter the mature mRNA and possibly the protein produced, and may or may not affect the protein's function and regulation. Similarly, it is difficult to predict the effect of a nonspecific point mutation or a premature stop codon. The text presents examples where these types of mutations have caused the activation of a proto-oncogene and resulted in an oncogene.

18.13   You have a culture of normal cells and a culture of cells dividing uncontrollably (isolated from a tumor). Experimentally, how might you determine whether uncontrolled growth was the result of an oncogene or a mutated pair of tumor suppressor alleles?

Answer: Using the method of Harris, one could experimentally fuse cells from the two cell lines and then test the resultant hybrids for their ability to form tumors. If the uncontrolled growth of the tumor cell line was due to a mutated pair of tumor suppressor alleles, the normal alleles present in the normal cell line would "rescue" the tumor cell-line defect. The hybrid line would grow normally and be unable to form a tumor. If the uncontrolled growth of the tumor cell line was due to an oncogene, the oncogene would also be present in the hybrid cell line. The hybrid line would grow uncontrollably and form a tumor.

18.14   What are the four main ways in which a proto-oncogene can be changed into an oncogene?

Answer: A proto-oncogene can be changed into an oncogene if there is an increase in the activity of its gene product or an increase in gene expression that leads to an increased amount of gene product. This can result from point mutation, deletion, gene amplification, and chromosomal translocation.

18.15   After a retrovirus that does not carry an oncogene infects a particular cell, northern blots indicate that the amount of mRNAs transcribed from a particular proto-oncogene became elevated approximately 13-fold compared with uninfected control cells. Propose a hypothesis to explain this result.

Answer: One hypothesis is that the proviral DNA has integrated near the proto-oncogene, and the expression of the proto-oncogene has come under the control of promoter and enhancer sequences in the retroviral LTR. This could be assessed by performing a whole-genome Southern blot analysis to determine whether the organization of the genomic DNA sequences near the proto-oncogene have been altered.

18.16 Explain how progression through the cell cycle is regulated by the phosphorylation of the retinoblastoma protein pRB. What phenotypes might you expect in cells where

a. pRB was constitutively phosphorylated?
b. pRB was never phosphorylated?
c. a severely truncated pRB protein was produced that could not be phosphorylated?
d. a normal pRB protein was produced at higher than normal levels?
e. a normal pRB protein was produced at lower than normal levels?

Answer: When unphosphorylated, pRB inhibits cell cycle progression by binding to a complex of the transcription factors E2F and DP1. This ensures that the cell remains in G_1 or in the quiescent G_0 state until it is ready to proceed to S. When progression into S phase is signaled, pRB is phosphorylated by a cyclin/Cdk complex. This prevents it from binding to E2F, which in turn allows E2F to activate transcription at genes needed for cell cycle progression. After S phase, pRB is dephosphorylated.

a. If pRB were constitutively phosphorylated, it would never bind to E2F, there would be no inhibition of cell cycle progression at G_1/S, and neoplastic growth would occur.
b. If pRB was never phosphorylated, cells would be stalled in the G_0 phase (and presumably, eventually undergo apoptosis).
c. If a truncated protein were produced, it would be unable to bind to E2F and DP1, and (regardless of its phosphorylation state) would be unable to inhibit cell cycle progression. Just as in part (a), this would result in neoplastic growth.
d. Higher levels of normal pRB could result in a longer cell cycle. If more pRB were present in the cell, more unphosphorylated pRB would be available to bind to E2F during G_1. In this event, if an unphosphorylated pRB molecule that was bound to a particular E2F molecule were phosphorylated by a cyclin/Cdk complex and the E2F molecule were released, another unphosphorylated pRB molecule present in the cell could bind to the same E2F molecule. This would prevent this particular E2F molecule from participating in activating the gene expression needed for progression into S phase. Only when enough pRB molecules are phosphorylated will a sufficient number of E2F molecules be released to provide for transcriptional activation. Since the number of pRB molecules is increased relative to the number of cyclin/Cdk complexes, it will take longer for the cyclin/Cdk complexes to phosphorylate enough pRB molecules to effect transcrip-

tional activation. If pRB levels are so high that the cyclin/Cdk complex is unable to phosphorylate enough of the pRB molecules present, cells could be stalled in the G_0 phase, just as in part (b).

    e. Lower levels of normal pRB might result in a shorter cell cycle.

18.17   Mutations in the *p53* gene appear to be a major factor in the development of human cancer.

    a. Explain what the normal cellular functions of the *p53* gene product are and how alterations in these functions can lead to cancer.

    b. Suppose cells in a cancerous growth are shown to have a genetic alteration that results in diminished *p53* gene function. Why can we not immediately conclude that the mutation *caused* the cancer? How would the affect of the mutation be viewed in light of the current, multistep model of cancer?

Answer:

    a. The *p53* gene product has multiple functions in tumor suppression. One of its chief roles is to maintain cells in G_0/G_1 arrest until DNA damage has been repaired, and, if such damage cannot be repaired, to signal cells to undergo apoptosis. Alterations in *p53* function can lead to cancer in three ways: failure to hold cells in G_0/G_1 arrest, failure to allow DNA repair prior to S (thus allowing mutations to be transmitted to the next generation), or failure to induce apoptosis appropriately.

    b. Cancerous cells typically have a number of genetic abnormalities, or lesions. The *p53* mutation may not be the initial genetic abnormality that occurred. Rather, it may have occurred subsequent to a mutation(s) that led to the activation of an oncogene, the introduction of a mutator gene, or the inactivation of alleles at a tumor suppressor gene. Hence, the *p53* mutation may not be the primary genetic lesion. Most cancers develop as a result of the accumulation of mutations in a number of genes, often over extended periods of time (decades). Such mutations accumulate in part due to the lack of successful DNA repair at the G_1/S checkpoint in the cell cycle.

18.18   Some tumor types have been very frequently associated with specific chromosomal translocations. In some cases, these translocations are found as the only cytogenetic abnormality. In each case examined to date, the chromosome breaks that occur result in a chimeric gene (pieces of two genes fused together) that encodes a fusion protein (a protein consisting of parts of two proteins fused together, corresponding to the coding sequences of the chimeric gene). A partial list of tumor-specific chromosomal translocations in bone and soft tissue tumors is given below.

TUMOR TYPE	TRANSLOCATION	CHARACTERISTIC	GENES
Ewings sarcoma	t(11;22) (q24;q12)	Malignant	*FLI1, EWS*
	t(21;22) (q22;q12)		*ERD, EWS*
Soft tissue clear cell carcinoma	t(7;21) (p22;q12)		*ATV1, EWS*

TUMOR TYPE	TRANSLOCATION	CHARACTERISTIC	GENES
Myxoid chrondro-sarcoma	t(9:22) (q22-31;q12)	Malignant	CHN, EWS
Desmoplastic small round cell tumor	t(11;22) (p13;q12)	Malignant	WT1, EWS
Synovial sarcoma	t(X;18) (p11.2;q11.2)	Malignant	SSX1, SSX2, SYT
Lipomas	t(var;12) (var;q13-15)	Benign	var, HMGI-C
Leiomomas	t(12;14) (q13-15)	Benign	HMGI-C, ?

a. What conclusions might you draw from the fact that in some cases, these translocations are found as the only cytogenetic abnormality?

b. How might the formation of a chimeric protein result in tumor formation?

c. Based on the data presented here, can you infer whether the genes near the breakpoints of these translocations are tumor-suppressor genes or proto-oncogenes? If so, which?

d. Can you speculate as to how multiple translocations involving the EWS gene result in different sarcomas?

e. It is often difficult to diagnose individual sarcoma types based solely on tissue biopsy and clinical symptoms. How might the cloning of the genes involved in translocation breakpoints associated with specific tumors have a practical value in improving tumor diagnosis and management?

Answer:

a. The fact that some translocations are found as the only cytogenetic abnormality in certain cancers most likely means that they represent a key event in tumor formation. It does not necessarily mean that they are the primary cause of the tumor, or the first of many mutational events.

b. A chimeric fusion protein may have different functional properties than either of the two proteins from which it derives. If it results in the activation of a proto-oncogene product into a protein that has oncogenic properties, or if it results in the inactivation of a tumor suppressor gene product, it could play a key role in the genetic cascade of events leading to tumor formation.

c. Before drawing conclusions as to whether these chromosomal aberrations inactivate the function of tumor suppressor genes, or activate quiescent proto-oncogenes, it is necessary to have additional molecular information on the effects of the translocation breakpoints on specific transcripts. Finding that the translocation breakpoints result in a lack of gene transcription or in transcripts that encode nonfunctional products would support the hypothesis that the translocation inactivated a tumor suppressor gene. Finding that the translocation breakpoints result in activation of gene transcription or in the production of an active fusion protein would support the hypothesis that the translocation activated a previously quiescent proto-oncogene.

d. One hypothesis is that the various fusion proteins that result from different translocations involving the EWS gene somehow result in the transcription activation of different proto-oncogenes, and this leads to the different sarcomas that are seen. (Sarcomas are cancers found in tissues that include, among others, muscle, bone, fat, and blood vessels.)

e. If translocation breakpoints are conserved within a tumor type, molecular-based diagnostics can be developed to identify the breakpoints relatively quickly from a tissue biopsy. For example, if the genes at the breakpoints have been cloned, PCR methods can be used to address whether the gene is intact or disrupted, using the DNA from cells of a tumor biopsy. Primers can be designed to amplify different segments of the normal gene. Then, PCR reactions containing these primers and either normal, control DNA or tumor-cell DNA can be set up to determine if each segment of a candidate gene is intact (a PCR product of the expected size is obtained) or disrupted (no PCR product will be obtained, because the gene has been rearranged).

Such molecular analyses would provide fast, accurate tumor diagnosis. If the different tumor types respond differentially to different regimens of therapeutic intervention, then a more rapid, unequivocal diagnosis of a particular tumor type should allow for the earlier prescription of a more optimized regime of therapeutic intervention. In addition, understanding the nature of the normal gene products of the affected genes may allow for the development of sarcoma-specific therapies.

18.19   What is apoptosis? Why is the cell death associated with apoptosis desirable, and how is it regulated?

Answer: Apoptosis is programmed, or suicidal, cell death. Cells targeted for apoptosis are those that have large amounts of DNA damage and so are at a greater risk for neoplastic transformation. (During the development of some tissues in multicellular organisms, cell death via apoptosis is a normal process.) Apoptosis is regulated by p53, among other proteins. In cells with large amounts of DNA damage, p53 is stabilized. This leads to the activation of *WAF1*, whose product, p21, causes cells to arrest in G_1 by binding to cyclin/Cdk complexes and blocking the kinase activity needed for progression from G_1 to S. If the DNA damage cannot be repaired, apoptosis will be induced by p53.

18.20   What mechanisms ensure that cells with heavily damaged DNA are unable to replicate?

Answer: To proceed from G_1 into S, one or more G_1 cyclins bind to the cyclin-dependent kinase CDC28/cdc2 and activate it. The cyclin-dependent kinase then phosphorylates key proteins that are needed for progression into S. In the presence of heavy DNA damage, p53 is stabilized. The p53 protein acts as a transcription factor to activate *WAF1*, which produces p21. The p21 protein binds to cyclin/Cdk complexes and blocks the kinase activity required to activate the genes needed for the cell to make the transition from G_1 to S. Thus, stabilization of p53 leads to cell cycle arrest at the G_1/S cell cycle checkpoint. This G_1 arrest allows the cell time to induce the necessary repair pathways and repair the DNA, or, if damage is too severe, to undergo apoptosis.

18.21   How do radiation and chemical carcinogens induce cancers?

Answer: Radiation and chemical carcinogens increase the amount of DNA damage in cells. If this damage is not repaired, or is repaired incorrectly, somatic mutations result. Increasing the amount of DNA damage therefore increases the chance of somatic mutation. Mutations in oncogenes or tumor suppressor genes will contribute to the induction of cancer.

Direct-acting chemical carcinogens bind to DNA and act as mutagens. In contrast, procarcinogens are converted metabolically to active derivatives, so-called ultimate carcinogens, most of which also bind to DNA and act as mutagens. Radiation carcinogens act directly to cause mutation in DNA.

19

DNA MUTATION AND REPAIR

CHAPTER OUTLINE

ADAPTATION VERSUS MUTATION

MUTATIONS DEFINED

Types of Point Mutations

Reverse Mutations and Suppressor Mutations

SPONTANEOUS AND INDUCED MUTATIONS

Spontaneous Mutations

Induced Mutations

Chemical Mutagens in the Environment

DNA REPAIR MECHANISMS

Direct Correction of Mutational Lesions

Repair Involving Excision of Base Pairs

HUMAN GENETIC DISEASES RESULTING FROM DNA MUTATIONS

DETECTING MUTATIONS

Visible Mutations

Nutritional Mutations

Conditional Mutations

Resistance Mutations

Molecular Screens

REVIEW OF KEY TERMS, SYMBOLS, AND CONCEPTS

In your own words, write a brief, precise definition of each term in the groups below. Check your definitions using the text. Then, develop a concept map using the terms in each list.

1	2
mutation	mutagen
adaptation	carcinogen
fluctuation test	spontaneous mutation
random mutation	mutation rate vs. mutation frequency
base-pair mutation, base-pair substitution	tautomer, tautomeric shift
somatic vs. germ-line mutation	depurination, deamination
gene vs. chromosomal mutation	mutational hot spot

1	2
point mutation	induced mutation
transition mutation	ionizing, nonionizing radiation
transversion mutation	thymine dimer
missense mutation	SOS system
nonsense mutation	base analog
neutral mutation	5BU, 2AP, AZT, MMS
silent mutation	base-modifying agent
frameshift mutation	nitrous acid, hydroxylamine
forward mutation	intercalating agent
reverse mutation (reversion)	acridine orange, proflavin
true reversion	site-specific *in vitro* mutagenesis
suppressor mutation, gene	reverse genetics
second-site mutation	Ames test
intragenic, intergenic suppressor	mitogenesis

3	4
DNA repair	mutant screen
proofreading	visible mutation
mutator mutation vs. mutator gene	replica plating
photoreactivation	nutritional mutation
light repair	auxotrophic mutation
excision (dark) repair	conditional mutation
alkylating repair	knockout mutants
glycosylase	targeted mutation
O^6-methyl-guanine methyltransferase	
AP site, AP endonuclease	
nick translation	
mismatch repair	
dam-methylase	
hemimethylation	
SOS response	
error-prone repair	
error-prone bypass synthesis	
xeroderma pigmentosum	
ataxia telangiectasia	
Fanconi's anemia	
Bloom's syndrome	
Cockayne syndrome	
hereditary nonpolyposis colon cancer	

THINKING ANALYTICALLY

Mutation is a fundamental process in genetics and evolution. In this chapter, the conceptual framework used by geneticists to consider the nature of mutation is presented. This is followed by a detailed discussion of the types and causes of mutation, strategies to identify mutants and mutagens, and the biological mechanisms used to repair mutations. Consequently, the material presented here is both highly conceptual and quite detailed. Focus first on the concepts, and as in previous chapters, learn to use the terms and definitions to explain the concepts. In order to follow some of the complicated processes described in this chapter, it is essential to have the precise meaning of each term well in mind.

As you consider the molecular basis of mutation, it will help to review the chemical structure of the bases to envision how each of the mutagens acts. Employ diagrams as you consider the effects of specific mutagens and repair processes on the structure of DNA. It will also be invaluable to use diagrams to follow how a mutant DNA sequence can result in specific alterations in codon usage in an mRNA. It is essential to proceed methodically (and slowly, so as not to overlook a subtle point such as changes in polarity) through any analysis involving base-pair changes. Use terms carefully, remembering that mutations affect the bases in DNA, and then, indirectly, the bases in transcribed RNA and the amino acids in proteins.

Two topics in this chapter, suppressor mutations and screening procedures used in the isolation of new mutations, warrant particularly careful attention. Proceed by carefully and methodically organizing the information that is presented. Then, supplement your reading with diagrams and flowcharts.

QUESTIONS FOR PRACTICE

Multiple Choice Questions

Match the best choice below to each of the statements for Questions 1–8.

a. missense mutation	e. nonsense mutation
b. transversion mutation	f. transition mutation
c. neutral mutation	g. frameshift mutation
d. forward mutation	h. suppressor mutation

1. A purine-pyrimidine base pair is mutated to a different purine-pyrimidine base pair.

2. A point mutation in the DNA that changes a codon in the mRNA and causes an amino acid substitution that does not alter the function of the translated protein.

3. A DNA change in which a GC base pair is replaced by a TA base pair.

4. A mutation that results in the addition or deletion of a base pair within the coding region of a gene.

5. Any point mutation that is expressed as a change from the wild type to the mutant phenotype.

6. A base-pair change in the DNA that results in the change of a mRNA codon to either UAG, UAA, or UGA.

7. A mutation in the DNA that changes a codon in the mRNA and causes an amino acid substitution that may or may not produce a change in the function of a translated protein.

8. Any new mutation that restores some or all of the wild-type phenotype to a previously isolated mutation.

9. The Ames test is used to screen for
   a. potential mutagens and carcinogens.
   b. the presence of enol forms of thymine and guanine.
   c. frameshift mutations.
   d. spontaneous mutations.

10. In the Ames test, rat liver extracts are used
    a. to chemically alter and detoxify potential mutagens.
    b. to chemically alter and toxify potential mutagens.
    c. to determine if an environmental chemical that itself is not mutagenic may become mutagenic when processed in the liver.
    d. all of the above.

11. A population of cells is subjected to UV irradiation and then placed in the dark. There will be significant
    a. production of base tautomers.
    b. breakage of phosphodiester bonds.
    c. formation of pyrimidine dimers.
    d. photolyase activity.

12. Single bacterial cells sensitive to the infection of a phage are inoculated into a large number of separate culture dishes, and allowed to grow in parallel. After many generations, a sample is taken from each culture, inoculated with the phage, and separately plated. Which result is expected?
    a. All plates will have similar numbers of bacterial colonies.
    b. No bacterial colonies will be seen on any of the plates.
    c. Only one plate in 10^6 will have bacterial colonies.
    d. Some plates will have no bacterial colonies, some will have a few, and some will have many.

Answers: 1f; 2c; 3b; 4g; 5d; 6e; 7a; 8h; 9a; 10d; 11c; 12d.

Thought Questions

1. What is the evidence that mutations occur spontaneously and at a low frequency, regardless of selection for or against them?

2. The proofreading ability of DNA polymerase is extremely good, but not quite perfect. What error rates are associated with DNA replication, from whence do they arise, and how might this be important in evolutionary terms?

3. Distinguish between a reversion mutation, an intragenic suppressor mutation, and an intergenic suppressor mutation.

4. Distinguish between a missense and a nonsense mutation, and between a missense, a silent, and a neutral mutation.

5. How would you classify the following mutations? (a) A single base change in a promoter region that affects the transcription of a gene. (b) A single base change in a pro-

moter region that has no effect. (c) An RFLP difference between two strains that has no apparent phenotypic effect.

6. What is the basis for the Ames test? What are its specific merits? Are there any kinds of mutagens that it might not detect? (e.g., "kinds of mutagens" refers to those that specifically cause point mutations, frameshifts, small deletions, chromosome rearrangements, etc.)

7. In the last several years, significant insight into how DNA is repaired has come from studies in bacteria and yeast, as well as from the molecular cloning of disease genes from humans with defective DNA repair. (a) Speculate as to the phenotype(s) of bacterial and yeast mutations that are defective in DNA repair. (b) How might comparison of these three systems be beneficial?

8. In *Drosophila*, the first mutations isolated (e.g., the first *white-eyed* mutant) were spontaneous. Currently, most new mutations are isolated by using mutagens. Why are mutagens currently employed, and what benefit do mutagens have for the study of genetics and development? How is site-specific *in vitro* mutagenesis used to study the function of cloned genes?

9. What spontaneous mutation rates are found in different organisms? Are these rates relatively similar or quite different? Why do you think this is so?

10. Dyes are routinely used to stain nuclei in bacteriological and histological preparations as well as to visualize DNA and RNA molecules separated by size using agarose gel electrophoresis. Some of these dyes bind to the backbone of nucleic acids while others intercalate between bases. How would you specifically test whether a particular dye is mutagenic? How would you use the results of the test to design general precautions for laboratory workers using these dyes?

11. If a substance is mutagenic, is it necessarily carcinogenic? Why or why not? If a substance is carcinogenic, is it necessarily mutagenic? Why or why not?

+

Thought Questions for Media

After reviewing the media on the *iGenetics* CD-ROM, try to answer these questions.

1. What are the consequence(s) of a nonsense mutation?
2. What are the consequence(s) of suppressing a nonsense mutation?
3. Suppose the mutation in the animation was an AT to GC transition instead of an AT to TA transversion.
   a. What would be the result of this mutation on the gene's protein product?
   b. Explain how this mutation could be suppressed using a mechanism similar to that illustrated in the animation.
4. The *Mutagenic Effects of 5BU* animation shows how 5BU can introduce mutations that are either AT to GC transition mutations or GC to AT transition mutations. For each type of mutation:

a. How many rounds of replication are involved in the formation of the mutation?

b. In which round(s) of replication is 5BU required to be in its normal form?

c. In which round(s) of replication is 5BU required to be in its rare form?

5. If 5BU is incorporated into DNA, but never shifts to its rare form during DNA replication, can it still cause a transition mutation?

6. Based on the information in the animation, is there a way for 5BU to cause a transversion mutation?

7. In principle, a mutagenic compound can cause either forward (new) mutations or reverse mutations.

a. Does the Ames test assess the frequency of reverse mutations (*his* to *his⁺*) or the frequency of forward mutations (say, *his⁺* to *his*)? How?

b. Why is it advantageous for the Ames test to assess this type of mutation frequency?

c. Does this strategy influence which types of mutagenic compounds can be detected using the Ames test?

8. According to the *Ames Test Protocol* animation, why is the S9 liver extract added to the bacteria during the Ames test?

1. In the iActivity, you observed that vinyl chloride causes a missense transversion mutation in the Ames test. Although the allowable EPA concentration of vinyl choride is two micrograms per liter, it is present at 140 micrograms per liter in the ground water of Russellville.

a. Can you infer that it is the vinyl chloride in the drinking water that causes missense transversion mutations in the residents of Russellville? Why or why not?

b. Suppose the concentration of vinyl chloride in a neighboring village is two micrograms per liter, the EPA allowable concentration. Is the water safe to drink? What concerns, if any, would you have?

c. Would your answers to **a** and **b** change if you knew that most of the adult residents of Russellville and the neighboring village smoked three packs of cigarettes a day?

2. In the iActivity, 1,2-dichloroethene was not mutagenic in the Ames test, but was found in the groundwater at about six times the allowable EPA concentration. Since its not mutagenic, why does the EPA bother to regulate how much 1,2-dichloroethene can be found in groundwater? What other factors might be used to determine the allowable groundwater concentration of a chemical?

3. Suppose that sequence analysis like that performed in the iActivity shows that a chemical causes a silent transition. Since it does not alter the amino acid sequence of a polypeptide, should you still be concerned about the chemical as a potential mutagen?

SOLUTIONS TO TEXT PROBLEMS

19.1   Mutations are (choose the correct answer)
a. caused by genetic recombination.
b. heritable changes in genetic information.
c. caused by faulty transcription of the genetic code.
d. usually but not always beneficial to the development of the individuals in which they occur.

Answer: b. Heritable changes in genetic information.

19.2   Answer true or false: Mutations occur more frequently if there is a need for them.

Answer: False. Mutations occur spontaneously at a more or less constant frequency, regardless of selective pressure. Once they occur, however, they can be selected for or against, depending on the advantage or disadvantage they confer. It is important not to confuse the frequency of mutations with selection.

19.3   Which of the following is *not* a class of mutation?
a. Frameshift
b. Missense
c. Transition
d. Transversion
e. None of the above (i.e., all are classes of mutation)

Answer: e. None of the above (i.e., all are classes of mutation)

19.4   Ultraviolet light usually causes mutations by a mechanism involving (choose the correct answer)
a. One-strand breakage in DNA.
b. Light-induced change of thymine to alkylated guanine.
c. Induction of thymine dimers and their persistence or imperfect repair.
d. Inversion of DNA segments.
e. Deletion of DNA segments.
f. All of the above.

Answer: c. Induction of thymine dimers and their persistence or imperfect repair. The key to this answer is the word "usually." The other choices might apply rarely, but not usually.

19.5   For the middle region of a particular polypeptide chain, the wild-type amino acid sequence and the amino acid sequence of several mutants were determined, as shown in the following table ("..." indicates additional, unspecified amino acids). For each mutant, say what DNA level change has occurred, whether the change is a base pair substitution mutation (transversion or transition, missense or nonsense) or a frameshift mutation, and in which codon the mutation occurred. (Refer to the codon dictionary in Figure 6.8.)

			1	2	3	4	5	6	7	8	9
							CODON				
a.	Normal:	...	Phe	Leu	Pro	Thr	Val	Thr	Thr	Arg	Trp
b.	Mutant 1:	...	Phe	Leu	His	His	Gly	Asp	Asp	Thr	Val
c.	Mutant 2:	...	Phe	Leu	Pro	Thr	Met	Thr	Thr	Arg	Trp
d.	Mutant 3:	...	Phe	Leu	Pro	Thr	Val	Thr	Thr	Arg	
e.	Mutant 4:	...	Phe	Pro	Pro	Arg					
f.	Mutant 5:	...	Phe	Leu	Pro	Ser	Val	Thr	Thr	Arg	Trp

Answer: Start methodically and write out the potential codons for the normal protein. Let N represent any nucleotide, R a purine (A or G) and Y a pyrimidine (C or U). Then the codons can be written as:

	1	2	3	4	5	6	7	8	9
Normal:	Phe	Leu	Pro	Thr	Val	Thr	Thr	Arg	Trp
CODON:	UUY	UUR or CUN	CCN	ACN	GUN	ACN	ACN	CGN or AGR	UGG

Mutant 1: The alteration of all of the amino acids after codon 2 suggests that this mutation is a frameshift, either a deletion or an addition of a base pair in the DNA region that codes for the mRNA near codons 2 and 3. His is CAY, which can be generated from CCN by the insertion of a single A between the two Cs. If this is the case, one has:

	1	2	3	4	5	6	7	8	9
Mutant 1:	Phe	Leu	His	His	Gly	Asp	Asp	Thr	Val
Frameshift:	UUY	UUR or CUN	C$_A$C	NAC	NGU	NAC	NAC	NCG or NGR	NUG or RUG

Now identify the unknown bases, given the amino acid sequence:

To code for His, the new fourth codon must be CAC.
To code for Gly, the new fifth codon must be GGU.
To code for Asp, the new sixth codon must be GAC.
To code for Asp, the new seventh codon must be GAC.
To code for Thr, the new eighth codon must be ACG.
To code for Val, the new ninth codon must be GUG.

Thus, one has:

	1	2	3	4	5	6	7	8	9
Mutant 1:	Phe	Leu	His	His	Gly	Asp	Asp	Thr	Val
CODON:	UUY	UUR or CUN	C**A**C	C**A**C	**G**GU	**G**AC	**G**AC	**A**CG	**G**UG

This analysis indicates that the codons used in the normal protein are:

	1	2	3	4	5	6	7	8	9
Normal:	Phe	Leu	Pro	Thr	Val	Thr	Thr	Arg	Trp
CODON:	UUY	UUR or CUN	CCC	ACG	GUG	ACG	ACA	CGG	UGG

Mutant 2: Codon 5 in mutant 2 encodes Met, instead of Val. This single change could be caused by a point mutation, where the G in codon GUG is changed to an A leading to an AUG codon. This would occur by a $CG \rightarrow TA$ transition in the DNA.

Mutant 3: Mutant 3 has a normal amino acid sequence, but is prematurely terminated, indicating that a nonsense mutation occurred. The nonsense mutation occurred in the ninth codon. If an A base is substituted (for one of the Gs) or inserted (before or after the first G), one could have either UAG or UGA. Thus, either a frameshift or base substitution ($CG \rightarrow TA$ transition) occurred.

Mutant 4: Mutant 4 shows premature termination at codon 5 (indicating a nonsense codon there), and has missense mutations at codons 2 and 4. Compare the possible sequences of the mutant with the normal sequence to see if one mutational event can account for all of these phenomena.

	1	2	3	4	5	6	7	8	9
Normal:	Phe	Leu	Pro	Thr	Val	Thr	Thr	Arg	Trp
Normal Codon:	UUY	UUR or CUN	CCC	A<u>CG</u>	<u>G</u>UG	<u>A</u>CG	ACA	CGG	UGG
Mutant 4:	Phe	Pro	Pro	Arg	Stop				
Possible Mutant Codons:	UUY	CCN (CCC)	CCN (CCA)	AGR or <u>CGN</u>	UAA UAG <u>UGA</u>				

Consider codon 2 carefully. In order for Pro to be encoded by CCN in the mutant protein, and be obtained by a single change from the second codon, Leu (in the normal protein) must be encoded by CUN. If the U were deleted (by an AT deletion in the DNA) and the N were a C, a CCC Pro codon and a frameshift would result.

Codon 3 would become CCA and still code for Pro, codon 4 would become CGG and code for Arg, and codon 5 would become UGA, a nonsense codon.

Mutant 5: Mutant 5 shows an alteration of only the fourth amino acid (Thr to Ser), suggesting a point mutation. If the fourth codon were changed from ACG to UCG (by a TA to an AT transversion in the DNA), this missense mutation would occur.

19.6   In mutant strain X of *E. coli*, a leucine tRNA that recognizes the codon 5'-CUG-3' in normal cells has been altered so that it now recognizes the codon 5'-GUG-3'. A missense mutation, which affects amino acid 10 of a particular protein, is suppressed in mutant X cells.
  a. What are the anticodons of the two Leu tRNAs, and what mutational event has occurred in mutant X cells?
  b. What amino acid would normally be present at position 10 of the protein (without the missense mutation)?
  c. What amino acid would be put in at position 10 if the missense mutation is not suppressed (that is, in normal cells)?
  d. What amino acid is inserted at position 10 if the missense mutation is suppressed (that is, in mutant X cells)?

  Answer:
  a. If the normal codon is 5'-CUG-3', the anticodon of the normal tRNA is 5'-CA<u>G</u>-3'. If a mutant tRNA recognizes 5'-GUG-3', it must have an anticodon that is 5'-CA<u>C</u>-3'. The mutational event was a CG to GC transversion.
  b. Since a leucine bearing (mutant) tRNA can suppress the mutation, one presumes that leucine is normally present at position 10.
  c. The mutant tRNA recognizes the codon 5'-GUG-3', which codes for Val. In normal cells, a Val.tRNA.Valine would recognize the codon.
  d. Leu.

19.7   A researcher using a model eukaryotic experimental system has identified a temperature-sensitive mutation, *rpIIA^{ts}*, in a gene that encodes a protein subunit of RNA polymerase II. This mutation results from a missense mutation. It has a recessive lethal phenotype at the higher, restrictive temperature, but allows growth at the lower, permissive (normal) temperature. To identify genes whose products interact with the subunit of RNA polymerase II, the researcher designs a screen to isolate mutations that will act as dominant suppressors of the temperature-sensitive recessive lethality.
  a. Explain how a new mutation in an interacting protein could suppress the temperature-sensitive lethality of the original mutation.
  b. In addition to mutations in interacting proteins, what other type of suppressor mutations might be found?
  c. Outline how the researcher might select for the new suppressor mutations.

d. Do you expect the frequency of suppressor mutations to be similar to, much greater than, or much less than the frequency of new mutations at a typical eukaryotic gene?

e. How might this approach be used generally to identify genes whose products interact in controlling transcription?

Answer:

a. The temperature sensitivity of the *rpIIA^{ts}* mutant could be due to a single amino acid change in the protein subunit of RNA polymerase II that causes it to be nonfunctional at the restrictive temperature. If its inability to function is due to a change in its secondary or tertiary structure that prevents it from interacting with another protein during transcription, then a mutation in this second, interacting protein might be compensatory. Such a mutation would effectively suppress the initial mutation, as it would allow for transcription even at the restrictive temperature.

b. A new mutation in a second protein would be an intergenic suppressor mutation. The original mutation could also be suppressed by reverting the missense mutation, or by an intragenic suppressor mutation. In an intragenic suppressor mutation, a particular second site within the protein would need to be mutated so as to compensate for the initial mutation.

c. One approach is to treat *rpIIA^{ts}/rpIIA^{ts}* individuals with a mutagen, and mate them to *rpIIA^{ts}/rpIIA^{ts}* individuals at the permissive temperature. A second-site suppressor could be selected for by removing the parents and shifting the progeny to the restrictive temperature. Since all of the offspring are *rpIIA^{ts}/rpIIA^{ts}*, only offspring carrying a new mutation capable of suppressing the recessive lethality of the *rpIIA^{ts}* mutation will survive.

d. Second-site suppressors will be quite rare, and will appear at a much lower frequency than mutations in a typical eukaryotic gene. To suppress a particular defect, a very specific new mutation must occur. Hence, the vast majority of mutations that are induced by a mutagen will lack the specific compensatory ability of a suppressor mutation.

e. Since intergenic suppressors may result from mutations in interacting proteins, this approach could be used to identify genes for proteins that interact during transcription.

19.8 The mutant *lacZ-1* was induced by treating *E. coli* cells with acridine, whereas *lacZ-2* was induced with 5BU. What kinds of mutants are these likely to be? Explain. How could you confirm your predictions by studying the structure of the β-galactosidase in these cells?

Answer: Acridine is an intercalating agent, and so can be expected to induce frameshift mutations. 5BU is incorporated into DNA in place of T. During DNA replication, it is likely to be read as C by DNA polymerase because of a keto-to-enol shift. This results in point mutations, usually TA to CG transitions. Considering these expectations, *lacZ-1* would probably result in a completely altered amino acid sequence after some point, although it might be truncated (due to the introduction–out of frame–of a nonsense codon). *lacZ-2* is likely to contain a single amino acid difference due to a missense mutation, although it too could contain a nonsense codon.

19.9

a. The sequence of nucleotides in an mRNA is:

5'-AUGACCCAUUGGUCUCGUUAG-3'

Assuming that ribosomes could translate this mRNA, how many amino acids long would you expect the resulting polypeptide chain to be?

b. Hydroxylamine is a mutagen that results in the replacement of an AT base pair for a GC base pair in the DNA; that is, it induces a transition mutation. When applied to the organism that made the mRNA molecule shown in part (a), a strain was isolated in which a mutation occurred at the 11th position of the DNA that coded for the mRNA. How many amino acids long would you expect the polypeptide made by this mutant to be? Why?

Answer:

a. The codons read as:

5' - AUG - ACC - CAU - UGG - UCU - CGU - UAG - 3'

The last codon is a nonsense (chain termination) codon, while the others are sense codons. The chain would be six amino acids long.

b. The new sequence would be

5' - AUG - ACC - CAU - UAG - ...

Since UAG is a nonsense (chain termination) codon, the new chain would be only three amino acids long.

19.10   In a series of 94,075 babies born in a particular hospital in Copenhagen, 10 were achondroplastic dwarfs (this is an autosomal dominant condition). Two of these 10 had an achondroplastic parent. The other 8 achondroplastic babies each had two normal parents. What is the apparent mutation rate at the achondroplasia locus?

Answer: There were eight new mutations in 94,073 normal couples. Since the phenotype is dominant, the phenotype is seen when just one of the parental genes is mutated. There were 2 x 94,073 copies of the gene that could have undergone mutation. Therefore, the apparent mutation rate at this locus is

$[8/(2 \times 94{,}073)] = 8/188{,}146 = 4 \times 10^{-5}$ mutations per locus per generation.

19.11   Three of the codons in the genetic code are chain-terminating codons for which no naturally occurring tRNAs exist. Just like any other codons in the DNA, though, these codons can change as a result of base pair changes in the DNA. Confining yourself to single base-pair changes at a time, determine which amino acids could be inserted in a polypeptide by mutation of these chain-terminating codons: (a) UAG, (b) UAA, and (c) UGA. (The genetic code is listed in Figure 6.8.)

Answer:

NUCLEOTIDE ALTERED	CODON					
	UAG	CODE	UAA	CODE	UGA	CODE
FIRST	AAG	Lys	AAA	Lys	AGA	Arg
	CAG	Gln	CAA	Gln	CGA	Arg
	GAG	Glu	GAA	Glu	GGA	Gly
SECOND	UUG	Leu	UUA	Leu	UUA	Leu
	UCG	Ser	UCA	Ser	UCA	Ser
	UGG	Trp	UGA	STOP	UAA	STOP
THIRD	UAC	Tyr	UAC	Tyr	UGC	Cys
	UAU	Tyr	UAU	Tyr	UGU	Cys
	UAA	STOP	UAG	STOP	UGG	Trp

19.12   The amino acid substitutions in the following figure occur in the α and β chains of human hemoglobin. Those amino acids connected by lines are related by single nucleotide changes. Propose the most likely codon or codons for each of the numbered amino acids. (Refer to the genetic code listed in Figure 6.8.)

Answer:

19.13   Yanofsky studied the tryptophan synthetase of *E. coli* in an attempt to identify the base sequence specifying this protein. The wild type gave a protein with a glycine in position 38. Yanofsky isolated two *trp* mutants, *A23* and *A46*. Mutant *A23* had Arg instead of Gly at position 38, and mutant *A46* had Glu at position 38. Mutant *A23* was plated on minimal medium, and four spontaneous revertants to prototrophy were obtained. The tryptophan synthetase from each of four revertants was isolated, and the amino acids at position 38 were identified. Revertant 1 had Ile, revertant 2 had Thr, revertant 3 had Ser, and revertant 4 had Gly. In a similar fashion, three revertants from *A46* were recovered, and the tryptophan synthetase from each was isolated and studied. At position 38 revertant, 1 had Gly, revertant 2 had Ala, and revertant 3 had Val. A summary of these data is given in the figure. Using the genetic code in Figure 6.8, deduce the codons for the wild type, for the mutants *A23* and *A46*, and for the revertants, and place each designation in the space provided in the figure.

Answer:

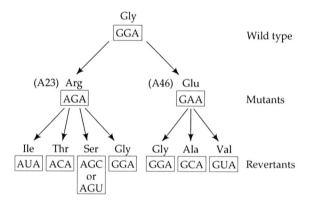

19.14   Consider an enzyme chewase from a theoretical microorganism. In the wild-type cell the chewase has the following sequence of amino acids at positions 39 to 47 (reading from the amino end) in the polypeptide chain:

```
-Met-Phe-Ala-Asn-His-Lys-Ser-Val-Gly-

 39   40   41   42   43   44   45   46   47
```

A mutant of the organism was obtained; it lacks chewase activity. The mutant was induced by a mutagen known to cause single base-pair insertions or deletions. Instead of making the complete chewase chain, the mutant makes a short polypeptide chain only 45 amino acids long. The first 38 amino acids are in the same sequence as the first 38 of the normal chewase, but the last 7 amino acids are as follows:

```
-Met-Leu-Leu-Thr-Ile-Arg-Val-
  39  40  41  42  43  44  45
```

A partial revertant of the mutant was induced by treating it with the same mutagen. The revertant makes a partly active chewase, which differs from the wild-type enzyme only in the following region:

```
-Met-Leu-Leu-Thr-Ile-Arg-Gly-Val-Gly-
  39  40  41  42  43  44  45  46  47
```

Using the genetic code given in Figure 6.8, deduce the nucleotide sequences for the mRNA molecules that specify this region of the protein in each of the three strains.

Answer: Using the genetic code, and letting N represent any nucleotide, R a purine, and Y a pyrimidine, the wild-type RNA can be denoted as:

```
-Met-Phe-Ala-Asn-His-Lys-Ser-Val-Gly-
  39   40  41  42  43  44  45  46  47
UCN
AUG UUY GCN AAY CAY AAR or GUN GGN
AGY
```

Since the mutants were obtained using a mutagen that causes single base-pair insertions or deletions, the mutants have frameshift mutations. Considering this fact and comparing the mutant amino acid sequence to that of the wild type, one expects a base pair to be missing or added in codon 40. Try various options to obtain an appropriate amino acid sequence after such a frameshift. If the Y of codon 40 was deleted, an appropriate sequence can be obtained, providing the unknown nucleotides are as specified below:

```
Met-Leu-Leu-Thr-Ile-Arg-Val-
 39  40  41  42  43  44  45
AUG UUG CNA AYC AYA ARA GYG UNG
N=U Y=C Y=U R=G Y=U N=A
```

This means that the original sequence was:

```
-Met-Phe-Ala-Asn-His-Lys-Ser-Val-Gly-
  39   40  41  42  43  44  45  46  47
AUG UUY GCU AAC CAU AAG AGU GUA GGN
```

In the revertant, the reading frame is restored at codon 46, the Val (GUG) at codon 45 is altered to a Gly (GGN), and the chain termination codon at position 46 (UAG) is altered to a Val (GUN). This would have occurred if a G was inserted before or after the first G in codon 45. One would have:

```
-Met-Leu-Leu-Thr-Ile-Arg-Gly-Val-Gly-
  39  40  41  42  43  44  45  46  47
AUG UUG CUA ACC AUA AGA GGU GUA GGN
```

19.15   DNA polymerases from different organisms differ in their fidelity of nucleotide insertion; however, even the best DNA polymerases make mistakes. These are usually mismatches. If such mismatches are not corrected, they can become fixed as mutations after the next round of replication.

   a.   How does DNA polymerase attempt to correct mismatches during DNA replication?

   b.   What mechanism is used to repair such mismatches if they escape detection by DNA polymerase?

   c.   How is the mismatched base in the newly synthesized strand distinguished from the correct base in the template strand?

   Answer:

   a.   Many, but not all, DNA polymerases have a proofreading capacity that causes them to stall at mismatches during DNA replication. When present, the 3'-to-5' exonuclease activity associated with the polymerase will excise mismatched bases, so that they can be replaced. See text discussion in Chapters 3 and 19, and Tables 3.1 and 3.4.

   b.   Shortly after DNA replication, mismatches can still be repaired by using a set of enzymes that recognize and excise mismatches in the newly synthesized DNA strand. In *E. coli*, mismatch repair is initiated when single base-pair mismatches or small base-pair additions or deletions in newly replicated DNA are bound by the MutS protein. The newly replicated strand is distinguished from the parental strand by the presence of an unmethylated A nucleotide in a 5'-GATC-3' sequence close to the mismatch. The MutL and MutH proteins bring the unmethylated GATC close to the mismatch and form a complex with MutS. MutH nicks the new, unmethylated DNA strand and a section of this DNA strand, including the mismatch, is excised by an exonuclease. DNA polymerase III and ligase repair the gap, producing the correct base pair. See Figure 19.18.

   c.   In *E. coli*, the parental strand can be distinguished from the newly replicated strand by methylation of the A in the sequence 5'-GATC-3'. As a newly replicated DNA strand is not methylated until a short time after its synthesis, hemimethylation at this frequently appearing site allows for the identification of which strand is newly synthesized. Since only the strand with the unmethylated A is nicked by the MutH protein and excised by an exonuclease during mismatch repair, only the newly synthesized strand and not the parental strand is re-synthesized by DNA polymerase III.

19.16   Two mechanisms in *E. coli* were described for the repair of thymine dimer formation after exposure to ultraviolet light: photoreactivation and excision (dark) repair. Compare these mechanisms, indicating how each achieves repair.

   Answer: Photoreactivation requires the enzyme photolyase, which, when activated by a photon of light with a wavelength between 320 and 370 nm, splits the dimers apart. Dark repair does not require light, but requires several different enzymes. First, the uvrABC endonuclease makes two single-stranded nicks, on the 5' side and the 3' side of the dimer. Then, an exonuclease excises the 12-nucleotide-long segment of one strand between the nicks, including the dimer. Next, DNA polymerase I fills in the single-stranded region in the 5'-to-3' direction. Finally, the gap is sealed by DNA ligase.

19.17 DNA damage by mutagens has very serious consequences for DNA replication. Without specific base pairing, the replication enzymes cannot specify a complementary strand, and gaps are left after the passing of a replication fork.

   a. What response has *E. coli* developed to large amounts of DNA damage by mutagens? How is this response controlled coordinately?

   b. Why is this response itself a mutagenic system?

   c. What effects would loss-of-function mutations in *recA* or *lexA* have on this response?

   Answer:

   a. *E. coli* has developed the SOS response to respond to large amounts of DNA damage. When such damage occurs, the RecA protein becomes activated and stimulates LexA to cleave itself. Since the LexA protein functions as a repressor for about 17 genes whose products are involved in DNA damage repair (it binds to a 20-nucleotide regulatory sequence called the SOS box), this results in the coordinate transcription of these genes. After the products of these genes "correct" the DNA damage, RecA is inactivated, and newly synthesized LexA represses the expression of the genes.

   b. The response is mutagenic because in some instances (e.g., in the repair of C^C dimers), the SOS repair system becomes stalled because of a mismatch. The delay is long enough for C to be deaminated to U. This results in a CG-to-TA transition.

   c. If there are loss-of-function mutations in <u>both *recA* and *lexA*,</u> or a loss-of-function mutation <u>only in *lexA*,</u> there would be no functional LexA protein to repress transcription of the 17 genes whose protein products are involved in the SOS response; this would result in constitutive activation of the SOS response. If the loss-of-function mutation is <u>only in *recA*,</u> however, heavy DNA damage would not result in activating the RecA protein, so RecA could not stimulate the LexA protein to cleave itself to induce the SOS response. Instead, the LexA protein would continue to repress the DNA repair genes in the SOS system. *E. coli* with a loss-of-function mutation in *recA* but with a normal *lexA* gene would, therefore, be deficient in SOS repair of heavy DNA damage and consequently would be sensitive to UV irradiation and to X rays. [*E. coli* with a *recA* loss-of-function mutation were observed to have this phenotype by Ann Dee Margulies and Alvin Clark, who discovered the *recA* gene in 1964.]

19.18 After a culture of *E. coli* cells was treated with the chemical 5-bromouracil, it was noted that the frequency of mutants was much higher than normal. Mutant colonies were then isolated, grown, and treated with nitrous acid; some of the mutant strains reverted to wild type.

a. In terms of the Watson-Crick model, diagram a series of steps by which 5BU may have produced the mutants.

b. Assuming the revertants were not caused by suppressor mutations, indicate the steps by which nitrous acid may have produced the back mutations.

Answer:

a. 5-bromouracil in its normal state is a T analog, base pairing with A. In its rare state, it resembles C and can base pair with G. It will induce an AT → GC transition as diagrammed below.

$$\begin{array}{ccccccc} \mid\mid & & \mid\mid & & \mid\mid & & \mid\mid \\ \text{A–T} & \rightarrow & \text{A–5BU} & \rightarrow & \text{G–5BU} & \rightarrow & \text{G–C} \\ \mid\mid & & \mid\mid & & \mid\mid & & \mid\mid \end{array}$$

b. Nitrous acid can deaminate C to U, resulting in a CG → TA transition.

19.19 A single, hypothetical strand of DNA is composed of the following base sequence, where A indicates adenine, T indicates thymine, G indicates guanine, C denotes cytosine, U denotes uracil, BU is 5-bromouracil, 2AP is 2-aminopurine, BU-enol is a tautomer of 5BU, 2AP-imino is a rare tautomer of 2AP, HX is hypoxanthine, X is xanthine, and 5' and 3' are the numbers of the free, OH-containing carbons on the deoxyribose part of the terminal nucleotides:

5'-T–HX–U–A–G–BU-enol–2AP–C–BU–X–2AP-imino-3'

a. Opposite the bases of the hypothetical strand, and using the shorthand of the base sequence, indicate the sequence of bases on a complementary strand of DNA.

b. Indicate the direction of replication of the new strand by drawing an arrow next to the new strand of DNA from part a.

c. When postmeiotic germ cells of a higher organism are exposed to a chemical mutagen before fertilization, the resulting offspring expressing an induced mutation are almost always mosaics for wild-type and mutant tissue. Give at least one reason that in the progenies of treated individuals these mosaics are found and not the so-called complete or whole-body mutants.

Answer:
a. and b.

```
5'–T–HX–U–A–G–BU-enol–2AP–C–BU–X–2AP-imino–3'
3'–A-  C–A–T–C–        G  –T –G  A–C-   C        –5'
    ←
```

c. If postmeiotic germ cells are treated, a single mutated site in one strand of the double helix will not be repaired until mitotic division begins during embryogenesis. Given the semiconservative replication of DNA, the normal strand will be replicated into two normal strands. If the mutated site on the other strand is not repaired, when the strand is replicated it will give rise to a double helix with two mutant strands. In this scenario, the products of DNA replication at the first mitotic division consist of one normal and one mutant helix. This will produce two different cell types, resulting in a mosaic individual.

For some mutagens, such as BU or 2AP, there is a variation in this method of mosaic production. If the BU (or 2AP) remains in the DNA strand it was incorporated into, the first mitotic division may result in a normal double helix (the new strand is copied from the old normal strand), and a double helix with the BU (or 2AP) paired to a "wrong" base (due to the rare form of BU). In this case, a mutant site will be produced on one of the daughter double helices that result after the second mitotic division (at the four-cell stage). In principle, a mutant cell could be introduced at any mitotic division when BU is incorporated in its rare form during DNA synthesis. In each case, a mosaic individual would be produced, but the later the developmental stage at which the mutation was introduced, the fewer the mutation-bearing cells.

The following information applies to Problems 19.20 through 19.24. A solution of single-stranded DNA is used as the template in a series of reaction mixtures. It has the following base sequence:

$$A \quad T \quad A \quad C \quad G \quad T$$

5' P ... OH 3'

where A = adenine, G = guanine, C = cytosine, T = thymine, H = hypoxanthine, and HNO_2 = nitrous acid. For Problems 19.20 through 19.24, use the shorthand system in the figure and draw the products expected from the reaction mixtures. Assume that a primer is available in each case.

19.20   The DNA template + DNA polymerase + dATP + dGTP + dCTP + dTTP + Mg^{2+}.

Answer:

3' OH ... 5'

T   A   T   G   C   A
A   T   A   C   G   T

5' P ... OH 3'

19.21   The DNA template + DNA polymerase + dATP + dGMP + dCTP + dTTP + Mg^{2+}.

Answer: The absence of dG<u>T</u>P leads to a block in polymerization after the first two bases.

19.22   The DNA template + DNA polymerase + dATP + dHTP + dGMP + dTTP + Mg^{2+}.

Answer: While the dHTP can substitute for dGTP, there is no dCTP, so polymerization cannot continue past the first base.

19.23   The DNA template is pretreated with HNO_2 + DNA polymerase + dATP + dGTP + dCTP + dTTP + Mg^{2+}.

Answer: Pretreatment of the template with HNO_2 deaminates G to X, C to U, and A to H. X will still pair with C, but U pairs with A, and H pairs with C, causing "mutations" in the newly synthesized strand.

19.24   The DNA template + DNA polymerase + dATP + dGMP + dHTP + dCTP + dTTP + Mg^{2+}.

Answer: The dHTP will substitute for the absence of dGTP, and pair with C.

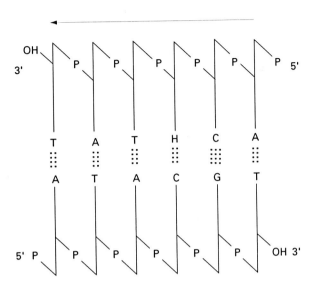

19.25   A strong experimental approach to determining the mode of action of mutagens is to examine the revertibility of the products of one mutagen by other mutagens. The following table represents collected data on revertibility of various mutagens on *rII* mutations in phage T2; "+" indicates majority of mutants reverted, "–" indicates almost no reversion; BU = 5-bromouracil, AP = 2-aminopurine, NA = nitrous acid, and HA = hydroxylamine. Fill in the empty spaces.

MUTATION INDUCED BY	PROPORTION OF MUTATIONS REVERTED BY				BASE-PAIR SUBSTITUTION INFERRED
	BU	AP	NA	HA	
BU	+			–	
AP		–	+		
NA	+	+		+	
HA			+	–	GC → AT

Answer: Answer this problem using only the data provided. First consider what is known about HA. HA causes a GC→AT transition, and cannot revert mutations it induces. Therefore, HA cannot cause AT→GC transitions. HA also cannot revert the BU mutation. Consequently, BU must have caused a GC→AT transition.

Now consider the relationship between NA and HA. Since HA can revert NA mutations, the NA mutation was an AT→GC transition. This is consistent with the observation that NA can revert the HA mutation.

Now consider AP. AP cannot revert its own mutation, but it can revert the AT→GC transition caused by NA. Therefore the AP mutation was a GC→AT transition, and AP cannot induce AT→GC transitions. The AP mutation cannot be reverted by HA, because HA cannot induce AT→GC transitions. AP also could not revert the GC→AT transitions caused by BU or HA.

Because BU can revert its own GC→AT mutation, it can induce AT→GC transitions. Therefore, BU can revert the GC→AT mutations caused by AP and HA.

Because NA can cause AT→GC transitions, NA could revert the GC→AT transition caused by BU. It cannot be determined from the data provided whether NA can induce GC→AT transitions. If it can induce GC→AT transitions, it could revert its own mutations; if it cannot, it would not be able to revert its own mutations.

MUTATION INDUCED BY	PROPORTION OF MUTATIONS REVERTED BY				BASE-PAIR SUBSTITUTION INFERRED
	BU	AP	NA	HA	
BU	+	−	+	−	GC → AT
AP	+	−	+	−	GC → AT
NA	+	+	?	+	AT → GC
HA	+	−	+	−	GC → AT

19.26

a. Nitrous acid deaminates adenine to form hypoxanthine, which forms two hydrogen bonds with cytosine during DNA replication. After treatment with nitrous acid, a mutant is recovered that contains a protein with an amino acid substitution: The amino acid valine (Val) is located in a position occupied by methionine (Met) in nonmutant organisms. What is the simplest explanation for this observation?

b. Hydroxylamine adds a hydroxyl (OH) group to cytosine, causing it to pair with adenine. Could mutant organisms like those in part (a) be back mutated (returned to normal) using hydroxylamine? Explain.

Answer:

a. The codon for Met is 5'-AUG-3'. This would be encoded by 3'-TAC-5' in the template DNA strand, which pairs with 5'-ATG-3' in the nontemplate DNA strand. In this case, the A in the nontemplate strand was deaminated to form hypoxanthine, and paired with C in the template strand. The new template was 3'-CAC-5' and the new codon was 5'-GUG-3', coding for Val.

b. In the mutant in (a), the template strand was 3'-CAC-5', and the nontemplate strand was 5'-GTG-3'. Since hydroxylamine acts on cytosine bases, it would act on the template strand. If it acted at the 3'-C, DNA replication would result in the nontemplate strand becoming 5'-ATG-3'. After an additional round of replication, one of the daughter cells would have a template strand that is 3'-TAC-5'. Thus, hydroxylamine could be used to obtain revertants.

19.27   A protein contains the amino acid proline (Pro) at one site. Treatment with nitrous acid, which deaminates C to make it U, produces two different mutants. One mutant has a substitution of serine (Ser) and the other has a substitution of leucine (Leu) at the site.

Treatment of the two mutants with nitrous acid produces new mutant strains, each with phenylalanine (Phe) at the site. Treatment of these new Phe-carrying mutants with nitrous acid produces no change. The results are summarized in the following figure:

Using the appropriate codons, show how it is possible for nitrous acid to produce these changes and why further treatment has no influence. (Assume only single nucleotide changes occur at each step.)

Answer: Nitrous acid deaminates C to make it U. U will pair with A, so that treatment with nitrous acid leads to CG→TA transitions. Analyze how this treatment would affect the codons of this protein. Use N to represent any nucleotide, and Y to represent a pyrimidine (U or C). Then, the codons for Pro are CCN, the (relevant) codons for Ser are UCN, the codons for Leu are CUN, and the codons for Phe are UUY. (Nucleotides are written in the 5'→3' direction unless specifically noted.)

The codon CCN for Pro would be represented by CCN in the nontemplate DNA strand. Deamination of the 5'-C would lead to a nontemplate strand of UCN, and a template strand of 3'-AGN-5'. This would produce a UCN codon, encoding Ser. Deamination of the middle C would lead to a nontemplate strand of CUN, and a template strand of 3'-GAN-5'. This would produce a CUN codon, encoding Leu.

Further treatment of either mutant would result in deamination of the remaining C, and a template strand of 3'-AAN-5'. This would result in a UUN codon. Since we are told Phe is obtained, N must be C or U, and the template strand must be 3'-AAA-5' or 3'-AAG-5'.

To explain why further treatment with nitrous acid has no effect, consider that nitrous acid acts via deamination and that T has no amine group. If the template strand was 3'-AAA-5', the nontemplate strand would have been TTT. Since T cannot be deaminated, nitrous acid will not have any effect on the non-template strand.

19.28   Three *ara* mutants of *E. coli* were induced by mutagen X. The ability of other mutagens to cause the reverse change (*ara* to *ara*⁺) was tested, with the results shown in the following table.

Frequency of *ara*⁺ Cells Among Total Cells After Treatment

	MUTAGEN				
MUTANT	NONE	BU	AP	HA	FRAMESHIFT
ara-1	1.5×10^{-8}	5×10^{-5}	1.3×10^{-4}	1.3×10^{-8}	1.6×10^{-8}
ara-2	2×10^{-7}	2×10^{-4}	6×10^{-5}	3×10^{-5}	1.6×10^{-7}
ara-3	6×10^{-7}	10^{-5}	9×10^{-6}	5×10^{-6}	6.5×10^{-7}

Assume all *ara*⁺ cells are true revertants. What base changes were probably involved in forming the three original mutations? What kind(s) of mutations are caused by mutagen X?

Answer: Use the revertant frequencies under "none" to estimate the spontaneous reversion frequency.

ara-1: BU and AP, but not HA or a frameshift, can revert *ara-1*. Both BU and AP cause CG→TA and TA→CG transitions, while HA only causes CG→TA transitions. If HA cannot revert *ara-1*, it must require a TA→CG transition to be reverted and be caused by a CG→TA transition.

ara-2: BU, AP, and HA, but not a frameshift, can revert *ara-2*. Since HA only causes CG→TA transitions, *ara-2* must have been caused by a TA→CG transition.

ara-3: By the same logic as for *ara-2*, *ara-3* must have been caused by a TA→CG transition.

Providing that this is a representative sample, mutagen X appears to cause both TA→CG and CG→TA transitions. It does not appear to cause frameshift mutations.

19.29   As genes have been cloned for a number of human diseases caused by defects in DNA repair and replication, striking evolutionary parallels have been found between human and bacterial DNA repair systems. Discuss the features of DNA repair systems that appear to be shared in these two organism types.

Answer: One of the most striking parallels between human and bacterial DNA repair systems has come from the analysis of mutations that affect mismatch repair (see problem 19.15). Mutations in any of the four human genes *hMSH2*, *hMLH1*, *hPMS1*, and *hPMS2* result in an increased accumulation of mutations in the genome and a hereditary predisposition to hereditary nonpolyposis colon cancer (HNPCC). Mutations in the *E. coli* genes *mutS* and *mutL* also result in an increased accumulation of mutations, and the normal alleles of these genes are essential for the initial stages of mismatch repair. The human gene *hMSH2* is homologous to *E. coli mutS*, and the other three human genes are homologous to *E. coli mutL*, indicating that aspects of mismatch repair are shared in these two organisms.

Examples of additional human genetic defects that lack functions required for DNA repair include xeroderma pigmentosum, ataxia telangiectasia, Fanconi's anemia, Bloom's syndrome, and Cockayne syndrome (see Table 19.1). While the specific DNA repair process affected by these mutations may not yet be sufficiently characterized for a direct comparison with a homologous process in *E. coli*, it has become clear that there are parallels in the types of repair processes that exist in the two organisms. For example, xeroderma pigmentosum and Fanconi's anemia both affect repair of DNA damage induced by UV irradiation, whose mechanism of repair is well understood in *E. coli*.

19.30   In the past few years, many knockout mice that lack specific gene functions have been bred. In addition to the knockouts for *p53* and the *CFTR* genes described in this chapter, knockouts for many different *Hox* genes (see Chapter 17), lysosomal hexosaminidase (the enzyme missing in Tay-Sachs disease), and many other enzymes have been made.

   a. Why is the ability to make knockout mice important for treating and curing of human disease?

   b. Consider a situation in which a dominant mutation causes a human disease such as Huntington disease. A hypothetical researcher clones the disease gene and discovers that a novel, abnormal protein is responsible for the disease phenotype. Would you expect the phenotype of a knockout mouse to be similar to the disease phenotype? Why or why not?

   Answer:

   a. The production of knockout mice allows for the development of an animal model system to investigate human disease. It allows for greater investigation into the consequences of not having a particular gene function, and also allows for the development of therapeutic approaches in a model system that closely parallels the human disease.

   b. Since knockout mice lack a particular gene function, the phenotype of a knockout mouse will not necessarily mimic the phenotype of a dominant mutation that has an additional, abnormal function. To design a mouse model in this instance, it is necessary to add a copy of a dominant allele into the normal genetic background, or replace a normal gene with the dominant allele. Only in this way would the aberrant protein product of the gene be expressed and the phenotype it causes be observed.

20

TRANSPOSABLE ELEMENTS

CHAPTER OUTLINE

GENERAL FEATURES OF TRANSPOSABLE ELEMENTS

TRANSPOSABLE ELEMENTS IN PROKARYOTES

Insertion Sequences

Transposons

IS Elements and Transposons in Plasmids

Bacteriophage Mu

TRANSPOSABLE ELEMENTS IN EUKARYOTES

Transposons in Plants

Ty Elements in Yeast

Drosophila Transposons

Human Retrotransposons

REVIEW OF KEY TERMS, SYMBOLS, AND CONCEPTS

In your own words, write a brief, precise definition of each term in the groups below. Check your definitions using the text. Then, develop a concept map using the terms in each list.

1	2
transposable element	transposon vs. retrotransposon
transposition	mutator gene
transposition event	bacteriophage Mu
insertion (IS) element	mutator
IS module	temperate bacteriophage
inverted terminal repeat	replicative vs. conservative transposition
transposase	homologous recombination
target site	deletion
target site duplication	inversion
transposon (Tn)	translocation
illegitimate recombination	*Mu1, Tam, Tgm* elements
composite transposon	*Ac, Ds* controlling elements
noncomposite transposon	null mutation
Tn*10*, Tn*3*	autonomous vs. nonautonomous element
replicative transposition	stable vs. unstable (mutable) allele

1	2
conservative (nonreplicative) transposition	donor site
simple insertion	*Ty* element
cointegrate	long terminal (direct) repeat
cointegration model	delta repeat, dropping
transposase	target site duplication
resolvase	retrovirus
β-lactamase	reverse transcriptase
IS element	mobile element
F factor	*copia* element
plasmid	hybrid dysgenesis
episome	*P* element
R plasmid	P, M cytotype
RTF region	LINEs, SINEs
	Alu, L1 elements

THINKING ANALYTICALLY

As the material in this chapter is broadly descriptive, it will be helpful to organize and categorize its information. Distinguish between the various categories of transposable elements by considering transposable elements from four perspectives: (1) structure, (2) mode of transposition, (3) the effect of a transposed element on the structure of a gene or a chromosome, and (4) the effect of a transposed element on the function of a gene. As you read the chapter, refer frequently to the text figures to visualize more clearly the different transposon structures and modes of transposition.

QUESTIONS FOR PRACTICE

Multiple Choice Questions

1. How are transposition and recombination fundamentally different?
    a. Recombination requires DNA homology but transposition does not.
    b. Transposition requires DNA homology but recombination does not.
    c. Only during transposition can a piece of DNA be moved from a virus to a cell.
    d. Only during recombination can a deletion occur.

2. Which of the following can result from the insertion of a transposon in bacteria?
    a. Gene inactivation
    b. An increase or a decrease in transcriptional activity of a gene
    c. Deletions or insertions
    d. All of the above

3. Which of the following can be consequences of transposition in eukaryotes?
    a. No effect on a nearby gene
    b. Production of a mutation by insertional mutagenesis
    c. Increased or decreased transcription from a nearby promoter
    d. All of the above

4. In what ways are bacterial IS and Tn elements alike?
    a. Both have inverted repeat sequences at their ends.
    b. Both integrate into target sites and cause a target site duplication.
    c. Both contain a transposase gene.
    d. Both contain antibiotic resistance genes.
    e. Both always use replicative transposition.
    f. a, b, and c.
    g. All of the above.

5. How might plasmids X and Y differ? X is an F factor in an F^+ bacterium sensitive to the antibiotics ampicillin, streptomycin, and tetracycline. Y is an R plasmid in a bacterium resistant to these antibiotics.
    a. Y is likely to be smaller in size.
    b. X is likely to lack the *tra* genes.
    c. Y is likely to have additional genes between flanking IS modules.
    d. Y is likely to lack the *RTF* genes.

6. Reverse transcriptase is used by which two of the following transposable elements?
    a. The *Ty* element in yeast.
    b. The *IS* element in bacteria.
    c. The *Tn*10 elementin bacteria.
    d. The *L1* element in humans.

7. In a bacterial *IS* element, how does transposase know the boundaries of the DNA to be transposed?
    a. There are special restriction sites at the ends of the *IS* element.
    b. It recognizes the target site of insertion.
    c. It recognizes the IR sequences.
    d. It recognizes the delta sequences.

8. Which of the following statements is *not* true about Mu?
    a. It is a temperate bacteriophage.
    b. Like λ, it is excised and replicated during lytic infection.
    c. It is a transposon that integrates by conservative transposition.
    d. Homologous recombination between two Mu elements can generate inversions.

9. In corn, the insertion of an autonomous element within a gene results in the production of an allele that mutates at high frequency. Why?
    a. Although an autonomous element cannot excise, it is highly mutable.
    b. An autonomous element has transposase and can excise, thereby causing a mutation.
    c. Autonomous alleles are unstable if nonautonomous elements are also in the genome.
    d. Autonomous alleles generally insert into promoter regions.

10. *Ty* elements in yeast are similar to retroviruses because (choose the correct answer):
    a. Both *Ty* elements and retroviruses utilize an RNA transposition intermediate.
    b. Both *Ty* elements and retroviruses utilize reverse transcriptase.

c. Introns are usually found in retroviruses and *Ty* elements.

d. More than one of the preceding.

11. Which of the following is true about hybrid dysgenesis in *Drosophila*?

a. It occurs in the progeny of M females after they are mated to P males.

b. It occurs in the progeny of P females after they are mated to M males.

c. It is a result of the mobilization of *P* elements in a P cytotype.

d. It is a result of the mobilization of *M* elements in a P cytotype.

12. Which of the following statements is *not* true about the L1 family of LINE elements in mammals?

a. They are retrotransposons.

b. They comprise about 5 percent of the genome.

c. All elements in one individual are full-length elements.

d. They are capable of causing disease by insertional mutagenesis during an individual's lifetime.

Answers: 1a; 2d; 3d; 4f; 5c; 6a,d; 7c; 8b; 9b; 10d; 11a; 12c.

Thought Questions

1. Contrast conservative and replicative transposition. How can conservative transposition of the *Ac* element result in gene duplication? Can particular IS sequences behave in both ways?

2. Consider how the distinction between direct and inverted repeats is central to the recognition of insertion sequences. The insertion sequence itself contains inverted terminal repeats. Thus, inverted repeats are present as a part of the transposable element both before and after the insertion. On the other hand, the act of insertion results in a staggered cut in the host DNA. When the gaps are filled in after insertion, direct repeats will be generated flanking the inverted terminals of the transposable element. Indeed, insertion sequences have been identified by the presence of a pair of inverted repeats flanked by direct repeats. Using this logic, find the insertion sequence in the following single-stranded length of DNA.

CGTAGCCATTTGCGATATGCATCCGAATATCGCAAGCCATGCCA

3. How is antibiotic resistance spread by transposable elements in *E. coli*?

4. What are the similarities and differences between antibiotic resistance factors in *Shigella* and fertility factors in *E. coli*?

5. In *Drosophila*, hybrid dysgenesis results in the mobilization of transposable elements. This in turn results in progeny flies that have normal somatic cells but are sterile. Why is the somatic tissue unaffected and only the germ line affected? Males from three *Drosophila* strains recently isolated from wild populations in different geographical areas are crossed with females from the same M cytotype laboratory strain. In the first cross, 12 percent of the progeny are sterile. In the second, 64 percent of the progeny are sterile. In the third, 97 percent of the progeny are sterile. Generate a hypothesis to address why different degrees of sterility are seen in these three strains.

6. In what situations can a nonautonomous element behave as an autonomous element? Give specific examples in corn and *Drosophila*.

7. Following the mobilization of *Ty* elements in yeast, two mutants were recovered that affected the activity of enzyme X. One of these mutants lacked enzyme activity, and was a null mutation. The other mutant had three times as much enzyme activity. Both mutants had a *Ty* element inserted into the *X* gene. Generate an hypothesis to explain how this is possible.

8. What differences and similarities are there between transposable elements that utilize an RNA intermediate and those that do not?

9. What kinds of repetitive elements are SINEs and LINEs? Support for a hypothesis that a particular repetitive element is a transposon often comes by analyzing its DNA sequence for open reading frames that encode transposase-like products. In humans, Alu sequences do not encode any of the enzymes that are presumably needed for retro-transposition. What aspects of their structure suggest that they might be capable of retrotransposition? What evidence is there that Alu sequences are retrotransposons capable of moving via an RNA intermediate, much like the yeast *Ty* element?

10. How has understanding the basis for hybrid dysgenesis and the transposition of *P* elements allowed for the development of methods for DNA-mediated transformation of *Drosophila*? How are transformants selected for?

11. In humans, insertion of transposable elements has occasionally been associated with disease. An *L1* element inserted into the gene for blood clotting factor VIII resulted in hemophilia in two separate individuals. An Alu element insertion disrupted pre-mRNA processing at the gene for neurofibromatosis. In each case, the insertion was not in either of the affected individual's parents, and so appeared to be a result of an insertional event during the affected individual's lifetime. Given that each of these classes of elements represents a substantial fraction of moderately repetitive DNA, how likely is it that most spontaneous mutations in humans are due to insertional mutagenesis by L1 elements? If it is not very likely, why not?

Thought Questions for Media

After reviewing the media on the *iGenetics* CD-ROM, try to answer these questions.

1. Suppose two different transposable elements are mobilized and insert them-selves itself into two different genes. In Gene A, transposon IS1 inserts itself into the translated region. In Gene B, transposon IS2 inserts itself at a site 3 base pairs downstream of the TATA box, but before the start of the transcribed region.
   a. What similarities do you expect to find between the sequences of the transposable element inserted in each gene?
   b. In addition to the sequence of the transposable elements, what sequence alterations do you expect to find in the region near the site of insertion?

c. What features do the sequence alterations in *b* have and how do they arise?

d. How might the transposon insertions influence the functions of genes A and B? Are they similar or different? Why?

1. The experiment in the iActivity allowed you to demonstrate that Tn10 transposition is conservative. Does it allow you to infer whether Tn10 transposition proceeds through a DNA or RNA intermediate?

2. Suppose you performed an experiment similar to the one described in the iActivity to identify the mode of transposition of an uncharacterized transposon. You observe that none of the colonies exhibit any sectoring, and that they are either blue or white. After picking several blue and several white colonies, you use PCR to amplify the region surrounding the *donor* DNA in each colony. You sequence the PCR products, and compare the sequences to that of the molecules used to generate the heteroduplexes. What do you find, and how do you explain your findings?

SOLUTIONS TO TEXT PROBLEMS

20.1   Distinguish between prokaryotic insertion elements and transposons. How do composite transposons differ from noncomposite transposons?

Answer: Insertion elements (IS elements) are simpler in structure than transposons, and have a transposase gene flanked by perfect or nearly perfect inverted repeat sequences (IR sequences). The more complex transposable elements (Tn elements) exist in two forms, composite transposons and noncomposite transposons. Composite transposons have a central gene-bearing region flanked by IS elements. Transposition of these elements, and the genes they contain (e.g., genes for antibiotic resistance), occurs because of the function of the IS elements. Noncomposite transposons also contain genes, but do not terminate with IS elements. However, they do have inverted terminal repeated sequences that are required for transposition.

Both types of elements can integrate into target sites with which they have no homology, where they cause target-site duplications. The transposition of IS elements and composite transposons requires use of the host cell's replicative enzymes and the transposase encoded in the element. Noncomposite transposons can transpose by two different mechanisms. Tn3-like noncomposite transposons utilize a replicative transposition mechanism employing a cointegrate—a fusion between a transposable element and the recipient DNA. Genes within Tn3 code for the enzymes transposase and resolvase that are needed for its transposition. Tn10-like composite transposons can move by a conservative (nonreplicative) transposition.

Upon insertion, all of the elements can cause mutations by a number of different mechanisms, including disruption of a gene's coding sequence or regulatory region.

20.2   What properties do bacterial and eukaryotic transposable elements have in common?

Answer: The structure and, at a general level, the function of eukaryotic and prokaryotic transposable elements is very similar. For example, both Tn and *Ac* elements have genes within them, and have inverted repeats at their ends. Both prokaryotic and eukaryotic elements may affect gene function in a variety of different ways, depending on the element involved and how it integrates into or nearby a gene. The integration events of eukaryotic elements, like those of most prokaryotic transposable elements, involve nonhomologous recombination. Some eukaryotic elements, such as *Ty* elements in yeast, and retrotransposons, move via an RNA intermediate, unlike the IS and Tn prokaryotic elements.

20.3   An IS element became inserted into the *lacZ* gene of *E. coli*. Later, a small deletion occurred in this gene, which removed 40 base pairs, starting to the left of the IS element. Ten *lacZ* base pairs were removed, including the left copy of the target site, and the 30 leftmost base pairs of the IS element were removed. What will be the consequence of this deletion?

Answer: The left inverted repeat of the IS element has been removed, so that the 2 ends of this IS element are no longer homologous. The element will not be able to move out of this location and insert into another site.

20.4   Although the detailed mechanisms by which transposable elements transpose differ widely, some features underlying transposition are shared. Examine the shared and different features by answering the following questions.
   a. Use an example to illustrate different transposition mechanisms that require
       i.   DNA replication of the element
       ii. no DNA replication of the element
       iii. an RNA intermediate
   b. What evidence is there that the inverted or direct terminal repeat sequences found in transposable elements are essential for transposition?
   c. Do all transposable elements generate a target site duplication after insertion?

Answer:
   a. i. The transposon Tn*3* is a transposable element whose transposition requires its DNA replication. Its transposition is illustrated in the cointegration model shown in Figure 20.6. When the donor DNA containing the transposable element fuses with the recipient DNA, the transposable element becomes duplicated, with one copy located at each junction between the donor and recipient DNA. After this cointegrate is resolved into two products, each has one copy of the transposable element.

ii. The bacterial Tn*10* element and the corn *Ac* element transpose without DNA replication using conservative transposition. After transposition, the element is lost from its original site of insertion.

iii. *Ty* elements in yeast and *copia* elements in *Drosophila* transpose by an RNA intermediate. After synthesis of an RNA copy of the integrated DNA sequence, reverse transcription results in a new element that integrates at a new chromosomal location.

b. Evidence that the inverted or direct terminal repeats found in transposable elements are essential for their transposition comes from the observation that mutations altering these sequences eliminate the ability of an element to transpose. These sequences are recognized by transposase during a transposition event.

c. Yes.

20.5   In addition to single gene mutations caused by the insertion of transposable elements, the frequency of chromosomal aberrations such as deletions or inversions can be increased when transposable elements are present. How?

Answer: Deletions, inversions, and translocations can occur when homologous recombination occurs between two identical transposons inserted in different locations in the genome. The production of deletions and inversions is illustrated in Figure 20.9. If two transposons are inserted in the same orientation in one chromosome, pairing and homologous recombination between them results in a deletion of the segment lying between them. If two transposons are inserted in an opposite orientation in one chromosome, pairing and homologous recombination between them results in an inversion of the segment lying between them. If two transposons are inserted in different chromosomes, pairing and homologous recombination between them will result in a reciprocal translocation. Whether the translocation results in two single-centromere chromosomes or in a dicentric and acentric chromosome will depend on the orientation and position of the elements relative to their respective centromeres.

20.6   An understanding of the molecular structures of *Ac* and *Ds* elements, together with an understanding of the basis for their transposition, has allowed for a clearer, molecular-based interpretation of Barbara McClintock's observations. Ponder the significance of this on the acceptance of her work, and use your understanding of transposition of *Ac* and *Ds* elements in corn to propose an explanation for the following.

Two different true-breeding strains of corn with colorless kernels A and B are crossed with each of two different true-breeding strains with purple kernels C and D.

The F₁ from each cross is selfed, with the following results:

P:	A × C	A × D
F_1:	all purple	all purple
F_2:	3 purple:1 colorless	3 purple:1 colorless

P:	B × C	B × D
F_1:	all purple	all purple
F_2:	3 purple:1 spotted*	3 purple:1 colorless

*spotted = kernels with purple spots in a colorless background

Answer:

a. As is described in Figure 20.11, the spotted-kernel phenotype arises from the transposition of *Ds* elements (incomplete transposons incapable of transposition themselves) out of the *C* gene during kernel development. This means that the mutation in colorless strain B is caused by an insertion of a *Ds* element in the *C* gene. It is able to transpose because the purple strain C has *Ac* elements, full-length transposons, that can activate *Ds* transposition.

Since spotted kernels are not seen in any of the other crosses, transposition of *Ds* elements is not occurring in them. There are two different explanations for this. Since spotted kernels are not seen in the A × C cross, the colorless phenotype in strain A is not caused by the insertion of a *Ds* element. (It could, for example, just be a point mutation in the *C* gene.) Since spotted kernels are not seen in the B × D cross, the D strain lacks *Ac* elements. For these reasons, the crosses A × C, A × D, and B × D all show only expected Mendelian patterns of inheritance.

20.7 A geneticist was studying glucose metabolism in yeast and deduced both the normal structure of the enzyme glucose-6-phosphatase (G6Pase) and the DNA sequence of its coding region. She was using a wild-type strain called A to study another enzyme for many generations when she noticed a morphologically peculiar mutant had arisen from one of the strain A cultures. She grew the mutant up into a large stock and found that the defect in this mutant involved a markedly reduced G6Pase activity. She isolated the G6Pase protein from these mutant cells and found that it was present in normal amounts but had an abnormal structure. The N-terminal 70 percent of the protein was normal. The C-terminal 30 percent was present but altered in sequence by a frameshift reflecting the insertion of 1 base pair, and the N-terminal 70 percent and the C-terminal 30 percent were separated by 111 new amino acids unrelated to normal G6Pase. These amino acids represented predominantly the AT rich codons (Phe, Leu, Asn, Lys, Ile, Tyr). There were also two extra amino acids added at the C-terminal end. Explain these results.

Answer: The extra 111 amino acids plus the one base-pair shift indicates that 334 base pairs were inserted into the G6Pase structural gene. This is the size of a "delta dropping." That is, this is consistent with an initial *Ty* transposition into the

G6Pase gene that was followed by recombination between the two deltas. Recombination between the two deltas would excise the *Ty* element but leave a delta dropping behind in the G6Pase gene. The delta elements are 334 base pairs long, and are 70 percent AT, the characteristics of the inserted sequence. If the delta element were positioned so that it would be translated and not generate a stop codon, it would yield 111 amino acids and one extra base pair, which would cause the frameshift. The two extra amino acids at the C-terminal end of G6Pase were added presumably because the frameshift did not allow the normal termination codon to be read.

20.8   Consider two theoretical yeast transposons, A and B. Each contains an intron. Each transposes to a new location in the yeast genome and then is examined for the presence of the intron. In the new locations, you find that A has no intron, but B does. What can you conclude about the mechanisms of transposon movement for A and B from these facts?

Answer: Since introns are spliced out only at the RNA level, a transposition event that results in the loss of an intron (such as that used by *Ty* elements) indicates that the transposition occurred via an RNA intermediate. Thus, A is likely to move via an RNA intermediate. The lack of intron removal during B transposition suggests that it uses a DNA→DNA transposition mechanism (either conservative or replicative, or some other mechanism).

20.9   When certain strains of *Drosophila melanogaster* are crossed, hybrid dysgenesis can result in mutations, chromosomal aberrations, and sterility. A curious feature of hybrid dysgenesis is that it has been seen when females from certain laboratory strains (M cytotype) are mated to males from wild populations (P cytotype), but not when males from the same laboratory strains are mated to females from wild populations.
   a. What occurs during the development of the F_1 hybrids to cause hybrid dysgenesis?
   b. Why does it occur only in F_1 hybrids from M females × P males, and not in F_1 hybrids from P females × M males?
   c. Why does hybrid dysgenesis affect only the F_1 germ line and not F_1 somatic cells?
   d. Some strains of P cytotype males are more potent at causing hybrid dysgenesis than others. Why might this be the case?
   e. How might you test your explanation in (c)? Assume that you have a plasmid vector with an intact *P* element cloned into it.

Answer:
   a. The mobilization of *P* elements within the germ line of the F_1 results in a large number of chromosomal breaks and *P* element insertions. These result in mutations (insertions that affect gene function) and chromosomal aberrations (see

answer to problem 20.5) in the gametes of the F_1, and which affect the phenotypes of the F_2. If the number of chromosome breaks is high enough, there will be sterility in the F_1.

b. In a cross of M females × P males, P males contribute chromosomes bearing *P* elements to an M cytotype. Since the M cytotype lacks a repressor, the *P* elements mobilize, causing hybrid dysgenesis. In the reciprocal cross, *P* elements remain in a P cytotype (contributed by the P female), where repressor exists, and therefore mobilization of *P* elements is repressed.

c. *P* element transposition is restricted to the germ line, and does not occur in somatic cells. (This occurs because transposase is produced only in germ-line cells due to the alternative splicing of the transposase pre-mRNA in germ-line cells.)

d. The degree of hybrid dysgenesis that is seen could be due to the number of intact *P* elements in the strain. The mobilization of a greater number of *P* elements would result in more chromosomal damage, and cause a greater degree of hybrid dysgenesis.

e. A genomic Southern blot analysis would assess the number of intact *P* elements in a strain. Isolate genomic DNA from a set of strains, cleave it with a restriction enzyme that does not cut within a *P* element, and separate the fragments by size using agarose gel electrophoresis. Blot the size-separated DNA to a membrane, and allow the DNA bound to the membrane to hybridize to a labeled probe made from the cloned *P* element DNA. Detect the sites that bind to the probe. Determine the number of different-sized fragments bound by the probe to estimate the number of *P* elements in the strain. Then determine whether there is a correlation between the number of *P* elements in a strain and the degree of hybrid dysgenesis it shows.

20.10 In the experiment described in Figure 20.18, a wild-type ry^+ (*rosy*$^+$) gene was introduced into a strain homozygous for a mutant *ry* allele by using *P* element-mediated gene transformation.

a. If a transformed male was mated to an M strain female (see Q20.8), would you expect the *P* element construct used in the experiment to transpose to another site in the genome of the F_1?

b. If a transformed male was mated to a P strain female (see Q20.8), would you expect the *P* element construct used in the experiment to transpose to another site in the genome of the F_1?

c. Crosses of transformed flies to well-defined laboratory strains are more often useful for experimentation than crosses to animals from wild populations. Based on your answers to (a) and (b), what problems could arise from using transformants obtained by the approach in Figure 20.18?

Answer:

a. Since the transformed male would be transmitting *P* elements into an M cytotype that lacks a repressor, there would be additional transposition events.

b. In a P cytotype, transposition is repressed. No additional transposition events would occur.

c. The answers to (a) and (b) suggest that it may be a problem to maintain stable lines of P elements in an M cytotype. This has been circumvented in two ways. First, backcrossing transformed lines repeatedly into strains having a P cytotype will result in animals with sufficient amounts of repressor that a stable line can be maintained. However, crosses must be done with other P cytotype strains or in one direction, P female × M male.

Second, methods have been developed to target DNA for insertion without linking the DNA to the gene for transposase, which is provided separately. In this method, two DNA segments are simultaneously injected into embryos. One DNA segment contains the gene for transposase, but itself is unable to be inserted into the genome (due to a lack of the 31-bp inverted repeats found in P elements; see Figure 20.17. The other DNA segment contains the gene targeted for insertion flanked by the 31-bp inverted repeats required for transposition by transposase.

20.11   After the discovery that P elements could be used to develop transformation vectors in *Drosophila melanogaster*, attempts were made to use them for the development of germ-line transformation in several different insect species. Recently, Savakis and his colleagues succeeded in using a different transposable element found in *Drosophila*, the *Minos* element, to develop germ-line transformation for both *Drosophila melanogaster* and the medfly, *Ceratitus capitata*, a major agricultural pest present in Mediterranean climates.

a. What is the value of developing a transformation vector for an insect pest?

b. What basic information about the *Minos* element would need to be gathered before it could be used for germ-line transformation?

Answer:

a. The ability to modify a pest species genetically may provide a means to develop better strategies for pest control. For insects harboring parasites that affect human and animal populations (e.g., mosquitoes that are hosts to malaria), the ability to modify the insect host genetically may provide a means to influence the reproduction of a human or animal pathogen.

b. By analogy with the information used to develop P element-mediated transformation in *Drosophila*, it is essential to understand the mode of transposition of the element and to have identified the essential features of the element that allow it to transpose (the nature of the transposase and its regulation, the sequences the transposase recognizes to mediate transposition, etc.).

21

CHROMOSOMAL MUTATIONS

CHAPTER OUTLINE

TYPES OF CHROMOSOMAL MUTATIONS
VARIATIONS IN CHROMOSOME STRUCTURE
    Deletion
    Duplication
    Inversion
    Translocation
    Position Effect
    Fragile Sites and Fragile X Syndrome
VARIATIONS IN CHROMOSOME NUMBER
    Changes in One or a Few Chromosomes
    Changes in Complete Sets of Chromosomes

REVIEW OF KEY TERMS, SYMBOLS, AND CONCEPTS

In your own words, write a brief, precise definition of each term in the groups below.
Check your definitions using the text. Then, develop a concept map using the terms in each
list.

1	2
chromosomal mutation, aberration	euploid
deletion	aneuploid
duplication	polyploid
translocation	diploid
inversion	haploid
position effect	nullisomy
karyotype	monosomy
polytene chromosomes, bands and interbands	trisomy
pseudodominance	tetrasomy
terminal tandem, reverse tandem duplication	autopolyploidy
multigene family	allopolyploidy
unequal crossing-over	allotetraploid
pericentric vs. paracentric inversion	odd-number polyploidy
dicentric bridge, acetric fragment	even-number polyploidy

1	2
intra-, interchromosomal translocation	chromosome
reciprocal vs. nonreciprocal translocation	centromere
alternate, adjacent-1, adjacent-2 segregation	distal to/from
semisterility	promixal to/from
fragile sites	p,q arms
triplet repeat amplification	Down syndrome
cri-du-chat syndrome	Patau syndrome
Prader-Willi syndrome	Edwards syndrome
Drosophila Bar mutation	Turner syndrome
Philadelphia chromosome	Klinefelter syndrome
Burkitt's lymphoma	familial Down syndrome
chronic myelogenous leukemia	Robertsonian translocation
oncogenes, c-abl, c-myc	
fragile X syndrome	
FMR-1	

THINKING ANALYTICALLY

In this chapter, it is crucial to be able to visualize the physical structure of chromosomes in the context of cellular processes such as meiosis and gene expression. Start by developing mental images of chromosomal aberrations: practice drawing inversions, transpositions, translocations, duplications and deletions.

In order to fully understand the impact of chromosomal mutations on gene expression and inheritance of traits, you will need a solid grasp of cellular processes involving chromosome movement. Review how chromosomes move and align during meiosis. Then consider how chromosomal aberrations and mutations affecting chromosome number alter the behavior of chromosomes during meiosis and thereby affect the inheritance of traits. The disruptions in meiosis that result from a particular chromosomal aberrations are best understood by drawing out the chromosomal mutation as it proceeds through meiosis. As you do the problems, take the time to draw out the consequences of crossing-over in inversion and translocation heterozygotes. To understand how chromosome aberrations affect gene expression and gene function, consider what happens when the structure of a gene is rearranged, and broken into two separate parts by a chromosomal aberration. Ask yourself - What are the possible consequences if a rearrangement breakpoint is in the amino-acid coding region of the gene, if it is in the promoter or other regulatory region, if it rearranges the gene nearby the enhancer of a different gene, or, if it fuses two unrelated genes in their intronic regions?

Aneuploidy and polyploidy have direct effects on gene dosage: a normal phenotype requires proper gene dosage. As you examine the consequences of different types of aneuploidy and polyploidy, consider how the different phenotypes that arise result from altering gene dosage.

QUESTIONS FOR PRACTICE

Multiple Choice Questions

1. The number of polytene chromosomes in dipterans, such as *Drosophila*, is characteristically
   a. twice the diploid number.
   b. hundreds or more times the diploid number.
   c. half the diploid number.
   d. the same as the diploid number.

2. The chromosomes that become polytene chromosomes are
   a. somatically paired.
   b. genetically inert.
   c. uniformly pycnotic.
   d. acentric.

3. Nonhomologous chromosomes that have exchanged segments are the products of a
   a. double deletion.
   b. reciprocal translocation.
   c. pericentric inversion.
   d. paracentric inversion.

4. The abbreviated karyotype, 2N - 1, describes
   a. nullisomy.
   b. monosomy.
   c. trisomy.
   d. haploidy.

5. The abbreviated karyotype, 2N + 1 + 1, describes
   a. double trisomy.
   b. tetrasomy.
   c. double monosomy.
   d. none of these.

6. All known monosomics in humans have been
   a. lethal.
   b. semi-lethal.
   c. treatable.
   d. deletion heterozygotes.

7. The cultivated bread wheat, *Triticum aestivum*, although a polyploid, is fertile because it
   a. has an odd number of chromosome sets.
   b. has an even multiple of chromosome sets.
   c. is a double hybrid.
   d. is propagated by grafting.

8. Cultivated bananas and Baldwin apples are
   a. double diploids.
   b. tetraploids.

   c. double haploids.

   d. triploids.

9. Down syndrome is associated with

   a. an inversion.

   b. a Robertsonian translocation.

   c. trisomy-21.

   d. both b and c.

10. Gene expression can be altered by

   a. an inversion.

   b. a duplication.

   c. a transposition.

   d. any of the above.

Answers: 1c; 2a; 3b; 4b; 5a; 6a; 7b; 8d; 9d; 10d.

Thought Questions

1. Identify and describe five examples of changes in chromosome structure that alter gene expression.

2. A chromosomal inversion in the heterozygous condition seems to act as a suppressor of crossing-over. Why might this be the case? How might such chromosomes be important for keeping a laboratory stock of three linked recessive mutations?

3. What are two modes by which Down syndrome can be caused? Why might one be more frequent than the other? If a normal female has a sibling with Down syndrome, what information would be critical in the assessment of the chances that she might have a Down syndrome child? How would the assessment be different if the assessed individual were a normal male with a Down syndrome sibling?

4. Consider the data presented in Table 21.2. Given this data, how do account for the fact that most children with Down syndrome are born to women under 25 years of age? Does this alter the need for caution and prenatal diagnosis in women over 35 years of age?

5. How do you account for the fact that polyploidy is significantly more common in plants than in animals? (Hint: What basic difference between sexual and asexual reproduction might be significant here?)

6. What might be the significance of the following in the evolutionary process of speciation? (1) autopolyploidy, (2) allopolyploidy, (3) inversions, (4) translocations. Provide an explanation that considers how animals might be affected differently than plants.

7. Chromosomal rearrangements such as inversions and translocations are sometimes associated with dominant or recessive phenotypes. How might such phenotypes be related to a "position effect"?

8. Consider the nature of a position effect, and offer a hypothesis as to why triplet repeats, such as those found in fragile X syndrome and Huntington disease, might only

result in an abnormal phenotype when a threshold number of triplet repeats is exceeded.

9. Many small deletions, when heterozygous, display a normal phenotype. Others display a mutant phenotype. For example, a small deletion that removes just the *Notch* gene in *Drosophila*, when heterozygous with a normal chromosome, displays a mutant phenotype of notched (nicked) wings. A nearby deletion that removes just the *white* gene, when heterozygous with a normal chromosome, displays the wild-type phenotype of deep-red eyes. Speculate why some heterozygous deletions might show a phenotype while others do not.

10. Which, if any, of the chromosomal aberrations discussed in this chapter are able to rever to a normal phenotype?

Thought Questions for Media

After reviewing the media on the *iGenetics* CD-ROM, try to answer these questions.

 After viewing the *Crossing Over in an Inversion Heterozygote* animation, consider the following two situations.

I. No crossovers occur in the inverted region of a pericentric inversion in an inversion heterozygote.

II. A single crossover occurs in the inverted region of a pericentric inversion in an inversion heterozygote.

1. Are different types of *viable* gametes produced in these two situations?
    a. Are the ratios of different types of *viable* gametes produced in these situations the same or different?
    b. Are *inviable* gametes produced in either of these situations? If so, how are they produced and why are they inviable?

2. In the *Meiosis in a Translocation Heterozygote* animation, the chromosomes in a reciprocal translocation heterozygote were depicted as N_1, N_2, T_1, and T_2. N_1 and N_2 were the normal ordered, nonhomologous chromosomes. T_1 and T_2 were the chromosomes in which a reciprocal translocation occurred. N_1 and T_1 have homologous centromeres, as do N_2 and T_2. In the animation, homologous regions of these chromosomes paired during Meiosis I and aligned in a cross-like figure. They were arranged with N_1 in the upper left-hand corner, N_2 in the lower right-hand corner, T_1 in the lower left-hand corner, and T_2 in the upper right-hand corner, as follows

$$N_1 \qquad T_2$$
$$T_1 \qquad N_2$$

Use this illustration as you answer the following questions.

a. The animation illustrated three different patterns of segregation of these chromosomes during Meiosis I called alternate, adjacent-1 and adjacent-2 segregation. Which chromosomes go to each pole in the different types of segregation?

   b. Which two types of segregation are most frequent? Which one type of segregation is rare?
   c. Which type(s) of segregation pattern produces balanced gametes? Which type(s) produces inviable gametes?
   d. Why are individuals with a reciprocal translocation semi-sterile?

1. Suppose Sonia and Ramon conceive a fetus that has the T(14;21) translocation. Can you tell, from this information alone, whether the child will have Down syndrome or be healthy? If not, what additional information about the karyotype would you need to know? If the child has Down syndrome, what can you infer about the chromosomes carried by the sperm used in fertilization?
2. Suppose Sonia and Ramon, having had one normal child, are interested in having a second child. They seek genetic counseling for advice. What advice should the counselor give them, and how, if at all, would it differ from any advice they might have received when attempting to have their first child?
3. What is the chance that Sonia and Ramon have a child with the same karyotype as Ramon? With the same karyotype as Sonia?

SOLUTIONS TO TEXT PROBLEMS

21.1   A normal chromosome has the following gene sequence:

$$A\ B\ C\ D\ E\ F\ G\ H$$

Determine the chromosomal mutation illustrated by each of the following chromosomes:

   a. $A\ B\ C\ F\ E\ \ D\ G\ H$
   b. $A\ D\ \ E\ F\ B\ C\ G\ H$
   c. $A\ B\ C\ D\ \ E\ F\ E\ F\ G\ H$
   d. $A\ B\ C\ D\ \ E\ F\ F\ E\ G\ H$
   e. $A\ B\ D\ \ E\ F\ G\ H$

Answer:
   a. pericentric inversion [inversion of D –(centromere) – E – F]
   b. nonreciprocal translocation [B – C moved from left to right arm]
   c. tandem duplication [E – F duplicated]
   d. reverse tandem duplication [E – F duplicated]
   e. deletion [C deleted]

21.2   Distinguish between pericentric and paracentric inversions.

Answer: A pericentric inversion is an inversion that includes the centromere, while a paracentric inversion is an inversion that is wholly within one chromosomal arm. See text Figure 21.9.

21.3   Very small deletions behave in some instances like recessive mutations.Why are some recessive mutations known not to be deletions?

Answer: Deletions, whether just a few bases or large segments of DNA, are unable to be reverted. Point mutations that affect only a single base can be reverted. If a recessive mutation is able to be reverted to a wild-type phenotype, it cannot be a deletion.

21.4   What would be the effect on protein structure if a small inversion were to occur within the amino acid-coding region of a gene?

Answer: In answering this question, it is important to keep in mind that DNA is composed of two strands that have opposite polarity (one is 5' to 3', the other 3' to 5'), and that the transcription of DNA into RNA always proceeds so that the RNA transcript is synthesized in the 5' to 3' direction using a 3' to 5' template strand. The sequence of bases in the mRNA transcript are then read as a triplet code and translated into an amino acid sequence.

There are several possible consequences of an inversion in the DNA of a single gene, all of them serious. This is because the polarity of DNA must be maintained to obtain the correct reading frame in the mRNA. Within the region of an inversion, the bases of the nontemplate strand of DNA would be inserted in the template strand (try drawing this out).After the DNA is transcribed, the mRNA transcript will be decoded during translation. The region of the transcript originating from the inverted region will encode an amino acid sequence that is quite different from the normal, uninverted region, and may have possible nonsense codons (translation termination signals) within it. Consequently, a nonfunctional or truncated protein may be produced.

21.5   Inversions are known to affect crossing-over. The following homologs with the indicated gene order are given (the filled and open circles are homologous centromeres):

A B C D E

A D C B E

a. Diagram the alignment of these chromosomes during meiosis.
b. Diagram the results of a single crossover between homologous genes B and C in the inversion.
c. Considering the position of the centromere, what is this sort of inversion called?

Answer:

a.

b. A crossover between B and C results in the following chromosomes:

    ●$\underline{A \ B \ C \ D \ E}$ (normal order)

    ●$\underline{A \quad B \quad C \quad D \quad A}$○ (dicentric, duplication for A, deletion for E)

    $\underline{E \quad B \quad C \quad D \quad E}$ (acentric, duplication for E, deletion for A)

    ○$\underline{A \quad D \quad C \quad B \quad E}$ (inverted order)

c. Paracentric inversion, because the centromere is not included in the inverted DNA segment.

21.6   Single crossovers within the inversion loop of inversion heterozygotes give rise to chromatids with duplications and deletions. What happens if, within the inversion loop, there is a two-strand double crossover in such an inversion heterozygote when the centromere is outside the inversion loop?

Answer: If a two-strand double crossover occurs within a paracentric inversion, the four products of meiosis have a complete set of genes, without duplications or deletions. No acentric or dicentric fragments are formed. Consequently, all four meiotic products are viable. This is illustrated in the following example:

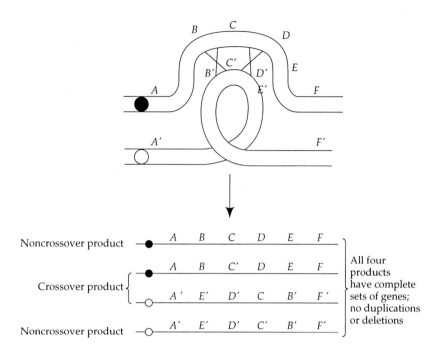

Noncrossover product — A B C D E F

Crossover product { A B C' D E F

A' E' D' C B' F'

Noncrossover product — A' E' D' C' B' F'

All four products have complete sets of genes; no duplications or deletions

21.7 An inversion heterozygote possesses one chromosome with genes in the normal order:

a b c d e f g h

It also contains one chromosome with genes in the inverted order:

a b f e d c g h

A four-strand double crossover occurs in the areas $e-f$ and $c-d$. Diagram and label the four strands at synapsis (showing the crossovers) and at the first meiotic anaphase.

Answer: Diagrammed below is a four-strand double crossover, where the crossover between *c* and *d* involves strands 2 and 4, and the crossover between *e* and *f* involves strands 1 and 3. The bridge strands will break at anaphase I as the centromeres move toward opposite poles of the cell.

Synapsis:

First Anaphase:

$\begin{matrix}1\\2\end{matrix}$ ● $\;a\;\;\;b\;\;\;c\;\;\;d^{\blacksquare}\;e^{\blacksquare}\;f'\;\;b'\;a'$ O $\begin{matrix}3\\4\end{matrix}$ double dicentric

$\quad\quad a\;\;\;b\;\;\;c\;\;\;d'\;\;e'\;\;f'\;\;b'\;a'$

$\quad\quad h\;\;\;g\;\;\;f\;\;\;e\;\;\;d\;\;\;c'\;\;g'\;\;h'$

$\quad\quad h\;\;\;g\;\;\;f\;\;\;e'\;\;d'\;\;c'\;\;g'\;\;h'$ acentric fragments

21.8   The following gene arrangements in a particular chromosome are found in *Drosophila* populations in different geographic regions. Assuming that the arrangement in part (a) is the original arrangement, in what sequence did the various inversion types probably arise?

a. *A B C D E F G H I*   d. *A B F C G H E D I*

b. *H E F B A G C D I*   e. *A B F E H G C D I*

c. *A B F E D C G H I*

Answer: One can envision a series of inversions occurring in the following sequence:

$$a \;\rightarrow\; c \;\rightarrow\; e \;\rightarrow\; d$$
$$\downarrow$$
$$b$$

The regions inverted in each step are illustrated below.

a. *A B C D E F G H I*

c. *A B F E D C G H I*

e. *A B F E H G C D I*

b. *H E F B A G C D I*   d. *A B F C G H E D I*

21.9   Human abnormalities associated with chromosomal mutations often exhibit a range of symptoms, of which only some subsets are shown in a particular individual. Recombinant 8 [Rec(8)] syndrome is an inherited chromosomal abnormality found primarily in individuals of Hispanic origin. Phenotypic characteristics associated with the syndrome can include congenital heart disease, urinary system abnormalities, eye abnormalities, hearing loss, and abnormal muscle tone. Most reported cases of Rec(8) have been found in the offspring of phenotypically normal parents who are heterozygous for an inversion of chromosome 8 with breakpoints at p23.1 and q22.1. Individuals with Rec(8) syndrome typically have a duplication of part of 8q (from q22.1 to the terminus of the q arm) and a deletion of 8p (from p23.1 to the terminus of the p arm).

a. Using diagrams, explain why individuals with Rec(8) syndrome typically have a duplication and a deletion for part of chromosome 8.

b. An individual is heterozygous for an inversion on chromosome 8 with breakpoints at p23.1 and q22.1. What is the chance, if a crossover occurs within the inverted region during a particular meiosis, that the resulting offspring will have Rec(8) syndrome?

c. Why might the phenotypes of Rec(8) individuals vary?

d. A child with some of the symptoms of Rec(8) syndrome is referred to a human geneticist. The karyotype of the child reveals heterozygosity for a large pericentric inversion in chromosome 8 with breakpoints at p23.1 and q22.1. Cytogenetic analysis of her phenotypically normal mother and maternal grandmother reveals a similar karyotype. According to the child's mother, the father has a normal phenotype, but he is unavailable for examination. Propose at least two explanations for why the child, but not her mother or maternal grandmother, is affected with some of the symptoms of Rec(8) syndrome.(Hint: Consider the limitations of karyotype analysis using G-banding methods and what is unknown about the father.)

Answer:

a. The chromosomal abnormalities associated with Rec(8) syndrome most often include an 8q22.1 to 8q–terminus (8q-ter) duplication and an 8p23.1 to 8p–terminus (8p-ter) deletion. Since parents of Rec(8) individuals are heterozygous for a pericentric inversion with breakpoints at 8p23.1 and 8q22.1, their 8q–duplication and 8p-deletion most likely arose from a single crossover within the pericentric inversion. Such an event is diagrammed in text Fig. 21.11.

b. As shown in text Fig. 21.11, if a single crossover occurs between two nonsister chromatids in an inversion heterozygote, two of the products will have the non-crossover chromosomes (one with the normal-ordered chromosome and one with the inversion chromosome) and two of the products will be duplication/deletion products. Here, one of these products (that having a duplication for 8q22.1 to 8q-ter, and a deletion for 8p23.1 to 8p-ter) will contribute to a viable zygote with Rec(8) syndrome.The other product (that having a deletion for 8p22.1 to 8p-ter, and a duplication for 8p23.1 to 8p-ter) is not discussed in the problem. It may be that if it is contributed to a zygote, the zygote will not survive. Then, of the surviving zygotes, 1/3 will have Rec(8) syndrome and 2/3 will be normal. One-half of the normal zygotes will have the chromosome 8 inversion.

c. The phenotypes of Rec(8) individuals could vary for one, or a combination, of reasons.

   i. There could be variation in the precise location of the inversion breakpoints in the parents of Rec(8) individuals, leading to differences in the genes that are duplicated and deleted in Rec(8) individuals. That is, there may be several different chromosome 8 inversions in the population that have breakpoints in the vicinity of 8q22.1 and 8p23.1.When single crossovers occur in inversion heterozygotes, the progeny would have different degrees of aneuploidy. This could result in different symptoms. In addition, slight variation in the precise location of the breakpoints could lead to gene activation or gene inactivation in different regions of chromosome 8.

ii. The genetic background in which the duplication and deletions are found could vary. That is, the addition or subtraction of a subset of genes could have different effects, depending on the genetic interactions between the genes present in three copies or one copy and other genes in the genome. For example, if there were genetic interactions between a key duplicated/deleted gene and another gene in the genome, allelic differences in either gene could strongly affect the phenotype seen. In this case, alleles inherited from the father that are different from those inherited from the mother and grandmother could contribute to the phenotype.

iii. There could be environmental effects that exacerbate the effects of the deleted and duplicated region. Since these effects are not uniform in the population of Rec(8) individuals, these could contribute to the observed phenotypic variability. Environment is used in a broad sense here to include the conditions present during fetal development, as many of the symptoms associated with Rec(8) syndrome are developmental abnormalities.

iv. There may be other, cytologically invisible mutations associated with the Rec(8) individuals. The presence or absence of additional mutations could strongly affect the phenotype.

d. Since the child has the chromosome 8 inversion, but not the duplication/deletion chromosome that results from a single crossover in an inversion heterozygote, she is an atypical Rec(8) individual. There are several explanations for why some of her symptoms overlap with those of Rec(8) syndrome. She may have an additional mutation near one of the Rec(8) breakpoints, in a region that is duplicated or deleted in Rec(8) syndrome, or in a gene that interacts with genes in the duplicated or deleted regions. Alternatively, it is possible that the inversion disrupts the function of a gene or genes at one or both breakpoints, and that normally, the inversion is an asymptomatic condition. In this case, the inversion chromosome (in her mother and grandmother) would bear a recessive mutation. If she had a new allelic mutation, or her paternally contributed chromosome had an allelic mutation, she would be affected. This could also explain why she has only some of the symptoms of Rec(8) syndrome; she would have fewer genes affected than most Rec(8) individuals.

Small deletions would be cytologically invisible, as would point mutations. Thus, the explanations given above could not be evaluated by karyotype analysis.FISH, STS, and/or DNA sequence analyses (see text Chapter 9) could to be used to evaluate the integrity of the chromosomal regions near the breakpoints.

21.10 A particular plant species that had been subjected to radiation for a long time in order to produce chromosome mutations was then inbred for many generations until it was homozygous for all of these mutations. It was then crossed to the original unirradiated plant, and the meiotic process of the F_1 hybrids was examined. It was noticed that the following structures occurred, at low frequency, in anaphase I of the hybrid: a cell with a dicentric chromosome (bridge) and a fragment.

a. What kind of chromosome mutation occurred in the irradiated plant? In your answer, indicate where the centromeres are.

b. Explain in words and with a clear diagram where crossover(s) occurred, and how the bridge chromosome of the cell arose.

Answer:

a. The irradiated chromosome has a paracentric inversion, with an inversion within one of its arms. Dicentric chromosomes and fragments arise as the result of single crossovers within paracentric inversions, and dicentric chromosomes with two bridges and two fragments result from a four-strand double crossover within paracentric inversions. An example of such a chromosome is diagrammed below.

b. The bridge chromosome would arise by a single crossover within an inversion loop during meiosis. In the above example, the crossover would occur between d and i. See text Figure 21.10b for an illustration of such a crossover.

21.11   On a normal-ordered chromosome, two loci a and b lie 15 map units apart on the left arm of a metacentric chromosome. A third locus, c, lies 10 map units to the right of b on the right arm of the chromosome. What frequency of progeny phenotypes do you expect to see in a testcross of an $a\ b\ c/a^+\ b^+\ c^+$ individual if the $a^+\ b^+\ c^+$ chromosome:

a. has a normal order?

b. has an inversion with breakpoints just proximal (towards the centromere) to a and just distal (away from the centromere) to b?

c. has an inversion with breakpoints just proximal to a and just proximal to c?

d. has an inversion with breakpoints just distal to a and just distal to c?

Answer: Since the crosses are three-point testcrosses, the progeny phenotypes are specified by the genotypes of the gametes of the trihybrid parent. In each case, it helps to diagram the two chromosomes of the trihybrid and then consider the different types of gametes that can be produced by crossovers in the trihybrid parent. Since an inversion is present in parts b, c, and d, some recombinant gametes will not be viable due to the aneuploidy that results when crossovers occur within the inverted region. As discussed below, this will alter the proportions of gamete genotypes relative to those seen in trihybrids with normal-ordered chromosomes.

a. The chromosomes can be diagrammed as:

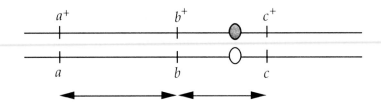

The trihybrid has no inversion, and its gametes will be exactly those expected from a trihybrid testcross. Since there are 15 mu between a and b, and 10 mu between b and c, 15% of the gametes will be single or double recombinants with crossovers between a and b, and 10% of the gametes will be single or double recombinants with crossovers between b and c. The remaining $[100 - (10 + 15)] = 75\%$ of the gametes will be parental types. This gives a frequency of 37.5% each of $a^+\ b^+\ c^+$ and $a\ b\ c$. Assuming that there is no interference, the expected frequency of double recombinants in the a–c interval is $0.10 \times 0.15 = 0.015$, or 1.5%.This gives a frequency of 0.75% each of $a^+\ b\ c^+$ and $a\ b^+\ c$. The remaining recombinants will result from single crossovers. There will be $15 - (1.5/2) = 14.25\%$ single recombinants in the a–b interval, giving 7.125% each of $a^+\ b\ c$ and $a\ b^+\ c^+$.There will be $10 - (1.5/2) = 9.25\%$ single recombinants in the b–c interval, giving 4.625% each of $a^+\ b^+\ c$ and $a\ b\ c^+$.

b. Here, nearly the entire region between a^+ and b^+ is inverted. The chromosomes can be diagrammed as indicated below, using a thick line with an open-headed arrowhead to represent the inverted region.

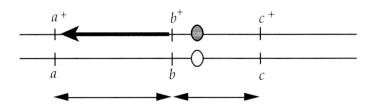

The inverted region is a paracentric inversion. As shown in text Figure 21.10, a single crossover within a paracentric inversion results in a dicentric bridge that produces deletion-bearing chromosomes. Gametes that receive these chromosomes are not viable.If this region were not inverted, nearly 15% of the gametes would be recombinant for the a–b interval. However, because of the inversion, these recombinants will not be recovered.As a consequence, the frequency of the remaining recombinant and parental gametes will not be the same as these gamete types in a trihybrid parent with normal-ordered chromosomes. Relative to a trihybrid parent with normal-ordered chromosomes, the frequency of the remaining recombinant and parental gametes will be increased by a factor of $[1/(1.00 - 0.15)] = 1.176$.

The only viable recombinant gametes from this trihybrid parent are those that result from crossovers between b and c. In a normal-ordered chromosome, since there are 10 mu between b and c, 10% of the gametes will be recombinant in this interval. Since 15% of the gametes are not seen in this trihybrid parent, there will be 1.176 x 10% = 11.76% recombinants in the *b–c* interval. The remaining gametes [1.176 x 90% = 88.24%] will be parental types. This gives 5.88% a^+ b^+ c, 5.88% a b c^+, 44.12% a^+ b^+ c^+, and 44.12% a b c.

c. Here, nearly the entire region between a^+ and c^+ has been inverted. The chromosomes can be diagrammed as shown below, using a thick line with an open-headed arrowhead to show the inverted region.

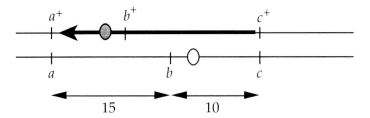

The inverted region is a pericentric inversion. As shown in text Figure 21.11, the only viable gametes that are produced from a meiosis with a single crossover within the inverted region are parental types (either normal-ordered or inversion-bearing chromosomes). Gametes with either of the two types of duplication/deletion-bearing chromosomes resulting from a single crossover are not viable. Thus, single crossovers occurring in nearly the entire *a–c* interval will not produce recombinant gametes.

Crossovers that occur simultaneously in each of the *a–b* and *b–c* intervals (double crossovers) may produce viable recombinants, depending on whether they are two-strand, three-strand, or four-strand double crossovers. As shown in the answer to problem 21.6, a two-strand double crossover will produce viable gametes. Half of the gametes from such a meiosis are double recombinants (a b^+ c and a^+ b c^+). As shown in the answer to problem 21.7, a four-strand double crossover will not produce any viable gametes. There are two possible types of three-strand double crossovers (see text Figure 13.8). These are diagrammed for an inversion heterozygote in the figure below.

I.

II.

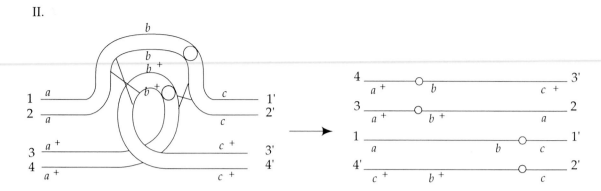

The three-strand double crossover shown in I will produce the doubly recombinant chromosome a b^+ c, two duplication/deletion chromosomes, and the parental-type chromosome a^+ b^+ c^+. The three-strand double crossover shown in II will produce the doubly recombinant chromosome a^+ b c^+, two duplication/deletion chromosomes, and the parental-type chromosome a b c. Thus, in a meiosis with either type of three-strand double crossover, two gametes will not be viable (the duplication/deletion-bearing gametes) and two gametes will be viable (one parental and one recombinant gamete). The results of meioses with each type of double crossover are summarized below:

TYPE OF DOUBLE CROSSOVER	NONVIABLE GAMETES	VIABLE GAMETES		
		RECOMBINANTS	PARENTALS	TOTAL
Two-strand	0	2	2	4
Three-strand (I)	2	1	1	2
Three-strand (II)	2	1	1	2
Four-strand	4	0	0	0

If each of the four types of double-crossover meioses occur equally frequently in a trihybrid with a heterozygous inversion, on average these meioses will produce 1/2 viable gametes and 1/4 doubly recombinant gametes. By comparison, double-crossover meioses in a trihybrid with normal-ordered chromosomes will produce on average all viable gametes and half doubly recombinant gametes. Thus, the pericentric inversion reduces both the number of gametes and the number of double recombinants by half. Since this pericentric inversion spans nearly the entire a–c interval, the observed number of double recombinants will be very close to half of the expected number of double recombinants in a normal-ordered trihybrid parent. From part a, a normal-ordered trihybrid parent has 1.25% doubly recombinant gametes, so here there will be 1/2 x 1.25% = 0.625%. This gives (100 - 0.625)/2 = 49.6875% each of a^+ b^+ c^+ and a b c, and 0.3125% each of a^+ b c^+ and a b^+ c.

d. Here, the inversion is only slightly larger than that in part c, as the inverted region extends distally just past a and c. The trihybrid chromosomes can be diagrammed as shown below, using a thick line with an open-headed arrowhead to show the inverted region.

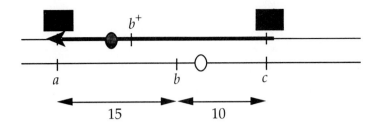

The frequency of progeny phenotypes will be very close to those observed in part c, since the inversion is very similar in size.

21.12 Mr. and Mrs. Lambert have not yet been able to produce a viable child. They have had two miscarriages and one severely defective child who died soon after birth. Studies of banded chromosomes of father, mother, and child showed that all chromosomes were normal except for pair number 6. The number 6 chromosomes of mother, father, and child are shown in the following figure.

Child   Mrs.   Mr.
          Lambert   Lambert

a. Does either parent have an abnormal chromosome? If so, what is the abnormality?
b. How did the chromosomes of the child arise? Be specific as to what events in the parents gave rise to these chromosomes.
c. Why is the child not phenotypically normal?
d. What can be predicted about future conceptions by this couple?

Answer:

a. Mr. Lambert is heterozygous for a pericentric inversion of chromosome 6. Relative to the centromere of the normal chromosome 6, one of the breakpoints is within the fourth light band up from the centromere, while the other is in the sixth dark band below the centromere. Mrs. Lambert's chromosomes are normal.

b. When Mr. Lambert's number 6 chromosomes paired during meiosis, they formed an inversion loop which included the centromere. Crossing-over occurred within the loop, and gave rise to the partially duplicated, partially deficient chromosome 6 that the child received.

c. The child's abnormalities stem from having three copies of some, and only one copy of other, chromosome 6 regions. The top part of the short arm is duplicated, and there is a deficiency of the distal part of the long arm in this case.

d. The inversion appears to cover more than half of the length of chromosome 6, so crossing-over will occur in this region in the majority of meioses. In the minority of meioses where there is a two-strand double crossover inside the loop, or where crossing-over occurs outside the loop, and in the cases where a crossover has occurred within the loop but the child receives a noncrossover chromosome, the child can be normal. There is significant risk of abnormality, so fetal chromosomes should be monitored.

21.13 Mr. and Mrs. Simpson have been trying for years to have a child but have been unable to conceive. They consulted a physician, and tests revealed that Mr. Simpson had a markedly low sperm count. His chromosomes were studied, and a testicular biopsy was done. His chromosomes proved to be normal, except for pair 12. The following figure shows Mrs. Simpson's normal pair of number 12 chromosomes and Mr. Simpson's number 12 chromosomes.

Mr.
Simpson

Mrs.
Simpson

a. What is the nature of the abnormality in Mr. Simpson's chromosomes of pair number 12?

b. What abnormal feature would you expect to see in the testicular biopsy (cells in various stages of meiosis can be seen)?

c. Why is Mr. Simpson's sperm count low?

d. What can be done about Mr. Simpson's low sperm count?

Answer:

a. Mr. Simpson has a paracentric inversion in the long arm of one of his number 12 chromosomes. Moving downward (distally) from the centromere of the normal chromosome, the breakpoints are in the first dark band and in the sixth light band.

b. Crossing-over within the inversion loop will produce dicentric chromatids which would form anaphase bridges. These chromatin bridges joining the two chromatin masses at the beginning of anaphase I would be visible in the testicular biopsy.

c. The inversion is large, so the frequency of crossing-over within it will be significant. Consequently, bridges will be formed in the majority of meioses. Cells in which bridges form do not complete meiosis or form sperm in mammals.

d. Nothing can be done to increase Mr. Simpson's sperm count. This might be an instance to consider *in vitro* fertilization.

21.14 Chromosome I in maize has the gene sequence *ABCDEF*, whereas chromosome II has the sequence *MNOPQR*. A reciprocal translocation resulted in *ABCPQR* and *MNODEF*. Diagram the expected pachytene (see Chapter 1) configuration of the F_1 of a cross of homozygotes of these two arrangements.

Answer:

```
            F ||  || F
            E ||  || E
            D ||  || D
      A B C ‖      ‖ O N M
      ───────      ───────

      A B C ‖      ‖ O N M
            P ||  || P
            Q ||  || Q
            R ||  || R
```

21.15 Diagram the pairing behavior at prophase of meiosis I (see Chapter 1) of a translocation heterozygote that has normal chromosomes of gene order *abcdefg* and *tuvwxyz* and has the translocated chromosomes *abcdvwxyz* and *tuefg*. Assume that the centromere is at the left end of all chromosomes.

Answer:

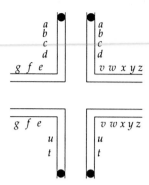

21.16   Mr. and Mrs. Denton have been trying for several years to have a child. They have experienced a series of miscarriages, and last year they had a child with multiple congenital defects. The child died within days of birth. The birth of this child prompted the Dentons' physician to order a chromosome study of parents and child. The results of the study are shown in the following figure. Chromosome banding was done, and all chromosomes were normal in these individuals except some copies of number 6 and number 12. The number 6 and number 12 chromosomes of mother, father, and child are shown in the figure (the number 6 chromosomes are the larger pair).

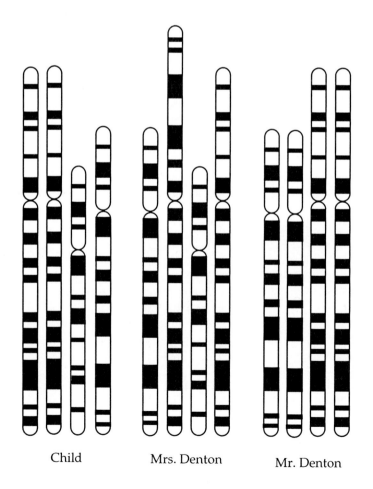

Child   Mrs. Denton   Mr. Denton

a. Does either parent have an abnormal karyotype? If so, which parent has it, and what is the nature of the abnormality?

b. How did the child's karyotype arise (what pairing and segregation events took place in the parents)?

c. Why is the child phenotypically defective?

d. What can this couple expect to occur in subsequent conceptions?

e. What medical help, if any, can be offered to them?

Answer:

a. Mr. Denton has normal chromosomes. Mrs. Denton is heterozygous for a balanced reciprocal translocation between chromosomes 6 and 12. Most of the short arm of chromosome 6 has been reciprocally translocated onto the long arm of chromosome 12. The breakpoints appear to be in the first thick, dark band just above the centromere of 6 and in the third dark band below the centromere of 12.

b. The child received a normal 6 and a normal 12 from his father. In prophase I of meiosis in Mrs. Denton, chromosome 6 and 12 and the reciprocally translocated 6 and 12 paired to form a cruciform-like structure. Segregation of adjacent, nonhomologous centromeres to the same pole ensued, so that the child received a gamete containing a normal 6 and one of the translocation chromosomes. See text Figure 21.13 for an illustration of adjacent-1 segregation.

c. The child has a normal 6 and a normal 12 chromosome from Mr. Denton. The child also has a normal 6 chromosome from Mrs. Denton. However, the child also has one of the translocation chromosomes from Mrs. Denton. With this chromosome, the child is partially trisomic as well as partially monosomic. It has three copies of part of the short arm of chromosome 6 and only one copy of most of the long arm of chromosome 12. This abnormality in gene dosage is the cause of its physical abnormality.

d. Segregation of adjacent homologous centromeres to the same pole is relatively rare. The segregation pattern seen in this child (adjacent-1 segregation) and alternate segregation (see text Figure 21.13) are more common. About half of the time, when alternate segregation occurs, the gamete will have a complete haploid set of genes, and the embryo should be normal. However, half of the gametes resulting from alternate segregation will be translocation heterozygotes.

e. Prenatal monitoring of fetal chromosomes could be done, and given the severity of the abnormalities (high probability of miscarriage and multiple congenital abnormalities), therapeutic abortion of chromosomally unbalanced fetuses would be a consideration.

21.17 Irradiation of *Drosophila* sperm produces translocations between the X chromosome and autosomes, between the Y chromosome and autosomes, and between different autosomes. Translocations between the X and Y chromosomes are not produced. Explain the absence of X-Y translocations.

Answer: Mature sperm either bear an X or a Y chromosome, not both. For X-Y translocations to be obtained, both chromosomes must be present in the same sperm cell.

21.18   Define the terms *aneuploidy*, *monoploidy*, and *polyploidy*.

Answer: An aneuploid cell or organism is one in which there is not an exact multiple of a haploid set of chromosomes, or one in which part or parts of chromosomes have been duplicated or deleted. It is one that does not have a *euploid* number of chromosomes. It is a general term used to describe a typically abnormal individual with an "unbalanced" chromosomal set.

A monoploid cell or individual has only one set of chromosomes. In humans, a monoploid cell would have 23 chromosomes instead of the normal diploid number of 46. In this case, a monoploid cell is also a haploid cell. A haploid number of chromosomes is typically the number of chromosomes in a gamete. Thus, in diploid individuals, a haploid gamete is also a monoploid cell. This is not always the case for nondiploid individuals. For example, in a hexaploid plant that has 36 chromosomes, a gamete will have 18 chromosomes (haploid number = 18), but the monoploid number will be 6.

A polyploid cell or individual has multiple sets of chromosomes. It is euploid, having multiple *complete* sets of chromosomes.

21.19   If a normal diploid cell is 2N, what is the chromosome content of the following:

a. a nullisomic   e. a double trisomic
b. a monosomic   f. a tetraploid
c. a double monosomic   g. a hexaploid
d. a tetrasomic

Answer:
a. 2N - 2 (two copies of the same chromosome are missing)
b. 2N - 1 (missing one chromosome)
c. 2N - 1 - 1 (one copy of each of two different chromosomes are missing)
d. 2N + 2 (two extra copies of one chromosome)
e. 2N + 1 + 1 (an extra copy of each of two different chromosomes)
f. 4N
g. 6N

21.20   In humans, how many chromosomes would be typical of nuclei of cells that are

a. monosomic   d. triploid
b. trisomic   e. tetrasomic
c. monoploid

Answer:
a. 45
b. 47
c. 23
d. 69
e. 48

21.21   An individual with 47 chromosomes, including an additional chromosome 15, is said
to be

a. triplet   c. triploid
b. trisomic   d. tricycle

Answer: b. trisomic

21.22   A color-blind man marries a homozygous normal woman, and after four joyful years
of marriage they have two children. Unfortunately, both children have Turner syndrome, although one has normal vision and one is color blind. The type of color
blindness involved is a sex-linked recessive trait.

a. For the color blind child, did nondisjunction occur in the mother or the father?
Explain your answer.
b. For the child with normal vision, in which parent did nondisjunction occur? Explain your answer.

Answer:

a. The cross can be written as $X^+ X^+$ x X^c Y. Turner syndrome children are XO. If
the child is color blind, it received its father's X^c via a chromosomally normal
X-bearing sperm. Therefore, the egg that was fertilized must have lacked an X,
and nondisjunction occurred in the mother.
b. If the child has normal vision, it must have received its mother's normal X^+. To
be XO, this must be the only X the embryo received, so that the egg must have
been fertilized by a nullo-X, nullo-Y sperm. Nondisjunction occurred in the father.

21.23   The frequency of chromosome loss in *Drosophila* can be increased by a recessive
chromosome 2 mutation called *pal*. The mutation causes the preferential loss of
chromosomes contributed to a zygote by *pal/pal* fathers. The paternally contributed chromosomes are lost during the first few mitotic divisions after fertilization.
What phenotypic consequences do you expect in offspring of the following crosses?
(Keep in mind how sex is determined in *Drosophila*, that loss of an entire chromosome 2 or chromosome 3 is lethal, and that loss of one copy of the small chromosome 4 is tolerated.)

a. X chromosome loss at the first mitotic division in a cross between a true-
breeding *yellow* (recessive, X-linked mutation causing yellow body color) female and a *pal/pal* father.
b. Chromosome 4 loss at the first mitotic division in a cross between a true-
breeding *eyeless* (recessive mutation on chromosome 4 causing reduced eye size)
female and a *pal/pal* father.
c. Chromosome 3 loss at the first mitotic division in a cross between a true-
breeding *ebony* (recessive mutation on chromosome 3 causing black body color)
female and a *pal/pal* father.

Answer: The *pal* mutation causes the loss (not nondisjunction) of paternally contributed chromosomes in the first few mitotic divisions after fertilization. It is *as if*

one of the paternal chromosomes is not replicated, and is passed on to one of the two daughter nuclei. Consequently, following chromosome loss, one daughter nucleus has a normal diploid set of chromosomes, while the other is monosomic for one chromosome. This problem considers what happens when a chromosome is lost at the very first mitotic division (and only at that division).

a. The cross is *y/y +/+* (female) x *+/Y pal/pal* (male), with progeny *y/+ pal/+* (daughters) and *y/Y pal/+* (sons). Since the paternally contributed X is only found in the *y/+ pal/+* daughter, we only need to consider the consequence of its loss in daughters. If a paternally contributed X chromosome (+) is lost during the first mitotic division in a *y/+ pal/+* zygote, one daughter cell will lose an X chromosome and be *y pal/+*. The other daughter cell will have two X chromosomes and be *y/+ pal/+*. The cell with two X chromosomes would be female (XX) and produce nonyellow cells (*y/+*), while the cell with one X chromosome would be male (XO) and produce yellow cells (*y*). The animal will be a mosaic with cells of two sex types that are marked by yellow (male) or grey (female) cuticle.

b. The cross is *+/+ eye/eye* (female) x *pal/pal +/+* (male), with progeny *pal/+ eye/+* (daughters and sons). The paternally contributed fourth chromosome is +. If it is lost during the first mitotic division in a *pal/+ eye/+* zygote, one daughter cell will lose a fourth chromosome and be *pal/+ eye*. The other daughter cell will have two fourth chromosomes and be normal, while the cell with one fourth chromosome will be *eye*. The animal will be a mosaic with some cells that are haploid for the fourth chromosome and some cells that are diploid for the fourth chromosome. If a patch of haplo-4 cells forms an eye during development, the eye will be reduced in size.

c. The cross is *+/+ e/e* (female) x *pal/pal +/+* (male), with progeny *pal/+ e/+*. The paternally contributed third chromosome is +. If it is lost during the first mitotic division in a *pal/+ e/+* zygote, one daughter cell will lose a third chromosome, and be *pal/+ e*. This cell is inviable, and so will not be recovered in the organism, should the organism survive. Consequently, if the organism survives, it will be phenotypically normal (*pal/+ e/+*).

21.24   Assume that *x* is a new mutant gene in corn. A female *x/x* plant is crossed with a triplo-10 individual (trisomic for chromosome 10) carrying only dominant alleles at the *x* locus. Trisomic progeny are recovered and crossed back to the *x/x* female plant.

a. What ratio of dominant to recessive phenotypes is expected if the *x* locus is not on chromosome 10?

b. What ratio of dominant to recessive phenotypes is expected if the *x* locus is on chromosome 10?

Answer:

a. If the new mutant is not on chromosome 10, the cross can be written as *x/x* x *+/+* (considering only the chromosome carrying the *x* gene). The progeny will be *x/+*, and the backcross will be *x/+* x *x/x*. A 1:1 ratio of *x/x* (recessive mutant) to *x/+* (normal) individuals will be seen.

b. If the new mutant is on chromosome 10, the cross can be written as $x/x \times +/+/+$. Trisomic progeny will be $x/+/+$, and the backcross can be written as $x/+/+ \times x/x$. In the trisomic $x/+/+$ individual, there will be four kinds of gametes produced depending on how chromosome 10 segregates during meiosis. In 1/3 of the meioses, x and $+/+$ gametes will be produced, giving 1/6 x and 1/6 $+/+$ gametes. In 2/3 of the meioses, $+$ and $+/x$ gametes will be produced, giving 1/3 $+/x$ and 1/3 $+$ gametes. When such gametes fuse with an x-bearing gamete (from the xx parent) at fertilization, 1/6 of the progeny will have the mutant phenotype (i.e., be x/x) and 5/6 will be normal (i.e., $+/+/x, +/x/x, +/x$). The phenotypic ratio would be 5 dominant:1 recessive mutant.

21.25 Why are polyploids with even multiples of the chromosome set generally more fertile than polyploids with odd multiples of the chromosome set?

Answer: Polyploids with even multiples of the chromosome set can better form chromosome pairs in meiosis I than can polyploids with odd multiples. Triploids, for example, will generate an unpaired chromatid pair for each chromosome type in the genome, so that chromosome segregation to the gametes is irregular and the resulting zygotes will not be euploid.

21.26 Select the correct answer from the key below for the following statement: One plant species (N = 11) and another (N = 19) produced an allotetraploid.
I.   The chromosome number of this allotetraploid is 30.
II. The number of linkage groups of this allotetraploid is 30.

Key:
A. Statement I is true and Statement II is true.
B. Statement I is true, but Statement II is false.
C. Statement I is false, but Statement II is true.
D. Statement I is false and Statement II is false.

Answer: To form the initial alloploid, gametes from each species fused, so that the initial alloploid had 11 + 19 = 30 chromosomes. A fertile, allotetraploid plant was produced by the doubling of this chromosome set, so that the allotetraploid plant has 60 chromosomes, two sets of 11 and two sets of 19. Thus Statement II is true, but Statement I is not. The allotetraploid has 60 chromosomes and 30 linkage groups (30 pairs of homologs). C is correct.

21.27 According to Mendel's first law, genes A and a segregate from each other and appear in equal numbers among the gametes. But Mendel did not know that his plants were diploid. In fact, since plants are frequently tetraploid, he could have been unlucky enough to have started with peas that were 4N rather than 2N. Let us assume that Mendel's peas were tetraploid, that every gamete contains two alleles, and that the distribution of alleles to the gamete is random. Suppose we have a cross of

AAAA x *aaaa*, where *A* is dominant, regardless of the number of *a* alleles present in an individual.

a. What will be the genotype of the F_1?

b. If the F_1 is selfed, what will be the phenotypic ratios in the F_2?

Answer:

a. The F_1 will be *AA aa*.

b. Label the four alleles in the F_1 as A^1, A^2, a^1, and a^2. These four gametes can segregate into gametes in six ways: A^1A^2, A^1a^1, A^1a^2, A^2a^1, A^2a^2, a^1a^2. 1/6 of the gametes will be *AA*, 4/6 of the gametes will be *Aa*, and 1/6 will be *aa*. Selfing the F_1 will give the following pairings:

	1/6 *AA*	4/6 *Aa*	1/6 *aa*
1/6 *AA*	1/36 *AAAA*	4/36 *AAAa*	1/36 *AAaa*
4/6 *Aa*	4/36 *AAAa*	16/36 *AAaa*	4/36 *Aaaa*
1/6 *aa*	1/36 *AAaa*	4/26 *Aaaa*	1/36 *aaaa*

This would give a phenotypic ratio of 35 *A*– :1 *aa*.

21.28 What phenotypic ratio of *A* to *a* is expected if *AAaa* plants are testcrossed against *aaaa* individuals? (Assume that the dominant phenotype is expressed whenever at least one *A* is present, no crossing-over occurs, and each gamete receives two chromosomes.)

Answer: Label the four alleles of the *AAaa* plant as A^1, A^2, a^1, and a^2. As in problem 21.28, these four alleles can segregate into gametes in six ways: A^1A^2, A^1a^1, A^1a^2, A^2a^1, A^2a^2, a^1a^2. 1/6 of the gametes will be *AA*, 4/6 of the gametes will be *Aa*, and 1/6 will be *aa*. When these gametes fuse with *aa* gametes at fertilization, the testcross progeny will be 1/6 *AAaa*, 4/6 *Aaaa*, and 1/6 *aaaa*. The phenotypic ratio will be 5 *A*: 1 *a*.

21.29 The root tip cells of an autotetraploid plant contain 48 chromosomes. How many chromosomes were contained by the gametes of the diploid from which this plant was derived?

Answer: The somatic cells of an autotetraploid plant have four identical sets of chromosomes. As root tip cells are mitotically dividing somatic cells, they too have four identical sets of chromosomes. Therefore, the gametes of the diploid from which this plant was derived had 12 chromosomes.

21.30 A number of species of the birch genus have a somatic chromosome number of 28. The paper birch is reported as occurring with several different chromosome numbers; *fertile* individuals with the somatic numbers 56, 70, and 84 are known. How should the 28-chromosome individuals be designated with regard to chromosome number?

Answer: Plants with 56, 70, and 84 chromosomes have gametes that have 28, 35, and 42 chromosomes, respectively. If these plants are fertile polyploids, they should have an even number of chromosome sets. This would be the case if the monoploid number of these plants is 7, and the 56, 70, and 84 chromosome plants have eight, ten, and twelve times the monoploid number of chromosomes. A plant with 28 chromosomes would therefore be tetraploid, and should be fertile.

21.31 How many chromosomes would be found in somatic cells of an allotetraploid derived from two plants, one with N = 7 and the other with N = 10?

Answer: The initial allopolyploid will have 17 chromosomes. After doubling, the somatic cells will have 34 chromosomes.

21.32 Plant species A has a haploid complement of four chromosomes. A related species B has five. In a geographic region where A and B are both present, C plants are found that have some characters of both species and somatic cells with 18 chromosomes. What is the chromosome constitution of the C plants likely to be? With what plants would they have to be crossed to produce fertile seed?

Answer: The C plants are allotetraploids, containing a diploid chromosome set from each of species A and species B. These plants should be fertile, as they will have no abnormal chromosome pairing or unpaired chromosomes. They should be able to produce gametes with 9 chromosomes (the four of species A and the five of species B), and can either be selfed or crossed to other C plants to produce fertile seed.

22

POPULATION GENETICS

CHAPTER OUTLINE

REVIEW OF KEY TERMS, SYMBOLS, AND CONCEPTS

In your own words, write a brief, precise definition of each term in the groups below. Check your definitions using the text. Then, develop a concept map using the terms in each list.

1	2	3
transmission genetics	models of genetic variation	Hardy-Weinberg equilibrium
molecular genetics	allele frequency cline	random mating
population genetics	classical model	nonrandom mating
quantitative genetics	balance model	positive assortative mating
genetic structure	neutral-mutation model	negative assortative mating
genotypic frequency	fitness	inbreeding
allelic frequency	polymorphic locus	mutation
Mendelian population	proportion of polymorphic loci	allelic frequency
gene pool	heterozygosity (H)	forward, reverse mutation
gene counting	RFLP	equilibrium frequency
Hardy-Weinberg law	nucleotide substitution	random genetic drift
infinitely large population	synonymous change	effective population size
migration	nonsynonymous change	sampling error
natural selection	coding sequence	founder effect
random mating	noncoding sequence	bottleneck effect
mutation	microsatellite, STRP	migration
genetic drift		gene flow
natural selection		population viability analysis
Hardy-Weinberg equilibrium		neutral theory of molecular evolution
		variance, standard error
		natural selection
		Darwinian fitness
		pleiotropy
		selection coefficient
		protected polymorphism
		heterosis
		overdominance
		heterozygote superiority

THINKING ANALYTICALLY

Population genetics considers patterns of genetic variation found among individuals within groups and how these patterns vary geographically and evolve over time. As you study population genetics your perspective will shift away from a direct consideration of the molecular and biochemical mechanisms that underlie the inheritance and expression of traits in a single individual or cell to a statistical evaluation of the *effects* of these processes at the level of the group, population, or species.

At the conceptual core of population genetics lies the Hardy-Weinberg law. Initially, focus your efforts on understanding its assumptions and predictions. Practice the examples given in the text and the text problems to become fluent in analyzing whether a population with two alleles at an autosomal locus is in Hardy-Weinberg equilibrium. Then, consider extensions of the law to loci with more than two alleles or loci with sex-linked alleles. Finally, investigate the different ways that the assumptions of the Hardy-Weinberg law may be violated, and the consequences of each to the genetic structure of a population.

Be aware that the allelic symbolism used in population genetics is often different from that used in Mendelian or molecular genetics. Consider the following example. In earlier chapters, the genotypes for normal and sickle-cell hemoglobin were written either as $\beta^A\beta^A$, $\beta^A\beta^S$ or $\beta^S\beta^S$ or $HbAHbA$, $HbAHbS$, $HbSHbS$. Here they are written as $Hb\text{-}A/Hb\text{-}A$, $Hb\text{-}A/Hb\text{-}S$, $Hb\text{-}S/Hb\text{-}S$. Similarly, care should be taken with the letters p and q, which symbolize the frequency within a population of dominant and recessive members of an allelic pair (but do not symbolize the alleles themselves!).

One of the main concerns of population genetics is how to model changes in allele and genotypic frequencies under a set of specified conditions. The models are often very elegant, and employ equations that identify relationships between a set of variables identified in a population. Memorization of the equations used to analyze changes in populations is by itself insufficient to understand the models. It will be difficult, if not impossible, to solve even moderately challenging word problems if you can only plug numbers into equations. While you will find it helpful to recognize by sight several of the equations, you need to do more. Take the time to understand the model that leads to the equation, and how the mathematical and statistical analysis in the model is related to a biological question.

A few hints for solving some of the problems are in order. First, you will often find that the frequency of one class of homozygote (usually the recessive homozygotes, given by q^2) is the only piece of hard data available. As you work back from this information, keep track of the assumptions that you are making. Otherwise, you may enter into the realm of circular reasoning. For example, you can legitimately calculate q as the square root of q^2, and if only two alleles exist, calculate p by equating it with $1 - q$. However, if you then determine that heterozygotes exist at a frequency of $2pq$, you are <u>assuming</u> that random mating is occurring and the conditions of Hardy-Weinberg equilibrium are satisfied. Further work with your calculated values of p^2, $2pq$, and q^2 will continue to reflect that assumption. Often, you will need to look for more information, or another approach, to prove that the population in question is in Hardy-Weinberg equilibrium. Second, doing the math requires care and, if you are not exceptionally fluent with it, patience. It will sometimes help to factor out common multipliers [e.g., $2pq^2 + q^2 = q^2(2p + 1)$]. At other times, it will be helpful to recognize members of a binomial expansion [e.g., $p^2 + 2pq + q^2 = (p + q)^2$].

After you have mastered the concepts underlying the Hardy-Weinberg law, focus on understanding how genetic variation can be measured. A number of important models have been developed that have been supported by data gathered using a variety of methods, including those of molecular genetics. Models have been proposed to address the substantial amount of genetic variation that exists in a population, and the factors that can lead to changes in a population's genetic structure. Some of these employ quantitative analysis and equations. Approach these models just as you did the Hardy-Weinberg law. First become familiar with the conceptual issues of the model, and then relate the variables in an equation to the key factors considered in the model.

QUESTIONS FOR PRACTICE

Multiple Choice Questions

1. In a small population, 30 percent of the individuals have blood type M, 40 percent of the individuals have blood type MN and 30 percent of the individuals have blood type N. If p equals the frequency of the L^M allele and q equals the frequency of the L^N allele, what are p and q?
   a. $p = 0.30$, $q = 0.30$.
   b. $p = 0.50$, $q = 0.50$.
   c. $p = 0.30$, $q = 0.70$.
   d. $p = 0.50$, $q = 0.30$.

2. Is the population described in question 1, above, in Hardy-Weinberg equilibrium?
   a. Yes, because the calculated genotypic frequencies equal the expected genotypic frequencies.
   b. Yes, because at equilibrium you always have equal numbers of recessive and dominant homozygotes.
   c. No; the frequency of heterozygotes is too large and the frequency of homozygotes is too low.
   d. No; the frequency of heterozygotes is too low and the frequency of homozygotes is too large.

3. Which of the following is *not* an assumption about a population in Hardy-Weinberg equilibrium?
   a. The population is isolated.
   b. Random mating occurs in the population.
   c. The population is free from mutation.
   d. The population is free from natural selection.
   e. The population is free from migration.

4. The frequency of one form of X-linked color-blindness varies among human ethnic groups. What can be said about whether each ethnic group is in Hardy-Weinberg equilibrium? (Let q = the frequency of the normal allele, and p = the frequency of the color-blind allele.)
   a. None of the ethnic populations can be in equilibrium, since all have different values for p and q.
   b. Only the entire human population is in equilibrium.
   c. Some of the ethnic populations may be in equilibrium, providing that the frequency of the trait in males is p and the frequency in females is p^2.
   d. Some of the ethnic populations may be in equilibrium, providing that the frequency of the trait in both sexes is p^2.

e. All of the ethnic populations will be in equilibrium, since each satisfies the criteria for a population in Hardy-Weinberg equilibrium.

5. In a large, randomly mating population, 80 percent of the individuals have dark hair and twenty percent are blond. Assuming that hair color is controlled by one pair of alleles, is the allele for dark hair <u>necessarily</u> dominant to the one for blond hair?

a. Yes, because otherwise the population would not be dominated by dark-haired individuals.

b. Yes, because more of something (in this case, hair color) is always dominant to less of that thing.

c. No, because relative frequencies of alleles in a randomly mating population are unrelated to issues of dominance and recessiveness.

d. No, because although there is a relationship between dominance and allele frequency, that relationship is not seen in this example.

6. The amounts of genetic variation in a population can be explained in a number of ways. In one model, a large amount of genetic variation is explained by recurrent mutation and random changes in allele frequencies. In this model, natural selection selects against some of the variation affecting fitness but does not select for or against much of the genetic variation. This model is termed

a. the classical model.

b. the balance model.

c. the neutral mutation model.

d. the random mutation model.

7. Which of the following populations are in Hardy-Weinberg equilibrium?

	GENOTYPES		
POPULATION	AA	Aa	aa
a	0.72	0.20	0.08
b	0.12	0.80	0.08
c	0.08	0.01	0.91
d	0.25	0.50	0.25

8. How is the rate of forward mutation likely to be related to the rate of reverse mutation?

a. The rate of forward mutation is generally lower because there is mutational pull back to a specific form.

b. The rate for forward mutation is generally higher because once an allele has changed, it is nearly as likely that a subsequent change will be to yet another new form.

c. The rate of forward and reverse mutations are codependent and usually equal.

d. The relative rates of forward and reverse mutation are so highly variable that one cannot formulate an accurate generalization comparing the two.

9. Which of the following can result in genetic drift?
   a. a sampling error
   b. random factors producing unexpected mortality
   c. the establishment of a population by a small number of breeding individuals
   d. a drastic reduction in the size of a population
   e. a change in environmental conditions that affects selection
   f. all of the above

10. What is the effective population size for a population consisting of 10 breeding males and 2 breeding females?
    a. 12
    b. 6
    c. 7
    d. 2

11. Which of the following is *not* true concerning the effect of migration among populations?
    a. Migration tends to increase the effective size of the populations, leading to a reduction in genetic drift.
    b. Migration is associated with gene flow, and introduces new alleles to the population.
    c. If the allelic frequencies of migrants and the recipient population differ, migration can lead to the further differentiation of two populations.
    d. Migration and genetic drift have opposite effects on size and variability. Migration effectively increases size and variability, whereas drift acts in opposition.

12. What can one generally state about measuring the fitness associated with a specific genotype?
    a. It is easy to assess, and can be based on the number of offspring of an individual.
    b. Since it is based on the reproductive ability of a genotype, it is an absolute term, which requires no assumptions.
    c. It will remain the same from generation to generation.
    d. It is difficult to measure because of pleiotropic effects.

13. Consider a recessive trait that results in a complete lack of reproductive success of homozygotes. How might such a recessive trait be maintained at a high level in a population?
    a. Through new mutation
    b. Through heterosis
    c. Through overdominance
    d. Through heterozygote superiority
    e. All of the above

14. For a given eukaryotic gene, which rate of DNA change is expected to be the lowest?
    a. the relative rate of change in nonfunctional pseudogenes
    b. the relative rate of change in introns
    c. the relative rate of change for synonymous substitutions in coding sequences
    d. the relative rate of change for nonsynonymous substitutions in coding sequences
    e. the relative rate of change in leaders and trailers

15. Which of the rates in Question 14 is expected to be the highest?

   Answers: 1b; 2d; 3a; 4c; 5c; 6c; 7d; 8b; 9f; 10c; 11c; 12d; 13e; 14d; 15a.

Thought Questions

1. Consider a population that is not in Hardy-Weinberg equilibrium for a pair of alleles. Show why equilibrium values for genotypic frequencies are reached in one generation after the onset of random mating for autosomal alleles, but more than one generation of random mating is required for sex-linked alleles.

2. Distinguish between heterozygosity and the proportion of polymorphic loci.

3. Mutation pressure is rarely the most important determinant of allelic frequency. What other factors are important?

4. Can a population be in Hardy-Weinberg equilibrium for one, but not another, pair of alleles?

5. What is the most likely explanation if the allelic frequencies agree with those predicted by the Hardy-Weinberg law, but the genotype frequencies do not? (Hint: Consider mating systems and heterosis.)

6. Why do mutation, migration, and drift not necessarily lead to adaptation?

7. What are five different molecular methods that can be used to measure genetic variation? What advantages and disadvantages are there to each?

8. Distinguish between nonrandom mating, positive assortative mating, negative assortative mating, and inbreeding.

9. What are the arguments for and against investing funds and human effort in a population viability analysis for an endangered species?

10. What are the values of preserving and promoting genetic diversity within a species? How does the development of genomics and technologies related to genomics affect our ability to assess and influence genetic diversity, both in our own species and other species?

Thought Questions for Media

After reviewing the media on the *iGenetics* CD-ROM, try to answer the following questions.

1. What assumptions of the Hardy-Weinberg law were illustrated by the animation?
2. Under these assumptions, what are the predictions of the Hardy-Weinberg law?
3. Which of these assumptions were not valid in the population of Darwin's finches under study by Dr. Grant?
4. What was the purpose of Dr. Grant's study of these finches?

5. The animation indicated that beak shape and size genetically complex. Some genes will have additive affects, some will be epistatic, and a few will show simple dominance and recessiveness. Why, for the purposes of the study, was it useful to assume the existence of a simple gene that, when homozygous recessive, contributes to a decrease in beak size?

6. Is fitness constant for a given trait such as beak length? If not, according to what conditions does it vary?

7. The animation describes how natural selection for small and large beak size in Darwin's finches is complex. For example, even though birds with larger beaks can crack harder seeds, in some years, there can still be selection for small beak size. Why might this be the case?

SOLUTIONS TO TEXT PROBLEMS

22.1   In the European land snail *Cepaea nemoralis*, multiple alleles at a single locus determine shell color. The allele for brown (C^B) is dominant to the allele for pink (C^P) and to the allele for yellow (C^Y). The dominance hierarchy among these alleles is $C^B > C^P > C^Y$. In one population sample of *Cepaea*, the following color phenotypes were recorded:

$$
\begin{array}{lr}
\text{Brown} & 236 \\
\text{Pink} & 231 \\
\underline{\text{Yellow}} & \underline{33} \\
\text{Total} & 500
\end{array}
$$

Assuming that this population is in Hardy-Weinberg equilibrium (large, randomly mating, and free from evolutionary processes), calculate the frequencies of the C^B, C^Y, and C^P alleles.

Answer: Equate the frequency of each color with the frequency expected in Hardy-Weinberg equilibrium, letting $p = f(C^B)$, $q = f(C^P)$, and $r = f(C^Y)$.

Brown: $f(C^BC^B) + f(C^BC^P) + f(C^BC^Y) = p^2 + 2pq + 2pr = 236/500 = 0.472$
Pink: $f(C^PC^P) + f(C^PC^Y) = q^2 + 2qr = 231/500 = 0.462$
Yellow: $f(C^YC^Y) = r^2 = 33/500 = 0.066$

Now solve for p, q, and r, knowing that $p + q + r = 1$.

$r^2 = 0.066$, so $r = \sqrt{0.066} = 0.26$

There are two approaches to solve for q. First, since $q^2 + 2qr = 0.462$, one can substitute in $r = 0.26$, giving $q^2 + 2q(0.26) = 0.462$. Recognize this as a quadratic equation and set it equal to 0, and solve for q: That is, solve the equation $q^2 + 0.52q - 0.462 = 0$.

Solving the quadratic equation for q, one has:

$$q = \frac{-0.52 \pm \sqrt{(0.52)^2 - 4(1)(-0.462)}}{2(1)} = 0.467$$

A second approach to solve for q is to realize that

$q^2 + 2qr = 0.462$ and
$r^2 = 0.066$.

Adding left and right sides of the equations together, one has
$q^2 + 2qr + r^2 = 0.066 + 0.462$
$(q + r)^2 = 0.528$
$q + r = 0.726$
$q = 0.726 - r = 0.726 - 0.26 = 0.467$

Since $p + q + r = 1$, $p = 1 - (q + r) = 1 - (0.26 + 0.467) = 0.273$.

22.2   Three alleles are found at a locus coding for malate dehydrogenase (MDH) in the spotted chorus frog. Chorus frogs were collected from a breeding pond, and each frog's genotype at the MDH locus was determined with electrophoresis. The following numbers of genotypes were found:

M^1M^1	8
M^1M^2	35
M^2M^2	20
M^1M^3	53
M^2M^3	76
M^3M^3	62
Total	254

a.   Calculate the frequencies of the M^1, M^2, and M^3 alleles in this population.
b.   Using a chi-square test, determine whether the MDH genotypes in this population are in Hardy-Weinberg proportions.

Answer:
a.   The tally for M^1 alleles is as follows:

GENOTYPE	# INDIVIDUALS	# M^1 ALLELES
M^1M^1	8	16
M^1M^2	35	35
M^1M^3	53	53
	Total	104

The total number of individuals is 254, thus the total number of alleles is 254×2, or 508. The frequency of M^1 alleles is $104/508 = 0.205$. The frequency of the other alleles is obtained similarly. One has $f(M^1) = 0.20 = p$, $f(M^2) = 0.30 = q$, and $f(M^3) = 0.50 = r$.

b. For three alleles with frequencies p, q, and r, a population in Hardy-Weinberg equilibrium will have $p^2 + 2pq + 2pr + q^2 + 2qr + r^2 = 1$. To test the hypothesis that the population is in Hardy-Weinberg equilibrium, calculate the numbers of individuals expected in each class using this relationship and the values for p, q, and r obtained in part (a). Calculate the value of χ^2 as shown in the following table.

GENOTYPE	OBSERVED VALUE (O)	EXPECTED FREQUENCY	EXPECTED VALUE (E)	d ($o-e$)	d^2/e
M^1M^1	8	$p^2 = 0.04$	10	−2	0.40
M^1M^2	35	$2pq = 0.12$	30	5	0.83
M^2M^2	20	$q^2 = 0.09$	23	−3	0.39
M^1M^3	53	$2pr = 0.20$	51	2	0.08
M^2M^3	76	$2qr = 0.30$	75	1	0.01
M^3M^3	62	$r^2 = 0.25$	64	−2	0.06
					$\chi^2 = 1.77$

Since the six phenotypic classes are completely specified by three allele frequencies, the number of phenotypes (6) minus the number of alleles (3) determines the degrees of freedom ($6 - 3 = 3$). With 3 degrees of freedom, $0.70 < P < 0.50$. The hypothesis is accepted as possible and it appears that the population is in Hardy-Weinberg equilibrium.

22.3   In a large interbreeding population 81 percent of the individuals are homozygous for a recessive character. In the absence of mutation or selection, what percentage of the next generation would be homozygous recessives? Homozygous dominants? Heterozygotes?

Answer: The conditions of this problem meet the requirements for a population in Hardy-Weinberg equilibrium. In such a population, if p equals the frequency of A, and q equals the frequency of a, one expects p^2 AA, $2pq$ Aa, and q^2 aa genotypes after random mating. Here, $q^2 = 0.81$, so $q = 0.9$. Since $p + q = 1$, $p = 1 - 0.9 = 0.1$. In the next generation, one would expect $p^2 = (0.1)^2 = 0.01$ (or 1%) AA genotypes, $2pq = 2(0.1)(0.9) = 0.18$ (or 18%) Aa genotypes and $q^2 = (0.9)^2 = 0.81$ (or 81%) aa genotypes.

22.4   Let A and a represent dominant and recessive alleles whose respective frequencies are p and q in a given interbreeding population at equilibrium (with $p + q = 1$).

a. If 16 percent of the individuals in the population have recessive phenotypes, what percentage of the total number of recessive genes exist in the heterozygous condition?

b. If 1.0 percent of the individuals were homozygous recessive, what percentage of the recessive genes would occur in heterozygotes?

Answer:

a. Since $q^2 = 0.16$, $q = \sqrt{0.16} = 0.40$. Since $p + q = 1$, $p = 0.60$. The frequency of heterozygotes is $2pq = 2(0.40)(0.60) = 0.48$. Each of the 48% of the heterozygotes has one recessive allele, while each of the 16% of the homozygous recessive individuals has two. Thus, the percentage of the total number of recessive alleles in heterozygotes is $(0.48)/[0.48 + 2(0.16)] = 0.48/0.80 = 0.60$, or 60%.

b. If $q^2 = 0.01$, then $q = 0.1$, and $p = 0.9$. $2pq = 2(0.1)(0.9) = 0.18$. The percentage of the total number of recessive alleles in heterozygotes is $(0.18)/[0.18 + 2(0.01)] = 0.18/0.20 = 0.90$, or 90%.

22.5   A population has eight times as many heterozygotes as homozygous recessives. What is the frequency of the recessive gene?

Answer: The frequency of heterozygotes in a population in equilibrium is $2pq$, and the frequency of homozygous recessives is q^2. Here, there are eight times as many heterozygotes as homozygous recessives, so $2pq = 8q^2$. Since $p + q = 1$, $p = 1 - q$, and one can substitute $1 - q$ for p. This gives $2(1 - q)q = 8q^2$. Dividing both sides by q, and multiplying through, one has $2 - 2q = 8q$. Thus, $2 = 10q$, and $q =$ the frequency of the recessive allele $= 0.20$.

22.6   In a large population of range cattle the following ratios are observed: 49 percent red (RR), 42 percent roan (Rr), and 9 percent white (rr).

a. What percentage of the gametes that give rise to the next generation of cattle in this population will contain allele R?

b. In another cattle population only 1 percent of the animals are white and 99 percent are either red or roan. What is the percentage of r alleles in this case?

Answer:

a. In the red, RR animals, all of the gametes contain the R allele, while in the roan, Rr animals, half of the gametes contain the R allele. Therefore, $[49 + (42/2)] = 70\%$ of the gametes will contain the R allele. Another way to look at this problem is to realize that the frequency of gametes bearing a certain allele is the same as the frequency of the allele in the population. Let p equal the frequency of R in the population. Since there are 49 percent red animals, $p^2 = 0.49$, so $p = 0.70$ (or 70%).

b. If one lets q represent the frequency of r, since 1 percent of the animals are white, one has $q^2 = 0.01$. Hence, $q = 0.1$.

22.7   In a gene pool the alleles A and a have initial frequencies of p and q, respectively. Show that the allelic frequencies and zygotic frequencies do not change from generation to generation as long as there is no selection, mutation, or migration, the population is large, and the individuals mate at random.

Answer: Let the frequency of allele A equal p and the frequency of allele a equal q, with $p + q = 1$. Then, in the initial generation, the frequency of AA genotypes is p^2, the frequency of aa genotypes is q^2. The frequency of the remaining genotypes (i.e., Aa heterozygotes) must be $1 - (p^2 + q^2)$. Since $p + q = 1$, $(p + q)^2 = 1^2$, and $p^2 + 2pq + q^2 = 1$. Therefore $1 - (p^2 + q^2) = 2pq$ and the frequency of Aa heterozygotes must be $2pq$.

Assume there is no selection, mutation, or migration and that the individuals mate at random. Since there are three different genotypes in the population, nine crosses are possible. The frequency of each type of cross is determined by the frequency of each parental genotype. The types of crosses, the frequency of each cross, the types of progeny, and the frequency of each progeny class are listed in the table below:

CROSS	CROSS FREQUENCY	PROGENY RATIOS			PROGENY FREQUENCIES		
		AA	Aa	aa	AA	Aa	aa
$AA \times AA$	$p^2 \times p^2 = p^4$	all			p^4		
$AA \times Aa$	$p^2 \times 2pq = 2p^3q$	1/2	1/2		p^3q	p^3q	
$AA \times aa$	$p^2 \times q^2 = p^2q^2$		all			p^2q^2	
$Aa \times AA$	$2pq \times p^2 = 2p^3q$	1/2	1/2		p^3q	p^3q	
$Aa \times Aa$	$2pq \times 2pq = 4p^2q^2$	1/4	1/2	1/4	p^2q^2	$2p^2q^2$	p^2q^2
$Aa \times aa$	$2pq \times q^2 = 2pq^3$		1/2	1/2		pq^3	pq^3
$aa \times AA$	$q^2 \times p^2 = p^2q^2$		all			p^2q^2	
$aa \times Aa$	$q^2 \times 2pq = 2pq^3$		1/2	1/2		pq^3	pq^3
$aa \times aa$	$q^2 \times q^2 = q^4$			all			q^4

To determine the frequency of a particular zygotic class, add up the frequency of the progeny in that class. Then factor out a common multiplier, and note that $p + q = 1$ and that $(p + q)^2 = p^2 + 2pq + q^2$. One has:

$$\text{frequency } (AA) = p^4 + 2p^3q + p^2q^2$$
$$= p^2(p^2 + 2pq + q^2)$$
$$= p^2(p + q)^2$$
$$= p^2(1)^2 = p^2$$

frequency (Aa) $= 2p^3q + 4p^2q^2 + 2pq^3$
$= 2pq(p^2 + 2pq + q^2)$
$= 2pq(p + q)^2$
$= 2pq(1)^2 = 2pq$

frequency (aa) $= pq + 2pq^3 + q^4$
$= q^2(p^2 + 2pq + q^2)$
$= q^2(p + q)^2$
$= q^2(1)^2 = q^2$

Thus, the zygotic frequencies do not change from one generation to the next.

Since all of the gametes of the AA parents and half of the gametes of the Aa parents will bear the A allele, the frequency of A in the gene pool of the next generation is $p^2 + pq = p(p + q) = p$. Since all of the gametes of the aa parents and half of the gametes of the Aa parents will bear the a allele, the frequency of a in the gene pool of the next generation is $q^2 + pq = q(q + p) = q$. Thus, the allelic frequencies do not change from one generation to the next.

22.8   The S-s antigen system in humans is controlled by two codominant alleles, S and s. In a group of 3,146 individuals the following genotypic frequencies were found: 188 SS, 717 Ss, and 2,241 ss.
a. Calculate the frequency of the S and s alleles.
b. Determine whether the genotypic frequencies are in Hardy-Weinberg equilibrium by using the chi-square test.

Answer:
a. Let p equal the frequency of S and q equal the frequency of s. Since homozygotes have two identical alleles and heterozygotes have one recessive and one dominant allele, one has:

$$p = \frac{2(188)[SS] + 717[Ss]}{2(3,146)} = \frac{1093}{6292} = 0.1737$$

$$q = \frac{717[Ss] + 2(2,241)[ss]}{2(3,146)} = \frac{5199}{6292} = 0.8263$$

b. Remember that in a χ^2 test, one uses the actual numbers of progeny observed and expected, and not the frequencies. With a hypothesis that the population is in Hardy-Weinberg equilibrium, one has:

CLASS	OBSERVED (o)	EXPECTED FREQUENCY	EXPECTED (e)	d ($o - e$)	d^2/e
SS	188	$p^2 = 0.0302$	95	93	91.0
Ss	717	$2pq = 0.287$	903	−186	38.3
$s\,s$	2,241	$q^2 = 0.683$	2,148	93	4.0
	3,146	1	3,146	0	133.3

There is only one degree of freedom because the three genotypic classes are completely specified by two allele frequencies, namely, p and q. (df. = number of phenotypes – number of alleles = 3 – 2 = 1.) The χ^2 value of 133.3, for one degree of freedom, gives $P<0.0001$. Therefore, the distribution of genotypes differs significantly from that expected if the population were in Hardy-Weinberg equilibrium.

22.9   Refer to Problem 22.8. A third allele is sometimes found at the S locus. This allele S^u is recessive to both the S and the s alleles and can be detected only in the homozygous state. If the frequencies of the alleles S, s, and S^u are p, q, and r, respectively, what would be the expected frequencies of the phenotypes $S-$, Ss, $s-$, and S^uS^u?

Answer: The frequencies are:
$$f(S-) = f(SS) + f(SS^u) = p^2 + 2pr$$
$$f(Ss) = 2pq$$
$$f(s-) = f(ss) + f(sS^u) = q^2 + 2qr$$
$$f(S^uS^u) = r^2.$$

22.10   In a large interbreeding human population, 60 percent of individuals belong to blood group O (genotype i/i). Assuming negligible mutation and no selective advantage of one blood type over another, what percentage of the grandchildren of the present population will be type O?

Answer: The conditions described in the problem indicate that the population is in Hardy-Weinberg equilibrium. Under equilibrium conditions, neither the allele nor the zygotic frequencies change from one generation to the next. Therefore, in two generations there should still be 60 percent type O individuals.

22.11   A selectively neutral, recessive character appears in 40 percent of the males and in 16 percent of the females in a large, randomly interbreeding population. What is the gene's frequency? What proportion of females are heterozygous for it? What proportion of males are heterozygous for it?

Answer: There are several possible explanations for the difference in the frequency of the trait in males and females. Two are sex linkage and autosomal linkage with males would be q, while the frequency in XX females would be q^2. Since the frequency in males is 0.4 and the frequency in females is $(0.4)^2 = 0.16$, the data fit a model of sex linkage with $q = 0.4$. The frequency of heterozygous XX (female) individuals is $2pq = 2(0.6)(0.4) = 0.48$. Since the trait appears to be sex linked, no heterozygous males exist.

22.12   Suppose you found two distinguishable types of individuals in wild populations of some organism in the following frequencies:

	TYPE 1	TYPE 2
Females	99%	1%
Males	90%	10%

The difference is known to be inherited. Are these dates compatible with the trait being X-linked?

Answer: As in problem 22.11, there are several explanations for differences in the frequency of a trait between males and females. Test the possibility of sex linkage first. Suppose the trait is sex linked and recessive and the population is in equilibrium. Let q equal the frequency of the recessive allele, and p equal the frequency of the dominant allele. If the gene is X-linked, one would expect XY males to express the recessive trait at a frequency of q, and XX females to express the recessive trait at a frequency of q^2. By inspecting the data given, one can see that the frequency of type 2 individuals in females is 0.01, which is the square of the frequency of type 2 individuals in males: $(0.10)^2 = 0.01$. Thus, this trait appears to be controlled by a sex-linked pair of alleles, occurring with allele frequencies of $q = 0.1$ recessive and $p = 0.9$ dominant.

22.13   Red-green color blindness is caused by sex-linked recessive gene. About 64 women out of 10,000 are color blind. What proportion of men would be expected to show the trait if mating is random?

Answer: Let q equal the frequency of the recessive allele, and p equal the frequency of the dominant allele. One expects homozygotes showing the trait to appear at a frequency of q^2 in a population at equilibrium. If $q^2 = 64/10,000 = 0.0064$, $q = 0.08$. Thus, one would expect 8 percent of XY, male individuals to show the trait.

22.14   About 8 percent of the men in a population are red-green color blind (because of a sex-linked recessive gene). Answer the following questions, assuming random mating in the population, with respect to color blindness.
   a. What percentage of women would be expected to be color blind?
   b. What percentage of women would be expected to be heterozygous?

22.14   About 8 percent of the men in a population are red-green color blind (because of a sex-linked recessive gene). Answer the following questions, assuming random mating in the population, with respect to color blindness.
   a. What percentage of women would be expected to be color blind?
   b. What percentage of women would be expected to be heterozygous?
   c. What percentage of men would be expected to have normal vision two generations later?

Answer:
   a. Let q equal the frequency of the recessive allele, and p equal the frequency of the dominant allele. The frequency of males with the trait will be q, and the frequency of females will be q^2. Here, $q = 0.08$, so $q^2 = 0.0064$, or 0.64 percent.
   b. Since $q = 0.08$, $p = 0.92$. The frequency of heterozygotes is $2pq = 0.1472$, or 14.72 percent. Only women can be heterozygotes, so the frequency of heterozygous women is 14.72 percent.
   c. If the population is in Hardy-Weinberg equilibrium, the frequencies of alleles and the frequency of zygotic phenotypes will not change in two generations. Since $p = 0.92$, 92 percent of the (XY) males will have normal vision.

22.15   List some of the basic differences in the classic, balance, and neutral mutation models of genetic variation.

Answer: In the classical model, natural populations possess little variation. Within each population, a single allele is strongly favored by natural selection because it "functions the best." This is the wild-type allele, and most individuals are homozygous for this allele. Occasionally, a mutation arises. Usually, this mutation is deleterious, and strong selection occurs against it. In the rare case that a new mutation is advantageous for survival or reproduction, the new allele will increase in frequency and eventually become the new wild type.

In the balance model, there is significant genetic variation within a population. Many alleles exist at each locus, and appear in the population in intermediate frequencies. Members of a population are heterozygous at numerous loci. Natural selection actively maintains genetic variation within a population by balancing selection to prevent any single allele from reaching a high frequency.

In a neutral-mutation model, there is also significant genetic variation within a population. As in the balance selection model, many alleles exist in intermediate frequencies and members of the population are heterozygous at numerous loci. In the neutral-mutation model, much of this genetic variation is explained by recurrent mutation and random changes in frequency of alleles which are physiologically equivalent, and not necessarily by natural selection. Hence, in this model, most variation is neutral with regard to selection.

22.16 Two alleles of a locus, A and a, can be interconverted by mutation:

$$A \xrightarrow[v]{u} a$$

where u is a mutation rate of 6.0×10^{-7}, and v is a mutation rate of 6.0×10^{-8}. What will be the frequencies of A and a at mutational equilibrium, assuming no selective difference, no migration, and no random fluctuation caused by genetic drift?

Answer: Let q equal the frequency of a, and p equal the frequency of A, with $q + p = 1$. As discussed in the text, when the population is at equilibrium, the frequency of p and q is given by:

$$q = \frac{u}{u + v} = \frac{6 \times 10^{-7}}{(6 \times 10^{-7}) + (6 \times \times 10^{-8})} = \frac{6 \times 10^{-7}}{(6 \times 10^{-7}) + (0.6 \times 10^{-7})} = \frac{6}{6.6} = 0.91$$

$p = 1 - q = 1 - 0.91 = 0.09$
Thus, the frequencies are 0.0081 AA, 0.1638 Aa, and 0.8281 aa.

22.17

    a. Calculate the effective population size (N_e) for a breeding population of 50 adult males and 50 adult females.

    b. Calculate the effective population size (N_e) for a breeding population of 60 adult males and 40 adult females.

    c. Calculate the effective population size (N_e) for a breeding population of 10 adult males and 90 adult females.

    d. Calculate the effective population size (N_e) for a breeding population of 2 adult males and 98 adult females.

Answer: As discussed in the text, the effective breeding size of a population is given by the equation:

$$N_e = \frac{4 \times N_f \times N_m}{N_f + N_m}$$

where N_f equals the number of breeding females and N_m equals the number of breeding males. Apply this equation to each of the situations described as follows:
    a. $(4 \times 50 \times 50)/100 = 100$
    b. $(4 \times 60 \times 40)/100 = 96$
    c. $(4 \times 10 \times 90)/100 = 36$
    d. $(4 \times 2 \times 98)/100 = 7.8$

22.18 In a population of 40 adult males and 40 adult females, the frequency of allele A is 0.6 and the frequency of allele a is 0.4.
    a. Calculate the 95 percent confidence limits of the allelic frequency for A.

c. What are the 95 percent confidence limits of A if the population consists of 76 females and 4 males?

Answer:

a.

$$N_e = \frac{4 \times N_f \times N_m}{N_f + N_m} = \frac{4 \times 40 \times 40}{40 + 40} = 80$$

$$2s_p = 2 \times \sqrt{\frac{pq}{2N_e}} = 2 \times \sqrt{\frac{0.6 \times 0.4}{2 \times 80}} = 2 \times 0.039 = 0.078$$

The 95% confidence limits of A are $p \pm 2s_p$, or 0.6 ± 0.078, or $0.522 \pounds\ p\ \pounds\ 0.678$.

b.

$$\frac{4 \times 4 \times 4}{4 + 4} = 8$$

$$2s_p = 2 \times \sqrt{\frac{0.6 \times 0.4}{2 \times 8}} = 0.245$$

The 95% confidence limits of A are 0.6 ± 0.245, or $0.355\ \pounds\ p\ \pounds\ 0.845$.

c.

$$\frac{4 \times 76 \times 4}{76 + 4} = 15.2$$

$$2s_p = 2 \times \sqrt{\frac{0.6 \times 0.4}{2 \times 15.2}} = 0.178$$

The 95% confidence limits of A are 0.6 ± 0.178, or $0.422\ \pounds\ p\ \pounds\ 0.778$.

22.19 The land snail *Cepaea nemoralis* is native to Europe but has been accidentally introduced into North America at several localities. These introductions occurred when a few snails were inadvertently transported on plants, building supplies, soil, or other cargo. The snails subsequently multiplied and established large, viable populations in North America.

  Assume that today the average size of *Cepaea* populations found in North America is equal to the average size of *Cepaea* populations in Europe. What predictions can you make about the amounts of genetic variation present in European and North American populations of *Cepaea*? Explain your reasoning.

Answer: Since the gene pool in the present, large North American population is derived from a small number of individuals, a founder effect is likely to have occurred. Thus, genetic drift (random change in allelic frequency due to chance) will influence the North American populations to a greater degree than the European populations. One would expect to see less variation within and greater genetic differentiation among the North American populations. The magnitude of the difference between the native North American population and the introduced population will depend on how many times different European populations were introduced. For example, if relatively large numbers of European snails from multiple localities were introduced many times, the founder effect would not be as marked as if a small number of snails were introduced just once from one location.

22.20   A population of 80 adult squirrels resides on campus, and the frequency of the Est^1 allele among these squirrels is 0.70. Another population of squirrels is found in a nearby woods, and there, the frequency of the Est^1 allele is 0.5. During a severe winter, 20 of the squirrels from the woods population migrate to campus in search of food and join the campus population. What will be the allelic frequency of Est^1 in the campus population after migration?

Answer: Let p_I equal the frequency of A in population I, and p_{II} equal the frequency of A in population II. If individuals in population I migrate to population II and make up proportion m of population II', the new frequency of A in population II' (p'_{II}) is given by:

$$p'_{II} = mp_I + (1 - m)p_{II}$$

Here, $p'_{II} = [20/(20 + 80)](0.50) + \{1 - [20/(20 + 80)]\}(0.70) = 0.66$.

22.21   Upon sampling three populations and determining genotypes, you find the following three genotype distributions. What would each of these distributions imply with regard to selective advantages of population structure?

POPULATION	AA	Aa	aa
1	0.04	0.32	0.64
2	0.12	0.87	0.01
3	0.45	0.10	0.45

Answer: For each population, determine the frequency of the A and a alleles, and compare how the population structure compares to that expected if no selection was occurring. To do this calculation, suppose there were 100 individuals in each population containing 200 alleles.

In population 1, there would be $(0.04)(100)(2) + (0.32)(100)(1) = 40$ A alleles, and $(0.64)(100)(2) + (0.32)(100)(1) = 160$ a alleles. Thus, $f(A) = p = 40/200 = 0.20$, and $f(a) = q = 160/200 = 0.80$. If the population was in Hardy-Weinberg equilibrium, one would expect $p^2 = 0.04$ AA, $2pq = 0.32$ Aa, and 0.64 aa individuals, as is observed. *If selection is acting at all*, it may be acting to maintain the observed frequencies of the A and a alleles in equilibrium.

tion is acting at all, it may be acting to maintain the observed frequencies of the *A* and *a* alleles in equilibrium.

In population 2, there would be $(0.12)(100)(2) + (0.87)(100)(1) = 111$ *A* alleles, and $(0.01)(100)(2) + (0.87)(100)(1) = 89$ *a* alleles. Here, $p = 0.555$ and $q = 0.455$. If the population was in Hardy-Weinberg equilibrium, one would expect $p^2 = 0.308$ *AA*, $2pq = 0.505$ *Aa*, and 0.207 *aa* individuals. The population is not in equilibrium, as there are far more heterozygotes, and far fewer homozygotes than would be expected. This suggests that the heterozygote is being selected for in this population.

In population 3, there would be $(0.45)(100)(2) + (0.10)(100)(1) = 100$ *A* alleles, and $(0.10)(100)(1) + (0.45)(100)(2) = 100$ *a* alleles. Here, $p = q = 0.5$. If the population was in Hardy-Weinberg equilibrium, one would expect $f(AA) = f(aa) = p^2 = q^2 = 0.25$ and $f(Aa) = 2pq = 0.50$. The population is not in equilibrium, as there are far more homozygotes (of either type) and far fewer heterozygotes than expected. This suggests that the heterozygote is being selected against in this population.

22.22   The frequency of two adaptively neutral alleles in a large population is 70 percent *A*: 30 percent *a*. The population is wiped out by an epidemic, leaving only four individuals, who produce many offspring. What is the probability that the population several years later will be 100 percent *AA*? (Assume no mutations.)

Answer: There are a variety of situations in which all individuals would become *AA*. One is that the four "founding" individuals are all *AA*. Since the probability of a single individual being *AA* is $(0.7)^2 = 0.49$, the probability of the four founding individuals being *AA* is $(0.49)^4 = 0.0576$, about $1/17$. Even if all four founding individuals are not *AA*, there will be some chance that the subsequent population may become all *AA*. For example, there is a low, but distinct probability that only *AA* offspring may be had by *Aa* × *AA* parents. Given that "many" offspring are produced, the likelihood of this will be less than $1/17$ [e.g., if ten offspring are produced, the likelihood of all being *AA* in such a cross would be $(1/2)^{10} = 1/1,024$]. Since the alleles are adaptively neutral, it would appear that $1/17$ is an upper bound for the likelihood of a population being 100 percent *AA*.

22.23   A completely recessive gene, through changed environmental circumstances, becomes lethal in a certain population. It was previously neutral, and its frequency was 0.5.
   a.   What was the genotype distribution when the recessive genotype was not selected against?
   b.   What will be the allelic frequency after one generation in the altered environment?
   c.   What will be the allelic frequency after two generations?

Answer:
   a.   Let $p = f(A)$, and $q = f(a)$. Initially, $p = q = 0.5$, so $p^2 = f(AA) = q^2 = f(aa) = (0.5)^2 = 0.25$. $f(Aa) = 2pq = 0.50$.

b. If *aa* individuals are now lethal, they will not contribute to the gene pool in the next generation. Only *AA* and *Aa* individuals will contribute to the gene pool in the next generation. The allele frequency will be

$$f(A) = \frac{(0.25 \times 2) + (0.50 \times 1)}{(0.25 \times 2) + (0.50 \times 2)} = \frac{1.0}{1.5} = 0.67$$

$$f(a) = \frac{(0.50 \times 1)}{(0.25 \times 2) + (0.50 \times 2)} = \frac{0.5}{1.5} = 0.33$$

c. Given the result of (b), the genotype of the progeny are $p^2 = (0.67)^2 = 0.449$ *AA*, $2pq = 2(0.67)(0.33) = 0.442$ *Aa*, and $q^2 = (0.33)^2 = 0.109$ *aa*. As in part (b), only *AA* and *Aa* individuals will contribute to the gene pool in the next generation. The allele frequency will be

$$f(A) = \frac{(0.449 \times 2) + (0.442 \times 1)}{(0.449 \times 2) + (0.442 \times 2)} = 0.75$$

$$f(a) = \frac{(0.442 \times 1)}{(0.449 \times 2) + (0.442 \times 2)} = 0.25$$

Can you show that the following statement is true under the conditions of this problem? If the last generation in the unaltered environment is considered to be generation number one, then after *n* generations, the frequency of *A* will be $n/(n+1)$ and the frequency of *a* will be $1/(n+1)$.

22.24 Human individuals homozygous for a certain recessive autosomal gene die before reaching reproductive age. Despite of this removal of all affected individuals, there is no indication that homozygotes occur less frequently in succeeding generations. To what might you attribute the continued presence of appearance of recessives?

Answer: There are several reasons recessives may appear in a constant frequency. (1) Perhaps most important is that new mutations of *A* to *a* could occur at a low, but constant rate. (2) There could also be a selective advantage to heterozygotes (overdominance). (3) There could be nonrandom mating within the population (e.g., positive assortative mating, inbreeding). (4) There could be a low, but steady frequency of migration of heterozygotes into the population. Each of these possibilities violates assumptions made for a population in Hardy-Weinberg equilibrium, and allows maintenance of a recessive allele that is deleterious as a homozygote. (Problem 22.23 considers the consequences of such an allele if the assumptions were not violated.) (5) If the homozygous recessive condition is a relatively rare occurrence, the frequency of *a* alleles in the population is very low. As a result, only a very small proportion of the *a* alleles would be found in homozygotes; almost all *a* alleles would be found in heterozygotes (protected polymorphism). The few generations for which data have been recorded may not be enough to see a decline in the number of homozygotes.

22.25   A completely recessive gene ($Q1$) has a frequency of 0.7 in a large population, and the $Q1Q1$ homozygote has a relative fitness of 0.6.
   a.   What will be the frequency of $Q1$ after one generation of selection?
   b.   If there is no dominance at this locus (the fitness of the heterozygote is intermediate to the fitnesses of the homozygotes), what will the allelic frequency be after one generation of selection?
   c.   If $Q1$ is dominant, what will the allelic frequency be after one generation of selection?

Answer: See Table 22.12. For parts (a) and (b), $p = 0.3$, $q = 0.7$, and $s = 1 - W = 0.4$.
   a.   If there is selection against the recessive homozygotes, after one generation,

$$Dq = \frac{-spq2}{1 - sq2} = \frac{-(0.4)(0.3)(0.7)2}{1 - (0.4)(0.7)2} = -0.073$$

$q1 = 0.7 - 0.073 = 0.627$

   b.   If there is selection with no dominance, so that the fitness of the heterozygote is intermediate between the two homozygotes,

$$Dq = \frac{-spq/2}{1 - sq} = \frac{-(0.4)(0.3)(0.7)/2}{1 - (0.4)(0.7)} = -0.0583$$

$q1 = 0.7 - 0.0583 = 0.642$

   c.   To select against $Q1$ as a dominant allele, let p equal the frequency of the dominant allele being selected against: $p = 0.7$, $q = 0.3$, and $s = 0.4$.

$$Dp = \frac{-spq2}{1 - s + sq2} = \frac{-(0.4)(0.7)(0.3)3}{1 - s + sq2} = \frac{-(0.4)(0.7)(0.3)2}{1 - 0.4 + (0.4)(0.3)2} = -0.04$$

$p1 = 0.70 - 0.04 = 0.66$

22.26   As discussed earlier in this chapter, the gene for sickle-cell anemia exhibits heterozygote advantage. An individual who is an *Hb-A/Hb-S* heterozygote has increased resistance to malaria and therefore has greater fitness than the *Hb-A/Hb-A* homozygote, who is susceptible to malaria, and the *Hb-S/Hb-S* homozygote, who has sickle-cell anemia. Suppose that the fitness values of the genotypes in Africa are as presented here:

   Hb-A/Hb-A = 0.88

   Hb-A/Hb-S = 1.00

   Hb-S/Hb-S = 0.14

Give the expected equilibrium frequencies of the sickle-cell gene (*Hb-S*).

Answer: From the text discussion, at equilibrium, $p = f(Hb\text{-}A) = t/(t + s)$, and $q = f(Hb\text{-}S) = s/(s + t)$, where t equals the selection coefficient of *Hb-S/Hb-S*, and s equals the selection coefficient of *Hb-A/Hb-A*. Since *fitness* = 1 − *selection coefficient*, $f(Hb\text{-}S) = 0.12/(0.12 + 0.86) = 0.122$.

22.27   Achondroplasia, a type of dwarfism in humans, is caused by an autosomal dominant gene. The mutation rate for achondroplasia is about 5×10^{-5}, and the fitness of achondroplastic dwarfs has been estimated to be about 0.2, compared with unaffected individuals. What is the equilibrium frequency of the achondroplasia gene based on this mutation rate and fitness value?

Answer: For a dominant allele, the frequency at equilibrium $\hat{p} = u/s$, where u equals the mutation rate, and s is the selection coefficient (= 1 − fitness). Here, $\hat{p} = 5 \times 10^{-5}/0.8 = 6.25 \times 10^{-5}$.

22.28   To answer the following questions, consider the spontaneous mutation frequencies tabulated in Table 22.6.
   a. In humans, why is the frequency of forward mutations to neurofibromatosis an order of magnitude larger than that for the other human diseases?
   b. In *E. coli*, why is the frequency of mutations to arabinose dependence two to four orders of magnitude larger than the frequency of mutations to leucine, arginine, or tryptophan independence?
   c. What factors influence the spontaneous mutation frequency for a specific trait?

Answer:
   a. There are many potential reasons. If all forms of the disease are caused by mutations in one gene, then that gene appears to be more highly mutable. This may be because the gene is very large, and so there is a larger amount of DNA that can be altered by randomly distributed point mutations, or because the gene may have some unusual sequence structure that results in mutation, for example, mutations due to DNA replication errors or transposon insertion. Alternatively, the rate could be large because mutations in any one of a number of genes can cause an identical disease phenotype.
   b. Arabinose dependence will result from mutations in any of the genes whose function is required to utilize arabinose, while mutations to leucine, arginine, or tryptophan independence require very specific synthetic functions to be "added" to the cell. The former is much more likely to occur by single new mutations than the latter.
   c. Factors include the number of genes that are required for the appearance of the trait, the size of those genes, the presence of genes that modify the mutation rate, and environmental factors.

22.29   The frequencies of the L^M and L^N blood group alleles are the same in each of the populations I, II, and III, but the genotypes' frequencies are not the same, as shown in the following table. Which of the populations is most likely to show each of the following characteristics: random mating, inbreeding, genetic drift? Explain your answers.

	$L^M L^M$	$L^M L^N$	$L^N L^N$
I	0.50	0.40	0.10
II	0.49	0.42	0.09
III	0.45	0.50	0.05

Answer: First calculate the frequencies of each allele. In population I, one has [(0.5 × 2) + (0.4 × 1)/2] = 0.7 *M*, and 0.3 *N*. Similarly, *M* = 0.7 and *N* = 0.3 in populations II and III also. A population in Hardy-Weinberg equilibrium would have $p^2 = (0.7)^2 = 0.49$ *M–M*, $2pq = 2(0.7)(0.3) = 0.42$ *M–N*, and $q^2 = (0.3)^2 = 0.09$ *N–N*. As population II shows these features, it must be in Hardy-Weinberg equilibrium, and would be expected to exhibit random mating. Inbreeding results in an increase in the frequency of homozygotes, and would be associated with population I (but not III). Genetic drift is random change in allelic frequency due to chance, and can be explained by random effects, a small effective population size, founder or bottleneck effects, or sampling error. Genetic drift could be associated with either population I or population III. Because the frequencies in populations I and III are fairly close to those of an equilibrium population, sampling error in a population in Hardy-Weinberg equilibrium could also explain the results seen.

22.30   DNA was collected from 100 people randomly sampled from a given human population and was digested with the restriction enzyme *Bam*HI; the fragments were separated by electrophoresis and then transferred to a membrane filter using the Southern blot technique. The blots were probed with a particular cloned sequence. Three different patterns of hybridization were seen on the blots. Some DNA samples (56 of them) showed a single band of 6.3 kb, others (6) showed a single band at 4.1 kb, and yet others (38) showed both the 6.3- and the 4.1- kb bands.
   a.   Interpret these results in terms of *Bam*HI sites.
   b.   What are the frequencies of the restriction site alleles?
   c.   Does this population appear to be in Hardy-Weinberg equilibrium for the relevant restriction sites?

Answer:
   a.   One explanation is that a restriction fragment length polymorphism exists in the population. On some chromosomes, an RFLP having a size of 4.1 kb is found, while on others, the 6.3 kb fragment is found. Individuals having just one size band are homozygotes, while individuals with two different-sized bands are heterozygous. The difference in sizes of the fragments could result from a miss-

ing site in the 6.3 kb individuals, or the insertion of a 2.2 kb piece of DNA between two sites that are normally 4.1 kb apart.

b. Homozygotes have two identical alleles, while heterozygotes have two different alleles. There are $(56 \times 2) + 38 = 150$, 6.3 kb alleles, and $(6 \times 2) + 38 = 50$, 4.1 kb alleles. Let q equal the frequency of 6.3 kb alleles, and p equal the frequency of 4.1 kb alleles. Then $q = 0.75$ and $p = 0.25$.

c. For a population in Hardy-Weinberg equilibrium, one would expect $q^2 = 0.5625$ 6.3 kb homozygotes (compared to the 0.56 seen), $2pq = 0.375$ heterozygotes (compared to the 0.38 seen) and $p^2 = 0.0625$ 4.1 kb homozygotes (compared to the 0.06 seen). The population appears to be in Hardy-Weinberg equilibrium.

22.31   Fifty tiger salamanders from one pond in west Texas were examined for genetic variation by using the technique of protein electrophoresis. The genotype of each salamander was determined for five loci (AmPep, ADH, PGM, MDH, and LDH-1). No variation was found at AmPep, ADH, and LDH-1; in other words, all individuals were homozygous for the same allele at these loci. The following numbers of genotypes were observed at the MDH and PGM loci.

MDH GENOTYPES	NUMBER OF INDIVIDUALS	PGM GENOTYPES	NUMBER OF INDIVIDUALS
AA	11	DD	35
AB	35	DE	10
BB	4	EE	5

Calculate the proportion of polymorphic loci and the heterozygosity for this population.

Answer: Since five loci were examined, and only two have more than one allele, $(2/5)(100\%) = 40\%$ of the loci are polymorphic. Heterozygosity is calculated by averaging the frequency of heterozygotes for each locus. The frequency of heterozygotes for the AmPep, ADH, and LDH-1 loci is zero. At MDH, 35 out of 50 individuals were heterozygous (0.70). At PGM, 10 out of 50 individuals were heterozygous (0.20). Thus, the average heterozygosity is

$$\frac{0 + 0 + 0 + 0.7 + 0.2}{5} = 0.18.$$

22.32   The success of a population depends in part on its reproductive rate, which may be affected by low genetic variability. Vyse and his colleagues have been interested in the conservation of small populations of grizzly bears, studying 304 members of 30 grizzly bear family groups in a population in northwestern Alaska. They have identified a set of polymorphic loci with these alleles, allele frequencies, and observed heterozygosities (obs. het.):

LOCUS *G1A*		LOCUS *G10X*		LOCUS *G10C*		LOCUS *G10L*	
Obs. het.: 0.776		Obs. het.: 0.783		Obs. het.: 0.770		Obs. het.: 0.651	
Allele	Frequency	Allele	Frequency	Allele	Frequency	Allele	Frequency
A194	0.398	X137	0.395	C105	0.355	L155	0.487
A184	0.240	X135	0.211	C103	0.257	L157	0.276
A192	0.211	X141	0.211	C111	0.240	L161	0.128
A180	0.086	X133	0.102	C113	0.092	L159	0.089
A190	0.036	X131	0.053	C107	0.043	L171	0.013
A200	0.016	X129	0.030	C101	0.010	L163	0.007
A186	0.007			C109	0.003		
A188	0.006						

The genotypes of a mother bear and her three cubs are shown here.

MOTHER	CUB #1	CUB #2	CUB #3
A184, A192	A184, A194	A184, A192	A184, A194
X135, X137	X135, X137	X133, X135	X137, X141
C105, C113	C105, C111	C105, C105	C111, C113
L155, L159	L155, L157	L159, L161	L155, L155

a. How do the observed heterozygosities compare with the expected heterozygosities? On the basis of this information, can you tell whether this grizzly bear population is in Hardy-Weinberg equilibrium?

b. What can you infer about the paternity of the mother's three cubs? How might paternity information affect the genetic variability and the effective population size in this population of grizzly bears?

Answer:

a. The expected heterozygosity is 1 – (frequency of expected homozygotes). If the frequency of alleles in the population are p_1, p_2, p_3 ... p_n, the expected frequency of homozygotes is $p_1^2 + p_2^2 + p_3^2 + ... p_n^2$. For locus *G1A*, the expected frequency of homozygotes is $(0.398)^2 + (0.240)^2 + (0.211)^2 + (0.086)^2 + (0.036)^2 + (0.016)^2 + (0.007)^2 + (0.006)^2 = 0.270$, and the expected heterozygosity is $1 - 0.270 = 0.730$. The expected heterozygosities for the other loci are *G10X*, 0.741; *G10C*, 0.740; *G10L*, 0.662. These are approximately the observed frequencies of heterozygosities. Since the numbers and types of different heterozygotes is not given, it is not possible to employ the chi-square test to directly evaluate if the population is in Hardy-Weinberg equilibrium. The population appears to be close to Hardy-Weinberg equilibrium.

b. The three cubs of the mother show evidence of multiple paternity. For each of the loci *G10X* and *G10L*, three alleles present in the cubs must have been contributed paternally (*G10X*: X133, X135 or X137, X141; *G10L*: L155, L157, L161). This could only have happened if the cubs were sired by at least two different fathers. Multiple paternity within one set of cubs would tend to increase the genetic variability in the population, as it would allow a larger number of males to contribute gametes seen in the next generation. Since $N_e = (4 \times N_f \times N_m)/(N_f + N_m)$, a larger N_m will tend to increase the effective population size.

22.33   What factors cause genetic drift?

Answer: Genetic drift arises from random change in allelic frequency due to chance. Random factors producing mortality in natural populations and sampling error can lead to genetic drift. Its causes include a small effective population size over many generations, a small number of founders (founder effect), and a reduction in population size (bottleneck effect).

22.34   What are the primary effects of the following evolutionary processes on the gene and genotypic frequencies of a population?
   a. mutation
   b. migration
   c. genetic drift
   d. inbreeding

Answer:
   a. Mutation will lead to change in allelic frequencies within a population if no other forces are acting. It will introduce genetic variation. If the effective population size is small, mutation may lead to genetic differentiation among populations.
   b. Migration will increase the population size, and has the potential to disrupt a Hardy-Weinberg equilibrium. It can increase genetic variation and may influence the evolution of allelic frequencies within populations. Over many generations, migration will reduce divergence among populations, and equalize allelic frequencies among populations.
   c. Genetic drift produces changes in allelic frequencies within a population. It can reduce genetic variation and increase the homozygosity within a population. Over time, it leads to genetic change. When several populations are compared, genetic drift can lead to increased genetic differences among populations.
   d. Inbreeding will increase the homozygosity within a population and decrease its genetic variation.

22.35   Explain how overdominance leads to an increased frequency of sickle-cell anemia in areas where malaria is widespread.

Answer: Overdominance results when a heterozygote genotype has higher fitness than either of the homozygotes. The two alleles of the heterozygote are maintained in a population because both are favored in the heterozygote genotype. In the case of the sickle-cell allele, heterozygotes for *Hb-A/Hb-S* are at a selective advantage because the hemoglobin mixture in these individuals provides an unfavorable environment for the growth of malarial parasites. Thus, heterozygotes have higher fitness than *Hb-A/Hb-A* homozygotes who are susceptible to malaria. Heterozygotes also have higher fitness than *Hb-S/Hb-S* homozygotes who suffer from sickle-cell anemia. The favoring of the sickle-cell allele *Hb-S* in the heterozygote results in its relatively high frequency in areas with malaria.

22.36   Since 1968, Pinter has studied the population dynamics of the montane vole, a small rodent in the Grand Teton mountains in Wyoming. For more than 25 years, severe periodic fluctuations in population density have been negatively correlated with precipitation levels: Vole density sharply declines every few years when spring precipitation is extremely high.

a. Propose several hypotheses concerning the genetic structure of the population of montane voles in two separate sampling sites if
   i.   there is negligible migration of voles between sampling sites
   ii   there is substantial migration of voles between sampling sites
b. How would you gather data to evaluate these hypotheses

Answer:

a. The cyclical decline in population density could cause a cyclically repeated bottleneck effect at each of the sampling sites. This would lead to the loss of some genes from the gene pool as a result of chance, and founder effects. If there were negligible migration between sampling sites, the populations would most likely diverge in their allelic frequencies through genetic drift. There would be more variance in allelic frequency among the small populations at each sampling site. If there were substantial migration between sampling sites, there would be reciprocal gene flow among the populations. This would increase the amount of genetic variation in the populations at each sampling site, and reduce the divergence between the populations. If there were cyclical, sharp declines in the vole population, it is unlikely that the population would be in Hardy-Weinberg equilibrium.

b. First, randomly trap a subset of the voles and sample tissue or blood from them. Then, identify a set of polymorphic loci (using protein electrophoresis, DNA sequencing, or RFLPs), and estimate the heterozygosity and allele frequencies at these loci. Use this information to compare populations sampled at each of the study sites, and estimate the degree of homogeneity or divergence of the two populations.

22.37   What are some of the advantages of using DNA sequences to infer the strength of evolutionary processes?

Answer: Using DNA sequence information to infer the strength of evolutionary processes has several advantages. DNA sequences provide highly accurate and reliable information, allow direct comparison of the genetic differences among organisms, are easily quantified, and can be used in all organisms.

22.38 Multiple, geographically isolated populations of tortoises exist on the Galapagos Islands off the coast of Ecuador. Several populations are endangered, partly because of hunting and partly because of illegal capture and trade. In principle, a significant number of tortoises in captivity (either in zoos or private collections) could be used to repopulate some of the endangered populations.

   a. Suppose you are interested in returning a particular captive tortoise to its native subpopulation, but you have no record of its capture. How could you determine its original subpopulation?

   b. A researcher planned to characterize one subpopulation of tortoises. In her first field season, she tagged and collected blood samples from all animals in the subpopulation. When she returns a year later, she cannot locate two animals. She learns that two untagged, smuggled tortoises are being held by U.S. customs officials. How can she assess whether the smuggled animals are from her field site?

Answer: In both instances, protein electrophoresis, RFLP analyses, microsatellite and DNA sequence analysis of specific genes could be used to gather information on the genotype of the captured individuals and members of each island population. In (a), the captured individual should be returned to the subpopulation from which it shows the least genetic variation. In (b), evaluate the genotype of the two missing tortoises using DNA from the previously collected blood samples, and compare these genotypes to the genotypes of the two captured tortoises. If a captured animal was taken from the field site, its genotype will exactly match a genotype obtained from one of the blood samples.

23

QUANTITATIVE GENETICS

CHAPTER OUTLINE

REVIEW OF KEY TERMS, SYMBOLS, AND CONCEPTS

In your own words, write a brief, precise definition of each term in the groups below. Check your definitions using the text. Then, develop a concept map using the terms in each list.

1	2	3
quantitative genetics	quantitative genetics	heritability
discontinuous trait	population	broad-sense heritability.
continuous trait	sample	narrow-sense heritability

1	2	3
polygenic trait	frequency distribution	phenotypic variance (V_P)
norm of reaction	normal distribution	genetic variance (V_G)
multifactorial trait	binomial distribution	environmental variance (V_E)
familial trait	binomial expansion	genetic-environmental
penetrance	mean	interaction(V_{GxE})
expressivity	variance	genetic-environmental
pleiotropy	standard deviation	covariation (COV_{GxE})
epistasis	analysis of variance	genetic variance (V_G)
polygene	(ANOVA)	additive genetic variance
contributing alleles	covariance	(V_A)
noncontributing alleles	correlation *vs.*	dominance variance (V_D)
polygene or multiple gene	cause and effect	interaction variance (V_I)
hypothesis for	correlation *vs.* identity	environmental variance (V_E)
quantitative inheritance	regression	general environmental
	regression line	effects (V_{Eg})
	regression coefficient	special environmental
	phenotypic correlation	Effects (V_{Es})
	genetic correlation	maternal effects (V_{Em})
	pleiotropy	evolution
	positive *vs.* negative	artificial selection
	correlation	selection response
		selection differential
		narrow-sense heritability

THINKING ANALYTICALLY

Quantitative genetics deals with important, but complex issues. Some of the concepts used in the analysis of quantitative traits are subtle. Throughout the chapter, clear and precise thinking is required. In order to sort out the basis for a quantitative trait, it is important to define the contribution of several different factors. These factors can include the environment as well as multiple genes that themselves may or may not interact. Central to the analysis of a quantitative trait is identifying the degree to which variation in a phenotype can be associated with one or more of these factors. Consequently, understanding how variation is measured and used is of the utmost importance in understanding quantitative genetics.

First, gain a solid understanding of the terms used and the concepts they convey. Geneticists have developed a substantial conceptual framework in which to consider quantitative traits. Some concepts are easy to misunderstand, and to understand what something *is*, it is often important to define what it *is not*. For example, the idea of heritability has important qualifications and limitations. Heritability is a measure of the *proportion of phenotypic variance* that results from genetic differences. It is *not* a measure of the extent to which a trait is genetic, or what proportion of an individual's phenotype is genetic. It is also not fixed for a particular trait, or a measurement of genetic differences between populations. The concepts underlying quantitative genetics have significant utility, but only if they are correctly and clearly applied.

Second, concentrate on understanding the statistical methods that are used to analyze data on quantitative traits. Your understanding should consist of more than just knowledge of how to crunch numbers by plugging them into an equation. You need to get a feel for what a statistic tells you about a data set.

Third, relate how measurements are made and analyzed to the concepts that have been developed to explain the inheritance of quantitative traits. For example, relate a measurement of heritability to a selection response. Then, explain how you would achieve a particular breeding objective through selection. By doing this, you will obtain a better understanding of the power and utility of quantitative genetics.

QUESTIONS FOR PRACTICE

Multiple Choice Questions

1. Which of the following could be used to describe coat colors in mice?
   a. continuous trait
   b. discontinuous trait
   c. polygenic trait
   d. quantitative trait
   e. both b and c

2. What can generally be said about quantitative traits such as crop yield, rate of weight gain, human birth weight, blood pressure, and the number of eggs laid by *Drosophila*?
   a. They are intractable to molecular genetics.
   b. They are multifactorial.
   c. They are discontinuous.
   d. They are not heritable because they are polygenic.

3. Which statement below best describes the aims of a quantitative genetic analysis of a trait?
   a. To determine whether genes or the environment control a trait
   b. To determine the best breeding strategy to retain a trait
   c. To determine how much of the phenotypic variation associated with a trait in a population is due to genetic variation and how much is due to environmental variation
   d. To determine whether a trait is controlled by nature versus nurture

4. The description of a population in terms of the number of individuals that display varying degrees of expression of a character or range of phenotypes is a
   a. polygraph.
   b. polynomial.
   c. normal distribution.
   d. frequency distribution.

5. The general expression for the binomial expansion is
   a. $(p + q)^n$.
   b. $(a^2 + b^2)$.

c. $(a + b)^2$.

d. $a2 + 2ab + b2$.

6. Which <u>two</u> of the following accurately describe the term *variance?*

a. It is a reflection of the accuracy of an estimated measurement.

b. It is a measure of how much a set of individual measurements is spread out around the mean.

c. It is the average value of a set of measurements.

d. It is equal to $(\Sigma x_i/n)$.

e. It is equal to $\dfrac{\Sigma(x_i - \bar{x})2}{n-1}$.

7. What is heritability?

a. The proportion of a population's phenotype that is attributable to genetic factors.

b. The proportion of a population's phenotypic variation that is attributable to genetic factors.

c. The degree to which family members resemble one another.

d. The degree to which a continuous trait is controlled by genetic factors.

8. The proportion of the phenotypic variance that consists of genetic variance, additive or otherwise, is called

a. heritability.

b. broad-sense heritability.

c. narrow-sense heritability.

d. phenotypic variance derived from genetic-environmental interactions.

9. The narrow-sense heritability of a trait is determined to be very close to 1.0. Which of the following inferences can be made?

a. The trait will be difficult to select for.

b. The trait can be readily selected for.

c. Most of the phenotypic variance results from additive genetic variance.

d. Most of the phenotypic variance results from environmental variance.

e. Both a and c.

f. Both b and c.

10. In a population of chickens raised under controlled conditions, body weight is negatively correlated with egg production, but positively correlated with egg weight. Because of market conditions, a farmer is interested in producing lots of small eggs. What selection strategy might be beneficial?

a. Select for smaller hens.

b. Select for larger hens.

11. Which one of the following statements is true?

a. Traits shared by family members show high heritability.

b. Artificial and natural selection can occur in a genetically uniform population.

c. If heritability is high in each of two populations and the populations differ markedly in a trait, the populations are genetically different.

d. The selection response depends on (1) the proportion of genetic variance that results from additive genetic variance and (2) the difference between the mean phenotypes of the selected parents and the mean phenotype of the unselected population.

Answers: 1e; 2b; 3c; 4d; 5a; 6b & e; 7b; 8b; 9f; 10a; 11d.

Thought Questions

1. Assume that mature fruit weight in pumpkins is a quantitative trait. In the following experiment, environmental factors (weather, soil, etc.) are uniform. Two pumpkin varieties, both of which produce fruit with a mean weight of 20 lb, are crossed. The F_1 produces 20-lb pumpkins. The F_2 plants, however, give the following results:

Mean fruit wt. (lb)	5	12.5	20	27.5	35
Number of plants	19	82	119	79	21

   Explain these results: Postulate how many genes are involved and how much each contributes to fruit weight.

2. Distinguish between heritability, broad-sense heritability, and narrow-sense heritability. In what ways can the latter two quantities be measured, and how can they be put to use by plant and animal breeders?

3. What statistics from a regression analysis are used to estimate narrow-sense heritability?

4. What sources contribute to the phenotypic variance associated with a quantitative trait?

5. Distinguish between a genetic correlation and a phenotypic correlation. In particular, address how a phenotypic correlation might exist when the trait is, or is not, influenced by a common set of genes.

6. Even though a positive correlation exists between alcohol consumption and the number of Baptist ministers, there is thought to be no causal relationship between these two phenomena. Can you think of other correlations that are likely to be true, but which clearly demonstrate that correlations (whether positive or negative) do not imply a cause and effect, and that a correlation is not the same thing as an identity?

7. Defend each of the following statements:
   a. Broad-sense heritability does not indicate the extent to which a trait is genetic.
   b. Heritability does not indicate what proportion of an individual's phenotype is genetic.
   c. Heritability is not fixed for a trait.
   d. If heritability is high in two populations, and the populations differ markedly in a particular trait, one cannot assume that the populations are genetically different.
   e. Familial traits do not necessarily have high heritability.

8. If a population is phenotypically homogeneous for a particular trait, can you predict whether it has a high narrow-sense heritability? If not, what additional information would you need?

9. Why is calculating narrow-sense heritability values for some quantitative human traits especially difficult?

10. Distinguish between a selection differential and a selection response.

11. The mean height in two separate populations A and B is identical and is five feet eight inches. The variance in population A is 14 inches while the variance in population B is 3 inches. In which population would a six-foot tall person be more uncommon?

12. In a single population, is it likely that artificial selection will be equally effective at producing changes in three different traits? Why or why not?

Thought Questions for Media

After reviewing the media on the *iGenetics* CD-ROM, try to answer these questions.

1. In the *Depicting Quantitative Inheritance* animation, a cross of wheat with red kernels to wheat with white kernels gave wheat with pink kernels. Why does this suggest that this trait shows incomplete dominance?
2. What data given in the animation allow one to rule out incomplete dominance as an explanation for the results illustrated in the animation?
3. An alternate explanation for the results illustrated in the animation was that two independently assorting genes controlled wheat-kernel color. Why was this explanation also ruled out?
4. In polygenic inheritance, what is a contributing allele? What is a noncontributing allele? How many contributing alleles can be present at one gene? How many contributing alleles can be present in one organism?
5. How does the explanation of two independently assorting genes with contributing and noncontributing alleles differ from the simpler explanation of two independently assorting genes?
6. Explain why, even though a contributing allele contributes a defined amount of pigment to the red color of the wheat kernel, wheat kernel color still appears to show continuous variation.

SOLUTIONS TO TEXT PROBLEMS

23.1   The following measurements of head width and wing length were made on a series of steamer-ducks:

SPECIMEN	HEAD WIDTH (cm)	WING LENGTH (cm)
1	2.75	30.3
2	3.20	36.2
3	2.86	31.4
4	3.24	35.7
5	3.16	33.4
6	3.32	34.8
7	2.52	27.2
8	4.16	52.7

a. Calculate the mean and the standard deviation of head width and of wing length for these eight birds.
b. Calculate the correlation coefficient for the relationship between head width and wing length in this series of ducks.
c. What conclusions can you make about the association between head width and wing length in steamer ducks?

Answer:

a. The mean is obtained by summing the individual values and dividing by the total number of values. The mean head width is $25.21/8 = 3.15$ cm, and the mean wing length is $281.7/8 = 35.21$ cm.

The standard deviation equals the square root of the variance (the square root of s^2). The variance is computed by squaring the sum of the difference between each measurement and the mean value, and dividing this sum by the number of measurements minus one. One has:

$$s_{headwidth} = \sqrt{s^2} = \sqrt{\frac{\Sigma(x_i - \bar{x})^2}{n-1}} = \sqrt{\frac{1.70}{7}} = \sqrt{0.24} = 0.49 \text{ cm}$$

$$s_{winglength} = \sqrt{s^2} = \sqrt{\frac{\Sigma(x_i - \bar{x})^2}{n-1}} = \sqrt{\frac{413.35}{7}} = \sqrt{59.05} = 7.68 \text{ cm}$$

b. The correlation coefficient, r, is calculated from the covariance, *cov*, of two quantities. Let head width be represented by x, and wing length be represented by y. r is defined as:

$$r = \frac{cov_{xy}}{s_x s_y} = \frac{\dfrac{\Sigma x_i y_i - \dfrac{1}{n}(\Sigma x_i \Sigma y_i)}{n-1}}{s_x s_y}$$

The first factor $(\Sigma x_i y_i)$ is obtained by taking the sum of the products of the individual measurements of head width and the corresponding measurements for wing length. The next factor $(\Sigma x_i \Sigma y_i)/n$ is the product of the sums of the two sets of measurements divided by the number of pairs of measurements. The difference between these values is then divided by $(n–1)$, and then by the products of the standard deviations of each measurement. One has:

$$r = \frac{\dfrac{913 - (1/8)(25.21 \times 281.7)}{7}}{0.49 \times 7.68} = \frac{3.61}{3.76} = 0.96$$

c. Head width and wing length show a strong positive correlation, nearly 1.0. This means that ducks with larger heads will almost always have longer wings, and ducks with smaller heads will almost always have smaller wings.

23.2   Answer the following questions:

a. In a family of six children, what is the probability that three will be girls and three will be boys?

b. In a family of five children, what is the probability that one will be a boy and four will be girls?

c. What is the probability that in a family of six children, all will be boys?

Answer:

a. Three boys and three girls can be obtained in a variety of different orders, and each of these must be considered to determine the probability of obtaining this result. One could determine the number of different orders that are possible, and then use the sum rule and add together the probability of obtaining three boys and three girls in each possible order. It is easier to use the binomial expansion than to work out all of the ways in which these offspring can be obtained. The binomial expansion is given by

$$p(s,t) = \frac{n!}{s!\,t!}\, a^s b^t$$

Here, s equals the number of the first class (here, say the number of girls, so $s = 3$), t equals the number of the other class (here, the number of boys, so $t = 3$), n equals the total number in both classes (here $n = 6$), a is the probability of the first event ($p(girl) = 1/2$) and b is the probability of the second event ($p(boy) = 1/2$). Substituting these values into the equation, one has:

$$p(3 \text{ girls}, 3 \text{ boys}) = [6!/(3!3!)] \times (1/2)^3 \times (1/2)^3 = 20/64 = 0.3125$$

b. Again, use the binomial expansion, with $n = 5$, $s = 4$, and $t = 1$. One has $p(4 \text{ girls}, 1 \text{ boy}) = [5!/(4!1!)] \times (1/2)^1 \times (1/2)^4 = 5/32 = 0.15625$.

c. One could again use the binomial expansion ($n = 6$, $s = 0$, $t = 6$, $a = b = 1/2$, note that $0! = 1$), but since there is only one way of obtaining six boys, it is straightforward to do this calculation without the binomial expansion. The chance of obtaining one boy is 1/2. The chance of obtaining six boys (use the product rule) is $(1/2)^6 = 1/64 = 0.015625$.

23.3   In flipping a coin, there is a 50 percent chance of obtaining heads and a 50 percent chance of obtaining tails on each flip. If you flip a coin 10 times, what is the probability of obtaining exactly 5 heads and 5 tails?

Answer: As in part (a) of Problem 23.2, there are a variety of different ways to obtain this result. Use the binomial expansion, with $n = 10$, $a = b = 1/2$, $s = t = 5$.

$$p = \frac{10!}{5!\,5!} \times \left(\frac{1}{2}\right)^5 \times \left(\frac{1}{2}\right)^5 = \frac{252}{1024} = 0.246$$

23.4   The F_1 generation from a cross of two pure-breeding parents that differ in a size character usually is no more variable than the parents. Explain.

Answer: The degree of phenotypic variability is related to the degree of genetic variability. Since each pure-breeding parent is homozygous for the genes (however many there are) controlling the size character, each parent is homogeneous in type. A cross of two pure-breeding strains will generate an F_1 heterozygous for those loci controlling the size trait. Since the F_1 consists of all heterozygotes, it is genetically as homogeneous as each of the parents. Therefore, it shows no greater variability than the parents.

23.5   If two pure-breeding strains, differing in a size trait, are crossed, is it possible for F_2 individuals to have phenotypes that are more extreme than either grandparent (i.e., be larger than the largest or smaller than the smallest in the parental generation)? Explain.

Answer: If the two grandparents of the F_2 individuals (i.e., the two parents in the parental generation) represent the two extremes for the size trait that is found in the population, the answer is no. However, if neither of the grandparental types is at an extreme end of the size range, and if each strain differs in the appropriate genes, then it is possible to obtain an F_2 that is more extreme than their grandparents. As an example, consider a quantitative trait that is specified by three allelic pairs: A/a, B/b, and C/c. Suppose each capital allele contributes a certain amount to the quantitative character. Then, individuals in the population with six capital alleles (*AA BB CC*) show one extreme, while individuals with six lowercase alleles (*aa bb cc*) show the other extreme. If the parental cross were *AA BB cc* × *aa bb CC*, the F_1 would be *Aa Bb Cc*, and some of the F_2 would be *AA BB CC* and *aa bb cc*. In this scenario, some of the F_2 would have more capital alleles than either grandparent, and so exhibit a more extreme phenotype. Similarly, some of the F_2 will have fewer capital alleles than either grandparent, and so exhibit a more extreme phenotype at the opposite end of the size range.

23.6   Two pairs of genes with two alleles each, A/a and B/b, determine plant height additively in a population. The homozygote *AA BB* is 50 cm tall, and the homozygote *aabb* is 30 cm tall.
a. What is the F_1 height in a cross between the two homozygous stocks?
b. What genotypes in the F_2 will show a height of 40 cm after an $F_1 \times F_1$ cross?
c. What will be the F_2 frequency of the 40-cm plants?

Answer:
a. Since the cross is *AA BB* × *aa bb*, the F_1 genotype will be *Aa Bb*. Since capital alleles determine height additively, and individuals with four capital alleles have a height of 50 cm, while individuals with no capital alleles have a height of

30 cm, each capital allele appears to confer $(50 - 30)/4 = 5$ cm of height over the 30-cm base. *Aa Bb* individuals with two capital alleles should have an intermediate height of 40 cm.

b. Any individuals with two capital alleles will show a height of 40 cm. Thus, *Aa Bb*, *AA bb*, and *aa BB* individuals will be 40 cm high.

c. In the F_2, 1/16 of the progeny are *AA bb*, 4/16 are *Aa Bb*, and 1/16 are *aa BB*. Thus, $6/16 = 3/8$ of the progeny will be 40 cm high.

23.7 Three independently segregating genes (*A, B, C*), each with two alleles, determine height in a plant. Each capital-letter allele adds 2 cm to a base height of 2 cm.

a. What are the heights expected in the F_1 progeny of a cross between homozygous strains *AA BB CC* (14 cm) x *aa bb cc* (2 cm)?

b. What is the distribution of heights (frequency and phenotype) expected in an F_1 x F_1 cross?

c. What proportion of F_2 plants will have heights equal to the heights of the original two parental strains?

d. What proportion of the F_2 will breed true for the height shown by the F_1?

Answer:

a. The cross *AA BB CC* x *aa bb cc* will produce all *Aa Bb Cc* progeny. The three capital letter alleles will add $3 \times 2 = 6$ cm to the 2-cm base height, giving a total of 8 cm.

b. There are a variety of ways to approach this problem. One way is to use a modified Punnett square and another is to use the binomial theorem [use the coefficients of $(a + b)^6$]. Shown here is still another approach, a branch diagram:

					# Capital	
$Aa \times Aa$	$Bb \times Bb$	$Cc \times Cc$		Proportion	Alleles	Ht. (cm)
		1/4 CC	→	1/64	6	14 cm
	1/4 BB	1/2 Cc	→	2/64	5	12 cm
		1/4 cc	→	1/64	4	10 cm
		1/4 CC	→	2/64	5	12 cm
1/4 AA	1/2 Bb	1/2 Cc	→	4/64	4	10 cm
		1/4 cc	→	2/64	3	8 cm
		1/4 CC	→	1/64	4	10 cm
	1/4 bb	1/2 Cc	→	2/64	3	8 cm
		1/4 cc	→	1/64	2	6 cm
		1/4 CC	→	2/64	5	12 cm
	1/4 BB	1/2 Cc	→	4/64	4	10 cm
		1/4 cc	→	2/64	3	8 cm
		1/4 CC	→	4/64	4	10 cm
1/2 Aa	1/2 Bb	1/2 Cc	→	8/64	3	8 cm
		1/4 cc	→	4/64	2	6 cm
		1/4 CC	→	2/64	3	8 cm
	1/4 bb	1/2 Cc	→	4/64	2	6 cm
		1/4 cc	→	2/64	1	4 cm
		1/4 CC	→	1/64	4	10 cm
	1/4 BB	1/2 Cc	→	2/64	3	8 cm
		1/4 cc	→	1/64	2	6 cm
		1/4 CC	→	2/64	3	8 cm
1/4 aa	1/2 Bb	1/2 Cc	→	4/64	2	6 cm
		1/4 cc	→	2/64	1	4 cm
		1/4 CC	→	1/64	2	6 cm
	1/4 bb	1/2 Cc	→	2/64	1	4 cm
		1/4 cc	→	1/64	0	2 cm

Add up the proportion of individuals with like heights to obtain:

$1/64 \rightarrow 14$ cm

$6/64 \rightarrow 12$ cm

$15/64 \rightarrow 10$ cm

$20/64 \rightarrow 8$ cm

$15/64 \rightarrow 6$ cm

$6/64 \rightarrow 4$ cm

$1/64 \rightarrow 2$ cm.

c. 1/64 are 2 cm and 1/64 are 14 cm, so the answer is 2/64.

d. None of the F_2 with the height of 8 cm can breed true, because this height depends upon a genotype having three capital-letter alleles, which in turn requires heterozygosity for at least one gene locus.

540   CHAPTER 23

23.8   Repeat Problem 23.7, but assume that each capital-letter allele doubles the existing height; for example, $Aa\ bb\ cc = 4$ cm, $AA\ bb\ cc = 8$ cm, $AA\ Bb\ cc = 16$ cm, and so on.

Answer:

a. Because the base height is 2 cm, the plant height $= 2^{n+1}$, where $n =$ the number of capital-letter alleles. The $Aa\ Bb\ Cc$ F_1 height $= 2^4 = 16$ cm.

b. $1/64 \rightarrow 128$ cm
$6/64 \rightarrow 64$ cm
$15/64 \rightarrow 32$ cm
$20/64 \rightarrow 16$ cm
$15/64 \rightarrow 8$ cm
$6/64 \rightarrow 4$ cm
$1/64 \rightarrow 2$ cm.

c. $2/64$

d. The 16-cm F_1 height is determined by the presence of three dominant alleles. This can only occur if one allelic pair is heterozygous. Consequently, the 16-cm strain could not breed true.

23.9   Assume that three equally and additively contributing pairs of alleles control flower length in nasturtiums. A completely homozygous plant with 10-mm flowers is crossed to a completely homozygous plant with 30-mm flowers. F_1 plants all have flowers about 20 mm long. F_2 plants show a range of lengths from 10 to 30 mm, with about $1/64$ of the F_2 having 10-mm flowers and $1/64$ having 30-mm flowers. What distribution of flower length would you expect to see in the offspring of a cross between an F_1 plant and the 30-mm parent?

Answer: Use the clue that $1/64$ of the F_2 progeny show either extreme trait. Note that (as in problems 23.7 and 23.8 and in text Table 23.5) in an F_2 resulting from a trihybrid cross, the proportion of one kind of homozygote is $1/64$. This suggests that three allelic pairs control this quantitative trait. The completely homozygous 10-mm plant would have six lowercase alleles at three loci, $aa\ bb\ cc$, while the completely homozygous 30-mm plant would have six capital alleles at three loci, $AA\ BB\ CC$. If each capital allele contributes $1/6$ of the 20-mm difference between the two extremes, or $20/6 = 3.33$ mm, the F_1 trihybrid individual would be 20 mm ($= 10$ mm base $+ 3 \times (3.33$ mm/capital allele) $= 20$ mm). Thus, the trait fits a model in which three capital alleles contribute additively to this quantitative trait.

If an F_1 plant is crossed to the 30-mm parent, one would have $Aa\ Bb\ Cc \times AA\ BB\ CC$. This cross would produce $1/8$ each of $Aa\ Bb\ Cc$, $Aa\ Bb\ CC$, $AA\ Bb\ Cc$, $Aa\ BB\ Cc$, $AA\ BB\ Cc$, $AA\ Bb\ CC$, $Aa\ BB\ CC$, and $AA\ BB\ CC$. Thus, there will be $1/8$ that are 30 mm long, $1/8$ that are 20 mm long, $3/8$ that are 23.33 mm long, and $3/8$ that are 26.67 mm long.

23.10   In a particular experiment the mean internode length in spikes (the floral structures) of the barley variety *asplund* was found to be 2.12 mm. In the variety *abed* *binder* the mean internode length was found to be 3.17 mm. The mean of the F_1 of a cross between the two varieties was approximately 2.7 mm. The F_2 gave a continuous range of variation from one parental extreme to the other. Analysis of the F_3 generation showed that in the F_2, 8 out of the total 125 individuals were of the *asplund* type, giving a mean of 2.19 mm. Eight other individuals were similar to the parent *abed binder*, giving a mean internode length of 3.24 mm. Is the internode length in spikes of barley a discontinuous or a quantitative trait? Why?

Answer: Internode length shows the characteristics of a quantitative trait. These characteristics include F_1 progeny that show a phenotype intermediate between the two parental phenotypes, and an F_2 showing a range of phenotypes with extremes in the range of the two parents.

23.11   Assume that the difference between a type of oats yielding about 4 g per plant and a type yielding 10 g is the result of three equal and cumulative multiple-gene pairs *AA BB CC*. If you cross the type yielding 4 g with the type yielding 10 g, what will be the phenotypes of the F_1 and the F_2? What will be their distribution?

Answer: If six equal and cumulatively acting capital alleles result in the addition of 6 g to the base weight of 4 g, each allele contributes 1 g. The F_1 will have the genotype *Aa Bb Cc*, and so have a yield of $4 + 3 = 7$ g. The F_2 will appear in a distribution with relative proportions according to the seven coefficients of the binomial expansion $(a + b)^6$ (see Table 23.5). One expects 1/64 = 4 g, 6/64 = 5 g, 15/64 = 6 g, 20/64 = 7 g, 15/64 = 8 g, 6/64 = 9 g, 1/64 = 10 g.

23.12   Assume that in squashes the difference in fruit weight between a 3-lb type and a 6-lb type results from three allelic pairs, *A/a*, *B/b*, and *C/c*. Each capital-letter allele contributes a half pound to the weight of the squash. From a cross of a 3-lb plant (*aa bb cc*) with a 6-lb plant (*AA BB CC*), what will be the phenotypes (weights) of the F_1 and the F_2? What will be their distribution?

Answer: The F_1 will have the genotype *Aa Bb Cc*, and so have a weight of 4.5 lb. The F_2 is expected to show a distribution predicted by the seven coefficients of the binomial expansion $(a + b)^6$ (see Table 23.5). One should see 1/64 = 3 lb, 6/64 = 3.5 lb, 15/64 = 4 lb, 20/64 = 4.5 lb, 15/64 = 5 lb, 6/64 = 5.5 lb, and 1/64 = 6 lb.

23.13   Refer to the assumptions stated in problem 23.12. Determine the range in fruit weight of the offspring in the following squash crosses: (a) *AA Bb CC × aa Bb Cc*; (b) *AA bb Cc × Aa BB cc*; (c) *aa BB cc × AA BB cc*.

Answer: In each case, one needs to consider the maximum and minimum number of capital-letter alleles that can be contributed to the progeny, noting that each contributes 0.5 lb above the 3-lb base weight.

a. *AA Bb CC* × *aa Bb Cc*. At least two, and at most five capital alleles can be contributed to the progeny. The progeny weights will range from 4.0 to 5.5 lbs.

b. *AA bb Cc* × *Aa BB cc*. At least two, and at most four capital alleles can be contributed to the progeny. The progeny weights will range from 4.0 to 5.0 lbs.

c. *aa BB cc* × *AA BB cc*. Exactly three capital alleles will be contributed to the progeny. The progeny weight will be 4.5 lbs.

23.14 Assume that the difference between a corn plant 10 dm (decimeters) high and one 26 dm high results from four pairs of equal and cumulative multiple alleles, with the 26-dm plants being *AA BB CC DD* and the 10-dm plants being *aa bb cc dd*.

a. What will be the size and genotype of an F_1 from a cross between these two true-breeding types?

b. Determine the limits of height variation in the offspring from the following crosses:
   (1) *Aa BB cc dd* × *Aa bb Cc dd*;
   (2) *aa BB cc dd* × *Aa Bb Cc dd*;
   (3) *AA BB Cc DD* × *aa BB cc Dd*;
   (4) *Aa Bb Cc Dd* × *Aa bb Cc Dd*.

Answer: Since four pairs of alleles are equally responsible for the 16-dm height increase, each allele contributes 2 dm.

a. A cross of *AA BB CC DD* × *aa bb cc dd* will produce *Aa Bb Cc Dd* progeny. With four capital-letter alleles, the F_1 height will be 18 dm.

b. (1) *Aa BB cc dd* × *Aa bb Cc dd*. The minimum number of capital alleles contributed to the progeny would be one, and the maximum number of capital alleles contributed to the progeny would be four. The height range would be 12 to 18 dm.

(2) *aa BB cc dd* × *Aa Bb Cc dd*. At least one and at most four capital alleles would be contributed to the progeny. The height range would be 12 to 18 dm.

(3) *AA BB Cc DD* × *aa BB cc Dd*. At least four and at most six capital alleles would be contributed to the progeny. The height range would be 18 to 22 dm.

(4) *Aa Bb Cc Dd* × *Aa bb Cc Dd*. A minimum of none and a maximum of seven capital alleles would be contributed to the progeny. The height range would be 10 to 24 dm.

23.15 Refer to the assumptions given in problem 23.14. For this problem two 14-dm corn plants, when crossed, give nothing but 14-dm offspring (case A). Two other 14-dm plants give one 18-dm, four 16-dm, six 14-dm, four 12-dm, and one 10-dm offspring (case B). Two other 14-dm plants, when crossed, give one 16-dm, two 14dm, and one 12-dm offspring (case C). What genotypes for each of these 14-dm parents (cases A, B, and C) would explain these results? Would it be possible to get a plant taller than 48 dm by selection in any of these families?

23.16

Answer: In each of cases A, B, and C, both 14-dm parents must have two capital-letter alleles. Consideration of the possible arrangement of these alleles leads to the solution of cases A, B, and C.

Case A: For two 14-dm plants only to give rise to more 14-dm plants, each of the plants must be homozygous for one of the capital alleles. Both plants could be homozygous for the same capital allele (e.g., *AA bb cc dd* × *AA bb cc dd*), or each could be homozygous for a different capital allele (e.g., *AA bb cc dd* × *aa bb CC dd*). The progeny plants would have two capital alleles, and be 14 dm high.

Case B: The 1 four-capital alleles:4 three-capital alleles:6 two-capital alleles:4 one-capital allele:1 no-capital allele proportions are the coefficients in the binomial expansion of $(a + b)^4$. This result suggests that the parents were heterozygous at the two (identical or different) loci, e.g., *Aa Bb cc dd* × *Aa Bb cc dd*, or *Aa Bb cc dd* × *aa bb Cc Dd*.

Case C: The 1 one-capital allele:2 two-capital alleles:1 three-capital allele proportions are the coefficients in the binomial expansion of $(a + b)^2$. One would expect this ratio if one of the parents was homozygous at one locus, and the other heterozygous at two loci. For example, the parents could be *aa BB cc dd* × *Aa Bb cc dd*, or *aa BB cc dd* × *Aa bb Cc dd*.

Since each capital aliele contributes 2 dm, plants would have to have at least five capital alleles to be taller than 18 dm. To be taller than 48 dm is simply not possible (they would need >(48 – 10)/2 = >17 capital alleles at only four genes!). At most, the plants can have 8 capital alleles and be 10 + 16 = 26-dm tall. In case B, 1/16 of the progeny of the cross *Aa Bb cc dd* x *aa bb Cc Dd* would have four capital alleles, and be 18-dm tall. If this is selfed, the F_2 would have 56/256 20-dm, 28/256 22-dm, 8/256 24-dm, and 1/256 26-dm tall plants.

23.16   Pigmentation in the imaginary river-bottom dweller *Mucus yuccas* is a quantitative character controlled by a set of five independently segregating polygenes with two alleles each: *A/a*, *B/b*, *C/c*, *D/d*, and *E/e*. Pigment is deposited at three different levels, depending on the threshold of gene products produced by the capital-lettered alleles. Greyish-brown pigmentation is seen if at least four capital alleles are present, light-tan pigmentation is seen if two or three capital alleles are present, and whitish-blue pigmentation is seen if these thresholds are not met. If an *AA BB CC DD EE* animal is crossed to a true-breeding *aa bb cc dd ee* animal and the progeny are selfed, what kinds of phenotypes are expected in the F_1 and F_2?

Answer: The F_1 is *A/a B/b C/c D/d E/e*, and so it is greyish-brown. The F_2 phenotypes are determined by the number of capital alleles contributed from each F_1 parent. Thus, determine the chance of obtaining 0, 1, 2, or 3 capital alleles from each F_1 parent: Since the parent is heterozygous at all five loci, the chance of obtaining any specified set of five alleles in one gamete is $(1/2)^5$. The chance of obtaining a particular number of capital alleles from an F_1 is the number of ways in which that number of alleles can be obtained multiplied by $(1/2)^5$. Consideration of all the possibilities reveals that there is one way to obtain 0 capital alleles, 5 ways to obtain

1 capital allele, 10 ways of obtaining two capital alleles, and 10 ways of obtaining three capital alleles. With this information, tabulate the ways in which the progeny can be formed:

| F$_1$ GAMETE #1 | | F$_1$ GAMETE #2 | | F$_2$ PROGENY | | |
Capital Alleles	Gamete Fraction	Capital Alleles	Gamete Fraction	Capital Alleles	F2 Fraction	Phenotype
0	$(1/2)^5$	0	$(1/2)^5$	0	$(1/2)^{10}$	whitish blue
0	$(1/2)^5$	1	$5(1/2)^5$	1	$5(1/2)^{10}$	whitish blue
1	$5(1/2)^5$	0	$(1/2)^5$	1	$5(1/2)^{10}$	whitish blue
0	$(1/2)^5$	2	$10(1/2)^5$	2	$10(1/2)^{10}$	light tan
1	$5(1/2)^5$	1	$5(1/2)^5$	2	$25(1/2)^{10}$	light tan
2	$10(1/2)^5$	0	$(1/2)^5$	2	$10(1/2)^{10}$	light tan
0	$(1/2)^5$	3	$10(1/2)^5$	3	$10(1/2)^{10}$	light tan
1	$5(1/2)^5$	2	$10(1/2)^5$	3	$50(1/2)^{10}$	light tan
2	$10(1/2)^5$	1	$5(1/2)^5$	3	$50(1/2)^{10}$	light tan
3	$10(1/2)^5$	0	$(1/2)^5$	3	$10(1/2)^{10}$	light tan

In the F$_2$, $11(1/2)^{10} = 11/1{,}024$ will be bluish white and $165(1/2)^{10} = 165/1{,}024$ will be light tan. The remaining $[1 - 176(1/2)^{10} =]$ $848/1{,}024$ F$_2$ progeny will be greyish brown.

A faster method to solve this problem is to use the coefficients of the binomial expansion to determine the proportion of progeny with different numbers of capital and lowercase alleles. Let n = total number of alleles, s = number of capital alleles, t = number of lowercase alleles, a = chance of obtaining a capital allele, b = chance of obtaining a lowercase allele, and $x! = (x)(x-1)(x-2)...(1)$, with $0! = 1$. Then the chance p of obtaining progeny with a specified number of each type of allele is given by:

$$p(s,t) = \frac{n!}{s!\,t!}\,a^s b^t$$

$$p(0,10) = \frac{10!}{0!10!}\left(\frac{1}{2}\right)^0\left(\frac{1}{2}\right)^{10} = \frac{1}{1024}$$
$$p(1,9) = \frac{10!}{1!9!}\left(\frac{1}{2}\right)^1\left(\frac{1}{2}\right)^9 = \frac{10}{1024}$$

$\left.\begin{array}{c}\end{array}\right\}\dfrac{11}{1024}$ whitish blue

$$p(2,8) = \frac{10!}{2!8!}\left(\frac{1}{2}\right)^2\left(\frac{1}{2}\right)^8 = \frac{45}{1024}$$
$$p(3,7) = \frac{10!}{3!7!}\left(\frac{1}{2}\right)^3\left(\frac{1}{2}\right)^7 = \frac{120}{1024}$$

$\left.\begin{array}{c}\end{array}\right\}\dfrac{165}{1024}$ light tan

$$1 - \frac{11+165}{1024} = \frac{848}{1024}$$ greyish brown

23.17   Alzheimer's disease (AD) is the leading cause of dementia in elderly individuals. Evidence that genetic alterations are involved in AD comes from three sources: the incidence of AD in first-degree relatives, the incidence in pairs of twins, and pedigree analysis. There is a 24–50 percent risk of AD by age 90 in first-degree relatives of AD individuals, a 40–50 percent risk of AD in the identical (monozygotic) twin of an AD individual, and a 10–50 percent risk of AD in the fraternal (dizygotic) twin of an AD individual. AD individuals in a subset of families showing AD have an alteration in the *APP* (amyloid protein) gene on chromosome 21. AD individuals in another subset of AD families have a particular allele (*E4*) at the *APOE* (apolipoprotein E) gene on chromosome 19. Individuals homozygous for the *E4* allele have increased risk of AD and earlier disease onset than heterozygotes. Population studies have shown that 40–50 percent of AD cases are associated with alterations in the *APOE* gene, but less than 1 percent of AD cases are associated with mutations in the *APP* gene.

a. In what sense might AD be considered a polygenic trait?

b. If AD has a genetic basis, why are identical twins not equally affected?

Answer:

a. From the data that are given, it appears that some proportion of cases of AD can be attributed to genetic factors. Multiple genes that increase the risk for AD have been identified, some of which appear to act in a dose-dependent manner. Thus, it could be that a number of different genes contribute to the onset of AD, with some having a greater contribution than others. This is somewhat similar to how polygenic traits control a phenotype, since there, alleles at multiple genes contribute in an additive, dose-dependent fashion to the phenotype.

b. Consider two explanations: First, if AD can be caused by environmental agents, mutation and/or a combination of both environmental agents and mutation, the presence of AD in both twins could be due to the presence of one or more abnormal alleles in both and/or the exposure of both twins to adverse environmental conditions. The presence of AD in only one twin may be due to differences in the exposure of that twin to a contributing or causative environmental agent(s). Second, the presence of a particular allele or a specific mutation may only increase the risk of disease, and not determine its occurrence, since an allele's penetrance may be strongly affected by the environment. In the case of AD, the environmental factors may not be clear cut or even small in number. There may be multiple environmental factors, some of which may be complex or subtle.

23.18   Alzheimer's disease (AD) is the leading cause of dementia in older adults. Evidence that genetic alterations are involved in AD comes from three sources: the incidence of AD in first-degree relatives, the incidence in pairs of twins, and pedigree analysis. There is a 24–50 percent risk of AD by age 90 in first-degree relatives of individuals with AD, a 40–50 percent risk of AD in the identical (monozygotic) twin of an individual with AD, and a 10–50 percent risk of AD in the fraternal (dizygotic) twin of an individual with AD. Individuals with AD in a subset of families showing AD have an alteration in the *APP* (amyloid protein) gene on chromosome 21. Individuals with AD in another subset of AD families have a particular allele (*E4*) at the *APOE* (apolipoprotein E) gene on chromosome 19. Individuals homozygous for the *E4* allele have increased risk of AD and earlier disease onset than heterozygotes. Population studies have shown that 40–50 percent of AD cases are associated with alterations in the *APOE* gene, but less than 1 percent of AD cases are associated with mutations in the *APP* gene.

a. In what sense might AD be considered a polygenic trait?

b. If AD has a genetic basis, why are identical twins not equally affected?

Answer:

a. From the data that are given, it appears that some proportion of cases of AD can be attributable to genetic factors. Multiple genes that increase the risk for AD have been identified, some of which appear to act in a dose-dependent manner. Thus, it could be that a number of different genes contribute to the onset of AD, with some having a greater contribution than others.

b. Consider two explanations: First, if AD can be caused by either environmental agents or mutation, the presence of AD in both twins could be due to the presence of an abnormal allele in both or exposure of both twins to adverse environmental conditions. The presence of AD in only one twin may be due to exposure of only one twin to the causative environmental agent(s). Second, the presence of a mutation may only increase the risk of disease, and not determine its occurrence. An allele's penetrance may be affected by the environment.

23.19   Because monozygotic twins share all their genetic material and dizygotic twins share, on average, half of their genetic material, twin studies sometimes can be useful for evaluating the genetic contribution to a trait. Consider the following two instances.

An intelligence quotient (IQ) assesses intellectual performance on a standardized test that involves reasoning ability, memory, and knowledge of an individual's language and culture. IQ scores are transformed so that the population mean score is 100 and 95 percent of the individuals have scores in the range between 70 and 130. Observations in the United States and England found that monozygotic twins had an average difference of 6 IQ points, dizygotic twins had an average difference of 11 points, and random pairs of individuals had an average difference of 21 points.

In a large sample of pairs of twins in the United States where one twin was a smoker, 83 percent of monozygotic twins both smoked, while 62 percent of dizygotic twins both smoked.

From these data, can you infer the genetic determination of IQ or smoking?

Answer: In neither of these cases is any information provided about the environments in which the twins were raised. While it would initially appear that there is some genetic component in each case, there is no way to evaluate the role of environment. It could be that the identical twins sampled in each case were raised in an identical environment, and this could account for the greater similarity in smoking behavior and IQ results for monozygotic twins than for dizygotic twins.

23.20 A quantitative geneticist determines the following variance components for leaf width in a population of wildflowers growing along a roadside in Kentucky:

Additive genetic variance (V_A)	=	4.2
Dominance genetic variance (V_D)	=	1.6
Interaction genetic variance (V_I)	=	0.3
Environmental variance (V_E)	=	2.7
Genetic-environmental variance ($V_{G \cdot E}$) =		0.0

a. Calculate the broad-sense heritability and the narrow-sense heritability for leaf width in this population of wildflowers.
b. What do the heritabilities obtained in part (a) indicate about the genetic nature of leaf width variation in this plant?

Answer:

a. The broad-sense heritability of a trait represents the proportion of the phenotypic variance in a particular population that results from genetic differences among individuals, while the narrow-sense heritability measures only the proportion of the phenotypic variance in that population that results from <u>additive</u> genetic variance.

Broad-sense heritability
    = genetic variance/phenotypic variance $= V_G/V_P$
    = (4.2 + 1.6 + 0.3)/(4.2 + 1.6 + 0.3 + 2.7 + 0.0)
    = 6.1/8.8 = 0.69

Narrow-sense heritability
    = additive genetic variance/phenotypic variance
    = V_A/V_P
    = 4.2/8.8 = 0.48

b. About 69 percent of the phenotypic variation in leaf width observed in this population is due to genetic differences among individuals. About 48 percent of the phenotypic variation is due to additive genetic variation. The phenotypic variation due to additive genetic variation represents the part of the phenotypic variance that responds to natural selection in a predictable manner.

23.21 Assume all genetic variance affecting seed weight in beans is genetically determined and is additive. From a population in which the mean seed weight was 0.88 g, a farmer selected two seeds, each weighing 1.02 g. He planted these and crossed the resulting plants to each other, then collected and weighed their seeds. The mean weight of their seeds was 0.96 g. What is the narrow-sense heritability of seed weight?

Answer: In this example, there was 0.96 – 0.88 = 0.08 g of change after one generation of selection. Thus, the selection response was 0.08 g. This selection response is dependent on both the narrow-sense heritability and the selection differential. The selection differential is the difference between the mean phenotype of the selected parents and the mean phenotype of the unselected population. In this case the selection differential is 1.02 – 0.88 = 0.14 g. The narrow-sense heritability is given by:

selection response = narrow-sense heritability x selection differential.

$$0.08 = h^2 \times 0.14$$
$$h^2 = 0.08/0.14 = 0.57$$

23.22   Members of the inbred rat strain SHR are salt sensitive: They respond to a high-salt environment by developing hypertension. Members of a different inbred rat strain, TIS, are not salt sensitive. Imagine that you placed a population consisting only of SHR rats in an environment that was variable in regard to distribution of salt, so that some rats would be exposed to more salt than others. What would be the heritability of blood pressure in this population?

Answer: SHR rats will continue to respond to salt by developing hypertension. Since the strain is inbred, any variation in blood pressure will result from the amount of exposure to salt, and not from genetic variation. Therefore, heritability for this population will be zero. Similarly, the inbred TIS rats would also have a heritability of zero (and retain a low blood pressure).

23.23   In Kansas a farmer is growing a variety of wheat called TK138. He calculates the narrow-sense heritability for yield (the amount of wheat produced per acre) and finds that the heritability of yield for TK138 is 0.95. The next year he visits a farm in Poland and observes that a Russian variety of wheat, UG334, growing there has only about 40 percent as much yield as TK138 grown on his farm in Kansas. Because he found the heritability of yield in his wheat to be very high, he concludes that the American variety of wheat (TK138) is genetically superior to the Russian variety (UG334), and he tells the Polish farmers that they can increase their yield by using TK138. What is wrong with his conclusion?

Answer: Heritability is a measurement of the genetic variance of a *particular* population in a *specific* environment. Heritability is not fixed for a specific trait. It depends on genetic makeup *as well as* the specific environment of the population in which it is measured. Consequently, heritability cannot be used to make inferences about the basis for the differences between two distinct populations. As the environmental conditions on the two farms differ, the heritability calculated for a population in Kansas cannot be used to infer the future performance of the same strain in another environment. The yield of TK138 grown in Poland would most likely be different than when grown in Kansas, perhaps even lower than the yield of the UG334 variety.

23.24 Dermatoglyphics are the patterns of the ridged skin found on the fingertips, toes, palms, and soles. (Fingerprints are dermatoglyphics.) Classification of dermatoglyphics frequently is based on the number of triradii; a triradius is a point from which three ridge systems separate at angles of 120°. The number of triradii on all ten fingers was counted for each member of several families, and the results are tabulated here.

FAMILY	MEAN NUMBER OF TRIRADII IN THE PARENTS	MEAN NUMBER OF TRIRADII IN THE OFFSPRING
I	14.5	12.5
II	8.5	10.0
III	13.5	12.5
IV	9.0	7.0
V	10.0	9.0
VI	9.5	9.5
VII	11.5	11.0
VIII	9.5	9.5
IX	15.0	17.5
X	10.0	10.0

a. Calculate the narrow-sense heritability for the number of triradii by the regression of the mean phenotype of the parents against the mean phenotype of the offspring.

b. What does your calculated heritability value indicate about the relative contributions of genetic variation and environmental variation to the differences observed in number of triradii?

Answer:

a. The narrow-sense heritability of the number of triradii will equal the slope, *b*, of the regression line of the mean offspring phenotype on the mean parental phenotype.

$$b = \frac{\text{cov}_{xy}}{(s_x)^2} = \frac{\dfrac{\Sigma x_i y_i - \frac{1}{n}(\Sigma x_i \Sigma y_i)}{n-1}}{\dfrac{\Sigma(x_i - \bar{x})^2}{n-1}} = \frac{\Sigma x_i y_i - \frac{1}{n}(\Sigma x_i \Sigma y_i)}{\Sigma(x_i - \bar{x})^2}$$

For this data set, *x* is the mean number of triradii in the parents and *y* is the mean number of triradii in the offspring. One has:

$$\bar{x} = 11.1 \qquad\qquad \Sigma x_i = 111$$
$$\Sigma(x_i - \bar{x})^2 = 51.4 \qquad\qquad \Sigma y_i = 108.5$$

$$\Sigma x_i y_i = 1{,}257.5 \qquad\qquad b = \frac{1257.5 - \dfrac{111 \times 108.5}{10}}{51.4} = 1.03$$

b. A narrow-sense heritability value of 1.03 indicates that all of the observed variation in phenotype can be attributed to additive genetic variation among the individuals.

23.25 A scientist wants to determine the narrow-sense heritability of tail length in mice. He measures tail length among the mice of a population and finds a mean tail length of 9.7 cm. He then selects the 10 mice in the population with the longest tails; mean tail length in these selected mice is 14.3 cm. He interbreeds the mice with the long tails and examines tail length in their progeny. The mean tail length in the F_1 progeny of the selected mice is 13 cm.

Calculate the selection differential, the response to selection, and the narrow-sense heritability for tail length in these mice.

Answer: The selection differential equals $14.3 - 9.7 = 4.6$ cm. The response to selection equals $13 - 9.7 = 3.3$ cm. The narrow-sense heritability equals $3.3/4.6 = 0.72$.

23.26 Suppose that the narrow-sense heritability of wool length in a breed of sheep is 0.92, and the narrow-sense heritability of body size is 0.87. The genetic correlation between wool length and body size is –0.84. If a breeder selects for sheep with longer wool, what will be the most likely effects on wool length and on body size?

Answer: The strong narrow-sense heritability of both wool length and body size indicates that these traits will respond to selection. The negative correlation coefficient between wool length and body size indicates that if longer wool is selected for, smaller body size will also be obtained.

23.27 The heights of nine college-age men and the heights of their fathers are presented below.

HEIGHT OF SON (INCHES)	HEIGHT OF FATHER (INCHES)
70	70
72	76
71	72
64	70
66	70
70	68
74	78
70	74
73	69

a. Calculate the mean and the variance of height for the sons and do the same for the fathers.

b. Calculate the correlation coefficient for the relationship between the height of father and height of son.

c. Determine the narrow-sense heritability of height in this group by regression of the son's height on the height of the father.

Answer:

a. Sons: mean = 70.0, variance = 10.25

Fathers: mean = 71.9, variance = 11.6

b. and c. Let y equal the height of the sons, and x equal the height of the fathers. One can calculate $\Sigma x_i y_i = 45{,}333$, $\Sigma x_i = 647$, $\Sigma y_i = 630$, and $n = 9$ so that

$$r = \frac{\text{cov}_{xy}}{s_x s_y} = \frac{\dfrac{\Sigma x_i y_i - \dfrac{1}{n}(\Sigma x_i \Sigma y_i)}{n-1}}{\sqrt{(s_x)^2 (s_y)^2}}$$

$$r = \frac{\dfrac{45333 - [(630)(647)/9]}{8}}{\sqrt{11.6 \times 10.25}} = \frac{5.375}{10.904} = 0.493$$

$$b = \frac{\text{cov}_{xy}}{(s_x)^2} = \frac{5.375}{11.6} = 0.463$$

When, as in this case, the mean phenotype of the offspring is regressed against the phenotype of only <u>one</u> parent, the narrow-sense heritability is $2b = 2(0.46) = 0.92$. Since $h2$ is very close to 1, most of the phenotypic variation is determined by genes with additive effects. Nonadditive factors (genes with dominance, genes with epistasis, environmental factors) contribute little to the phenotypic variation.

23.28   The narrow-sense heritability of egg weight in a particular flock of chickens is 0.60. A farmer selects for increased egg weight in this flock. The difference in the mean egg weight of the unselected chickens and the selected chickens is 10 g. How much should egg weight increase in the offspring of the selected chickens?

Answer: Selection response = narrow-sense heritability × selection differential

Selection response = 0.60 x 10 g = 6 g.

23.29   Members of a strain of white leghorn chickens are selectively crossed to produce two lines, A and B, that show improved egg production. The progeny from a cross of lines A and B are used for commercial egg production. The selection strategy is shown in Figure 23.A. The mean number of eggs produced in the first egg production year and the mean egg weight (in grams) from hens at an age of 240 days is given for animals at each step of the selection procedure.

year and the mean egg weight (in grams) from hens at an age of 240 days is given for animals at each step of the selection procedure.

Parental White Leghorn Strain (196 eggs, 51 g)
→ Select Set A (279 eggs, 57 g)   →   Select Set B (310 eggs, 53 g)
    ↓   ↓

    F$_1$ (208 eggs, 54 g)   F$_1$ (217 eggs, 52 g)
→ Select F$_1$ (271 eggs, 60 g)   → Select F$_1$ (310 eggs, 55 g)
    ↓ ↓

    F$_2$ (214 eggs, 55 g)   F$_2$ (224 eggs, 53 g)
→ Select F$_2$ (292 eggs, 61 g)   → Select F$_2$(315 eggs, 57 g)
    ↓   ↓

    Line A (218 eggs, 56 g)   Line B (230 eggs, 54 g)

Figure 23.A

Line A × Line B → Hybrid used for commercial production (262 eggs, 57 g)
a. What is the narrow-sense heritability for the traits at each selection step?
b. Why does the response of the traits to selection change during the selection process?
c. What percentage increase in the number of eggs produced is obtained when lines A and B are crossed?
d. With the possible exception of dairy cattle, commercial livestock are hybrids produced by crossing breeds, lines, or strains already selected for a set of desirable traits. Why?

Answer:
a. The narrow-sense heritability is given in the table below:

Selection Step	LINE A		LINE B	
	Number of Eggs	Egg Weight	Number of Eggs	Egg Weight
Initial Selection	0.145	0.50	0.184	0.50
F$_1$ Selection	0.095	0.17	0.075	0.33
F$_2$ Selection	0.051	0.17	0.066	0.25

b. The response changes because the selection process decreases the amount of genetic variation within the population.
c. Compared to the mean of traits in lines A and B, there is a 17 percent increase in the number of eggs produced, and a 3.6 percent increase in egg weight.
d. When different lines are crossed, an increase due to heterosis, or heterozygote advantage, may be obtained (see Chapter 22). If there are multiple alleles that contribute to increased egg production and size, it is possible that different alleles were selected for in the two lines. Combining these advantageous alleles could lead to further increases, as well as decrease the effects of recessive, deleterious alleles.

23.30 The following variances were determined for measurements of body length, antenna bristle number, and egg production in a moth species. Which of these characters would be most rapidly changed by natural selection? Which character would be most slowly affected by natural selection?

VARIANCE	BODY LENGTH	ANTENNA BRISTLE NUMBER	EGG PRODUCTION
Phenotypic (V_P)	798	342	145
Additive (V_A)	132	21	21
Dominance (V_D)	122	126	24
Interaction (V_I)	118	136	34
Genetic-environmental (V_{GxE})	81	23	21
Maternal effects (V_{Em})	345	36	45

Answer: The variance that responds to selection is the additive genetic variance. The narrow-sense heritability for each of the traits is V_A/V_P, and can be used to predict how a trait will respond to selection. This is 0.165 for body length, 0.061 for antenna bristle number, and 0.144 for egg production. Thus, body length will respond most to selection, and antenna bristle number will respond least to selection.

24

MOLECULAR EVOLUTION

CHAPTER OUTLINE

PATTERNS AND MODES OF SUBSTITUTIONS

Nucleotide Substitutions in DNA Sequences

Rates of Nucleotide Substitutions

Variation in Evolutionary Rates Between Genes

Rates of Evolution in Mitochondrial DNA

Molecular Clocks

MOLECULAR PHYLOGENY

Phylogenetic Trees

Reconstruction Methods

Phylogenetic Trees on a Grand Scale

ACQUISITION AND ORIGINS OF NEW FUNCTIONS

Multigene Families

Gene Duplication and Gene Conversion

Arabidopsis Genome Results

REVIEW OF KEY TERMS, SYMBOLS, AND CONCEPTS

In your own words, write a brief, precise definition of each term in the groups below. Check your definitions using the text. Then, develop a concept map using the terms in each list.

1	2	3
molecular evolution	nucleotide substitution	molecular phylogeny
population, species	homologous proteins, genes	morphological phylogeny
gene	sequence alignment	evolutionary relationship
evolutionary time, history	computer algorithm	convergent evolution
population genetics	optimal alignment	phenotype
Hardy-Weinberg equilibrium	indel	phylogenetic tree
mutation vs. substitution	Jukes/Cantor Model	branch, node
gene duplication	substitution rate	rooted, unrooted trees
gene conversion	evolutionary rate	taxa
transposition	divergence time	gene vs. species tree
unequal crossing over	transition, transversion	inferred tree

1	2	3
phylogenetic relationship	coding, noncoding sequence	distance matrix
natural selection	leader, trailer region	parsimony
multigene family	pseudogene	unweighted-pair-group
globin, myoglobin genes	synonymous site, codon	method (UPGMA)
ancestral gene	nonsynonymous site, codon	transformed distance
domain shuffling	mutation vs. substitution	method
exon shuffling	comparative genome	neighbor-joining method
internal duplication	analysis	clustering
exon, intron	genome project	informative site
Bacteria, Archaea, Eukarya	codon usage bias	noninformative site
	stochastic factor	tree of maximum parsimony
	natural selection	bootstrap test
	diversifying selection	confidence level
	McDonald-Kreitman test	tree of life
	functional constraint	"out of Africa" theory
	major histocompatibility	"mitochondrial Eve"
	complex (MHC)	"Y chromosome Adam"
	mitochondrial DNA	
	error prone replication	
	proof reading ability	
	molecular clock	
	molecular clock hypothesis	
	relative rate test	
	outgroup	

THINKING ANALYTICALLY

Perhaps the most striking element in the field of molecular evolution is the time scale in which the mechanisms of evolution operate. Almost throughout this text, we have considered genetic mechanisms that act over relatively short time frames. The replication of the genetic material, its transcription, and the production of gene products through translation occur in time scales that are on the order of seconds and minutes. Genetic crosses may take several generations, but even for organisms that have relatively long life spans, the time scales are on the order of years or tens of years. Molecular evolution occurs over many, many generations, and the time scales being considered are on the order of tens of thousands to millions of years. In this space of time, much can happen. Some say that if you can think of it, nature has had time to try it. With genomes serving as historical records of molecular evolution, it may be possible to find evidence of it as well. Having said this, consider that small alterations in events that occur quickly, can, over a long period of time, result in major effects. For example, variation in the bonding energy associated with the instantaneous interaction between codons and the anticodons of isoacceptor tRNAs can effect the efficiency of translation. Over many, many generations, this may lead to the selection of a species' codon usage bias.

It is therefore helpful to keep in mind the time scales that are associated with molecular evolution. The text presents data documenting that rates of evolutionary change are not constant between regions of a gene, between different positions of codons within the coding region of a gene, between genes, between species, and between mitochondrial and nuclear genomes. Where possible, relate differences in the rate of evolutionary change to the time frames associated with molecular evolution. Focus on why rates are different – what functional differences or constraints exist that preclude uniform rates? As you do this, draw on everything you have learned about the mechanisms of inheritance and gene expression, since these can not only influence molecular evolution, but have also been derived through molecular evolution and therefore represent the tuning of existing biological instruments.

QUESTIONS FOR PRACTICE

Multiple Choice Questions

1. Why does the molecular clock run at different rates in different proteins?
   a. Neutral substitution rates differ among proteins.
   b. Some proteins have resulted from gene duplication followed by sequence divergence.
   c. Some species have shorter generation times.
   d. Codon usage varies between proteins.

2. Two homologous proteins are found in two different species. These proteins
   a. perform identical functions in the different species.
   b. share a common ancestor.
   c. arose by gene duplication.
   d. have only synonymous substitutions in their genes.

3. An indel is
   a. a gap in a sequence alignment caused by either by an insertion or a deletion.
   b. a gap in a sequence alignment caused by a deletion in just one of the sequences.
   c. a gap in a sequence alignment caused by an insertion in just one of the sequences.
   d. a deletion that removes an intron.

4. What issues does the Jukes-Cantor model address?
   a. The rate of the molecular clock in different proteins.
   b. Whether nucleotide substitutions are adaptive or random.
   c. The relationship between the observed and actual number of substitutions.
   d. Whether an inferred phylogenetic tree is robust.

5. What is generally true about synonymous and nonsynonymous substitutions?
   a. In coding regions, synonymous substitutions are more frequent than nonsynonymous substitutions.
   b. In coding regions, synonymous and nonsynonymous substitutions are equally frequent.
   c. Synonymous substitutions in coding regions and substitutions in intronic regions are equally frequent.
   d. Both a and c are true.

6. Which one of the following sequences of a gene exhibits the highest rate of evolution?
   a. the 3'untranslated, but transcribed, region of the gene.
   b. introns within the gene
   c. the 5' flanking region of the gene
   d. nonfunctional pseudogenes related to the gene

7. Why might codon usage bias have evolved?
   a. The tRNA for one codon is more abundant than an isoacceptor tRNA for another codon.
   b. The bonding energy between pairs of codons and anticodons differ, leading to increased translation efficiency of certain pairs.
   c. The required abundant expression of some genes favors selection of codons that provide efficient translation.
   d. All of the above.

8. Which of the following statements is true?
   a. An outgroup is a species that a phylogenetic analysis using maximum parsimony shows is a common ancestor to two existing species.
   b. The molecular clock typically runs at the same rate in different proteins.
   c. The synonymous substitution rate in mammalian mitochondrial genes is about ten-fold greater than that in nuclear genes.
   d. The length of a species' generation time is unlikely to affect its evolutionary rate.

9. What is the best description of convergent evolution?
   a. Mutations that introduce the same polymorphism into two species after they diverged from a common ancestor.
   b. The evolution of similar phenotypes in distantly related species.
   c. The finding that there are parallel gene duplications in two unrelated species.
   d. The slowing of the molecular clock in an existing species such as humans.

10. In phylogenetic analysis, how do rooted and unrooted trees differ?
    a. When a given number of taxa are being analyzed, there are more possible unrooted than rooted trees.
    b. A rooted tree is based on relationships between genes, while an unrooted tree is based on relationships between species.
    c. Outgroups can be used only in unrooted trees.
    d. A rooted tree specifies one internal node as representing a common ancestor to all the other nodes on the tree. An unrooted tree specifies only the relationship between the nodes, and does not indicate the evolutionary path that was taken.

11. Which approach to phylogenetic reconstruction first determines the distance between taxa, and then repeatedly clusters the two taxa with the smallest distance separating them into a single, composite taxa until all the taxa are grouped together?
    a. The maximum parsimony method.
    b. The UPGMA method.
    c. The bootstrap method.
    d. The neighbor-joining method.

Answers: 1a; 2b; 3a; 4c; 5a; 6d; 7d; 8c; 9b; 10d; 11b.

Thought Questions

1. Gene duplication provides a mechanism that allows for the evolution of new protein functions. How does this mechanism affect our view of which proteins are homologous? How can one infer which proteins encoded by a multigene family present in each of two organisms are homologous?

2. What are the relationships between the fields of comparative genomics and molecular evolution?

3. How do the results of the *Arabidopsis* genome project add to our understanding of molecular evolution and how new gene functions evolve?

4. Suppose you have identified a sequence that can be translated and appears to encode an open reading frame (ORF). How could you use an analysis of codon usage bias to infer whether it was likely to be translated?

5. What problems in dating the times of existence of common ancestors are posed by variable molecular clocks in different taxonomic groups?

6. Why is the parsimony approach to phylogenetic tree reconstruction able to give some insight into the nature of long-dead organisms? Are other methods, such as distance matrix-based approaches, also able to do this?

7. What role does gene conversion play in the evolution of new gene functions?

8. Does the proposition that domain shuffling provides a mechanism for the generation of new protein function require that introns once existed in primitive life forms? If so, why might they no longer exist in the simpler Bacteria and Archaea?

9. Do phylogenetic reconstructions tell us anything about the mechanisms of speciation? If so, what?

10. What are the general types of functional constraints that restrict proteins from undergoing rapid evolution? Consider in your answer the histones, which evolve so slowly that the human histone H4 protein can functionally replace its homolog in yeast.

Thought Questions for Media

After reviewing the media on the *iGenetics* CD-ROM, try to answer these questions

1. The iActivity illustrates how the sequence of ancient DNA is obtained by using PCR. Fragments averaging 100-200 base pairs in length are cloned, the cloned segments are sequenced and aligned, and a *consensus nucleotide sequence* is determined from the aligned sequences.
    a. What is a *consensus nucleotide sequence* and why is it necessary to use one in this type of analysis?
    b. In this analysis, sequences from the control region of mitochondrial DNA were amplified. Why is mitochondrial DNA used, and why might the control region be specifically chosen for analysis?
    c. What types of errors might be introduced when amplifying ancient DNA templates? How might you assure yourself that a sequence accurately reflects the sequence in the ancient DNA, and is not an artifact?

2. Suppose a bone sample from a new, non-Neanderthal, extinct hominid species called *ML* (for *missing link*) was made available to you.

    a. Outline how you would test if *ML* was a direct ancestor of modern humans?

    b. Suppose you undertook an analysis similar to that of the iActivity and compared DNA sequences in the control region of mitochondrial DNA. You find 12 differences in mitochondrial DNA between *ML* and modern European sequences, 11 differences between *ML* and modern African sequences, and 7 differences between the modern European and modern African DNA sequences. What would you conclude? Be as specific as possible.

3. In the iActivity, you were able to estimate the time of divergence of modern Europeans and Africans, and the time of divergence of Neanderthals and modern humans.

    a. What assumptions did you make in this analysis?

    b. How did you estimate the rate of nucleotide evolution? That is, what was the basis for relating the number of observed mutations to the times of divergence between the European, African and Neanderthal populations?

    c. How would your estimates of the times of divergence between the European, African and Neanderthal populations differ if the rate of nucleotide evolution in hominid species is not constant, but tripled, relative to a previously constant rate, in the last 300,000 years?

SOLUTIONS TO TEXT PROBLEMS

24.1   The following sequence is that of the first 45 codons from the human gene for pre-proinsulin. Using the genetic code (Chapter 6), determine what fraction of mutations at the first, second, and third positions of these 45 codons will be synonymous.

```
ATG GCC CTG TGG ATG CGC CTC CTG CCC CTG CTG GCG CTG CTG GCC CTC TGG
GGA CCT GAC CCA GCC GCA GCC TTT GTG AAC CAA CAC CTG TGC GGC TCA CAC
CTG GTG GAA GCT CTC TAC CTA GTG TGC GGG GAA
```

At which position is natural selection likely to have the greatest effect and are nucleotides most likely to be conserved?

Answer: A synonymous mutation or substitution is a change in nucleotide sequence that does not affect the amino acid sequence in a polypeptide chain. Due to the redundancy of the genetic code, more than one codon can code for one amino acid. Inspection of a table of the genetic code (Chapter 6) shows that at one extreme, some amino acids, such as methionine and tryptophan, are only coded by one codon (AUG and UGG, respectively), while at the other extreme, some amino acids, such as leucine and serine, are coded for by six codons. Other amino acids are coded for by two, three, or four codons. Say the codon in question codes for leucine and is CUG. Then, since the codons for leucine are UAA, UGG, CUU, CUC, CUA, and CUG, any of three coding strand changes in the third nucleotide (G → T,

G $\rightarrow$ A, or G $\rightarrow$ C) and a change of C $\rightarrow$ T in the first nucleotide would still result in leucine being inserted into the polypeptide chain. Hence, any of these substitutions would be synonymous.

To get some sense of which substitutions will be synonymous, inspect the genetic code and look for some general principles. For amino acids coded for by four codons, variation in the third position results in a synonymous substitution; for amino acids coded for by two codons, variation in the third position by one base only (a purine or a pyrimidine) results in a synonymous mutation. For amino acids coded for by either two or four codons, variations in the first or second positions results in a nonsynonymous substitution. Similar, but not identical patterns are seen for amino acids coded for by either three or six codons. The sense that synonymous changes are mostly associated with substitutions in the third position is confirmed by a more systematic analysis. The following table lists the number of possible nonsynonymous (NS) and synonymous (S) mutations at each position of each codon for the amino acids in question.

Coding Strand	mRNA Codon	Amino Acid	Position 1		Position 2		Position 3	
			NS	S	NS	S	NS	S
ATG	AUG	methionine	3	0	3	0	3	0
GCC	GCC	alanine	3	0	3	0	0	3
CTG	CUG	leucine	2	1	3	0	0	3
TGG	UGG	tryptophan	3	0	3	0	3	0
ATG	AUG	methionine	3	0	3	0	3	0
CGC	CGC	arginine	3	0	3	0	0	3
CTC	CUC	leucine	3	0	3	0	0	3
CTG	CUG	leucine	2	1	3	0	0	3
CCC	CCC	proline	3	0	3	0	0	3
CTG	CUG	leucine	2	1	3	0	0	3
CTG	CUG	leucine	2	1	3	0	0	3
GCG	GCG	alanine	3	0	3	0	0	3
CTG	CUG	leucine	2	1	3	0	0	3
CTG	CUG	leucine	2	1	3	0	0	3
GCC	GCC	alanine	3	0	3	0	0	3
CTC	CUC	leucine	3	0	3	0	0	3
TGG	UGG	tryptophan	3	0	3	0	3	0
GGA	GGA	glycine	3	0	3	0	0	3
CCT	CCU	proline	3	0	3	0	0	3
GAC	GAC	aspartate	3	0	3	0	2	1
CCA	CCA	proline	3	0	3	0	0	3
GCC	GCC	alanine	3	0	3	0	0	3
GCA	GCA	alanine	3	0	3	0	0	3
GCC	GCC	alanine	3	0	3	0	0	3
TTT	UUU	phenylalanine	3	0	3	0	2	1
GTG	GUG	valine	3	0	3	0	0	3
AAC	AAC	asparagine	3	0	3	0	2	1

Coding Strand	mRNA Codon	Amino Acid	Position 1		Position 2		Position 3	
			NS	S	NS	S	NS	S
CAC	CAC	histidine	3	0	3	0	2	1
CTG	CUG	leucine	2	1	3	0	0	3
TGC	UGC	cysteine	3	0	3	0	2	1
GGC	GGC	glycine	3	0	3	0	0	3
TCA	UCA	serine	3	0	3	0	0	3
CAC	CAC	histidine	3	0	3	0	2	1
CTG	CUG	leucine	2	1	3	0	0	3
GTG	GUG	valine	3	0	3	0	0	3
GAA	GAA	glutamate	3	0	3	0	2	1
GCT	GCU	alanine	3	0	3	0	0	3
CTC	CUC	leucine	3	0	3	0	0	3
TAC	UAC	tyrosine	3	0	3	0	2	1
CTA	CUA	leucine	2	1	3	0	0	3
GTG	GUG	valine	3	0	3	0	0	3
TGC	UGC	cysteine	3	0	3	0	2	1
GGG	GGG	glycine	3	0	3	0	0	3
GAA	GAA	glutamate	3	0	3	0	2	1
		TOTAL	124	11	135	0	34	101
		Percent	91.8	8.2	100	0	25.2	74.8

From this analysis, 8.2% of mutations in the first position, none of the mutations in the second position and 74.8% of mutations in the third position will be synonymous. Since none of the mutations in the second position will be synonymous, all mutations in this position will affect the amino acid inserted into a polypeptide chain. Natural selection is therefore likely to have the greatest effect on mutations in the second position, and nucleotides in this position are the most likely to be conserved.

24.2   The following sequences represent an optimum alignment of the first 50 nucleotides from the human and sheep preproinsulin genes. Estimate the number of substitutions that have occurred in this region since humans and sheep last shared a common ancestor, using the Jukes-Cantor model.

```
Human: ATGGCCCTGT GGATGCGCCT CCTGCCCCTG CTGGCGCTGC TGGCCCTCTG
Sheep: ATGGCCCTGT GGACACGCCT GGTGCCCCTG CTGGCCCTGC TGGCACTCTG
```

Answer: Inspection of the sequences reveals that there are six differences (underlined):

```
Human: ATGGCCCTGT GGATGCGCCT CCTGCCCCTG CTGGCGCTGC TGGCCCTCTG
Sheep: ATGGCCCTGT GGACACGCCT GGTGCCCCTG CTGGCCCTGC TGGCACTCTG
```

The Jukes and Cantor model estimates the number of substitutions per site (K) based on the fraction of nucleotides that are different between two sequences (p), taking into account that a particular site can undergo multiple changes. According to this model, $K = -(3/4) \ln[1 - (4/3)(p)]$. Here, $p = 6/50 = 0.12$, so $K = -3/4 \ln[1 - (4/3)(0.12)] = 0.1308$. Since $K = 0.1308$, the estimated number of substitutions is $50 \times 0.1308 = 6.54$.

24.3   Using the alignment in Question 24.2 and assuming that humans and sheep last shared a common ancestor 80 million years ago, estimate the rate at which the sequence of the first fifty nucleotides in their preproinsulin genes have been accumulating substitutions.

Answer: Since substitutions are assumed to accumulate simultaneously and independently in both sequences, the substitution rate (r) is obtained by dividing the number of substitutions between the homologous sequences by $2T$, where T = divergence time: $r = K/2T$. Here, $K = 0.1308$ and $T = 80 \times 10^6$, so $r = 0.1308 / (2 \times 80 \times 10^6) = 8.175 \times 10^{-10}$ substitutions/year.

24.4   Would the mutation rate be greater or less than the observed substitution rate for a sequence of a gene such as the one shown in Question 24.2? Why?

Answer: The mutation rate reflects changes in DNA sequence due to errors in replication or repair processes, while the substitution rate reflects changes in DNA sequence (i.e., mutations) that have passed through the filter of natural selection. Since mutations that are not synonymous may be selected against, an estimate of the number of substitutions in a coding region, such as in this analysis, is likely to be lower than the mutation rate. Therefore, the mutation rate is likely to be greater than the observed substitution rate.

24.5   If the rate of nucleotide evolution along a lineage is 1.0 percent per million years, what is the rate of substitution per nucleotide per year? What would be the observed rate of divergence between two species evolving at that rate since they last shared a common ancestor?

Answer: Using the assumption of the Jukes/Cantor model that each nucleotide is just as likely to change into any other nucleotide, when the rate of change to any one of three alternative nucleotides is α, the overall rate of substitution for any given nucleotide is 3α. Here, if the rate of nucleotide evolution is interpreted to be the observed rate of substitution - mutations that have passed through the filter of selection –, $3\alpha = 0.01$ substitutions/10^6 years = 1×10^{-8} substitutions/year, so $\alpha = 3.3 \times 10^{-9}$ substitutions/year. If the observed rate of substitution within each lineage in two diverging species is 3.3×10^{-9}, then, since substitutions accumulate simultaneously and independently in two diverging sequences, the observed rate of divergence will be 6.6×10^{-9}.

24.6   The average synonymous substitution rate in mammalian mitochondrial genes is approximately ten times the average value for synonymous substitutions in nuclear genes. Why would it be better to use comparisons of mitochondrial sequences when studying human migration patterns and nuclear genes when studying the phylogenetic relationships of mammalian species that diverged 80 million years ago?

Answer: There are two broad issues to consider here. First, sequence differences must be able to be observed within the time period being assessed, and there must be a sufficient number of them so that meaningful conclusions can be drawn from their analysis. For the analysis of human migration patterns, the time scale is on the order of tens of thousands of years, while for the analysis of mammalian phylogenetic relationships, the time scale is on the order of millions of years. The average synonymous substitution rate in the mitochondrial genome is high enough for differences between different human populations to be observed, and provides for a sufficient number of differences for a meaningful analysis to be performed. The average synonymous substitution rate in the nuclear genome may be too low to identify a sufficient number of differences for a meaningful analysis to be performed.

Second, over time, synonymous nucleotide substitutions will change repeatedly and will include changes back to their ancestral state. If the substitution rate is too high relative to the time period being examined, it may be difficult to clearly identify relationships due to noise in the data from this phenomenon. The average synonymous substitution rate in nuclear genes is high enough for differences to be observed among mammalian species over periods of millions of years, yet not so high that multiple substitutions cloud their phylogenetic interpretation. The rate of synonymous mutations in mitochondrial genes is so high that multiple substitutions cloud their phylogenetic interpretation. In summary, the rapid and regular rate of accumulation of nucleotide sequence differences in mitochondrial genomes allows for the phylogenetic analysis of closely related lineages, but for more distant lineages, it is better to use less rapidly changing sequences, such as those in the nuclear genome.

24.7   Why might mitochondrial DNA sequences accumulate substitutions at a faster rate than nuclear genes in the same organism?

Answer: The increased rate of substitutions in animal mtDNA may result from a higher mutation rate due to error prone replication and DNA repair, since mitochondrial DNA polymerases lack proofreading ability; from increased concentrations of mutagens, such as free radicals resulting from mitochondrial metabolic processes; and/or from relaxed selection pressure, since most cells have at least several dozen mitochondria, each of which has multiple copies of the mitochondrial genome.

24.8   Why might substitution rates differ from one species to another, and how would such differences depart from Zuckerkandl and Pauling's assumptions for molecular clocks?

Answer: Substitution rates may differ between species because their generation times are different, and so the number of germ-line DNA replications (which occur once per generation) are different; because the species are different in their average repair efficiency; because the species have different average exposure to mutagens; and/or because the species are exposed to different opportunities to adapt to new ecological niches and environments.

Zuckerkandl and Pauling's molecular clock hypothesis was based on initial data suggesting that substitution rates were constant in homologous proteins, that is, that there is a steady rate of change between two sequences. If this were generally true, the number of differences between two homologous proteins could be correlated with the amount of time since speciation caused them to diverge independently. If the hypothesis were correct, it would facilitate the determination of the phylogenetic relationships between species and the times of their divergence. However, the molecular clock is not uniform for all species, and so molecular divergence cannot always be used for phylogenetic analysis and to date the times recent common ancestors existed. Before making these types of inferences, it is necessary to demonstrate that the species being examined have a uniform molecular clock.

24.9   Suppose we examine the rates of nucleotide substitution in two nucleotide sequences isolated from humans. In the first sequence (sequence A) we find a nucleotide substitution rate of 4.88×10^{-9} substitutions per site per year. The substitution rate is the same for synonymous and nonsynonymous substitutions. In the second sequence (sequence B), we find a synonymous substitution rate of 4.66×10^{-9} substitutions per site per year and a nonsynonymous substitution rate of 0.70×10^{-9} substitutions per site per year. Referring to Table 24.1, what might you conclude about the possible roles of sequence A and sequence B?

Answer: Nonsynonymous substitutions are those that code for different amino acids, while synonymous substitutions code for the same amino acid. In sequence A, the finding of the same, relatively high rate for synonymous and nonsynonymous substitutions suggests that this sequence may not code for a functional protein, and may derive from a pseudogene. The rate seen for synonymous and nonsynonymous substitutions in sequence A is similar to that seen for pseudogenes shown in Table 24.1.

The different rates seen for synonymous and nonsynonymous substitutions in sequence B (and in particular, the much lower rate of nonsynonymous substitutions) suggest that this sequence encodes a protein. A low nonsynonymous substitution rate would be expected if nonsynonymous changes resulted in changes in protein function that were detrimental to fitness. Since most nonsynonymous substitutions would not "improve" a protein's function, such mutations would be eliminated by the filter of natural selection. Synonymous substitutions would be tolerated and seen at a higher frequency, as they would not alter protein function.

24.10   What evolutionary process might explain a coding region in which the rate of amino acid replacement is actually greater than the rate of synonymous substitution?

Answer: If there is evolutionary pressure, or natural selection, for diversity, then the rate of amino acid replacement, driven by nonsynonymous substitution, may be greater than the rate of synonymous substitution. This is seen at the major histocompatibility complex (MHC) in mammals, which is involved in immune function where diversity favors fewer individuals vulnerable to an infection by any single virus; and in viruses which utilize error-prone replication coupled with diversifying selection. In both cases, this serves as a response to pressure for rapid evolution.

24.11   Natural selection does not always act just at the level of amino acid sequences in proteins. Ribosomal RNAs, for instance, are functionally dependent on extensive and specific intramolecular secondary structures that form when complementary nucleotide sequences within a single rRNA interact. Would the regions involved in such pairing accumulate mutations at the same rate as unpaired regions? Why?

Answer: While the sequences of rRNA regions that interact and provide for ribosomal function by pairing will be subject to mutation at the same rates as sequences that do not pair, mutations that disrupt pairing will be selected against. Such mutations will alter ribosomal function, and this provides a basis for selection against them. Consequently, substitutions in paired regions will not accumulate, unless there are two simultaneous, complementary mutations – one in each of the two sites that pair. A high degree of conservation of nucleotides at particular sites within the rRNA genes therefore indicates that these nucleotides are functionally important.

24.12   The following three-way alignment is of the nucleotide sequences from the beginning of the human, rabbit, and duck α-globin genes. Given that humans and rabbits are known to be more closely related to each other than they are to ducks (an outgroup), use the relative rate test to determine whether there has been a difference in the rate of substitution in this region of the human and rabbit genomes since they last shared a common ancestor.

```
Human: ATGGTGCTCT CTCCTGCCGA CAAGACCAAC GTCAAGGCCG CCTGGGACAA
Rabbit:ATGGTGCTGT CTCCCGCTGA CAAGACCAAC ATCAAGACTG CCTGGGAAAA
Duck:  ATGGTGCTGT CTGCGGCTGA CAAGACCAAC GTCAAGGGTG TCTTCTCCAA
```

Answer: First identify how many differences exist between pairs of the sequences. In the annotation below, H represents human; R represents rabbit; D represents duck; an underlined base indicates a base that is different between the mammalian and duck sequence; and an "x" below the aligned sequences identifies the position of a base that is different between the indicated pair of species.

```
H:      ATGGTGCTCT CTCCTGCCGA CAAGACCAAC GTCAAGGCCG CCTGGGACAA
R:      ATGGTGCTGT CTCCCGCTGA CAAGACCAAC ATCAAGACTG CCTGGGAAAA
D:      ATGGTGCTGT CTGCGGCTGA CAAGACCAAC GTCAAGGGTG TCTTCTCCAA
H vs. D:           x x  x                        xx  x  xxxx
R vs. D:           x x                    X       xx  x  xxxxx
H vs. R:             x  x                 x        x x         x
```

Based on this analysis, there are 10 substitutions between humans and ducks, 11 substitutions between rabbits and ducks, and 6 substitutions between humans and rabbits. With ducks as an outgroup, we can draw a species tree as follows:

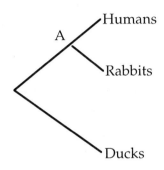

If the molecular clock hypothesis is correct, then $d_{A\text{-Humans}} = d_{A\text{-Rabbits}}$ (d in these equations represents "distance": $d_{A\text{-Humans}}$ is the distance between the point of common ancestry (A) to humans). The path by which the distances are calculated should not matter if the molecular clocks throughout the tree are uniform. Check this by inserting the numbers of substitutions determined from the analysis of the sequences into equations that trace the paths in the species tree. These equations are presented in the text, and reflect the relationships between distances in the species tree.

$$d_{A\text{-Humans}} = (d_{\text{Humans-Rabbits}} + d_{\text{Humans-Ducks}} - d_{\text{Rabbits-Ducks}}) / 2$$
$$= (6 + 10 - 11)/2$$
$$= 2.5$$

$$d_{A\text{-Rabbits}} = (d_{\text{Humans-Rabbits}} + d_{\text{Rabbits-Ducks}} - d_{\text{Humans-Ducks}}) / 2$$
$$= (6 + 11 - 10)/2$$
$$= 3.5$$

This analysis indicates that although $d_{A\text{-Humans}}$ and $d_{A\text{-Rabbits}}$ are similar, they are not identical. This suggests that there is a difference in the rate of substitution in this region of the rabbit and human genomes since they last shared a common ancestor.

24.13 What are some of the advantages of using DNA sequences to infer evolutionary relationships?

Answer: Using DNA sequence information to infer evolutionary relationships has several advantages. First, DNA sequences serve as historical records that can be unraveled to identify the dynamics of evolutionary history. Second, since they do not rely on phenotypes for comparison of genetic relatedness, they circumvent problems associated with phylogenetic classification in organisms based solely on phenotypes. These include: problems in the identification of usable phenotypes in organisms which either lack phenotypes that correlate with their degree of genetic relatedness or for which there is no fossil record evidence (e.g., the eubacteria and the archaeabacteria); problems in the identification of usable phenotypes in groups of organisms where few characters are shared (e.g., the bacteria and mammals); and problems associated with convergent evolution, where distantly related organisms can share similar phenotypes. Third, they allow for an abundance of parameters that can be measured so that theories can be tested, as they provide highly accurate and reliable information, allow direct comparison of the genetic differences among organisms, are easily quantified, and can be used for all organisms.

24.14   As suggested by the popular movie *Jurassic Park*, organisms trapped in amber have proven to be a good source of DNA from tens and even hundreds of millions of years ago. However, when using such sequences in phylogenetic analyses it is usually not possible to distinguish between samples that come from evolutionary "dead ends" and those that are the ancestors of organisms still alive today. Why would the former be no more useful than simply including the DNA sequence of another living species in an analysis? Including the DNA sequence of an evolutionary "dead end" is no more useful in a phylogenetic analysis than simply including the DNA sequence of another living species because neither one represents an ancestral group to which living species can be linked.

Answer: An evolutionary "dead end" represents a taxon that is on a separate, no-longer existing branch of the tree of life. In this sense, it serves just as another species for comparison, much as does a living species on a separate, existing branch of the tree of life. Phylogenetic analyses can not distinguish between existing and extinct species, since they only describe species relatedness.

24.15   In the phylogenetic analysis of a group of closely related organisms, the conclusions drawn from one locus were found to be at odds with those from several others. What might account for the discordant locus?

Answer: Sequence polymorphisms that result in divergence within genes often predate speciation events. If an ancestral polymorphism at a locus predates the split between two species, some members of a species may have retained the ancestral polymorphism, while others may have not retained it, having accumulated a newer polymorphism at the locus that occurred following speciation. Consequently, for certain loci, some members of a species will be more similar to other species than to their own or more closely related species. For these loci, phylogenetic trees made from a single gene will not always reflect the relationships between species. This is why it is important to use multiple loci when constructing species trees.

24.16   What is the chance of randomly picking the one rooted phylogenetic tree that describes the true relationship between a group of six organisms? Are the odds better or worse for randomly picking from among all the possible unrooted trees for those organisms?

Answer: Refer to Table 24.3 and the accompanying text. The number of possible rooted (N_R) and unrooted (N_U) trees for n taxa are given by the equations:

$$N_R = (2n-3)!/2^{n-2} (n-2)! \text{ and } N_U = (2n-5)!/2^{n-3} (n-3)!$$

For $n = 6$, $N_R = 9!/2^4\,4! = 945$ and $N_U = 7!/2^3\,3! = 105$. The chance of picking the one rooted tree that describes the true relationship between a group of six organisms is 1/945 (0.11%). The odds are better in picking a random unrooted tree: 1/105 (0.95%).

24.17   Increasing the amount of sequence information available for analysis usually has little effect on the length of time computer programs use to generate phylogenetic trees with the parsimony approach. Why doesn't the amount of sequence information have an effect on the total number of possible rooted and unrooted trees?

Answer: The total number of possible rooted and unrooted trees is based on the number of taxa considered, not the amount of sequence information provided for each taxa. If n is the number of taxa considered, then the total number of rooted trees is $N_R = (2n-3)!/2^{n-2} (n-2)!$ and the total number of unrooted trees is $N_U = (2n-5)!/2^{n-3} (n-3)!$ The amount of time required for computer generation of phylogenetic trees with the parsimony approach is not affected much by the amount of sequence information because in parsimony-based approaches, not all sites are used when considering molecular data. Rather, only informative sites – sites that have at least two different nucleotides present at least twice – are used. Simply increasing the amount of sequence information does not necessarily dramatically increase the number of informative sites since there is no guarantee that the sequences that are added harbor informative sites. It is more important to identify regions that have informative sites, and add these to the analysis. Once informative sites within an alignment are determined, the parsimony approach is used - the unrooted tree that invokes the fewest number of mutations for each of the sites is determined. Restricting the analysis to informative-only sites, and invoking parsimony quickly eliminates many trees from further consideration.

24.18   When bootstrapping is used to assess the robustness of branching patterns in a tree of maximum parsimony, why is it more important to use sequences that have as many informative sites as possible than to simply use longer sequences?

Answer: Bootstrap tests draw repeatedly on different subsets of the original data and infer trees from the newly selected incomplete data set. Repeating this process hundreds or thousands of times identifies which portions of the inferred, maximum parsimony tree have the same groupings as many of the repetitions. These are the regions of the inferred tree that are especially well supported by the entire data set. When maximum parsimony is used, only informative sites – sites that have at least two different nucleotides present at least twice – are used for the analysis. Other sequence sites are not used in the analysis, as they are not considered to be biologically informative characters. Consequently, simply using longer sequences does not necessarily add any additional information to the analysis. It is more important to identify subsets of sequences that harbor a high density of informative sites, and add these to the analysis. This will increase the size of the data set that can be selected from during the bootstrap analysis, and therefore be more useful in assessing the robustness of the inferred tree.

24.19   What are the advantages of gene duplication (in whole or in part) in generating genes with new functions? Suggest an alternative way in which genes with new functions could arise.

Answer: Following a gene duplication event, two functional copies of a gene are present. Providing that one of them continues to provide a required function, the other may undergo changes in sequence, as it is free from the constraint of providing a required function. Not all of the changes of course will be desirable or lead to new functions – many may result in a loss of function and result in a pseudogene. However, some may result in a modified function that serves the organism. Subsequent misalignments between the altered, duplicated gene or a pseudogene and the retained functional gene provide an opportunity for recombination and gene conversion events to "repair" inactivated copies of a gene. Thus, a mutated, duplicated gene/pseudogene can have its function restored.

When only part of a gene is duplicated, there is a potential for domain shuffling. Domain shuffling is the duplication and rearrangement of domains in proteins that provide specific functions. This can lead to the assemblage of proteins with more complex domain arrangements, which can result in proteins with novel functions.

While gene duplications are therefore advantageous as a mechanism to generate genes with new functions because they provide a short cut for modifying existing proteins. Rather than starting to build a gene "from scratch," duplications provide a template that already serves a function. The template can be tinkered with, repeatedly if recombination and gene conversion occur, in a manner that is largely free from selection. Of course, if the new function is deleterious to the organism (e.g., a dominant mutation resulting from a gain-of-function or new function) it will be selected against. Partial gene duplications are advantageous since they allow combinations of existing functional domains to be reassembled into new arrangements, and so effectively provide a set of building blocks for the assembly of new functions.

Additional mechanisms for the generation of genes with new functions could include the transposition, inversion or translocation of chromosome segments that rearrange the transcriptional structure of an existing gene, either by placing it under the control of another gene's regulatory elements (e.g., altering the times or tissues it is expressed in during development and thereby providing "new functions" where none were previously); creating a novel fusion protein or introducing sites for mRNA processing that were previously not present; the insertion of copies of existing or foreign genes via viral retrotransposons which could then, much like duplications, change over time; the insertion and/or partial deletion of mobile repetitive elements into exonic or intronic regions that would introduce new regulatory and or RNA processing signals; and, of course, point, small deletion and insertion mutations that could alter the function of an existing gene or modify the way existing RNA processing sites are used.